Cells and Heredity: Teacher's Edition

Contents in Brief

Teacher's Edition

Student Edition

Prentice Hall Science Explorer

Series Tables of Contents

The Nature of Science and Technology

Life Science

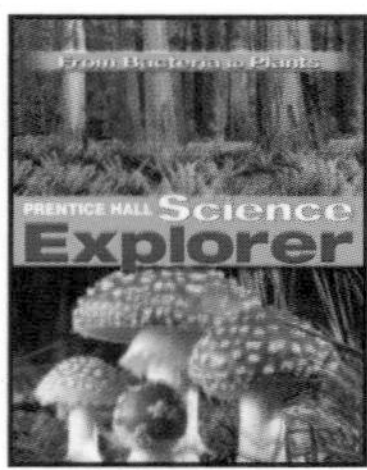

From Bacteria to Plants

Animals

Cells and Heredity

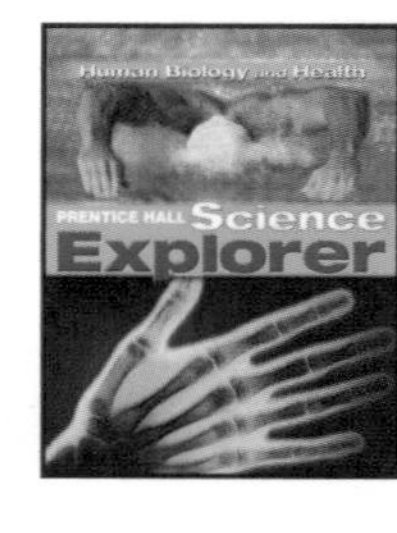

Human Biology and Health

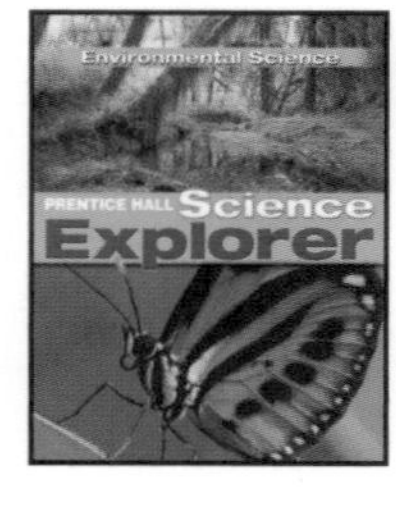

Environmental Science

Earth Science

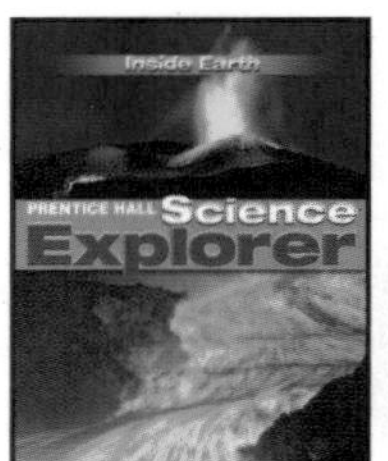

Inside Earth

Earth's Changing Surface

Earth's Waters

Weather and Climate

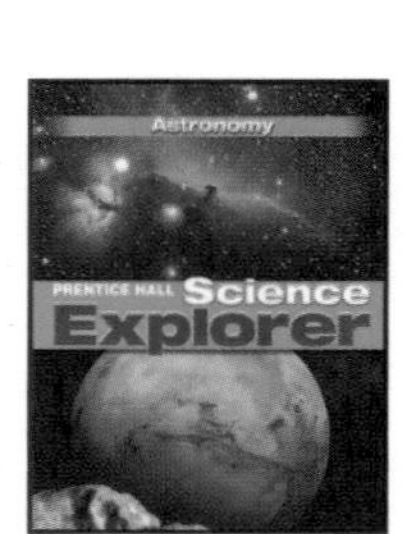

Astronomy

Physical Science

Chemical Building Blocks

Chemical Interactions

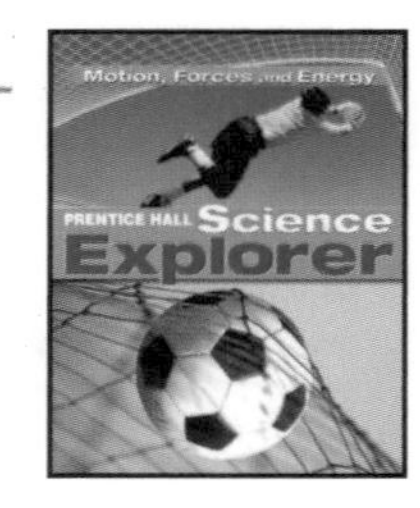

Motion, Forces, and Energy

Electricity and Magnetism

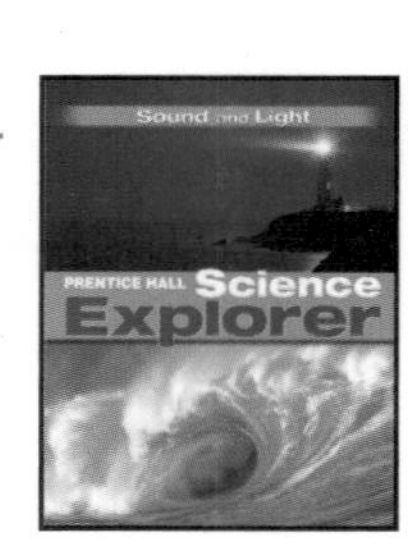

Sound and Light

Teacher's Edition

Boston, Massachusetts
Upper Saddle River, New Jersey

ISBN 0-13-201164-6

3 4 5 6 7 8 9 10 10 09 08 07

Pacing Options

PRENTICE HALL
TeacherEXPRESS™
Plan • Teach • Assess

SCIENCE EXPLORER offers many aids to help you plan your instruction time, whether regular class periods or block scheduling. Section-by-section lesson plans for each chapter include suggested times for Student Edition activities. TeacherExpress™ and the Lab zone™ Easy Planner CD-ROM will help you manage your time electronically.

Pacing Chart

	PERIODS	BLOCKS
Careers in Science: An Unfolding Mystery	1	1/2
Chapter 1 Cell Structure and Function		
Chapter 1 Project *Egg-speriment with a Cell*	Ongoing	Ongoing
1 Discovering Cells	2–3	1–1 1/2
2 Looking Inside Cells	3–4	1 1/2–2
3 Integrating Chemistry: Chemical Compounds in Cells	2–3	1–1 1/2
4 The Cell in Its Environment	1–2	1/2–1
Chapter 1 Review and Assessment	1	1/2
Chapter 2 Cell Processes and Energy		
Chapter 2 Project *Shine On!*	Ongoing	Ongoing
1 Photosynthesis	2–3	1–1 1/2
2 Respiration	2–3	1–1 1/2
3 Cell Division	3–4	1 1/2–2
4 Integrating Health: Cancer	2–3	1–1 1/2
Chapter 2 Review and Assessment	1	1/2
Chapter 3 Genetics: The Science of Heredity		
Chapter 3 Project *All in the Family*	Ongoing	Ongoing
1 Mendel's Work	2–3	1–1 1/2
2 Integrating Mathematics: Probability and Genetics	2–3	1–1 1/2
3 The Cell and Inheritance	2–3	1–1 1/2
4 The DNA Connection	2–3	1–1 1/2
Chapter 3 Review and Assessment	1	1/2
Chapter 4 Modern Genetics		
Chapter 4 Project *Teach Others About a Trait*	Ongoing	Ongoing
1 Human Inheritance	2–3	1–1 1/2
2 Human Genetic Disorders	2–3	1–1 1/2
3 Tech and Design: Advances in Genetics	2–3	1–1 1/2
Chapter 4 Review and Assessment	1	1/2
Chapter 5 Changes Over Time		
Chapter 5 Project *Life's Long Calendar*	Ongoing	Ongoing
1 Darwin's Theory	2–3	1–1 1/2
2 Evidence of Evolution	2–3	1–1 1/2
3 Integrating Earth Science: The Fossil Record	2–3	1–1 1/2
Chapter 5 Review and Assessment	1	1/2
Interdisciplinary Exploration: Dogs—Loyal Companions	2–3	1–1 1/2

Research-Based and Proven to Work

As the originator of the small book concept in middle school science, and as the nation's number one science publisher, Prentice Hall takes pride in the fact that we've always listened closely to teachers. In doing so, we've developed programs that effectively meet the needs of your classroom.

As we continue to listen, we realize that raising the achievement level of all students is the number one challenge facing teachers today. To assist you in meeting this latest challenge, Prentice Hall has combined the very best author team with solid research to create a program that meets your high standards and will ensure that no child is left behind.

With Prentice Hall, you can be confident that your students will not only be motivated, inspired, and excited to learn science, but that they will also achieve the success needed in today's environment of the No Child Left Behind (NCLB) legislation and testing reform.

On the following pages, you will read about the key elements found throughout *Science Explorer* that truly set this program apart and ensure success for you and your students.

As we continue to listen, we realize that raising the achievement level of all students is the number one challenge facing teachers today.

A Science Program Backed by Research

In developing Prentice Hall *Science Explorer*, we used research studies as a central, guiding element. Research on *Science Explorer* indicated key elements of a textbook program that ensure students' success: support for reading and mathematics in science, consistent opportunities for inquiry, and an ongoing assessment strand. This research was conducted in phases and continues today.

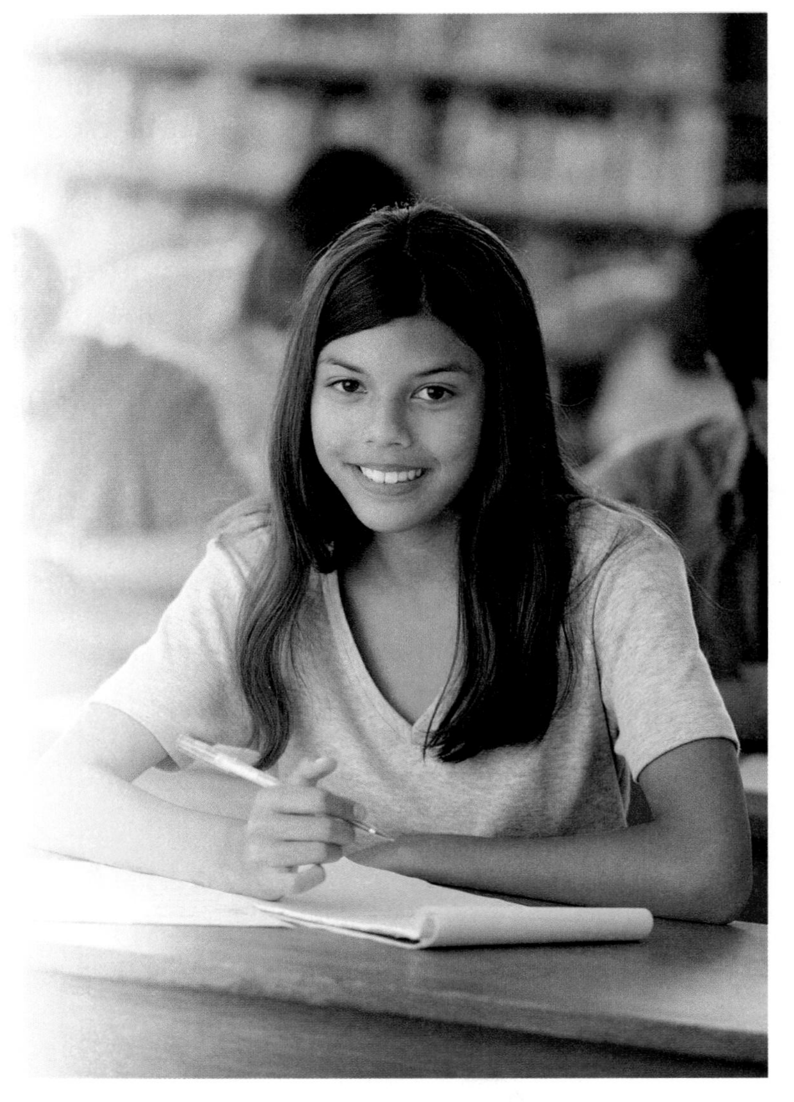

1. Exploratory: Needs Assessment

Along with periodic surveys concerning state and national standards as well as curriculum issues and challenges, we conducted specific product development research, which included discussions with teachers and advisory panels, focus groups, and quantitative surveys. We explored the specific needs of teachers, students, and other educators regarding each book we developed in Prentice Hall *Science Explorer*.

2. Formative: Prototype Development and Field-Testing

During this phase of research, we worked to develop prototype materials. Then we tested the materials by field-testing with students and teachers and by performing qualitative and quantitative surveys. In our early prototype testing, we received feedback about our lesson structure. Results were channeled back into the program development for improvement.

3. Summative: Validation Research

Finally, we conducted and continue to conduct long-term research based on scientific, experimental designs under actual classroom conditions. This research identifies what works and what can be improved in the next revision of Prentice Hall *Science Explorer*. We also continue to monitor the program in the market. We talk to our users about what works, and then we begin the cycle over again. The next section contains highlights of this research.

A Science Program With Proven Results

In a year-long study in 2000–2001, students in six states using Prentice Hall *Science Explorer* outscored students using other science programs on a nationally normed standardized test.

The study investigated the effects of science textbook programs at the eighth-grade level. Twelve eighth-grade science classes with a total of 223 students participated in the study. The selected classes were of similar student ability levels.

Each class was tested at the beginning of the school year using the TerraNova CTBS Basic Battery Plus, and then retested at the end of the school year. The final results, shown in the graph, show a significant improvement in test scores from the pre-test to the post-test evaluation.

- All tests were scored by CTB/McGraw-Hill, the publisher of the TerraNova exam. Statistical analyses and conclusions were performed by an independent firm, Pulse Analytics, Inc.

In Japan, Lesson Study Research has been employed for a number of years as a tool for teachers to improve their curriculum. In April 2003, Prentice Hall adapted this methodology to focus on a lesson from this edition. Our goal was to test the effectiveness of lesson pedagogy and improve it while in the program development stage. In all three classrooms tested, student learning increased an average of 10 points from the pre- to the post-assessment.

- Detailed results of these studies can be obtained at **www.PHSchool.com/research.**

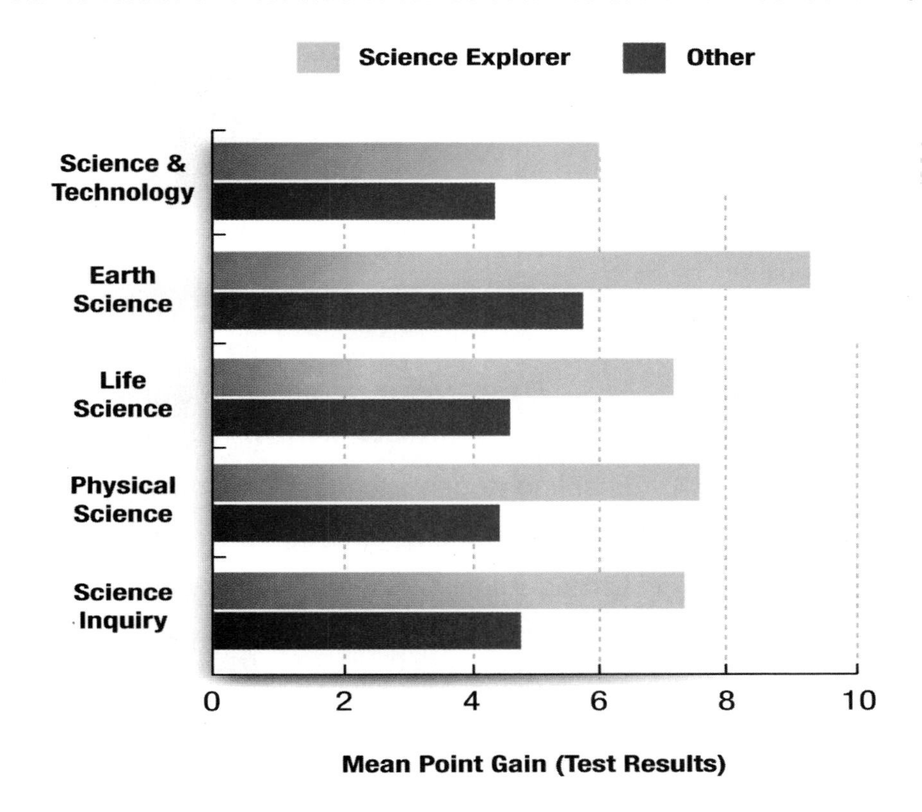

Foundational Research: Inquiry in the Science Classroom

"How do I know if my students are inquiring?" "If students are busy doing lots of hands-on activities, are they using inquiry?" "What is inquiry, anyway?" If you're confused, you are not alone. Inquiry is the heart and soul of science education, with most of us in continuous pursuit of achieving it with our students!

Defining Science Inquiry

What is it? Simply put, inquiry is the intellectual side of science. It is thinking like a scientist—being inquisitive, asking why, and searching for answers. The National Science Education Content Standards define inquiry as the process in which students begin with a question, design an investigation, gather evidence, formulate an answer to the original question, and communicate the investigative process and results. Since it is often difficult to accomplish all this in one class period, the standards also acknowledge that at times students need to practice only one or two inquiry components.

Understanding Inquiry

The National Research Council in Inquiry and the National Science Education Standards (2000) identified several "essential features" of classroom inquiry. We have modified these essential features into questions to guide you in your quest for enhanced and more thoughtful student inquiry.

1. ***Who asks the question?*** In most curricula, these focusing questions are an element given in the materials. As a teacher you can look for labs that, at least on a periodic basis, allow students to pursue their own questions.
2. ***Who designs the procedures?*** To gain experience with the logic underlying experimentation, students need continuous practice with designing procedures. Some labs in which the primary target is content acquisition designate procedures. But others should ask students to do so.
3. ***Who decides what data to collect?*** Students need practice in determining the data to collect.
4. ***Who formulates explanations based upon the data?*** Students should be challenged to think—to analyze and draw conclusions based on their data, not just copy answers from the text materials.
5. ***Who communicates and justifies the results?*** Activities should push students not only to communicate but also to justify their answers. Activities also should be thoughtfully designed and interesting so that students want to share their results and argue about conclusions.

Making Time for Inquiry

One last question—Must each and every activity have students do all of this? The answer is an obvious and emphatic "No." You will find a great variety of activities in *Science Explorer*. Some activities focus on content acquisition, and thus they specify the question and most of the procedures. But many others stress in-depth inquiry from start to finish. Because inquiry is an intellectual pursuit, it cannot merely be characterized by keeping students busy and active. Too many students have a knack for being physically but not intellectually engaged in science. It is our job to help them engage intellectually.

Michael J. Padilla, Ph.D.
Program Author of *Science Explorer*
Professor of Science Education
University of Georgia
Athens, Georgia

"Because inquiry is an intellectual pursuit, it cannot merely be characterized by keeping students busy and active."

Evaluator's Checklist

Does your science program promote inquiry by—

- ✔ Enabling students to pursue their own questions
- ✔ Allowing students to design their own procedures
- ✔ Letting students determine what data are best to collect
- ✔ Challenging students to think critically
- ✔ Pushing students to justify their answers

Inquiry in *Science Explorer*

Science Explorer offers the most opportunities to get students to think like a scientist. By providing inquiry opportunities throughout the program, *Science Explorer* enables students to enhance their understanding by participating in the discovery.

Student Edition Inquiry

Six lab and activity options are included in every chapter, structured from directed to open-ended—providing you the flexibility to address all types of learners and accommodate your class time and equipment requirements. As Michael Padilla notes, some activities focus on content acquisition, and thus the question and most of the procedures are specified. But many others stress in-depth inquiry from start to finish. The graph below shows how, in general, inquiry levels are addressed in the Student Edition.

Science Explorer encourages students to develop inquiry skills across the spectrum from teacher-guided to open-ended. Even more opportunities for real-life applications of inquiry are included in Science & Society, Technology & Society, Careers in Science, and Interdisciplinary Exploration features.

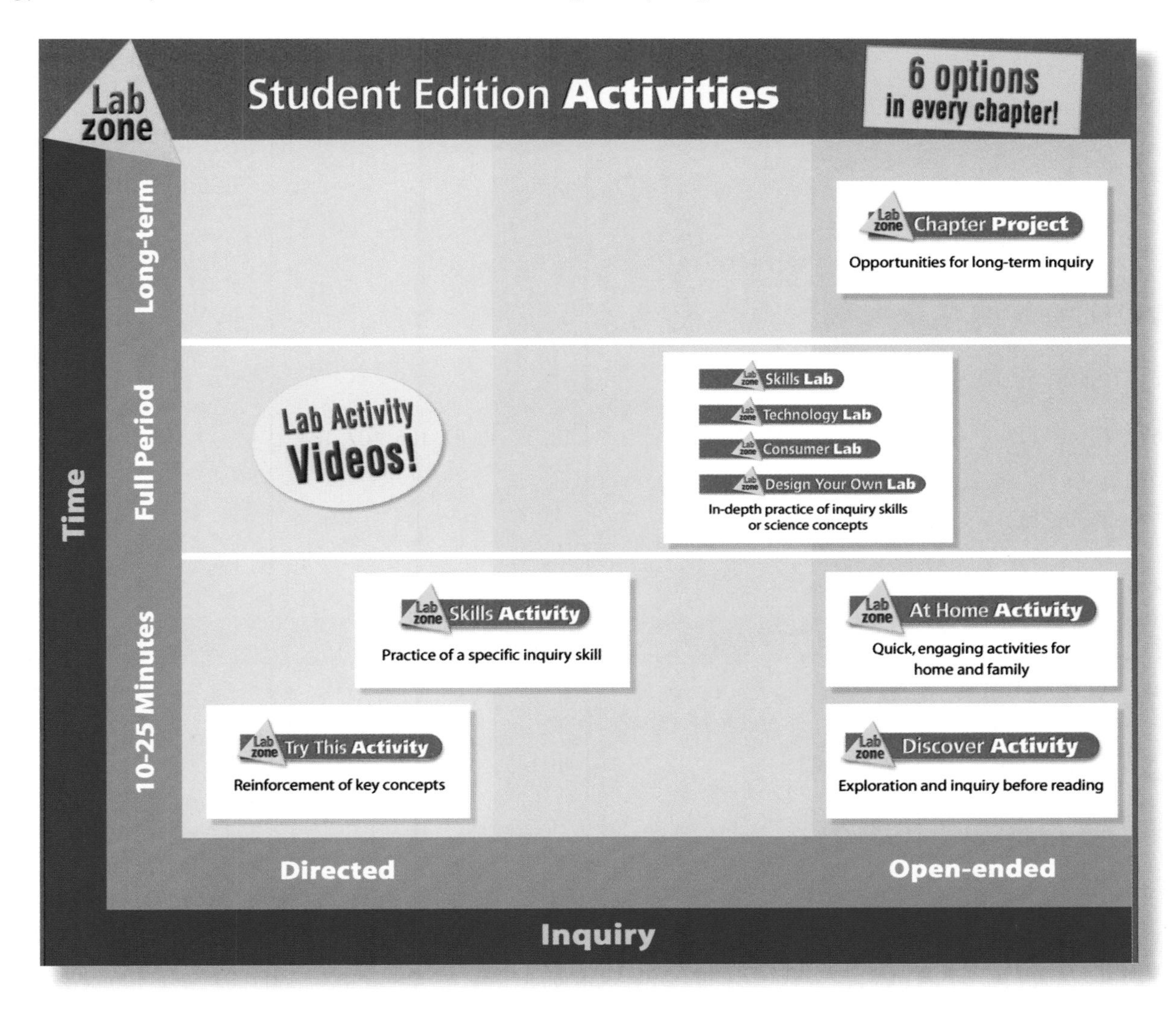

Inquiry Skills Chart

SCIENCE EXPLORER provides comprehensive teaching, practice, and assessment of science skills, with an emphasis on the process skills necessary for inquiry. This chart lists the skills covered in the program and cites the page numbers where each skill is covered.

	Student Text: Projects and Labs	Student Text: Activities	Student Text: Caption and Review Questions	Teacher's Edition: Extensions
Basic Process SKILLS				
Observing	4–5, 15, 31, 42–43, 82–83, 146–147	6, 11, 22, 49, 53, 123, 128	40	12, 19, 34, 47, 76, 78, 80, 87, 143, 150
Inferring	31, 74–75, 129	16, 28, 35, 44, 47, 76, 88, 110, 117, 141, 155, 156	19, 24, 30, 40, 53, 62, 67, 72, 80, 103, 106, 120, 134, 153, 166	26, 56, 79, 99, 115, 148, 160
Predicting	4–5, 54, 74–75, 90–91, 122, 146–147	50, 64, 80, 84, 118	34, 40, 53, 72, 89, 106, 153, 166	57, 92
Classifying		138, 148	30, 61, 89, 96, 163	8
Making Models	74–75, 90–91, 108–109, 136–137, 146–147	18, 56, 92, 143, 163		19, 27, 28, 36, 58, 59, 61, 67, 93, 95, 99, 101, 102, 114, 119, 120, 127, 151, 157, 159
Communicating	14–15, 31, 54, 63, 74–75, 90–91, 108–109, 122, 129, 136–137, 146–147	30, 53, 67, 81, 127, 128		9, 11, 17, 21, 45, 76, 77, 85, 101, 113, 127, 139, 141, 143, 149, 161
Measuring	4–5, 42–43, 54		41	51
Calculating	63, 136–137, 146–147	33, 85, 88, 125	12, 37, 40, 87, 106, 107, 134, 166	57, 67, 158
Creating Data Tables	63, 82–83, 146–147		106	33
Graphing	4–5, 42–43	29, 60, 88	72	
Advanced Process SKILLS				
Posing Questions				
Developing Hypotheses	82–83	32, 55, 125	40, 145	
Designing Experiments	31, 42–43, 54, 63, 82–83, 147	113		144

Advanced Process SKILLS (continued)				
	Student Text: Projects and Labs	Student Text: Activities	Student Text: Caption and Review Questions	Teacher's Edition: Extensions
Controlling Variables	54			
Forming Operational Definitions		25, 97		
Interpreting Data	31, 63, 82–83, 90–91, 122, 154	29, 60, 86, 158	72, 73, 134, 166	
Drawing Conclusions	4–5, 14–15, 31, 42–43, 54, 63, 82–83, 91, 122, 129, 154	29, 60, 99, 150	106, 116, 153, 166	
Critical Thinking SKILLS				
Comparing and Contrasting	63, 90–91	103, 117	13, 20, 23, 24, 30, 37, 40, 48, 52, 53, 58, 67, 72, 81, 96, 102, 116, 121, 140, 141, 145, 149, 153, 163, 166	20, 22, 32, 36, 51, 52, 55, 67, 68, 88, 94, 140, 142, 148
Applying Concepts	15, 108–109	30, 53, 128	7, 13, 24, 26, 37, 40, 48, 57, 72, 81, 89, 93, 106, 115, 116, 120, 124, 128, 144, 145, 153, 163, 166	11, 19, 113, 124, 127, 152, 161
Interpreting Diagrams, Graphs, Photographs, and Maps	4–5, 42–43	88, 158	11, 17, 36, 40, 46, 51, 62, 66, 77, 79, 88, 94, 96, 98, 100, 106, 111, 113, 119, 120, 126, 134, 135, 138, 150, 152, 159, 163, 167	20, 21, 22, 35, 45, 46, 51, 58, 61, 79, 87, 88, 93, 94, 95, 98, 100, 111, 112, 114, 119, 126, 141, 143, 158, 160
Relating Cause and Effect		138	13, 30, 37, 45, 53, 65, 67, 72, 81, 89, 103, 106, 116, 128, 143, 145, 156, 162, 163, 166	
Making Generalizations			27, 48	
Making Judgments			72, 166	
Problem Solving	15		134	
Informational Organizational SKILLS				
Concept Maps			39, 105, 133	29, 38, 70, 79, 98, 104, 132, 164
Compare/Contrast Tables			71	126, 142
Venn Diagrams				36
Flowcharts			104, 165	
Cycle Diagrams		55	52, 58–59	

The ***Science Explorer*** program provides additional teaching, reinforcement, and assessment of skills in the *Inquiry Skills Activities Book* and the *Integrated Science Laboratory Manual*.

A National Look at Science Education

Project 2061 was established by the American Association for the Advancement of Science (AAAS) as a long-term project to improve science education nationwide. A primary goal of Project 2061 is to define a "common core of learning"—the knowledge and skills we want all students to achieve. Project 2061 published *Science for All Americans* in 1989 and followed this with *Benchmarks for Science Literacy* in 1993. *Benchmarks* recommends what students should know and be able to do by the end of grades 2, 5, 8, and 12. Project 2061 clearly states that *Benchmarks* is not a curriculum but a tool for designing successful curricula.

The National Research Council (NRC) used *Science for All Americans* and *Benchmarks* to develop the National Science Education Standards (NSES), which were published in 1996. The NSES are organized into six categories (Content, Teaching, Assessment, Professional Development, Program, and System) to help schools establish the conditions necessary to achieve scientific literacy for all students.

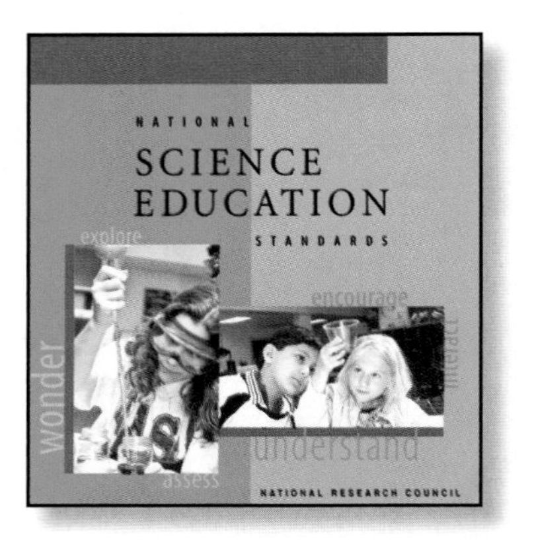

Michael Padilla, the program author of *Science Explorer,* guided one of six teams of teachers whose work led to the publication of *Benchmarks.* He also was a contributing writer of the National Science Education Standards. Under his guidance, *Science Explorer* has implemented these standards through its inquiry approach, a focus on student learning of important concepts and skills, and teacher support aligned with the NSES teaching standards.

Neither *Benchmarks* nor the NSES requires a single, uniform national curriculum, and in fact there is a great diversity nationwide in science curricula. The correlations that follow are designed to help you use the *Science Explorer* program to meet your particular curriculum needs.

Meeting the National Science Education Standards

CELL STRUCTURE AND FUNCTION

Science as Inquiry (Content Standard A)

- **Think critically and logically to make relationships between evidence and explanations** Students investigate how various materials enter or leave a cell, using an egg as a model of the cell. *(Chapter Project—Egg-speriment with a Cell)*

Life Science (Content Standard C)

- **Structure and function in living systems** All living things are composed of cells. Each of the various structures in a cell has a different function. Important organic compounds found in living things are carbohydrates, lipids, proteins, and nucleic acids. *(Discovering Cells; Looking Inside Cells; Chemical Compounds in Cells)*
- **Regulation and behavior** Substances can move into and out of a cell by diffusion, osmosis, or active transport. *(The Cell in Its Environment)*

Science and Technology (Content Standard E)

- **Understandings about science and technology** The invention of the microscope enabled people to discover and learn about cells. *(Discovering Cells; Tech & Design in History)*

CELL PROCESSES AND ENERGY

Science as Inquiry (Content Standard A)

- **Design and conduct a scientific investigation** Students investigate how different light conditions affect plants. *(Chapter Project—Shine On!)*
- **Use appropriate tools and techniques to gather, analyze, and interpret data** Students investigate how long the stages of the cell cycle take. *(Skills Lab—Multiplying by Dividing)*

Life Science (Content Standard C)

- **Structure and function in living systems** Photosynthesis occurs inside chloroplasts in the cells of plants and some other organisms. During respiration, cells break down food molecules and release the energy they contain. The regular sequence of growth and division that cells undergo is called the cell cycle. Cancer is a disease in which cells grow and divide uncontrollably. *(Chapter Project—Shine On!; Photosynthesis; Respiration; Cell Division; Cancer; Skills Lab—Multiplying by Dividing)*
- **Populations and ecosystems** Nearly all living things obtain energy either directly or indirectly from the energy of sunlight captured during photosynthesis. Photosynthesis and respiration form a cycle that keeps the levels of oxygen and carbon dioxide fairly constant in the atmosphere. *(Photosynthesis; Respiration)*

A National Look at Science Education *(continued)*

Science in Personal and Social Perspectives (Content Standard F)

- **Science and technology in society** Students consider the issue of when new medicines should be made available. *(Science and Society)*

GENETICS: THE SCIENCE OF HEREDITY

Science as Inquiry (Content Standard A)

- **Use appropriate tools and technology to gather, analyze, and interpret data** Students investigate genetic traits among classmates and have the option of sharing their data online. *(Skills Lab—Take a Class Survey)*
- **Develop descriptions, explanations, predictions, and models using evidence** Students model genetic crosses. Students predict the possible results of genetic crosses. *(Chapter Project—All in the Family; Skills Lab—Take a Class Survey; Skills Lab—Make the Right Call!)*
- **Use mathematics in all aspects of scientific inquiry** Geneticists use Punnett squares to determine the probability of a particular outcome. *(Chapter Project—All in the Family; Mendel's Work; Skills Lab—Take a Class Survey; Skills Lab—Make the Right Call!)*

Life Science (Content Standard C)

- **Structure and function in living systems** Meiosis is the process by which the number of chromosomes is reduced by half to form sex cells. During protein synthesis, the cell uses information from genes to produce proteins. *(The Cell and Inheritance; The DNA Connection)*
- **Reproduction and heredity** The passing of traits from parents to offspring is called heredity. Genes are carried from parents to offspring on chromosomes. Mutations can be a source of genetic variety. *(Chapter Project—All in the Family; Mendel's Work; The Cell and Inheritance; The DNA Connection; Skills Lab—Take a Class Survey; Skills Lab—Make the Right Call!)*

History and Nature of Science (Content Standard G)

- **History of science** The genetic principles that Mendel discovered still stand to this day. *(Mendel's Work; Probability and Genetics)*

MODERN GENETICS

Science as Inquiry (Content Standard A)

- **Develop descriptions, explanations, predictions, and models using evidence** Students create a pedigree for an imaginary family, investigate inheritance patterns in families and model DNA fingerprinting. *(Skills Lab—Family Puzzles; Skills Lab—Guilty or Innocent?)*

Life Science (Content Standard C)

- **Reproduction and heredity** Human traits can be controlled by single genes, multiple alleles, or many genes. A pedigree is used to trace the inheritance of traits. Genetic disorders are caused by mutations. People have used selective breeding, cloning, and genetic engineering to develop organisms with desirable traits. *(Human Inheritance; Human Genetic Disorders; Advances in Genetics; Skills Lab—Family Puzzles; Skills Lab—Guilty or Innocent?)*

Science and Technology (Content Standard E)

- **Understandings about science and technology** Doctors use tools such as karyotypes to help detect genetic disorders. In genetic engineering, genes from one organism are transferred into the DNA of another organism. DNA can be used to identify individuals. *(Human Genetic Disorders; Advances in Genetics; Skills Lab—Family Puzzles; Skills Lab—Guilty or Innocent?)*
- **Science and technology in society** Students examine the use of DNA fingerprinting. *(Technology and Society)*

CHANGES OVER TIME

Science as Inquiry (Content Standard A)

- **Develop descriptions, explanations, predictions, and models using evidence** Students create timelines of Earth's history. Students model how natural selection leads to changes in a species over time. Students compare the structure of a protein in several animals to determine their evolutionary relationships. *(Chapter Project—Life's Long Calendar; Skills Lab—Nature at Work; Skills Lab—Telltale Molecules)*

Life Science (Content Standard C)

- **Diversity and adaptations of organisms** Over a long period of time, natural selection can lead to evolution. A species is extinct if no members of that species are still alive. Scientists compare fossils, body structures, early development, DNA sequences and protein structure to determine evolutionary relationships. *(Darwin's Theory; The Fossil Record; Evidence of Evolution; Skills Lab—Nature at Work; Skills Lab—Telltale Molecules)*

Earth and Space Science (Content Standard D)

- **Earth's history** The fossil record provides clues about how and when new groups of organisms evolved. *(Chapter Project—Life's Long Calendar; The Fossil Record)*

History and Nature of Science (Content Standard G)

- **History of science** Charles Darwin theorized that evolution occurs by means of natural selection. *(Darwin's Theory)*

Note: To see how the Benchmarks are supported by *SCIENCE EXPLORER*, go to **PHSchool.com.**

Reading

Reading Comprehension in the Science Classroom

Q&A

Q: Why are science texts often difficult for students to read and comprehend?

A: In general, science texts make complex literacy and knowledge demands on learners. They have a more technical vocabulary and a more demanding syntax, and place a greater emphasis on inferential reasoning.

Q: What does research say about facilitating comprehension?

A: Studies comparing novices and experts show that the conceptual organization of experts' knowledge is very different from that of novices. For example, experts emphasize core concepts when organizing knowledge, while novices focus on superficial details. To facilitate comprehension, effective teaching strategies should support and scaffold students as they build an understanding of the key concepts and concept relationships within a text unit.

Q: What strategies can teachers use to facilitate comprehension?

A: Three complementary strategies are very important in facilitating student comprehension of science texts. First, guide student interaction with the text using the built-in strategies. Second, organize the curriculum in terms of core concepts (e.g., the **Key Concepts** in each section). Third, develop visual representations of the relationships among the key concepts and vocabulary that can be referred to during instruction.

Nancy Romance, Ph.D.
Professor of Science Education
Florida Atlantic University
Fort Lauderdale, Florida

"Effective teaching strategies should support and scaffold students as they build an understanding of the key concepts and concept relationships within a text unit."

Evaluator's Checklist

Does your science program promote reading comprehension with—

- ✔ Text structured in an outline format and key concepts highlighted in boldface type
- ✔ Real-world applications to activate prior knowledge
- ✔ Key concepts, critical vocabulary, and a reading skill for every section
- ✔ Sample graphic organizers for each section
- ✔ Relevant photos and carefully constructed graphics with questions
- ✔ Reading checkpoints that appear in each section
- ✔ Scaffolded questions in section assessments

Reading Support in *Science Explorer*

The latest research emphasizes the importance of activating learners' prior knowledge and teaching them to distinguish core concepts from less important information. These skills are now more important than ever, because success in science requires students to read, understand, and connect complex terms and concepts.

Before students read—

Reading Preview introduces students to the key concepts and key terms they'll find in each section. The **Target Reading Skill** is identified and applied with a graphic organizer.

During the section—

Boldface Sentences identify each key concept and encourage students to focus on the big ideas of science.

Reading Checkpoints reinforce students' understanding by slowing them down to review after every concept is discussed.

Caption Questions draw students into the art and photos, helping them connect the content to the images.

After students read—

Section Assessment revisits the **Target Reading Skill** and encourages students to use the graphic organizer.

Each review question is scaffolded and models the way students think, by first easing them into a review and then challenging them with increasingly more difficult questions.

Math in the Science Classroom

Why should students concern themselves with mathematics in your science class?

Good science requires good data from which to draw conclusions. Technology enhances the ability to measure in a variety of ways. Often the scientist must measure large amounts of data, and thus an aim of analysis is to reduce the data to a summary that makes sense and is consistent with established norms of communication—i.e., mathematics.

Calculating measures of central tendency (e.g., mean, median, or mode), variability (e.g., range), and shape (graphic representations) can effectively reduce 500 data points to 3 without losing the essential characteristics of the data. Scientists understand that a trade-off exists between precision and richness as data are folded into categories, and so margins of error can be quantified in mathematical terms and factored into all scientific findings.

Mathematics is the language used by scientists to model change in the world. Understanding change is a vital part of the inquiry process. Mathematics serves as a common language to communicate across the sciences. Fields of scientific research that originated as separate disciplines are now integrated, such as happened with bioengineering. What do the sciences have in common? Each uses the language of mathematics to communicate about data and the process of data analysis. Recognizing this need, *Science Explorer* integrates mathematics practice throughout the program and gives students ample opportunity to hone their math skills.

Clearly, mathematics plays an important role in your science classroom!

William Tate, Ph.D.
Professor of Education and Applied Statistics and Computation
Washington University
St. Louis, Missouri

"Mathematics is the language used by scientists to model change in the world."

Integrated Math Support

In the Student Edition

The math instruction is based on principles derived from Prentice Hall's research-based mathematics program.

Sample Problems, Math Practice, Analyzing Data, and a Math Skills Handbook all help to provide practice at point of use, encouraging students to Read and Understand, Plan and Solve, and then Look Back and Check.

Color-coded variables aid student navigation and help reinforce their comprehension.

In the Teacher's Edition

Math teaching notes enable the science teacher to support math instruction and math objectives on high-stakes tests.

In the Guided Reading and Study Workbook

These unique worksheets help students master reading and enhance their study and math skills. Students can create a record of their work for study and review.

Evaluator's Checklist

Does your science program promote math skills by—

- ✔ Giving students opportunities to collect data
- ✔ Providing students opportunities to analyze data
- ✔ Enabling students to practice math skills
- ✔ Helping students solve equations by using color-coded variables
- ✔ Using sample problems to apply science concepts

Technology and Design

Technology and Design in the Science Classroom

Much of the world we live in is designed and made by humans. The buildings in which we live, the cars we drive, the medicines we take, and often the food we eat are products of technology. The knowledge and skills needed to understand the processes used to create these products should be a component of every student's basic literacy.

Some schools offer hands-on instruction on how technology development works through industrial arts curricula. Even then, there is a disconnect among science (understanding how nature works), mathematics (understanding data-driven models), and technology (understanding the human-made world). The link among these fields of study is the engineering design process—that process by which one identifies a human need and uses science knowledge and human ingenuity to create a technology to satisfy the need. Engineering gives students the problem-solving and design skills they will need to succeed in our sophisticated, three-dimensional, technological world.

As a complement to "science as inquiry," the National Science Education Standards (NRC, 1996) call for students at all age levels to develop the abilities related to "technology as design," including the ability to identify and frame a problem and then to design, implement, and evaluate a solution. At the 5–8 grade level, the standards call for students to be engaged in complex problem-solving and to learn more about how science and technology complement each other. It's also important for students to understand that there are often constraints involved in design as well as trade-offs and unintended consequences of technological solutions to problems.

As the *Standards for Technological Literacy* (ITEA, 2000) state, "Science and technology are like conjoined twins. While they have separate identities they must remain inextricably connected." Both sets of standards emphasize how progress in science leads to new developments in technology, while technological innovation in turn drives advances in science.

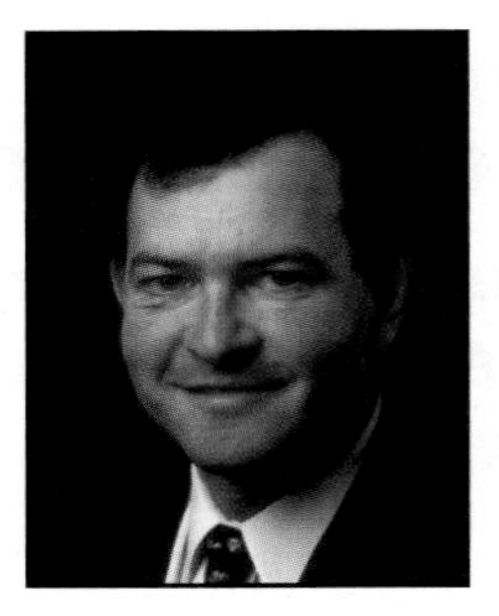

Ioannis Miaoulis, Ph.D.
President
Museum of Science
Boston, Massachusetts

"Engineering gives students the problem-solving and design skills they will need to succeed in our sophisticated, three-dimensional, technological world."

Evaluator's Checklist

Does your science program promote technology and design by—

- ✔ Incorporating technology and design concepts and skills into the science curriculum
- ✔ Giving students opportunities to identify and solve technological design problems
- ✔ Providing students opportunities to analyze the impact of technology on society
- ✔ Enabling students to practice technology and design skills

Technology and Design in *Science Explorer*

How often do you hear your students ask: "Why do I need to learn this?" Connecting them to the world of technology and design in their everyday life is one way to help answer this question. It is also why so many state science curricula are now emphasizing technology and design concepts and skills.

Science Explorer makes a special effort to include a technology and design strand that encourages students to not only identify a need but to take what they learned in science and apply it to design a possible solution, build a prototype, test and evaluate the design, and/or troubleshoot the design. This strand also provides definitions of technology and engineering and discusses the similarities and differences between these endeavors and science. Students will learn to analyze the risks and benefits of a new technology and to consider the tradeoffs, such as safety, costs, efficiency, and appearance.

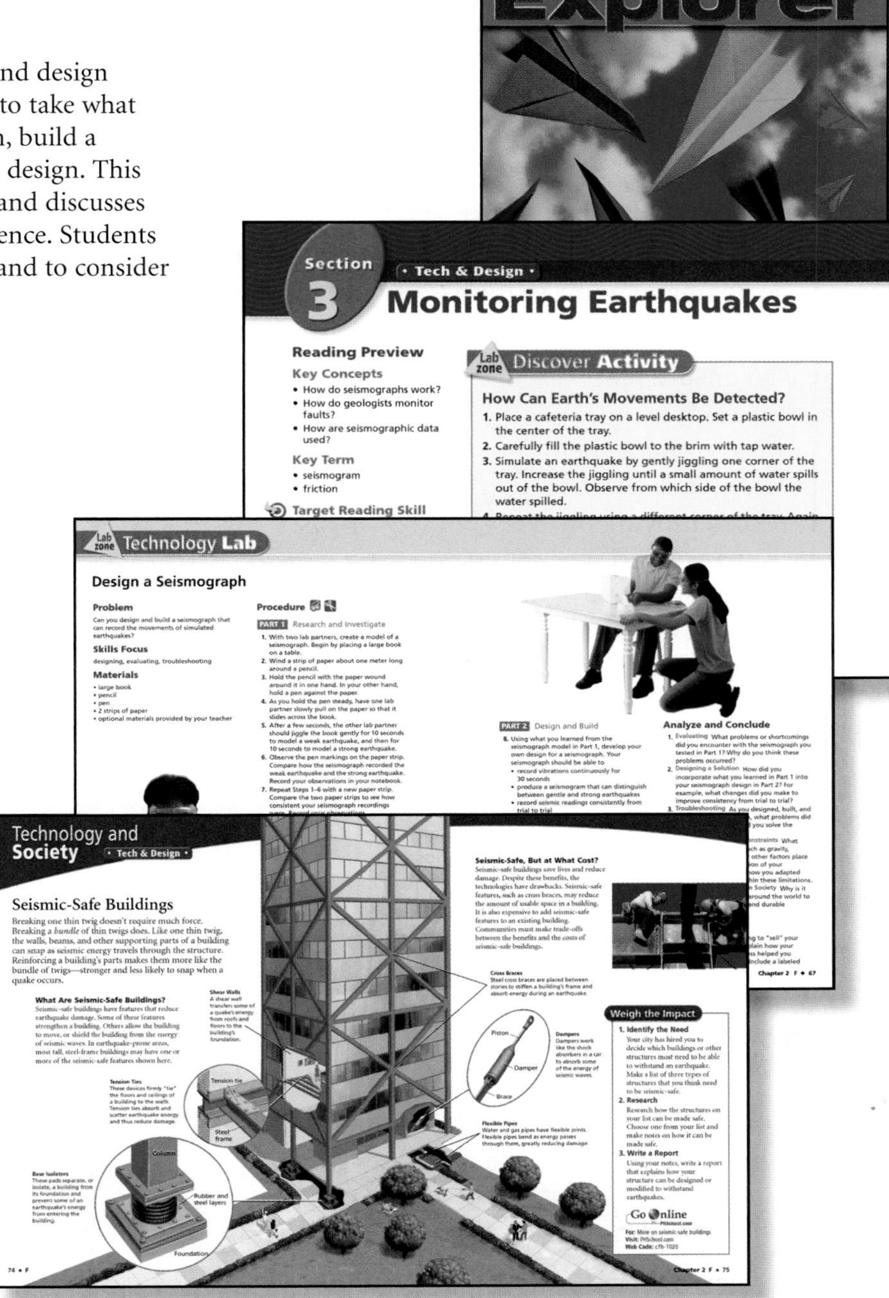

In the Student Edition

Integrated Technology & Design Sections

Sections throughout *Science Explorer* specifically integrate technology and design with the content of the text. For example, students not only learn how seismographs work but also learn what role seismographs play in society and how people use the data that are gathered.

Technology Labs

These labs help students gain experience in designing and building a device or product that meets a particular need or solves a problem. Students follow a design process of Research and Investigate, Design and Build, and Evaluate and Redesign.

Chapter Projects

Chapter Projects work hand-in-hand with the chapter content. Students design, build, and test based on real-world situations. They have the opportunity to apply the knowledge and skills learned to building a product.

Special Features

This technology and design strand is also reflected in Technology & Society and Science & Society features as well as Science & History timelines and Tech & Design in History timelines. These highly visual features introduce a technology and its impact on society. For example, students learn how a hybrid car differs from a traditional car.

Assessment in the Science Curriculum

No Child Left Behind clearly challenges school districts across the nation to raise expectations for all students with testing of student achievement in science beginning in 2007–2008.

A primary goal of NCLB is to provide classroom teachers with better data from scientifically valid assessments in order to inform instructional planning and to identify students who are at risk and require intervention. It has been a common practice to teach a science lesson, administer a test, grade it, and move on. This practice is a thing of the past. With the spotlight now on improving student performance, it is essential to use assessment results as a way to identify student strengths and challenges. Providing student feedback and obtaining student input is a valuable, essential part of the assessment process.

Assessment is a never-ending cycle, as is shown in the following diagram. Although you may begin at any point in the assessment cycle, the basic process is the same.

An important assessment strategy is to ensure that students have ample opportunities to check their understanding of skills and concepts before moving on to the next topic. Checking for understanding also includes asking appropriate, probing questions with each example presented. This enables students and teachers to know whether the skills or concepts being introduced are actually understood.

ASSESS: Use a variety of assessment tools to gain information and strengthen student understanding.

ANALYZE: Analyze assessment results to create a picture of student strengths and challenges.

TARGET: Choose a target to create a focused path on which to proceed.

STRATEGIZE: Identify strategies to achieve the target, create a plan for implementation, and choose assessments tools.

IMPLEMENT: Implement the plan with a focus on gathering and using assessment information throughout.

Eileen Depka
Supervisor of Standards and Assessment
Waukesha, Wisconsin

"Meeting the NCLB challenge will necessitate an integrated approach to assessment with a variety of assessment tools."

Evaluator's Checklist

Does your science program include assessments that—

- ✔ Are embedded before, during, and after lesson instruction
- ✔ Align to standards and to the instructional program
- ✔ Assess both skill acquisition and understanding
- ✔ Include meaningful rubrics to guide students
- ✔ Mirror the various formats of standardized tests

Prentice Hall *Science Explorer* now includes Success Tracker, an online tool to help teachers monitor and assess student progress with built-in remediation. Ask your sales rep about Success Tracker today!

Success  Tracker™

Online at PHSchool.com

Assessment in *Science Explorer*

Science Explorer's remarkable range of strategies for checking progress will help teachers find the right opportunity for reaching all their students.

The assessment strategies in *Science Explorer* will help both students and teachers alike ensure student success in content mastery as well as high-stakes test performance. A wealth of opportunities built into the Student Edition helps students monitor their own progress. Teachers are supported with ongoing assessment opportunities in the Teacher's Edition and an easy-to-use, editable test generator linked to content objectives. These integrated, ongoing assessment tools assure success.

Especially to support state and national testing objectives, Prentice Hall has developed test preparation materials that model the NCLB approach.

- **Diagnostic Assessment** tools provide in-depth analysis of strengths and weaknesses, areas of difficulty, and probable underlying causes that can help teachers make instructional decisions and plan intervention strategies.
- **Progress Monitoring** tools aligned with content objectives and state tests provide ongoing, longitudinal records of student achievement detailing individual student progress toward meeting end-of-year and end-of-schooling grade level, district, or state standards.
- **Outcomes** tools that mimic state and national tests show whether individual students have met the expected standards and can help a school system judge whether it has made adequate progress in improving its performance year by year.

Caption Questions enhance critical thinking skills.

Reading Checkpoints reinforce students' understanding.

Scaffolded Section Assessment Questions model the way students think.

Comprehensive Chapter Reviews and Assessments provide opportunities for students to check their own understanding and practice valuable high-stakes test-taking skills.

***ExamView®* Computer Test Bank CD-ROM** provides teachers access to thousands of modifiable test questions in English and Spanish.

Test Preparation Blackline Masters and Student Workbook include diagnostic and prescription tools, progress-monitoring aids, and practice tests that help teachers focus on improving test scores.

Section 3 Assessment

Target Reading Skill Sequencing Refer to your flowchart about seismographs as you answer Question 1.

Reviewing Key Concepts

1. a. Defining What is a seismogram?
   b. Explaining How can geologists tell apart the different types of seismic waves on a seismogram?
   c. Comparing and Contrasting Two identical seismographs are located 1,000 km and 1,200 km from an earthquake's epicenter. How would the two seismograms for the earthquake compare?
2. a. Reviewing What changes are measured by the instruments used to monitor faults?
   b. Describing How are satellites used to measure movements along a fault?
   c. Inferring A satellite that monitors a fault detects an increasing tilt in the land surface along the fault. What could this change in the land surface indicate?
3. a. Listing What are three ways in which geologists use seismographic data?
   b. Explaining How do geologists use seismographic data to make maps of faults?
   c. Making Generalizations Why is it difficult to predict earthquakes?

Writing in Science

Dialogue Geologists in Alaska have just detected an earthquake and located the earthquake's epicenter. Write a dialogue in which the geologists notify a disaster response team that will help people in the earthquake area.

Chapter 2 F ◆ 65

Standardized Test Prep

Test-Taking Tip

When answering questions about diagrams, read all parts of the diagram carefully, including title, captions, and labels. Make sure that you understand the meaning of arrows and other symbols. Determine exactly what the question asks. Then eliminate those answer choices that are not supported by the diagram.

Practice answering this question.

The diagram shows how stress affects a mass of rock in a process called
A compression.
B tension.
C squeezing.
D shearing.

The correct answer is D because the arrows show rock being pulled in opposite directions.

Choose the letter that best answers the question or completes the statement.

1. In a strike-slip fault, rock masses along the fault move
   A in the same direction.
   B down only.
   C together.
   D sideways past each other.
2. Stress will build until an earthquake occurs if friction along a fault is
   F decreasing. G high.
   H low. J changed to heat.

Use the information below and your knowledge of science to answer Questions 3 and 4.

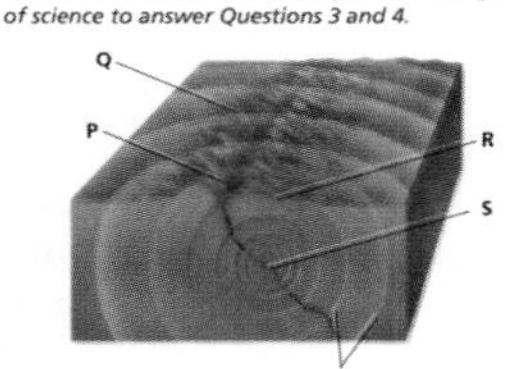

3. When an earthquake occurs, seismic waves travel
   A from P in all directions.
   B from R to S.
   C from S in all directions.
   D from Q to P.
4. At point R, seismic waves from an earthquake would be
   F weaker than at P.
   G likely to cause little damage.
   H weaker than at Q.
   J likely to cause the most damage.
5. To estimate the total energy released by an earthquake, a geologist should use the
   A Mercalli scale. B Richter scale.
   C epicenter scale. D moment magnitude scale.

Constructed Response

6. A geologist discovers a large fault beneath a major city. Why would this information be helpful in determining earthquake risk in the area? What three safety steps should the geologist recommend?

Chapter 2 F ◆ 79

Master Materials List

SCIENCE EXPLORER offers an abundance of activity options in the Student Edition so you can pick and choose those that suit your needs. Prentice Hall has worked with Neo/SCI Corporation to develop Consumable Kits and Nonconsumable Kits that precisely match the needs of the ***SCIENCE EXPLORER*** labs. Use this Master Materials List or the Materials Ordering CD-ROM to help order your supplies. For more information on materials kits for this program, contact your local Prentice Hall sales representative or Neo/SCI Corporation at 1-800-526-6689 or **www.neosci.com**.

Consumable Materials

Description	Textbook Section(s)	Quantity per Class
*Air freshener, spray	1-4 (DIS)	1
Bag, paper, 10 x 20 x 7.5 cm	3-2 (Lab)	10
*Bar code	4-3 (Lab)	25
Bromthymol blue, 30 mL	2-2 (Lab)	5
*Cellophane, colored, roll	2-1 (CP)	1
Chemical compounds, variety (i.e., baking soda, chalk, salt)	1-3 (DIS)	15
Coffee filter, paper	2-1 (TT)	5
Cotton swab, pkg	1-3 (Lab)	50
Coverslip, 1 oz	1-1 (SA), 2-3 (DIS)	1
*Crackers, unsalted soda, box	1-3 (TT)	1
Cup, clear, plastic, large, 16 oz	2-2 (SA), 2-2 (Lab)	5
Cup, clear, plastic, small, 7 oz	1-4 (TT), 2-1 (TT)	5
*Cup, paper, 7 oz	1-3 (Lab), 5-1 (TT)	15
*Dips, fat-containing (complete with nutrition labels)	1-3 (Lab)	5
Dropper, plastic, pkg/10	1-1 (SA), 1-4 (TT), 2-3 (DIS)	1
*Egg, uncooked	1-1 (CP)	5
Fat-testing strips, pkg/75	1-3 (Lab)	1
Food coloring, red, 30 mL	1-1 (CP), 1-4 (TT)	1
Forceps, plastic	5-1 (TT)	5
*Fresh fruit	5-3 (TT)	50
Gelatin, colorless, package	1-2 (TT)	5
*Glue	3-1 (CP)	5
Index card, blank, 3" x 5"	4-2 (Lab)	60
Ink pad	4-3 (DIS)	5
*Leaf	2-1 (SA)	5
*Markers, colored art, pkg	3-1 (CP), 4-1 (CP)	5
Marker, permanent	1-3 (Lab), 3-2 (Lab), 3-3 (DIS), 4-2 (Lab), 5-1 (Lab)	5
*Materials, craft, miscellaneous	1-2 (TT)	5
Methylene blue stain, 30 mL	2-3 (DIS)	1
Microscope slide, pkg/72	1-1 (SA), 2-3 (DIS)	1
*Newspaper	1-1 (DIS), 1-1 (Lab)	1
*Paper towel, roll	1-3 (Lab), 2-2 (Lab)	1
Paper, construction, black, sheet	1-1 (Lab)	10
Paper, construction, blue, sheet	3-1 (CP), 5-1 (Lab)	50
*Paper, construction, variety pkg	2-3 (TT), 4-1 (CP)	1
Paper, construction, yellow, sheet	3-1 (CP), 5-1 (Lab)	55
*Paper, graph	4-1 (DIS)	30
*Paper, white, ream	3-3 (DIS), 4-3 (DIS), 5-1 (SA)	1
*Pencil, colored, pkg/4	2-3 (Lab), 3-1 (CP)	5
Pin, hair	5-1 (TT)	5
Pipe cleaners, color variety, pkg	2-3 (TT)	1
*Plant	2-1 (CP)	5
Plate, paper, 9"	5-1 (TT)	5
Pond culture, dry mix	1-1 (SA)	1
Potting soil, bag	2-1 (CP)	1
*Raisins, box, small	5-1 (TT)	5
Rubbing alcohol, 30 mL	2-1 (TT)	1
*Seeds, bean, pkt.	2-1 (CP)	5
*Seed, bird, 1 box	5-1 (TT)	1
Seed, sunflower, 30 g	5-1 (DIS)	1
Stick, craft	3-3 (DIS)	20
Straw, drinking, wrapped	2-2 (DIS), 2-2 (Lab)	20
*String, ball	1-1 (CP)	1

KEY: CP: Chapter Project; **DIS:** Discover; **SA:** Skills Activity; **TT:** Try This; **Lab**: Skills, Consumer, Design Your Own, and Technology & Design
* = School Supplied

Quantities based on five groups of six students per class.

Master Materials List

Consumable Materials (continued)

Description	Textbook Section(s)	Quantity per Class
Sugar, granulated, 454 g	2-2 (DIS)	1
Tape, masking, roll	1-1 (Lab), 2-4 (DIS), 3-2 (TT)	1
Vinegar, 125 mL	1-1 (CP)	1
Yeast, dry baking, 25 g	2-2 (DIS), 2-3 (DIS)	1

Nonconsumable Materials

Description	Textbook Section(s)	Quantity per Class
Beaker, 250 mL	2-2 (Lab)	10
Button, black	5-1 (SA)	75
Button, white	5-1 (SA)	75
*Calculator	1-2 (DIS), 2-3 (Lab), 5-1 (CP)	5
Calculator, solar-powered	2-1 (DIS)	1
*Clip, hair	5-1 (TT)	5
*Clothespin	5-1 (TT)	5
Container, plastic, with lids	1 (CP), 1-3 (DIS), 5-3 (TT)	15
*Dime	2-1 (TT), 3-2 (TT), 3-2 (DIS)	20
*Goggles, safety	2-2 (DIS)	30
Graduated cylinder, polypropylene, 25 mL	2-2 (Lab)	5
Hand lens	1-1 (Lab), 1-1 (DIS), 4-3 (DIS), 4-3 (Lab), 5-1 (DIS)	10
*Lens, magnifying, high-power	1-1 (Lab)	5
*Lens, magnifying, low-power	1-1 (Lab)	5
*Marble, blue	3-2 (Lab)	15
*Marble, white	3-2 (Lab)	15
Meter stick, 1/2	2-4 (DIS), 4-1 (DIS), 5-1 (CP)	5
*Metric tape	5-1 (CP)	1
*Microscope	1-1 (DIS), 1-1 (SA), 1-2 (TT), 2-3 (DIS), 2-3 (Lab)	5
Mirror, 7.5 cm x 12.5 cm	3-1 (Lab)	5
*Nutrition labels, food	1-3 (Lab)	5
Pan, aluminum, rectangular, 9 x 7 x 2"	1-2 (TT)	5
Pan, aluminum, round, 9"	1-2 (TT)	5
*Pen	5-2 (DIS)	40
*Plant light	2-1 (CP)	1
*Plant pots	2-1 (CP)	5
Rack, test tube	2-2 (DIS)	5
Ruler, 15 cm	1-1 (CPLab), 1-2 (DIS), 2-1 (CP), 2-1 (TT), 4-1 (DIS), 5-1 (DIS)	5
*Scissors	1-1 (DIS), 2-1 (TT), 3-1 (CP), 3-2 (TT), 4-2 (Lab), 5-1 (Lab)	5
Slide, prepared, animal cell	1-2 (TT)	5
Slide, prepared, cork section	1-1 (SA)	5
Slide, prepared, onion root tip undergoing cell division	2-3 (Lab)	5
Slide, prepared, plant cell	1-2 (TT)	5
Stopper, rubber, size 6	2-2 (DIS)	10
*Stopwatch	1-3 (Lab), 2-2 (Lab), 5-1 (TT), 5-1 (SA)	5
Test tube, with stopper, 18 x 150 mm	2-2 (DIS)	10
*Watering can	2-1 (CP)	1

KEY: CP: Chapter Project; **DIS:** Discover; **SA:** Skills Activity; **TT:** Try This; **Lab**: Skills, Consumer, Design Your Own, and Technology & Design
* = School Supplied

Quantities based on five groups of six students per class.

Cells and Heredity

Book-Specific Resources

Student Edition
StudentExpress™ with Interactive Textbook
Teacher's Edition
All-in-One Teaching Resources
Color Transparencies
Guided Reading and Study Workbook
Student Edition on Audio CD
Discovery Channel School® Video
Lab Activity Video
Consumable and Nonconsumable Materials Kits

Program Print Resources

Integrated Science Laboratory Manual
Computer Microscope Lab Manual
Inquiry Skills Activity Books
Progress Monitoring Assessments
Test Preparation Workbook
Test-Taking Tips With Transparencies
Teacher's ELL Handbook
Reading Strategies for Science Content

Differentiated Instruction Resources

Adapted Reading and Study Workbook
Adapted Tests
Differentiated Instruction Guide for Labs and Activities

Program Technology Resources

TeacherExpress™ CD-ROM
Interactive Textbooks Online
PresentationExpress™ CD-ROM
ExamView®, Computer Test Bank CD-ROM
Lab zone™ Easy Planner CD-ROM
Probeware Lab Manual With CD-ROM
Computer Microscope and Lab Manual
Materials Ordering CD-ROM
Discovery Channel School® DVD Library
Lab Activity DVD Library
Web Site at PHSchool.com

Spanish Print Resources

Spanish Student Edition
Spanish Guided Reading and Study Workbook
Spanish Teaching Guide With Tests

Acknowledgments appear on page 210, which constitutes an extension of this copyright page.

ISBN 0-13-201145-X
2 3 4 5 6 7 8 9 10 10 09 08 07 06

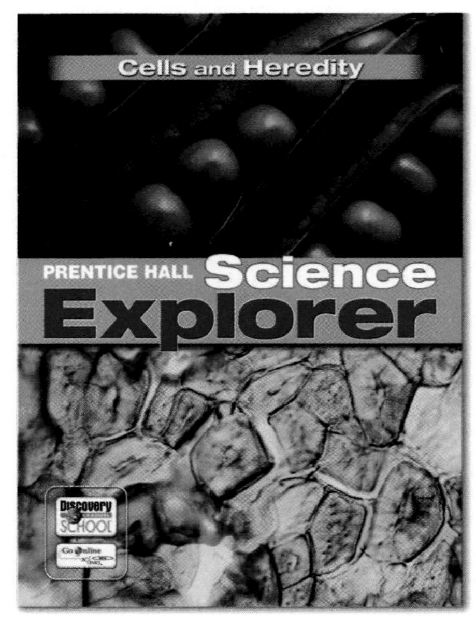

Cover
Ripe peas represent both the end and the beginning of a reproductive cycle (top). The thick walls of pea seed cells protect the cells' contents (bottom).

Program Authors

Michael J. Padilla, Ph.D.
Professor of Science Education
University of Georgia
Athens, Georgia

Michael Padilla is a leader in middle school science education. He has served as an author and elected officer for the National Science Teachers Association and as a writer of the National Science Education Standards. As lead author of Science Explorer, Mike has inspired the team in developing a program that meets the needs of middle grades students, promotes science inquiry, and is aligned with the National Science Education Standards.

Ioannis Miaoulis, Ph.D.
President
Museum of Science
Boston, Massachusetts

Originally trained as a mechanical engineer, Ioannis Miaoulis is in the forefront of the national movement to increase technological literacy. As dean of the Tufts University School of Engineering, Dr. Miaoulis spearheaded the introduction of engineering into the Massachusetts curriculum. Currently he is working with school systems across the country to engage students in engineering activities and to foster discussions on the impact of science and technology on society.

Martha Cyr, Ph.D.
Director of K–12 Outreach
Worcester Polytechnic Institute
Worcester, Massachusetts

Martha Cyr is a noted expert in engineering outreach. She has over nine years of experience with programs and activities that emphasize the use of engineering principles, through hands-on projects, to excite and motivate students and teachers of mathematics and science in grades K–12. Her goal is to stimulate a continued interest in science and mathematics through engineering.

Book Author

Donald Cronkite, Ph.D.
Professor of Biology
Hope College
Holland, Michigan

Contributing Writer

Thomas R. Wellnitz
Science Instructor
The Paideia School
Atlanta, Georgia

Consultants

Reading Consultant

Nancy Romance, Ph.D.
Professor of Science Education
Florida Atlantic University
Fort Lauderdale, Florida

Mathematics Consultant

William Tate, Ph.D.
Professor of Education and Applied Statistics and Computation
Washington University
St. Louis, Missouri

C • iii

Reviewers

Tufts University Content Reviewers

Faculty from Tufts University in Medford, Massachusetts, developed *Science Explorer* chapter projects and reviewed the student books.

Astier M. Almedom, Ph.D.
Department of Biology

Wayne Chudyk, Ph.D.
Department of Civil and Environmental Engineering

John L. Durant, Ph.D.
Department of Civil and Environmental Engineering

George S. Ellmore, Ph.D.
Department of Biology

David Kaplan, Ph.D.
Department of Biomedical Engineering

Samuel Kounaves, Ph.D.
Department of Chemistry

David H. Lee, Ph.D.
Department of Chemistry

Douglas Matson, Ph.D.
Department of Mechanical Engineering

Karen Panetta, Ph.D.
Department of Electrical Engineering and Computer Science

Jan A. Pechenik, Ph.D.
Department of Biology

John C. Ridge, Ph.D.
Department of Geology

William Waller, Ph.D.
Department of Astronomy

Content Reviewers

Paul Beale, Ph.D.
Department of Physics
University of Colorado
Boulder, Colorado

Jeff Bodart, Ph.D.
Chipola Junior College
Marianna, Florida

Michael Castellani, Ph.D.
Department of Chemistry
Marshall University
Huntington, West Virginia

Eugene Chiang, Ph.D.
Department of Astronomy
University of California – Berkeley
Berkeley, California

Charles C. Curtis, Ph.D.
Department of Physics
University of Arizona
Tucson, Arizona

Daniel Kirk-Davidoff, Ph.D.
Department of Meteorology
University of Maryland
College Park, Maryland

Diane T. Doser, Ph.D.
Department of Geological Sciences
University of Texas at El Paso
El Paso, Texas

R. E. Duhrkopf, Ph.D.
Department of Biology
Baylor University
Waco, Texas

Michael Hacker
Co-director, Center for Technological Literacy
Hofstra University
Hempstead, New York

Michael W. Hamburger, Ph.D.
Department of Geological Sciences
Indiana University
Bloomington, Indiana

Alice K. Hankla, Ph.D.
The Galloway School
Atlanta, Georgia

Donald C. Jackson, Ph.D.
Department of Molecular Pharmacology, Physiology, & Biotechnology
Brown University
Providence, Rhode Island

Jeremiah N. Jarrett, Ph.D.
Department of Biological Sciences
Central Connecticut State University
New Britain, Connecticut

David Lederman, Ph.D.
Department of Physics
West Virginia University
Morgantown, West Virginia

Becky Mansfield, Ph.D.
Department of Geography
Ohio State University
Columbus, Ohio

Elizabeth M. Martin, M.S.
Department of Chemistry and Biochemistry
College of Charleston
Charleston, South Carolina

Joe McCullough, Ph.D.
Department of Natural and Applied Sciences
Cabrillo College
Aptos, California

Robert J. Mellors, Ph.D.
Department of Geological Sciences
San Diego State University
San Diego, California

Joseph M. Moran, Ph.D.
American Meteorological Society
Washington, D.C.

David J. Morrissey, Ph.D.
Department of Chemistry
Michigan State University
East Lansing, Michigan

Philip A. Reed, Ph.D.
Department of Occupational & Technical Studies
Old Dominion University
Norfolk, Virginia

Scott M. Rochette, Ph.D.
Department of the Earth Sciences
State University of New York, College at Brockport
Brockport, New York

Laurence D. Rosenhein, Ph.D.
Department of Chemistry
Indiana State University
Terre Haute, Indiana

Ronald Sass, Ph.D.
Department of Biology and Chemistry
Rice University
Houston, Texas

George Schatz, Ph.D.
Department of Chemistry
Northwestern University
Evanston, Illinois

Sara Seager, Ph.D.
Carnegie Institution of Washington
Washington, D.C.

Robert M. Thornton, Ph.D.
Section of Plant Biology
University of California
Davis, California

John R. Villarreal, Ph.D.
College of Science and Engineering
The University of Texas – Pan American
Edinburg, Texas

Kenneth Welty, Ph.D.
School of Education
University of Wisconsin–Stout
Menomonie, Wisconsin

Edward J. Zalisko, Ph.D.
Department of Biology
Blackburn College
Carlinville, Illinois

Teacher Reviewers

David R. Blakely
Arlington High School
Arlington, Massachusetts

Jane E. Callery
Two Rivers Magnet Middle School
East Hartford, Connecticut

Melissa Lynn Cook
Oakland Mills High School
Columbia, Maryland

James Fattic
Southside Middle School
Anderson, Indiana

Dan Gabel
Hoover Middle School
Rockville, Maryland

Wayne Goates
Eisenhower Middle School
Goddard, Kansas

Katherine Bobay Graser
Mint Hill Middle School
Charlotte, North Carolina

Darcy Hampton
Deal Junior High School
Washington, D.C.

Karen Kelly
Pierce Middle School
Waterford, Michigan

David Kelso
Manchester High School Central
Manchester, New Hampshire

Benigno Lopez, Jr.
Sleepy Hill Middle School
Lakeland, Florida

Angie L. Matamoros, Ph.D.
ALM Consulting, Inc.
Weston, Florida

Tim McCollum
Charleston Middle School
Charleston, Illinois

Bruce A. Mellin
Brooks School
North Andover, Massachusetts

Ella Jay Parfitt
Southeast Middle School
Baltimore, Maryland

Evelyn A. Pizzarello
Louis M. Klein Middle School
Harrison, New York

Kathleen M. Poe
Fletcher Middle School
Jacksonville, Florida

Shirley Rose
Lewis and Clark Middle School
Tulsa, Oklahoma

Linda Sandersen
Greenfield Middle School
Greenfield, Wisconsin

Mary E. Solan
Southwest Middle School
Charlotte, North Carolina

Mary Stewart
University of Tulsa
Tulsa, Oklahoma

Paul Swenson
Billings West High School
Billings, Montana

Thomas Vaughn
Arlington High School
Arlington, Massachusetts

Susan C. Zibell
Central Elementary
Simsbury, Connecticut

Safety Reviewers

W. H. Breazeale, Ph.D.
Department of Chemistry
College of Charleston
Charleston, South Carolina

Ruth Hathaway, Ph.D.
Hathaway Consulting
Cape Girardeau, Missouri

Douglas Mandt, M.S.
Science Education Consultant
Edgewood, Washington

Activity Field Testers

Nicki Bibbo
Witchcraft Heights School
Salem, Massachusetts

Rose-Marie Botting
Broward County Schools
Fort Lauderdale, Florida

Colleen Campos
Laredo Middle School
Aurora, Colorado

Elizabeth Chait
W. L. Chenery Middle School
Belmont, Massachusetts

Holly Estes
Hale Middle School
Stow, Massachusetts

Laura Hapgood
Plymouth Community Intermediate School
Plymouth, Massachusetts

Mary F. Lavin
Plymouth Community Intermediate School
Plymouth, Massachusetts

James MacNeil, Ph.D.
Cambridge, Massachusetts

Lauren Magruder
St. Michael's Country Day School
Newport, Rhode Island

Jeanne Maurand
Austin Preparatory School
Reading, Massachusetts

Joanne Jackson-Pelletier
Winman Junior High School
Warwick, Rhode Island

Warren Phillips
Plymouth Public Schools
Plymouth, Massachusetts

Carol Pirtle
Hale Middle School
Stow, Massachusetts

Kathleen M. Poe
Fletcher Middle School
Jacksonville, Florida

Cynthia B. Pope
Norfolk Public Schools
Norfolk, Virginia

Anne Scammell
Geneva Middle School
Geneva, New York

Karen Riley Sievers
Callanan Middle School
Des Moines, Iowa

David M. Smith
Eyer Middle School
Allentown, Pennsylvania

Gene Vitale
Parkland School
McHenry, Illinois

Contents

Cells and Heredity

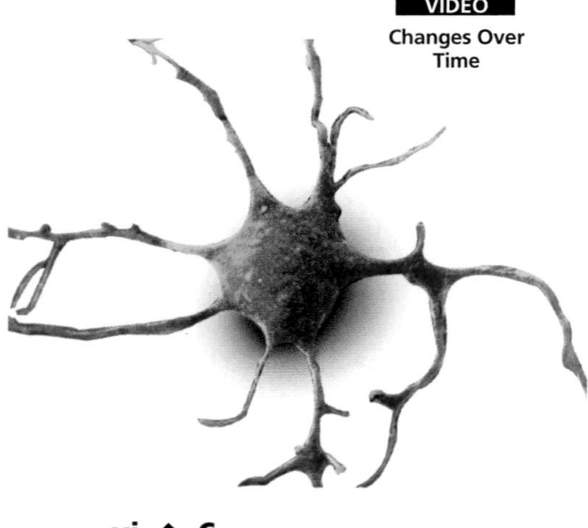

Reference Section

VIDEO

Enhance understanding through dynamic video.

Preview Get motivated with this introduction to the chapter content.

Field Trip Explore a real-world story related to the chapter content.

Assessment Review content and take an assessment.

Web Links

Get connected to exciting Web resources in every lesson.

SCI LINKS NSTA Find Web links on topics relating to every section.

Active Art Interact with selected visuals from every chapter online.

Planet Diary® Explore news and natural phenomena through weekly reports.

Science News® Keep up to date with the latest science discoveries.

Experience the complete textbook online and on CD-ROM.

Activities Practice skills and learn content.

Videos Explore content and learn important lab skills.

Audio Support Hear key terms spoken and defined.

Self-Assessment Use instant feedback to help you track your progress.

Activities

Lab zone™ Chapter Project — Opportunities for long-term inquiry

Lab zone Discover Activity — Exploration and inquiry before reading

Lab zone Try This Activity — Reinforcement of key concepts

Lab zone Skills Activity — Practice of specific science inquiry skills

viii ◆ C

Lab zone Labs — In-depth practice of inquiry skills and science concepts

Lab zone At-Home Activity — Quick, engaging activities for home and family

• Tech & Design • — Design, build, test, and communicate

Math — Point-of-use math practice

Analyzing Data

Math Skills

active art — Illustrations come alive online

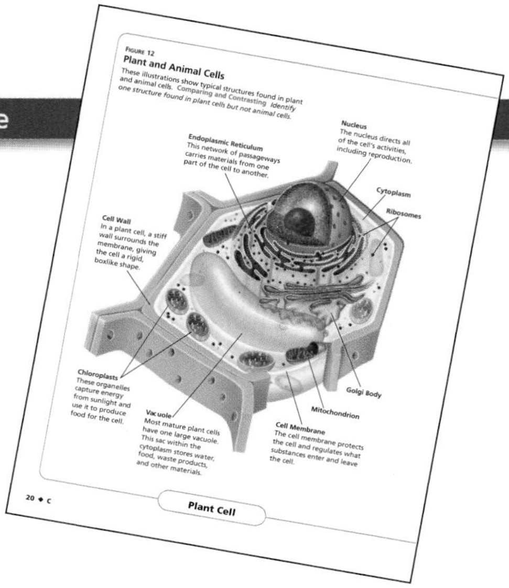

C • ix

Careers in Science

An Unfolding Mystery

Inquiry and Proteins

Biochemist Wilfredo Colón conducts research on the causes of certain human diseases. By reading about his work, students will gain insights about how research is done. They will read about how Dr. Colón plans and conducts his research. They will also learn about lab work, laboratory equipment, and analyzing data. The skills that Dr. Colón uses every day are the same inquiry skills that students need to become successful young scientists.

Build Background Knowledge

Proteins

Explain to students that proteins are an important building block of body cells. Ask: **What do you think would happen to a cell if the structure of its proteins were faulty?** Lead students to understand that when that happens, an organism can develop diseases.

Introduce the Career

Before students read the feature, let them read the title, examine the pictures, and read the captions on their own. Then ask: **What questions came into your mind as you looked at these pictures?** *(Students might suggest questions about how proteins fold, how misfolded proteins can lead to disease, and what a spectrophotometer is.)* **Why do you think it is important that a protein be folded correctly?** *(If a protein is not folded correctly, it cannot perform its function and may lead to disease.)*

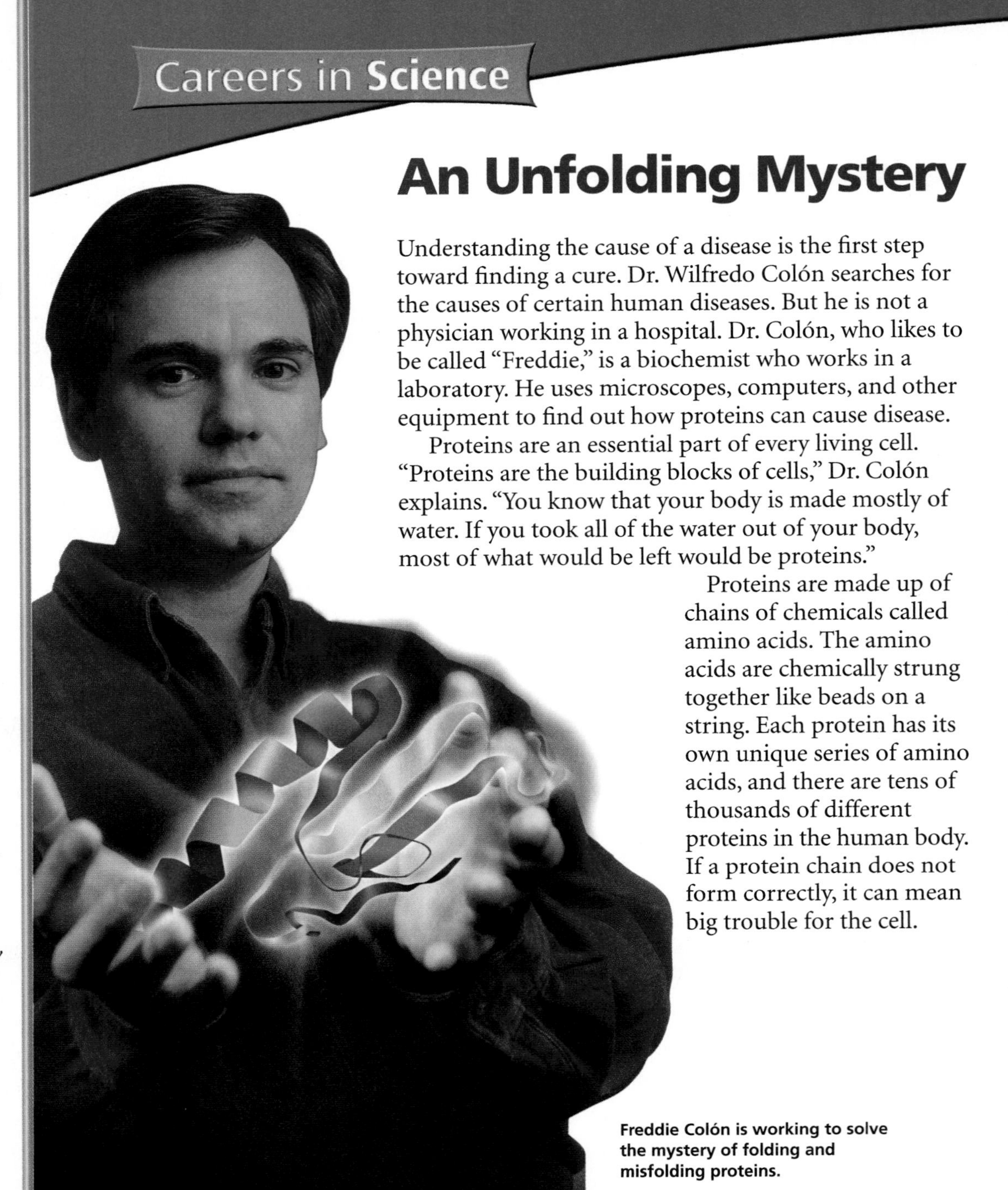

An Unfolding Mystery

Understanding the cause of a disease is the first step toward finding a cure. Dr. Wilfredo Colón searches for the causes of certain human diseases. But he is not a physician working in a hospital. Dr. Colón, who likes to be called "Freddie," is a biochemist who works in a laboratory. He uses microscopes, computers, and other equipment to find out how proteins can cause disease.

Proteins are an essential part of every living cell. "Proteins are the building blocks of cells," Dr. Colón explains. "You know that your body is made mostly of water. If you took all of the water out of your body, most of what would be left would be proteins."

Proteins are made up of chains of chemicals called amino acids. The amino acids are chemically strung together like beads on a string. Each protein has its own unique series of amino acids, and there are tens of thousands of different proteins in the human body. If a protein chain does not form correctly, it can mean big trouble for the cell.

Freddie Colón is working to solve the mystery of folding and misfolding proteins.

Background

Facts and Figures Biochemistry is the study of the chemistry of organisms. The goal of biochemistry is to provide an understanding of the structure and function of living things at the molecular level.

Biochemists identify biological problems and then develop and apply appropriate techniques to solve them at the molecular level. Biochemistry is used in clinical and forensic science and in the food and drug industries. Biochemists play an important role in a variety of areas, including health agriculture, and the environment.

Scientists created this computer model of protein folding.

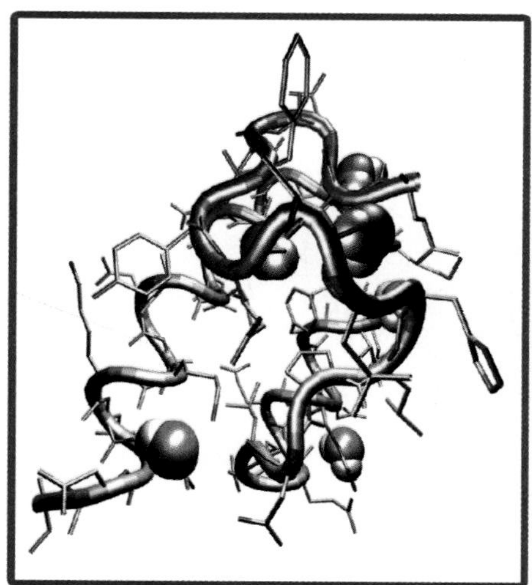

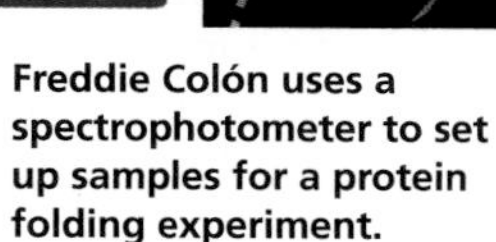

Freddie Colón uses a spectrophotometer to set up samples for a protein folding experiment.

Career Path

Wilfredo Colón was born in New York City and moved with his family to Puerto Rico when he was 10 years old. He received his bachelor's degree at the University of Puerto Rico at Mayagüez. Now he is an associate professor of chemistry at Rensselaer Polytechnic Institute, in Troy, New York. In 2000, Freddie received the Presidential Early Career Award for Scientists and Engineers. In 2002, he received a federal grant for one million dollars to fund his research into ALS.

Talking with Wilfredo Colón

Why is protein shape important?

As a protein chain forms inside the cell, it folds into a shape particular to that protein. The shape of a protein is sometimes compared to a key that fits into a lock. If the shape of the lock is incorrect, the key will no longer work. If the shape of a protein is wrong, it won't function properly. Disease may result. "No one knows exactly what makes normal proteins fold the way they do," says Freddie. "Until we know that, we won't fully understand how to cure diseases that occur when the folding goes wrong."

What happens when proteins misfold?

Misfolded proteins tend to stick together in clumps that are useless to the cell. The clumping of improperly folded, or misfolded, proteins is similar to what happens to an egg white when an egg is boiled. An egg white is mainly water and protein. When you first crack open an uncooked egg, the white is clear and runny. But when you cook an egg, the proteins it contains change shape, and the egg white becomes hard and is no longer clear. These changes are like the changes that occur when a protein folds incorrectly.

Explore the Career

Choose from among the teaching strategies on these pages as you help your students explore the practical application of inquiry skills.

Use Visuals Direct students' attention to the illustration of a protein folding. Help students see that if both ends of the protein were stretched out, it would form a chain composed of different parts. But as shown in the picture, the protein is made of many folds.

Class Activity After students read these two pages, ask: **Why is it important that a protein has a proper shape?** *(A protein's shape enables it to do its job.)* Explain that the shape of a protein enables it to bind with specific receptors on or in a cell. These receptors have a complimentary shape to that of the protein. To illustrate this, cut index cards in half, using a variety of cutting patterns. Place the cut cards in a bag and have each student choose one card. Then allow students to walk around the room comparing card halves until they find a match.

Discuss Remind students that when proteins lose their shape, they can no longer do their jobs. Explain that one factor that can cause a protein to lose its shape is an increase or decrease in temperature. Tell students that if the temperature returns to normal after an increase or decrease, smaller proteins may return to their normal shape. But because larger proteins have a more complex folding pattern, they do not return to normal as often after a temperature change. Ask: **What do you think might happen to the proteins in the cells of the human body if a person runs a high fever for an extended period?** *(Proteins may lose their shape permanently and not be able to do their job.)*

Background

Facts and Figures Proteins have four levels of structural organization. The first level is the unique sequence of amino acids that make up the protein. If the sequence of amino acids in a protein is not correct, diseases such as sickle-cell anemia can result. The second level of organization involves the folding of the amino acids into a spiral or pleated sheets. The third level describes the overall folding pattern of the amino acids into a three-dimensional shape. Each protein has a unique structure that determines how it will function. The fourth level of organization describes how a group of large protein chains are arranged relative to each other.

Discuss Ask: **According to the information in the feature what kind of equipment, and for what purpose, does Dr. Colón use in his research?** (*Computers to make models, spectrophotometers to tell when a protein has folded correctly or if it has clumped, a high-power microscope to look at the shape of the clumped proteins)*

Use Visuals Ask a volunteer to read the captions in the diagram as other students follow along in their own text. Then ask: **What happens to misfolded proteins?** *(They clump together.)* **What is the effect of this clumping?** *(Disease)* **How do misfolded proteins cause ALS?** *(The misfolded proteins are too large for the nerve cell to get rid of, so they build up in the cell. As a result, nerve cells can no longer send or receive signals so muscles cannot move. Over time as more nerve cells die, the muscles completely lose their ability to move.)*

Research Interested students may want to research more information about the diseases mentioned in the feature or other diseases that may be caused by improperly folded proteins. Diseases mentioned in the feature include Parkinson's disease, type II diabetes, and Alzheimer's disease. What are the symptoms of the disease? How is it currently treated? What research is currently being done on the disease? How does this research move us closer to finding a cure for the disease?

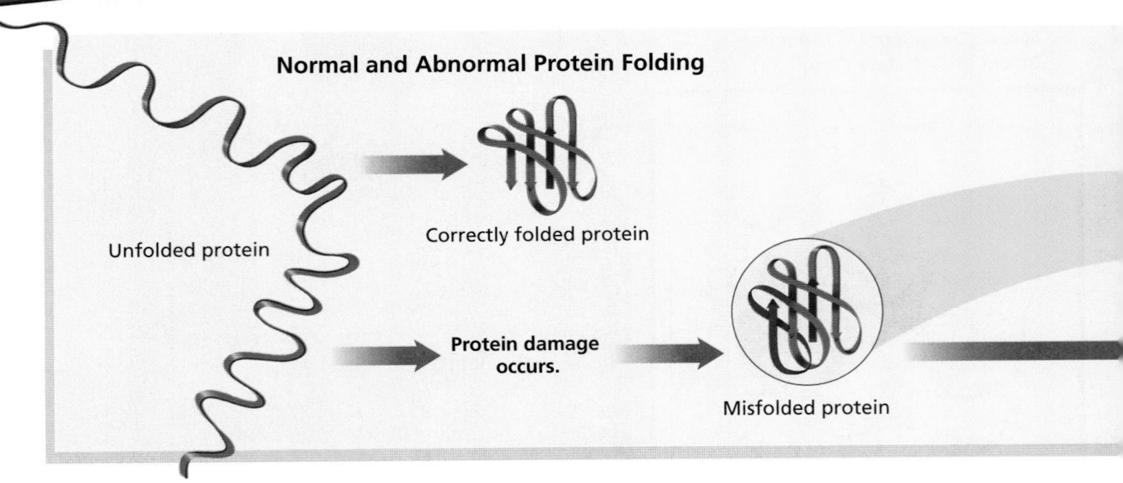

What diseases are caused by misfolding?

Diseases that may be caused by improperly folded proteins include Parkinson's disease, type II diabetes, and Alzheimer's disease. Dr. Colón is especially interested in finding out how misfolded proteins may cause a disease called amyotrophic lateral sclerosis (ALS), which is also known as Lou Gehrig's disease.

Lou Gehrig, who played first base for the New York Yankees, was one of baseball's greatest players. He died at age 38. The disease that took his life was named after him.

What is ALS?

"ALS is a disease of the nerve cells that tell your muscles to move," Freddie explains. "A person with ALS slowly loses the ability to move. The disease is always fatal. Many scientists hypothesize that ALS may be caused by proteins that do not fold correctly." On average, ALS strikes people who are around 50 years of age.

What causes ALS?

In ALS, the misfolded proteins appear to poison nerve cells, the cells that control movement. Misfolded proteins are too large for the cell to get rid of, so they build up inside the cell. Nerve cells that contain too many protein clumps can no longer receive signals from the brain.Without instruction from the brain, muscles cannot move. Over time, as more and more nerve cells die, the muscles completely lose their ability to move.

How do you research proteins?

"We are researching two areas," Freddie explains. "First, we are trying to understand how proteins fold correctly.

Background

Facts and Figures Amyotrophic Lateral Sclerosis (ALS) affects about 20,000 Americans with an estimated 5,000 people in the United States diagnosed each year. Men are about one and a half times more likely to develop ALS than women. Early symptoms of ALS include muscle cramping, twitching, and stiffness; muscle weakness in the arms or legs; slurred speech; and difficulty chewing or swallowing. As the disease progresses patients lose the ability to control voluntary muscles and later when the muscles involved in breathing weaken, respiration becomes difficult. Most ALS patients die as a result of respiratory failure. A patient's mental abilities, including memory and intelligence, remain intact. There is no known cure for ALS.

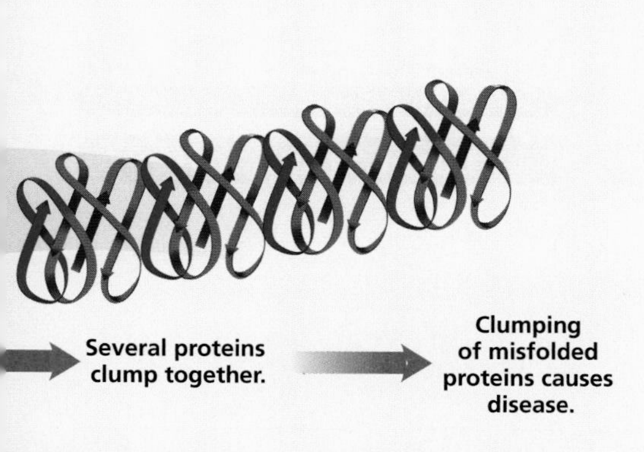

"Second, we are testing the hypothesis that certain ALS cases are caused by the misfolding of a particular protein. Since we can't see protein molecules with our eyes, we use a machine called a spectrophotometer.

"The spectrophotometer can tell us when the protein is folded correctly or when it misfolds and clumps up. We use an atomic force microscope to look at the shape of the clumped protein.

"If we can unlock the mystery of how the ALS protein behaves, we may begin to understand how it causes disease. We could begin to look for medicines that would slow the progress of this disease. This information would help us better understand other diseases that seem to be caused by protein misfolding."

Did you always want to be a scientist?

"No!" Freddie exclaims. "I always wanted to be a physician, to cure diseases. But, when I took a chemistry class in my second year of college, that subject really came alive for me. Then I saw an ad for an undergraduate research assistant in a laboratory and applied for the job. This opportunity to do research was a turning point for me, and I decided on a career in chemistry. Now I work on chains of amino acids that make up proteins. So, instead of a physician, now I'm a scientist!"

What qualities make a good scientist?

"I can think of four things that make a good scientist," says Freddie. "First, scientists need to be hardworking. In my job, I do whatever my work requires. Often that means long hours. Second, scientists need to have perseverance. You have to realize that many of your experiments won't work! Perseverance means to keep going even when nothing is going right. Third, I think scientists have to be able to see many aspects of a problem and put them together toward a possible solution. Finally, and most important, a scientist needs confidence. If you want to be a scientist, go for it!"

Writing in Science

Career Link Freddie listed four qualities that make a good scientist. One of those qualities is perseverance. Someone with perseverance doesn't give up when faced with difficulties. In a paragraph, describe how perseverance might help in a science career.

For: More on this career
Visit: PHSchool.com
Web Code: ceb-3000

Discuss Dr. Colón mentions four things that make a good scientist: the motivation to work hard, perseverance, the ability to problem solve, and confidence. Help students understand that some of the qualities needed for success in any career are not always about academic material. Ask: **How do all of these qualities help you accomplish other goals in your life?** *(Student responses may vary but could include ideas such as meeting a goal in sports, meeting a goal in academics, meeting a goal at work, or meeting a personal goal.)*

Writing in Science

Writing Mode Description
Scoring Rubric
4 Includes a definition of the word *perseverance* and several examples of how having perseverance is important to pursuing a science career
3 Includes several examples of how having perseverance is important to pursuing a science career
2 Includes one example of how having perseverance is important to pursuing a science career
1 Includes only a definition of the word *perseverance* and no examples of how having perseverance is important to pursuing a science career

Go Online PHSchool.com
For: More on this career
Visit: PHSchool.com
Web Code: ceb-3000

Students can do research on this career and others that are related to the study of biochemistry.

Chapter at a Glance

Technology

Local Standards

 *Egg-speriment With a Cell*

All in One Teaching Resources

- Chapter Project Teacher Notes, pp. 40–41
- Chapter Project Student Overview, pp. 42–43
- Chapter Project Student Worksheets, pp. 44–45
- Chapter Project Scoring Rubric, p. 46

Video Preview

2–3 periods
1–1 1/2 blocks

Discovering Cells

C.1.1.1 Tell what cells are.

C.1.1.2 Explain how the invention of the microscope contributed to scientists' understanding of living things.

C.1.1.3 State the cell theory.

C.1.1.4 Describe how microscopes produce magnified images.

3–4 periods
1 1/2–2 blocks

Looking Inside Cells

C.1.2.1 Identify the role of the cell wall and the cell membrane in the cell.

C.1.2.2 Describe the functions of cell organelles.

C.1.2.3 Explain how cells are organized in many-celled organisms.

C.1.2.4 Tell how bacterial cells differ from plant and animal cells.

Video Field Trip

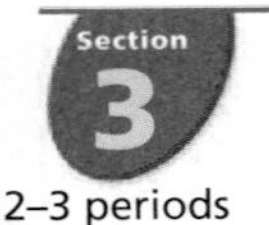

2–3 periods
1–1 1/2 blocks

Chemical Compounds in Cells

C.1.3.1 Define elements and compounds.

C.1.3.2 Identify the four main kinds of organic compounds in living things.

C.1.3.3 Explain how water is important to the function of cells.

1–2 periods
1/2–1 block

The Cell in Its Environment

C.1.4.1 Describe how most small molecules cross the cell membrane.

C.1.4.2 Explain why osmosis is important to cells.

C.1.4.3 Tell the difference between passive transport and active transport.

Review and Assessment

All in One Teaching Resources

- Key Terms Review, p. 78
- Transparency C11
- Performance Assessment Teacher Notes, p. 87
- Performance Assessment Scoring Rubric, p. 88
- Performance Assessment Student Worksheet, p. 89
- Chapter Test, pp. 90–94

Video Assesment

Test Preparation

Test Preparation

Chapter Activities Planner

For more activities
LAB ZONE Easy Planner CD-ROM

Student Edition	Inquiry	Time	Materials	Skills	Resources
Chapter Project, p. 5	Open-Ended	Ongoing (2 weeks)	**All in One Teaching Resources,** p. 40	Predicting, observing, measuring, graphing	**Lab zone Easy Planner** **All in One Teaching Resources,** Support pp. 40–41
Section 1					
Discover Activity, p. 6	Guided	10 minutes	Black and white newspaper photograph, hand lens, microscope, scissors	Observing	**Lab zone Easy Planner**
Skills Activity, p. 11	Guided	10 minutes	Blank slide, coverslip, microscope, plastic dropper, pond water, prepared slide of cork	Observing	**Lab zone Easy Planner**
Technology Lab, pp.14–15	Open-Ended	40 minutes	Book, metric ruler, 1 low-power magnifying lens, 1 high-power magnifying lens, 2 cardboard tubes from paper towels (or black construction paper), tape	Building a prototype, observing, evaluating	**Lab zone Easy Planner** **Lab Activity Video** **All in One Teaching Resources,** Technology Lab: *Design and Build a Microscope*, pp. 54–55
Section 2					
Discover Activity, p. 16	Directed	10 minutes	Calculator, metric ruler	Inferring	**Lab zone Easy Planner**
Try This Activity, p. 18	Open-Ended	10 minutes first day; 10 minutes the next	Packet of colorless gelatin, warm water, craft-type materials, stirrer, rectangular or round pan	Making models	**Lab zone Easy Planner**
Try This Activity, p. 22	Guided	15 minutes	Microscope, prepared slide of animal cells, prepared slide of plant cells	Observing	**Lab zone Easy Planner**
Section 3					
Discover Activity, p. 25	Directed	10 minutes	Labeled containers of chemical compounds such as baking soda, chalk, salt, and zinc oxide sun block	Forming operational definitions	**Lab zone Easy Planner**
Try This Activity p. 28	Guided	5 minutes	Unsalted soda cracker	Inferring	**Lab zone Easy Planner**
Consumer Lab, p. 31	Guided	Prep 20 minutes; Class 30 minutes	Fat-testing test strips with color key, dips containing fat, paper towels, cotton swabs, clock or watch with second hand, permanent marker	Interpreting data, inferring	**Lab zone Easy Planner** **Lab Activity Video** **All in One Teaching Resources,** Consumer Lab: *Which Foods Are Fat Free?*, pp. 70–71
Section 4					
Discover Activity, p. 32	Directed	5 minutes	Air freshener spray	Developing hypotheses	**Lab zone Easy Planner**
Try This Activity, p. 35	Directed	10 minutes	Cold water; food coloring, small, clear plastic cup; plastic dropper	Inferring	**Lab zone Easy Planner**

Section 1 Discovering Cells

2–3 periods, 1–1 1/2 blocks

ABILITY LEVELS
- L1 Basic to Average
- L2 For All Students
- L3 Average to Advanced

Local Standards

Objectives

C.1.1.1 Tell what cells are.

C.1.1.2 Explain how the invention of the microscope contributed to scientists' understanding of living things.

C.1.1.3 State the cell theory.

C.1.1.4 Describe how microscopes produce magnified images.

Key Terms

• cell • microscope • cell theory

Preteach

Build Background Knowledge

Help students appreciate the great number of cells in an organism and the size of individual cells.

Is Seeing Believing? 

Targeted Print and Technology Resources

All in One Teaching Resources
- L2 Reading Strategy Transparency C1: Sequencing

 **PresentationExpress™ CD-ROM**

Instruct

An Overview of Cells Ask questions to help students define a cell and its functions.

First Observations of Cells Identify what early scientists learned by studying living things under a microscope.

Development of the Cell Theory Examine the contributions of scientists leading to the cell theory.

Light and Electron Microscopes Use a diagram to explain how microscopes magnify images.

Lab zone Technology Lab *Design and Build a Microscope* 

Targeted Print and Technology Resources

All in One Teaching Resources
- L2 Guided Reading, pp. 49–51
- L2 Transparency C2
- L2 Technology Lab: *Design and Build a Microscope,* pp. 54–55

Lab Activity Video/DVD
Technology Lab: *Design and Build a Microscope*

www.SciLinks.org Web Code: scn-0311

Student Edition on Audio CD

Assess

Section Assessment Questions

Have students use their flowcharts showing the work of scientists to answer the questions.

Reteach

Use the Technology and History timeline to discuss the development of microscopes and the development of the cell theory.

Targeted Print and Technology Resources

All in One Teaching Resources
- • Section Summary, p. 48
- L1 Review and Reinforce, p. 52
- L3 Enrich, p. 53

Section 2 Looking Inside Cells

3–4 periods, 1 1/2–2 blocks

ABILITY LEVELS
- L1 Basic to Average
- L2 For All Students
- L3 Average to Advanced

Local Standards

Objectives

C.1.2.1 Identify the role of the cell wall and the cell membrane in the cell.
C.1.2.2 Describe the functions of cell organelles.
C.1.2.3 Explain how cells are organized in many-celled organisms.
C.1.2.4 Tell how bacterial cells differ from plant and animal cells.

Key Terms

• organelle • cell wall • cell membrane • nucleus • cytoplasm • mitochondria
• endoplasmic reticulum • ribosome • Golgi body • chloroplast • vacuole
• lysosome

Preteach

Build Background Knowledge

Relate division of labor among cell structure to division of labor in a community.

Discover Activity *How Large Are Cells?*  L1

Targeted Print and Technology Resources

Teaching Resources
- L2 Reading Strategy Transparency C3: Previewing Visuals

PresentationExpress™ CD-ROM

Instruct

Enter the Cell Use illustrations to identify the functions of the cell wall and cell membrane.

Sail on to the Nucleus Use a diagram of the nucleus to analyze its functions.

Organelles in the Cytoplasm Ask questions to help students synthesize how organelles work together to perform their functions.

Specialized Cells Explain how cells are organized into tissues, then organs, then organ systems.

Bacterial Cells Use an illustration to examine how bacterial cells differ from plant and animal cells.

Targeted Print and Technology Resources

All in One Teaching Resources
- L2 Guided Reading, pp. 58–60
- L2 Transparencies C4, C5

PHSchool.com Web Code: cep-3012

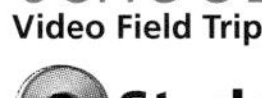
Discovery Channel School Video Field Trip

Student Edition on Audio CD

Assess

Section Assessment Questions

Have students use their graphic organizer of questions and answers about cells to answer the questions.

Reteach

Show photographs of different types of cells for students to classify.

Targeted Print and Technology Resources

All in One Teaching Resources
- Section Summary, p. 57
- L1 Review and Reinforce, p. 61
- L3 Enrich, p. 62

Section 3 Chemical Compounds in Cells

2–3 periods, 1–1 1/2 blocks

ABILITY LEVELS
- L1 Basic to Average
- L2 For All Students
- L3 Average to Advanced

Local Standards

Objectives

C.1.3.1 Define elements and compounds.

C.1.3.2 Identify the four main kinds of organic compounds in living things.

C.1.3.3 Explain how water is important to the function of cells.

Key Terms

• element • compound • carbohydrate • lipid • protein
• amino acid • enzyme • nucleic acid • DNA • RNA

Preteach

Build Background Knowledge

Model the difference between an element and a compound.

 *What Is a Compound?*

Targeted Print and Technology Resources

All in One Teaching Resources
- L2 Reading Strategy Transparency C6: Comparing and Contrasting

Instruct

Elements and Compounds Discuss elements, compounds, and water.

Carbohydrates Discuss which elements make up carbohydrates and the role of carbohydrates.

Lipids Identify the elements in lipids and how lipids function in living things.

Proteins Describe proteins and their various functions in cells.

Nucleic Acids Compare RNA and DNA, and discuss their role in cells.

Water and Living Things Consider the many ways that water is important to living things.

Lab zone Consumer Lab *Which Foods Are Fat Free?* L2

Targeted Print and Technology Resources

All in One Teaching Resources
- L2 Guided Reading, pp. 65–67
- L2 Transparency C7
- L2 Consumer Lab: *Which Foods Are Fat Free?* pp. 70–71

Lab Activity Video/DVD
Consumer Lab: *Which Foods Are Fat Free?*

www.SciLinks.org Web Code: scn-0313

Student Edition on Audio CD

Assess

Section Assessment Questions

Have students use their graphic organizers comparing and contrasting carbohydrates, proteins, and lipids to answer the questions.

Reteach

Compare and contrast the main types of organic compounds in living things.

Targeted Print and Technology Resources

All in One Teaching Resources
- Section Summary, p. 64
- L1 Review and Reinforce, p. 68
- L3 Enrich, p. 69

Section 4 The Cell in Its Environment

1–2 periods, 1/2–1 block

ABILITY LEVELS
- L1 Basic to Average
- L2 For All Students
- L3 Average to Advanced

Objectives

C.1.4.1 Describe how most small molecules cross the cell membrane.
C.1.4.2 Explain why osmosis is important to cells.
C.1.4.3 Tell the difference between passive transport and active transport.

Local Standards

Key Terms

• selectively permeable • diffusion • osmosis • passive transport
• active transport

Preteach

Build Background Knowledge

Compare the cell membrane to a sieve.

 *How Do Molecules Move?* 

Targeted Print and Technology Resources

All in One Teaching Resources
- L2 Reading Strategy: Building Vocabulary

PresentationExpress™ CD-ROM

Instruct

Diffusion Describe how diffusion causes molecules to move in or out of a cell membrane.

Osmosis Use visuals to explain how water moves in osmosis and why this is important.

Active Transport Compare and contrast active and passive transport.

Targeted Print and Technology Resources

All in One Teaching Resources
- L2 Guided Reading, pp. 74–75
- L2 Transparencies C8, C9, C10

PHSchool.com Web Code: ced-3014

Student Edition on Audio CD

Assess

Section Assessment Questions

Have students use their definitions to answer the questions.

Reteach

Summarize the three ways substances can move into and out of a cell.

Targeted Print and Technology Resources

All in One Teaching Resources
- Section Summary, p. 73
- L1 Review and Reinforce, p. 76
- L3 Enrich, p. 77

Chapter 1 Content Refresher

Section 1 Discovering Cells

Resolution in Light and Electron Microscopes In biological study, resolution, or resolving power, is the capability of lenses to distinguish individual objects within a specimen. In the study of cells, this includes the fine structures such as membranes, ribosomes, and even macromolecules.

The resolving power of both light and electron microscopes is limited by the source of illumination, that is, light waves and streams of vibrating electrons, respectively. In order for two adjacent objects to be resolved as two, light waves or electrons must pass between the objects without being scattered. When scattering occurs, the image is still visible, but the two objects will appear as a single fuzzy one. If objects are closer together than half the wavelength of light or electrons, the waves will be scattered.

Because of this physical limitation, the resolving power of light microscopes turns out to be no greater than half the wavelength of visible light. This translates into a useful magnification of about 1,000 X. You can magnify an image much greater than this by photographic enlargement, but you will not be able to see more detail. For this reason, many biological structures cannot be seen through even the finest light microscopes.

The wavelength of oscillating electrons in their stream is much smaller than the wavelengths of visible light, so electrons will easily pass between and resolve adjacent cell structures. As a result, the electron microscope's useful magnification is in the neighborhood of 250,000 X.

Section 2 Looking Inside Cells

Endosymbiotic Model

Some scientists have developed a model that may explain the origins of plant and animal cells. Bacterial cells are prokaryotic organisms, meaning that their genetic information is not enclosed within a nucleus and they do not have membrane-bound organelles, such as mitochondria and chloroplasts. All other cells, including plant and animal cells, are eukaryotic, meaning they have a nucleus and contain membrane-bound organelles.

Address Misconceptions

Some students may think that different types of cells within an organism contain different genetic material. However, every cell of an organism has exactly the same genetic material. For a strategy for overcoming this misconception, see **Address Misconceptions** in the section Looking Inside Cells.

The endosymbiotic model suggests that eukaryotic cells came from a mutually beneficial (symbiotic) relationship between different kinds of prokaryotic cells. That is, ancient bacterial cells enveloped smaller bacterial cells, and they functioned together as a unit. The model suggests that they evolved together, eventually becoming present-day eukaryotic cells. This model is supported by the fact that mitochondria and chloroplasts contain enzymes, ribosomes, and membranes that are similar to those of existing prokaryotes. Furthermore, mitochondria and chloroplasts have their own DNA and reproduce themselves within the eukaryotic cell in the same way that bacterial cells do.

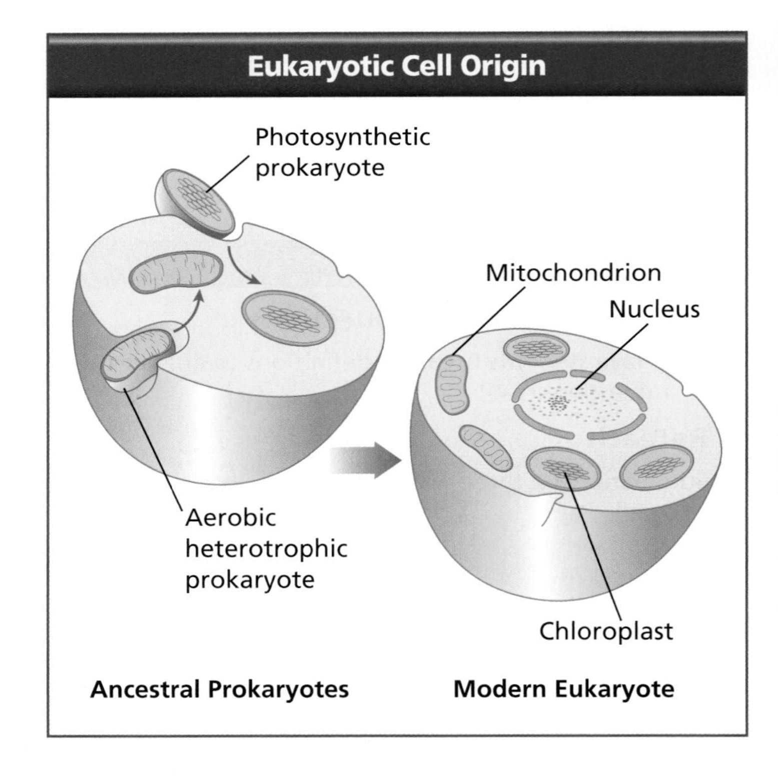

Section 3 Chemical Compounds in Cells

Biopolymers Complex carbohydrates, proteins, and nucleic acids are often called biopolymers. A biopolymer is a large biological molecule consisting of many similar units bonded together. These units are called monomers. Complex carbohydrates, such as starches, are made up of many simple sugars chemically combined in long strands or branching molecules. Cellulose, a complex carbohydrate that makes up the cell walls of plants, consists of many identical units of glucose (a simple sugar) bonded together in a long, unbranching strand.

Nucleic Acid Structure

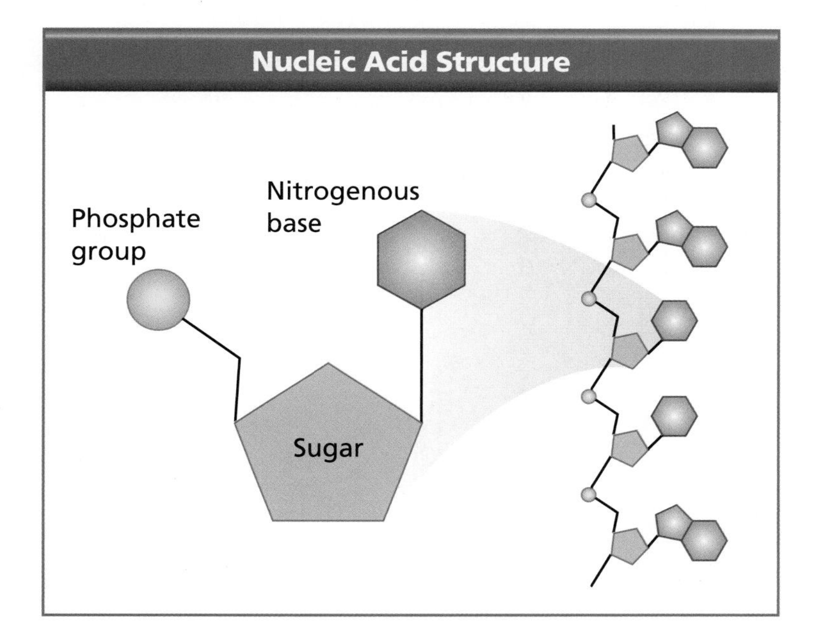

Nucleic acids are polymers made up of nucleotide units. Each nucleotide monomer consists of a sugar, a nitrogen-containing base, and a phosphate group, as you can see in the illustration. The nucleotide units are bonded together by their sugar and phosphate groups, making nucleic acids a sugar-phosphate chain with exposed nitrogenous bases. These nitrogenous bases can attract bases on a nearby chain, giving DNA molecules their double-stranded structure.

Proteins are polymers made up of amino acid monomers. The amino acids that make up proteins vary in structure and therefore chemical characteristics. Thus, the great variety of sequences of amino acids that make up different proteins gives rise to the great variety of protein shapes and functions.

Section 4 The Cell in Its Environment

Transport Proteins The cell membrane is a lipid bilayer, which means that it is composed of two layers of lipid molecules. The structure is such that some molecules (such as oxygen, carbon dioxide, water, and many organic compounds) can easily pass through the cell membrane, while other substances (such as ions and large, water-soluble organic compounds) cannot pass through on their own. Instead, these substances must pass from one side of the cell membrane to the other via transport proteins.

Transport proteins are specific to the substances they allow into and out of the cell. The transport protein simply acts like a key-activated gate—only particles of a specific size, shape, or chemical makeup can use them. Some transport proteins do not require cellular energy. The process by which such transport proteins carry out their function is called facilitated diffusion. Like simple diffusion, the substance that crosses the membrane goes from an area of high concentration to one of low concentration.

Help Students Read

Active Comprehension

Engaging Interest in a Topic

Strategy Stimulate students' interest in a topic prior to reading by having them generate questions based on their curiosity. Interest is thus translated into a purpose for reading. Looking for answers to the questions during reading helps keep students engaged. Before students begin reading, choose an opening paragraph from one of the sections in this chapter.

Example

1. Have a student read the paragraph.
2. Ask the group what more they would like to know about the topic. Make a list of responses.
3. Tell students to read the remainder of the section, keeping the questions in mind as they read.
4. After reading, discuss the extent to which each question was answered by the text. Also ask students to comment on any new information they learned that was surprising.
5. Have students work in small groups, applying the active comprehension strategy to the reading of other sections of the chapter.

Interactive Textbook

- Complete student edition
- Video and audio
- Simulations and activities
- Section and chapter reviews

Chapter 1 Cell Structure and Function

Chapter Preview

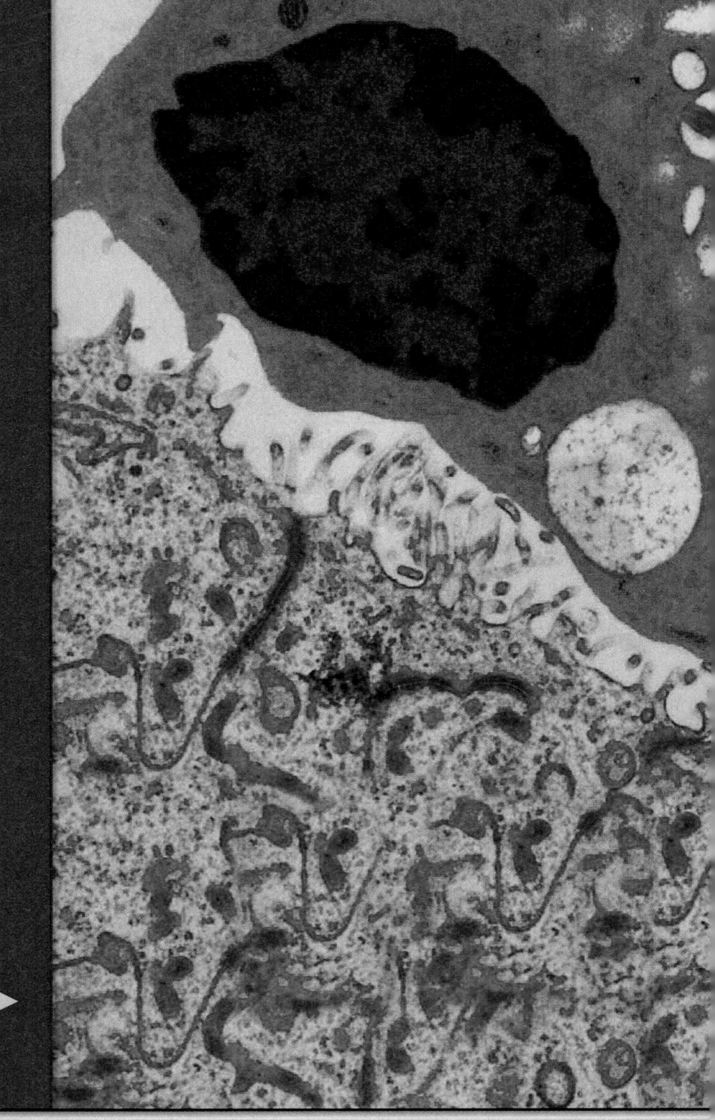

The cell that has been colored red is found in blood. This kind of cell destroys bacteria.

Lab zone Chapter Project

L3

Objectives

This project will allow students to observe how fluids pass back and forth across the semi-permeable membrane surrounding a raw egg. Students will gain an understanding of osmosis and will appreciate the importance of the cell membrane. After this Chapter Project, students will be able to

- predict and observe how various liquids will affect an egg
- measure and record changes in the egg
- graph and interpret data of the egg's circumference
- draw conclusions about what processes occurred during the project

Skills Focus

predicting, observing, measuring, making and interpreting graphs, drawing conclusions

Project Time Line 2 weeks

All in One Teaching Resources

- Chapter Project Teacher Notes
- Chapter Project Overview
- Chapter Project Worksheet 1
- Chapter Project Worksheet 2
- Chapter Project Scoring Rubric

Developing a Plan

On the first day, have students read about the project in their text and plan how they will observe, measure, and record data. Allow a few minutes of class time every day for students to share their observations and ask questions. Set aside additional class time for group work if students are working in groups.

Possible Materials

- Students will need clean plastic containers with lids; various liquids, such as corn syrup, milk, orange juice, and shampoo; flexible cloth or vinyl tape or a piece of string and a ruler to measure the eggs.
- Large eggs will show a greater change in size, making it easier to observe the results of osmosis. Make sure eggs are not cracked to begin with.

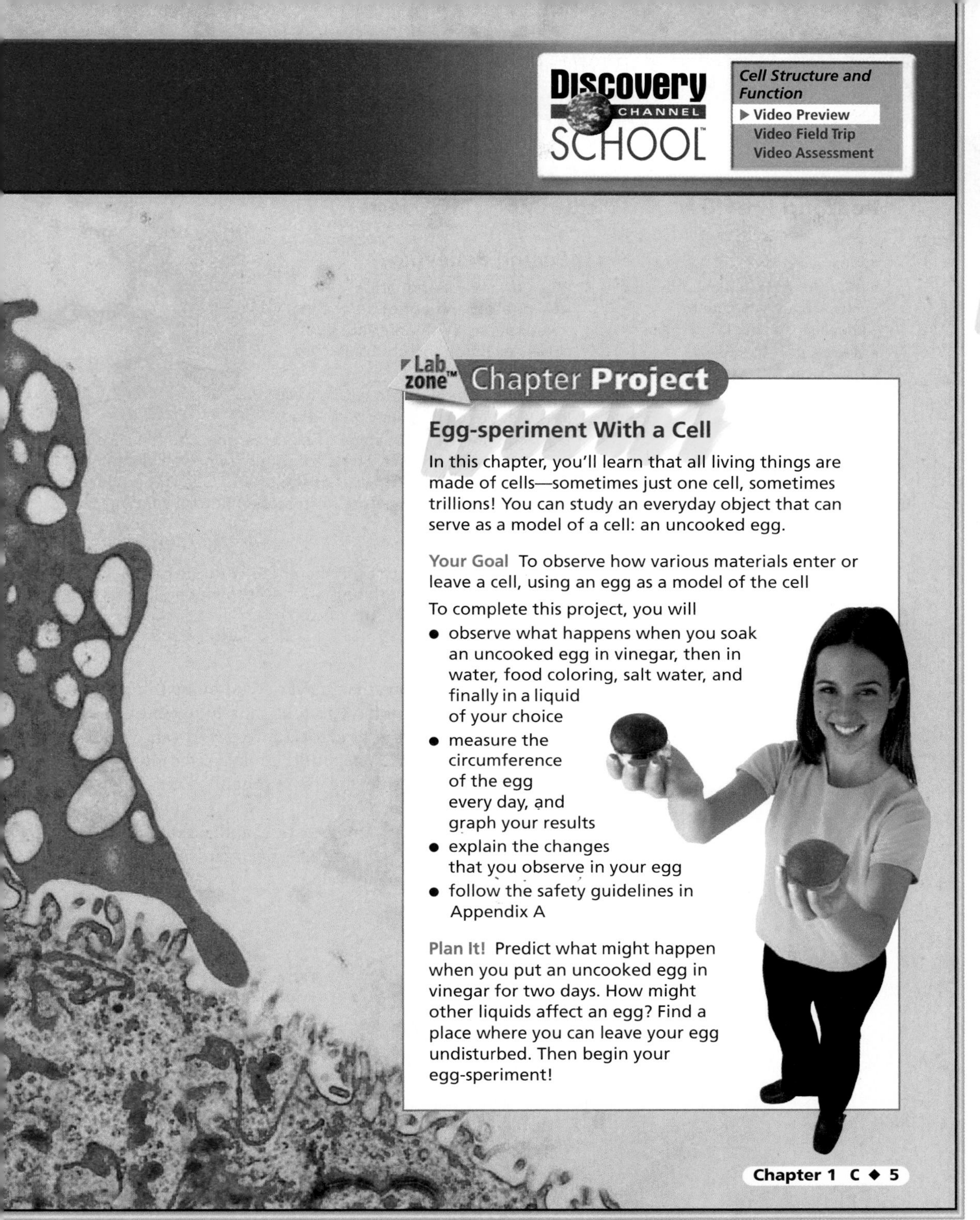

Discovery Channel School

Cell Structure and Function

▶ Video Preview

Video Field Trip

Video Assessment

Lab zone™ Chapter **Project**

Egg-speriment With a Cell

In this chapter, you'll learn that all living things are made of cells—sometimes just one cell, sometimes trillions! You can study an everyday object that can serve as a model of a cell: an uncooked egg.

Your Goal To observe how various materials enter or leave a cell, using an egg as a model of the cell

To complete this project, you will

- observe what happens when you soak an uncooked egg in vinegar, then in water, food coloring, salt water, and finally in a liquid of your choice
- measure the circumference of the egg every day, and graph your results
- explain the changes that you observe in your egg
- follow the safety guidelines in Appendix A

Plan It! Predict what might happen when you put an uncooked egg in vinegar for two days. How might other liquids affect an egg? Find a place where you can leave your egg undisturbed. Then begin your egg-speriment!

Chapter 1 C ◆ 5

Cell Structure and Function

Show the Video Preview to introduce the topic of cells.

Possible Shortcuts

In a group project, each student can soak his or her egg in a different liquid, after first soaking the eggs in vinegar for two days. Then all students can pool their results. Or make this a class project by assigning different students to perform different tasks each day.

Launching the Project

Show students a chicken egg. Tell students that they will study it to learn more about how cells function. Ask: **Why do you think you will be using a chicken egg instead of an actual cell, such as a human skin cell?** *(Most cells are too small to be seen without a microscope.)* Emphasize that a chicken egg is not just one cell, however; it is being used as a model only.

Performance Assessment

The Chapter Project Scoring Rubric will help you evaluate how well students complete the Chapter Project. You may want to share the scoring rubric with your students so they are clear about what will be expected of them. Students will be assessed on

- how accurately and consistently they make measurements and record their data
- the neatness and accuracy of their graphs and diagrams
- how well their conclusions display an understanding of the functions of a cell membrane
- their participation in a group, if they worked in groups

Portfolio

Section 1 Discovering Cells

Objectives

After this lesson, students will be able to

C.1.1.1 Tell what cells are.

C.1.1.2 Explain how the invention of the microscope contributed to scientists' understanding of living things.

C.1.1.3 State the cell theory.

C.1.1.4 Describe how microscopes produce magnified images.

Target Reading Skill

Sequencing Explain that organizing information from beginning to end helps students understand a step-by-step process.

Answer

One possible way to complete the flowchart:

Discovering Cells

Hooke sees cells in cork; Leeuwenhoek sees many one-celled organisms; Schleiden concludes that all plants are made of cells; Schwann concludes that all animals (and all living things) are made of cells; Virchow proposes that new cells form only from cells that already exist.

All in One Teaching Resources

- Transparency C1

Preteach

Build Background Knowledge

Numbers of Cells L1

Ask: **How many individual grains of sand do you think make up a beach?** *(Students probably will say billions or trillions.)* Point out that humans and many other living things are composed of trillions of tiny components as well. These components, called cells, are too small to be easily seen without a microscope.

Section 1 Discovering Cells

Reading Preview

Key Concepts

- What are cells?
- How did the invention of the microscope contribute to knowledge about living things?
- What is the cell theory?
- How do microscopes produce magnified images?

Key Terms

- cell
- microscope
- cell theory

Target Reading Skill

Sequencing A sequence is the order in which a series of events occurs. As you read, construct a flowchart showing how the work of Hooke, Leeuwenhoek, Schleiden, Schwann, and Virchow contributed to scientific understanding of cells.

Discovering Cells

Hooke sees cells in cork.
↓
[ ]
↓
[ ]

Lab zone Discover Activity

Is Seeing Believing?

1. Cut a black-and-white photograph out of a page in a newspaper. With only your eyes, closely examine the photo. Record your observations.
2. Examine the same photo with a hand lens. Again, record your observations.
3. Place the photo on the stage of a microscope. Use the clips to hold the photo in place. Shine a light down on the photo. Focus the microscope on part of the photo. (See Appendix B for instructions on using the microscope.) Record your observations.

Think It Over

Observing What did you see in the photo with the hand lens that you could not see with only your eyes? What additional details could you see with the microscope?

A forest is filled with an amazing variety of living things. Some are easy to see, but you have to look closely to find others. If you look carefully at the floor of a forest, you can often find spots of bright color. A beautiful pink coral fungus grows beneath tall trees. Beside the pink fungus, a tiny red newt perches on a fallen leaf.

What do you think a fungus, a tree, and a red newt have in common? They are all living things, or organisms, and, like all organisms, they are made of cells.

FIGURE 1
Newt and Coral Fungus
All living things are made of cells, including this pink fungus and the red newt that perches next to it.

Lab zone Discover Activity

Skills Focus Observing L1

Materials black and white newspaper photograph, hand lens, microscope, scissors

Time 10 minutes

Tips CAUTION: *Advise students to be careful when using the scissors.* Set up several microscopes around the room and review with students how to use them.

Expected Outcome Students can see the individual dots of ink that make up the photograph. This will help them appreciate how the hand lens and microscope allow them to see very small objects.

Think It Over The black and grey shaded areas in the picture are made up of separate tiny dots of ink. Additional details may include things such as fibers or flaws in the paper.

An Overview of Cells

You are made of cells. **Cells are the basic units of structure and function in living things.** This means that **cells** form the parts of an organism and carry out all of an organism's processes, or functions.

Cells and Structure When you describe the structure of an object, you describe what it is made of and how its parts are put together. The structures of many buildings, for example, are determined by the way in which bricks, steel beams, and other materials are arranged. The structures of living things are determined by the amazing variety of ways in which cells are put together. A tall tree, for example, consists of cells arranged to form a high trunk and leafy branches. A red newt's cells form a body with a head and four legs.

Cells and Function An organism's functions are the processes that enable it to stay alive and reproduce. Some functions in organisms include obtaining oxygen, getting rid of wastes, obtaining food, and growing. Cells are involved in all these functions. For example, cells in your digestive system absorb food. The food provides your body with energy and materials needed for growth.

Many and Small Figure 2 shows human skin cells. One square centimeter of your skin's surface contains more than 100,000 cells. But no matter how closely you look with your eyes alone, you won't be able to see individual skin cells. That is because, like most cells, those of your skin are very small. Until the late 1600s, no one knew cells existed because there was no way to see them.

What are some functions that cells perform in living things?

FIGURE 2
Skin Cells
Your skin is made of cells such as these. Applying Concepts *What are cells?*

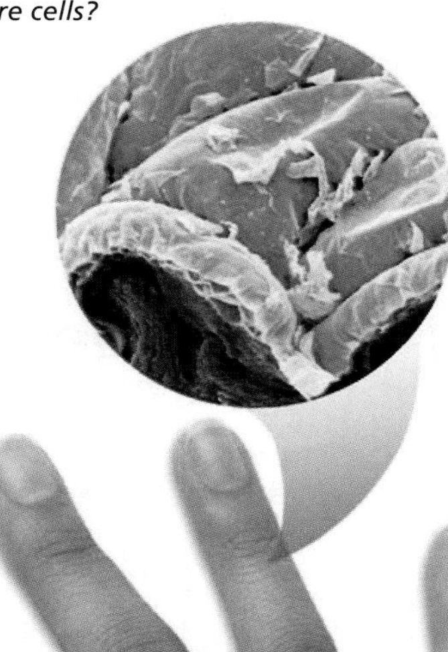

First Observations of Cells

Around 1590, the invention of the microscope enabled people to look at very small objects. **The invention of the microscope made it possible for people to discover and learn about cells.** A **microscope** is an instrument that makes small objects look larger. Some microscopes do this by using lenses to focus light. The lenses used in light microscopes are similar to the clear, curved pieces of glass or plastic used in eyeglasses. A simple microscope contains only one lens. A light microscope that has more than one lens is called a compound microscope.

Instruct

An Overview of Cells L2

Help Students Read

Active Comprehension Refer to the Content Refresher for guidelines on using Active Comprehension. Have students read the first paragraph in this section. Ask: **What would you like to know about cells?** *(Possible answers: What do cells do? How do microscopes work?)* Write student responses on the board. After students have finished reading the section, ask them to respond to each question.

Teach Key Concepts L2

Cell Structure and Function

Focus Call students' attention to the photograph of the hand and the close up image of human skin cells.

Teach Ask: **Why do you need a microscope to see most cells?** *(They are too small to be seen with the naked eye.)* **What are cells?** *(The basic units of structure and function in living things)* **What are some functions of cells?** *(Obtaining oxygen, getting rid of waste, obtaining food, growing)*

Apply Explain that cells are so small that scientists use the micron, one thousandth of one millimeter, to measure cells. **learning modality: verbal**

Independent Practice L2

All in One Teaching Resources

- Guided Reading and Study Worksheet: *Discovering Cells*

Student Edition on Audio CD

Differentiated Instruction

Special Needs L1

Magnifying Objects Have students choose a suitable object, such as a strand of human hair, to place on a slide with a coverslip and view under the microscope, first at low and then at high power. For students whose movements are limited, you can use a microprojector to project the images on a screen, or pair students with students who can adjust and turn the knobs on the microscope. Have students orally describe what they see under each magnification. **learning modality: visual**

Monitor Progress L2

Writing Ask students to write a definition of cells using an analogy similar to the building materials analogy in the text.

Answers

Figure 2 The basic units of structure and function in living things

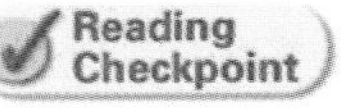

Cells obtain oxygen, get rid of wastes, obtain food, and grow.

First Observations of Cells

Teach Key Concepts L2

Discovery of the Cell

Focus Remind students that without instruments to make them visible, cells were unknown until the microscope was invented.

Teach Ask: **What was Robert Hooke's contribution to the study of cells?** *(Hooke was one of the first people to observe cells. He gave them their name.)* **What did Anton van Leeuwenhoek use his microscope to study?** *(Lake water, scrapings from his teeth and gums, water from rain gutters, and tiny, moving organisms that he named animalcules.)* **How did the invention of the microscope help advance the study of life science?** *(The invention of the microscope made it possible to discover and learn about cells.)*

Apply Hooke published drawings of the cells he saw in a book, which became a bestseller. Ask: **Why do you think people were so interested in seeing Hooke's drawings?** *(They were drawings of things that up until then had been invisible, so the book opened up a whole new world to people.)* **learning modality: visual**

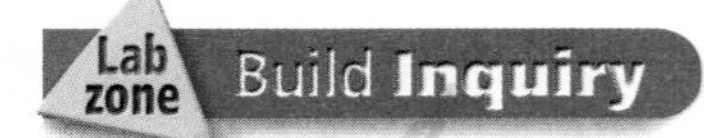

Classifying Images L2

Materials Photocopies of images produced by different types of microscopes (available in high school and college-level textbooks)

Time 10 minutes

Focus Review the magnifications of the microscopes featured in the text.

Teach Provide a set of the images to each group of students. Have them classify the images according to which microscope they think took them.

Apply Ask: **Why are light microscopes still used?** *(Possible answer: Light microscopes are less expensive. Also, sometimes you do not want the level of detail you get with higher magnifications, such as when looking at feathers or insect legs. In such cases, you want to look at overall structure.)* **learning modality: visual**

Robert Hooke One of the first people to observe cells was the English scientist and inventor Robert Hooke. Hooke built his own compound microscope, which was one of the best microscopes of his time. In 1663, Hooke used his microscope to observe the structure of a thin slice of cork. Cork, the bark of the cork oak tree, is made up of cells that are no longer alive. To Hooke, the empty spaces in the cork looked like tiny rectangular rooms. Therefore, Hooke called the empty spaces *cells,* which is a word meaning "small rooms."

Hooke described his observations this way: "These pores, or cells, were not very deep, but consisted of a great many little boxes. . . ." What most amazed Hooke was how many cells the cork contained. He calculated that in a cubic inch there were about twelve hundred million cells—a number he described as "almost incredible."

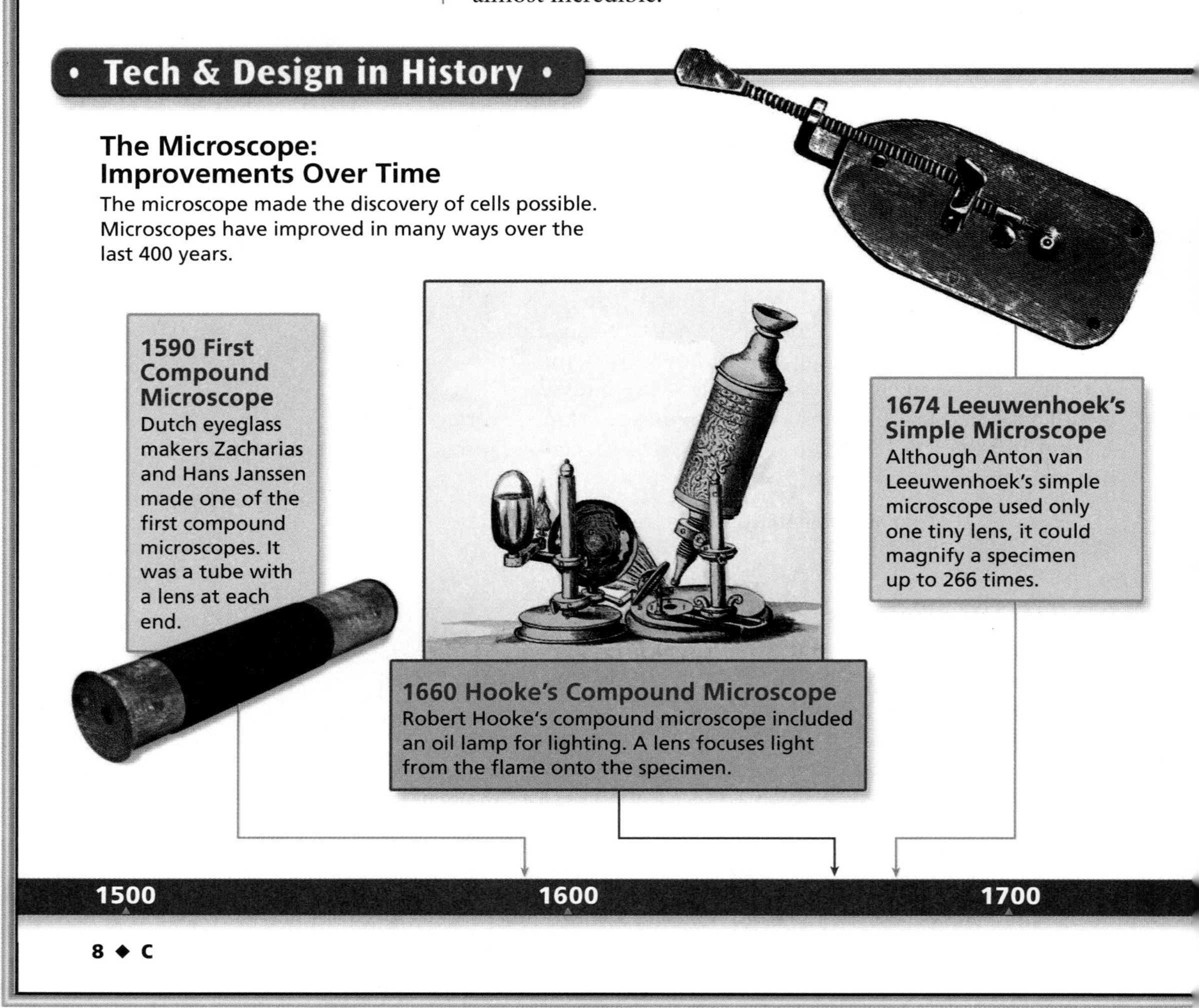

Background

Facts and Figures To differentiate among particular cell structures under a microscope, scientists may stain the tissue to be examined. Different stains color different structures inside cells. For example, a stain called hematoxylin colors the cell's nucleus, the area where most nucleic acids in the cell are found. After staining the tissue, a scientist shaves off extremely thin slices with a precision cutting instrument called a microtome. The microtome can cut slices so thin that they are less than one cell thick. This allows a clear view of even the tiniest cell structures.

Anton van Leeuwenhoek At about the same time that Robert Hooke made his discovery, Anton van Leeuwenhoek (LAY vun hook) also began to observe tiny objects with microscopes. Leeuwenhoek was a Dutch businessman who sold cloth. In his spare time, he built simple microscopes.

Leeuwenhoek looked at drops of lake water, scrapings from teeth and gums, and water from rain gutters. In many materials, Leeuwenhoek was surprised to find a variety of one-celled organisms. Leeuwenhoek noted that many of these tiny organisms moved. Some whirled, some hopped, and some shot through water like fast fish. He called these moving organisms *animalcules* (an ih MAL kyoolz), meaning "little animals."

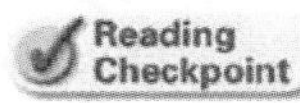
Which type of microscope—simple or compound—did Leeuwenhoek make and use?

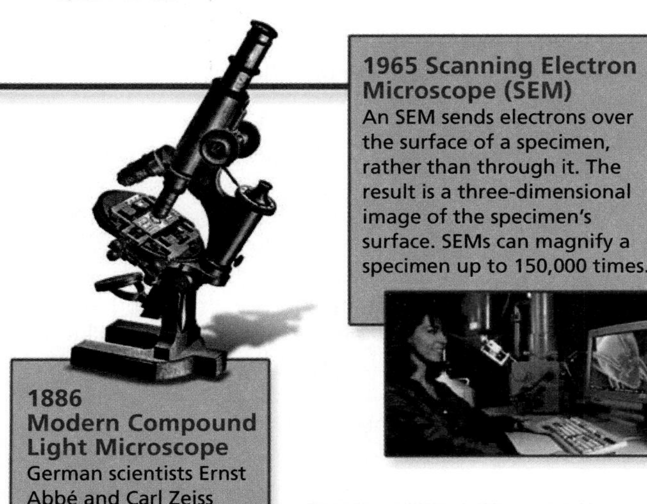

1886 Modern Compound Light Microscope
German scientists Ernst Abbé and Carl Zeiss made a compound light microscope with complex lenses that greatly improved the image. A mirror focuses light up through the specimen. Modern compound microscopes can effectively magnify a specimen up to 1,000 times.

1933 Transmission Electron Microscope (TEM)
German physicist Ernst Ruska created the first electron microscope. TEMs send electrons through a very thinly sliced specimen. TEMs can magnify a specimen up to 500,000 times.

1965 Scanning Electron Microscope (SEM)
An SEM sends electrons over the surface of a specimen, rather than through it. The result is a three-dimensional image of the specimen's surface. SEMs can magnify a specimen up to 150,000 times.

1981 Scanning Tunneling Microscope (STM)
An STM measures electrons that leak, or "tunnel," from the surface of a specimen. STMs can magnify a specimen up to 1,000,000 times.

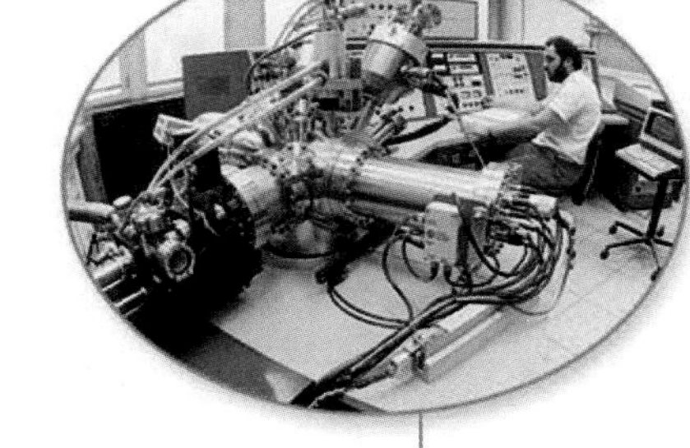

1800 1900 2000

Writing in Science

Research and Write Find out more about one of the microscopes. Then write an advertisement for it that might appear in a popular science magazine. Be creative. Emphasize the microscope's usefulness or describe the wonders that can be seen with it.

• Tech & Design in History •

Focus Ask student volunteers to read the entries on the timeline.

Teach Ask: **How did each advance influence the next scientist's work?** *(The work of each scientist built upon the work and knowledge of the previous scientist.)* **How do electron microscopes differ from light microscopes?** *(Instead of using light, electron microscopes use electrons to produce an image of an object.)* **How has each type of microscope contributed to knowledge about cells?** *(The compound microscope led to the discovery of cells. The modern compound light microscope increased magnification. The TEM, SEM, and STM all further increased magnification. The SEM provided a three-dimensional image of a surface.)*

Writing in Science

Writing Mode Persuasion

Scoring Rubric

4 Includes a detailed description of the uses of the type of microscope; written with persuasive language
3 Includes all criteria but lacks creativity
2 Includes brief but accurate description
1 Includes inaccurate description

Differentiated Instruction

Gifted and Talented L3
Investigating Electron Microscopes Have students prepare a presentation on electron microscopes to share with their classmates. The presentation should explain in simple terms how electron microscopes work and why electron microscopes can magnify so greatly. Students may wish to discuss differences in mechanisms, resulting images, and uses of scanning electron microscopes, transmission electron microscopes, and scanning tunneling microscopes. **learning modality: verbal**

Monitor Progress L2

Writing Have students explain how the invention of the microscope led to the discovery of the cell. Have students place their explanations in their portfolios.

Portfolio

Answer

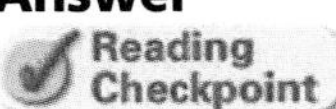
Simple

Development of the Cell Theory

For: Links on cell theory
Visit: www.SciLinks.org
Web Code: scn-0311

Download a worksheet to guide students' review of cell theory.

Teach Key Concepts L2

Understanding the Cell Theory

Focus Remind students that even after Hooke viewed cork cells, scientists still did not understand cells and their importance.

Teach Draw a simple timeline on the board that begins with Hooke's observation of cork cells in 1663. Ask: **How did Schleiden, Schwann, and Virchow contribute to the understanding of cells?** *(In 1838, Schleiden concluded that all plants are made of cells. In 1839, Schwann concluded that all animals are made of cells. In 1855, Virchow proposed that all new cells are formed from existing cells.)* As students answer, add each contribution to the timeline. Point out that almost 200 years separated the contributions of Hooke and Virchow. Ask: **What is the cell theory?** *(All living things are composed of cells. Cells are the basic units of structure and function in living things. All cells are produced from other cells.)*

Apply Ask: **Why do you think it took almost 200 years after cells were discovered for scientists to conclude that all living things consist of cells?** *(Sample answer: There were far fewer scientists and microscopes than there are today, and scientists had to examine thousands of samples of living things before they could reasonably conclude that all living things are made of cells.)* **learning modality: visual**

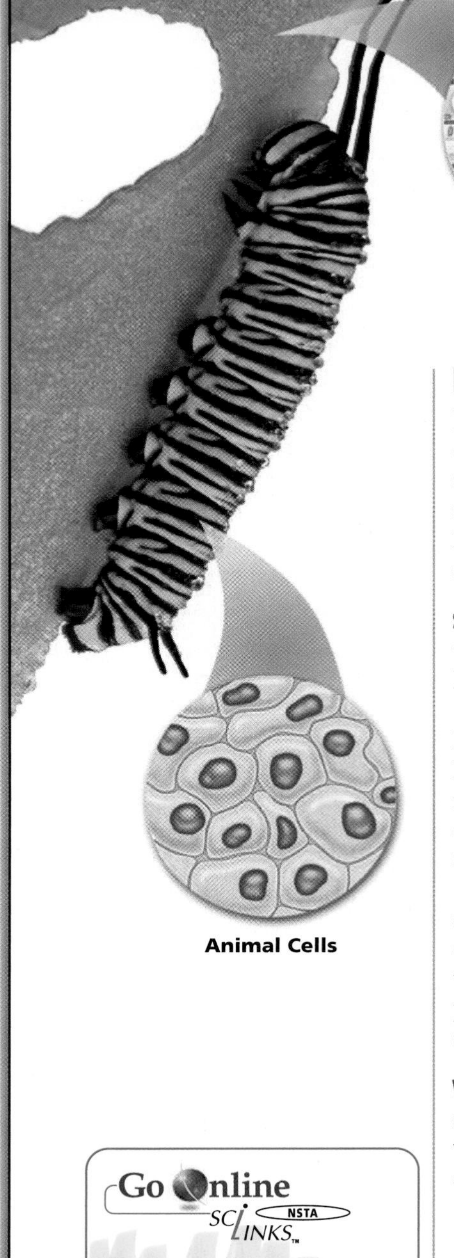

FIGURE 3
Monarch and Milkweed
The monarch butterfly caterpillar and the milkweed leaf that the caterpillar nibbles on are both made of cells.

Development of the Cell Theory

Leeuwenhoek's exciting discoveries caught the attention of other researchers. Like Hooke, Leeuwenhoek, and all good scientists, these other researchers were curious about the world around them, including things they couldn't normally see. Many other people began to use microscopes to discover what secrets they could learn about cells.

Schleiden, Schwann, and Virchow Three German scientists made especially important contributions to people's knowledge about cells. These scientists were Matthias Schleiden (SHLY dun), Theodor Schwann, and Rudolf Virchow (FUR koh). In 1838, Schleiden concluded that all plants are made of cells. He based this conclusion on his own research and on the research of others before him. The next year, Theodor Schwann concluded that all animals are also made up of cells. Thus, stated Schwann, all living things are made up of cells.

Schleiden and Schwann had made an important discovery about living things. However, they didn't explain where cells came from. Until their time, most people thought that living things could come from nonliving matter. In 1855, Virchow proposed that new cells are formed only from cells that already exist. "All cells come from cells," wrote Virchow.

What the Cell Theory Says Schleiden, Schwann, Virchow, and others helped develop the cell theory. The **cell theory** is a widely accepted explanation of the relationship between cells and living things. **The cell theory states the following:**

- **All living things are composed of cells.**
- **Cells are the basic units of structure and function in living things.**
- **All cells are produced from other cells.**

For: Links on cell theory
Visit: www.SciLinks.org
Web Code: scn-0311

The cell theory holds true for all living things, no matter how big or how small. Since cells are common to all living things, they can provide information about the functions that living things perform. Because all cells come from other cells, scientists can study cells to learn about growth and reproduction.

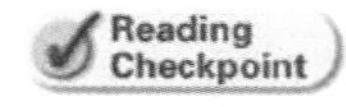
What did Schleiden and Schwann conclude about cells?

Light and Electron Microscopes

The cell theory could not have been developed without microscopes. For a microscope to be useful, it must combine two important properties—magnification and resolution. Scientists today use two kinds of microscopes: light microscopes and electron microscopes.

Magnification and Lenses The first property, magnification, is the ability to make things look larger than they are. **The lenses in light microscopes magnify an object by bending the light that passes through them.** If you examine a hand lens, such as the one in Figure 4, you will see that the lens is curved, not flat. The center of the lens is thicker than the edge. A lens with this curved shape is called a convex lens. The light passing through the sides of the lens bends inward. When this light hits the eye, the eye sees the object as larger than it really is.

Lab zone Skills Activity

Observing

1. Read about using the microscope (Appendix B) before beginning this activity.
2. Place a prepared slide of a thin slice of cork on the stage of a microscope.
3. Observe the slide under low power. Draw what you see.
4. Place a few drops of pond water on another slide and cover it with a coverslip.
5. Observe the slide under low power. Draw what you see. Wash your hands after handling pond water.

How does your drawing in Step 3 compare to Hooke's description of cells on page 8? Based on your observations in Step 5, why did Leeuwenhoek call the organisms he saw "little animals"?

Convex lens

Incoming light rays bend as they pass through a convex lens.

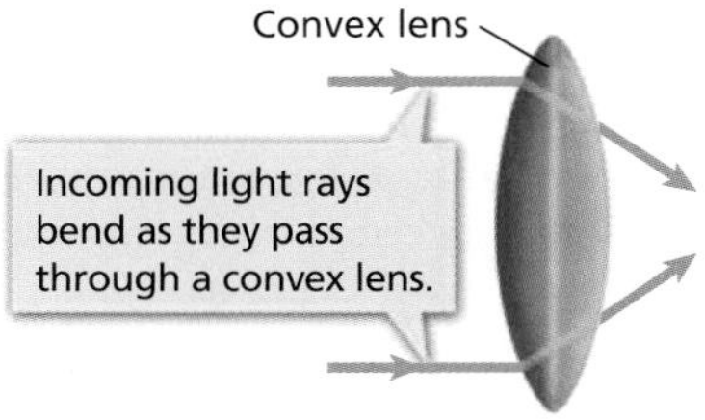

FIGURE 4
A Convex Lens
A magnifying glass is a convex lens. The lines in the diagram represent rays of light, and the arrows show the direction in which the light travels.
Interpreting Diagrams *Describe what happens to light rays as they pass through a convex lens.*

Light and Electron Microscopes

Teach Key Concepts
L2

How Microscopes Magnify Images

Focus Remind students that cells were visible only after the invention of microscopes.

Teach Refer students to the inset in Figure 4. Ask: **What shape is the lens?** *(Convex)* **What does it do to light passing through?** *(Bends it inward)* **What two properties does a light microscope need to work?** *(Magnification and resolution)* **How does an electron microscope magnify?** *(By using a beam of electrons)*

Apply Ask: **When might you use a light microscope instead of an electron microscope?** *(When you do not need great magnification)* **learning modality: verbal**

All in One Teaching Resources
- Transparency C2

Lab zone Build Inquiry
L1

Applying How Microscopes Work

Focus Use Appendix B to point out the parts of a microscope.

Teach Have students name its parts and describe its functions.

Apply Ask students to write a paragraph describing how microscopes magnify images. **learning modality: kinesthetic**

Monitor Progress

Oral Presentation Call on students to describe the cell theory in their own words.

Answers

Figure 4 The light rays bend inward.

Reading Checkpoint Schleiden: All plants are made of cells; Schwann: all animals are made of cells.

Skills Focus Observing L2

Materials blank slide, coverslip, microscope, plastic dropper, pond water, prepared slide of cork

Time 10 minutes

Tips Caution students that glass slides are fragile. Make sure students have focused the microscope and can see the cells clearly before they start their drawings.

Expected Outcome Drawings of cork cells should resemble Hooke's drawing. Leeuwenhoek called the organisms he saw "little animals" because they moved as animals move.

Extend Ask students to examine a drop of tap water under the microscope. Most likely, the water will not contain microorganisms, but it could possibly contain non-disease-causing ones, as treated tap water is not sterile. **learning modality: visual**

L2

Observing with a Microscope

Materials compound microscope, prepared slides of various cells and microscopic organisms

Time 10 minutes

Focus Review how to determine the magnification of an object using a compound microscope.

Teach Caution students that glass slides are fragile. Have students view the slides first at low power and then at high power. Ask them to calculate the magnification of each. Ask: **What does the microscopic view allow you to see that the naked eye does not?** *(The microscope allows you to see the smaller details and tinier parts of the object.)* Point out that smaller magnifications are useful for viewing an entire organism, such as the water flea in Figure 6.

Apply Have students draw and label a simple sketch of what they see under each magnification, then share their drawings with the class. **learning modality: visual**

L2

Integrating Physics

Show students a concave lens and have students contrast its structure to that of a convex lens. Group students in pairs, and instruct one student to hold a hand lens (convex lens) steady at about 10 cm above a page. Tell the other student to move closer to or farther from the lens until the letters on the page come into focus. At this point, have both students note the relative positions of the eye, lens, and page. By moving farther back from the lens, students can see the difference between magnification and resolution. Ask: **How does the object appear now?** *(Even larger but blurry, or out of focus)* Have students switch positions and repeat the activity. **learning modality: kinesthetic**

Less Proficient Readers

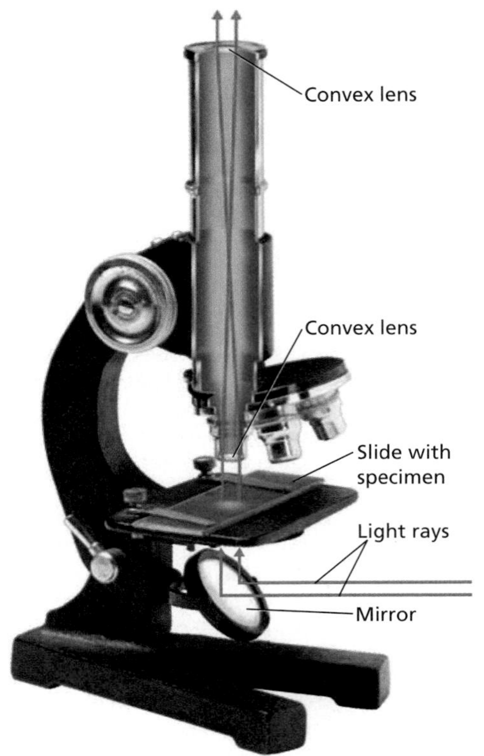

FIGURE 5
A Compound Microscope
A compound microscope has two convex lenses.
Calculating *If one lens has a magnification of 10, and the other lens has a magnification of 50, what is the total magnification?*

Compound Microscope Magnification Since a compound microscope uses more than one lens, it can magnify an object more than one lens by itself. Light passes through a specimen and then through two lenses, as shown in Figure 5. The first lens, near the specimen, magnifies the object. Then a second lens, near the eye, further magnifies the enlarged image. The total magnification of the microscope is equal to the magnifications of the two lenses multiplied together. For example, suppose the first lens makes an object look 10 times bigger than it actually is, and the second lens makes the object look 40 times bigger than it actually is. The total magnification of the microscope is 10×40, or 400.

Resolution To create a useful image, a microscope must also help you see individual parts clearly. The ability to clearly distinguish the individual parts of an object is called resolution. Resolution is another term for the sharpness of an image. For example, a photograph in a newspaper is really made up of a collection of small dots. If you put the photo under a microscope, you can see the dots. You see the dots not only because they are magnified but also because the microscope improves resolution. Good resolution is needed when you study cells.

FIGURE 6
Light Microscope Photos
The pictures of the water flea and the threadlike *Spirogyra* were both taken with a light microscope.

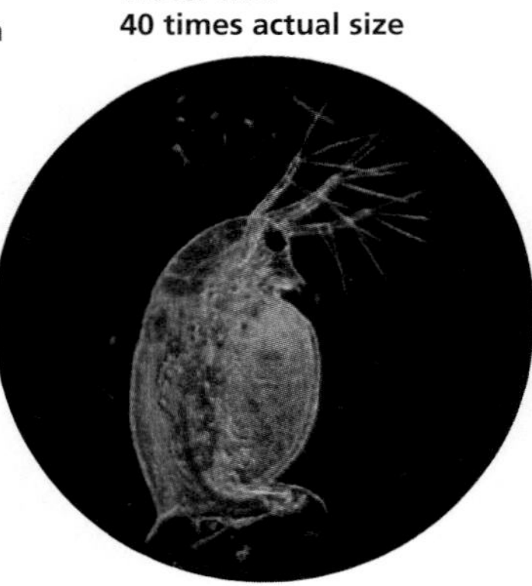

Water flea
40 times actual size

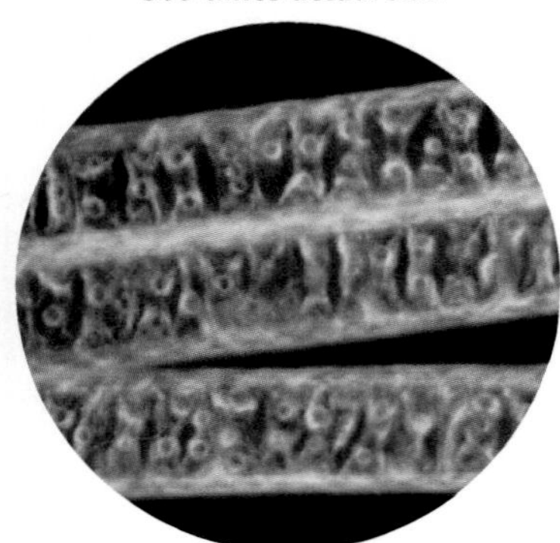

Spirogyra
300 times actual size

12 ◆ C

Differentiated Instruction

Reading in Pairs L1 Parts of the chapter, such as the paragraphs under the heading Light and Electron Microscopes, contain advanced words and concepts that some students may find difficult. Pair these students with more proficient readers. Have each student read a paragraph in the section independently. Next, have the students discuss what they have read with their partners. Encourage them to discuss the main ideas of what they read as well as any questions they may have about it. Then have them write a paragraph in their own words that describes how microscopes magnify images. **learning modality: verbal**

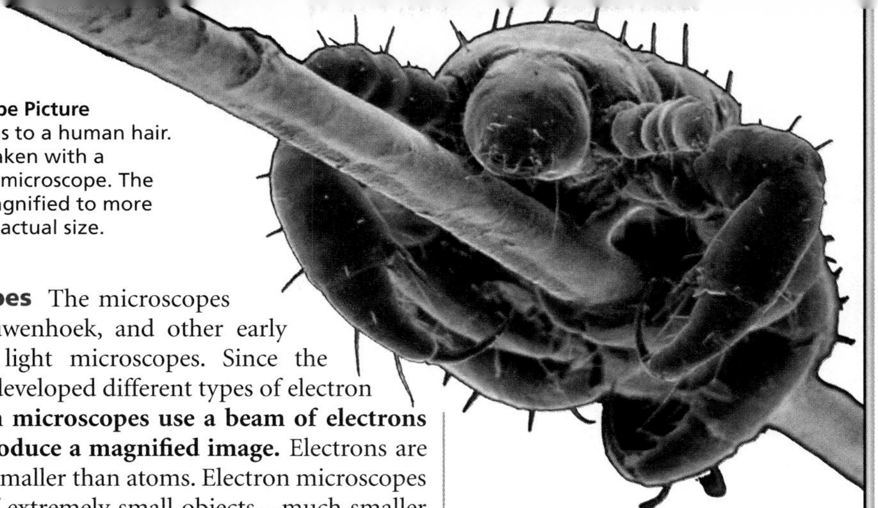

FIGURE 7
Electron Microscope Picture
A head louse clings to a human hair. This picture was taken with a scanning electron microscope. The louse has been magnified to more than 100 times its actual size.

Electron Microscopes The microscopes used by Hooke, Leeuwenhoek, and other early researchers were all light microscopes. Since the 1930s, scientists have developed different types of electron microscopes. **Electron microscopes use a beam of electrons instead of light to produce a magnified image.** Electrons are tiny particles that are smaller than atoms. Electron microscopes can obtain pictures of extremely small objects—much smaller than those that can be seen with light microscopes. The resolution of electron microscopes is much better than the resolution of light microscopes.

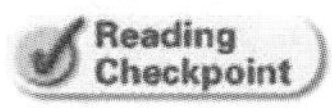
What do electron microscopes use to produce magnified images?

Section 1 Assessment

Target Reading Skill Sequencing Review your flowchart and use it to answer Questions 2 and 3 below.

Reviewing Key Concepts

1. a. Defining Define *structure* and *function*.
   b. Explaining Explain this statement: Cells are the basic units of structure and function in organisms.
   c. Applying Concepts In what important function are the cells in your eyes involved?
2. a. Reviewing What does a microscope enable people to do?
   b. Summarizing Summarize Hooke's observations of cork under a microscope.
   c. Relating Cause and Effect Why would Hooke's discovery have been impossible without a microscope?
3. a. Reviewing What are the main ideas of the cell theory?
   b. Explaining What did Virchow contribute to the cell theory?
   c. Applying Concepts Use the ideas of Virchow to explain why plastic plants and stuffed animals are not alive.
4. a. Defining What is magnification?
   b. Comparing and Contrasting Contrast the way light microscopes and electron microscopes magnify objects.

Writing in Science

Writing an Award Speech Suppose you are a member of a scientific society that is giving an award to one of the early cell scientists. Choose the scientist, and write a speech that you might give at the award ceremony. Your speech should describe the scientist's accomplishments.

Monitor Progress L2

Answers
Figure 5 10 × 50, or 500
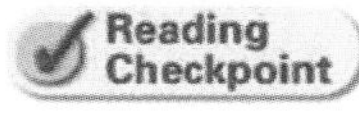
A beam of electrons

Assess

Reviewing Key Concepts

1. a. Structure is what an object or organism is made of and how its parts are put together. A function is a process that enables an organism to stay alive and reproduce. **b.** Cells form the parts of an organism and carry out all of its functions. **c.** Sight
2. a. Microscopes make it possible for people to discover and learn about tiny things, such as cells. **b.** Hooke saw that the cork was made up of many tiny, rectangular spaces, which he called cells. **c.** The human eye is not able to see such small structures.
3. a. All living things are made up of cells, which are the basic units of structure and function in living things. Cells come from other cells. **b.** Virchow proposed that cells are produced from other cells. **c.** Plastic plants and stuffed animals are not made up of cells. Their parts do not produce similar parts in the same way that cells produce other cells. Instead, the parts of plastic plants and stuffed animals are human-made.
4. a. Magnification is the ability to make things look larger than they are. **b.** Light microscopes use lenses to bend light rays to magnify objects, while electron microscopes use a beam of electrons.

Reteach L1

Use the Tech & Design in History timeline to present and discuss the different types of microscopes. Have students identify where in the timeline the cell theory was developed.

Performance Assessment L2

Skills Check Have students compare and contrast light microscopes and electron microscopes.

All in One Teaching Resources
- Section Summary: *Discovering Cells*
- Review and Reinforce: *Discovering Cells*
- Enrich: *Discovering Cells*

Lab zone Chapter Project

Keep Students on Track Make sure students have started soaking their eggs in vinegar. Remind them to measure and record the circumferences of their eggs every day after rinsing their eggs in water. Also check that they are measuring the eggs in the same way each time. Remind students to handle the eggs gently. If an egg breaks, have them start over with another egg.

Writing in Science

Writing Skill Description
Scoring Rubric
4 Includes accomplishments and goes beyond requirements in some way, for example, by researching other accomplishments
3 Includes all criteria but does not go beyond requirements
2 Includes only brief description
1 Includes inaccurate or incomplete description

Design and Build a Microscope

Prepare for Inquiry

Key Concept
You can build a working microscope using two different lenses.

Skills Objectives
After this lab, students will be able to
- build a working microscope using high-and low-powered magnifying lenses
- make observations using the microscope
- evaluate the usefulness of the design

Class Time 40 minutes

All in One Teaching Resources
- Lab Worksheet: *Design and Build a Microscope*

Safety

Review the safety guidelines in Appendix A.

Guide Inquiry

Invitation
Remind students of the general structure of a compound light microscope. Have them examine Figure 5 and conclude that compound microscopes contain two convex lenses.

Introduce the Procedure
Review the terms *magnification* and *resolution* and how they relate to microscopy. Make sure students know how to use a compound microscope. Ask: **If you know the magnification of the two lenses in the microscope, how do you determine the overall magnification?** *(You multiply the magnifications of the lenses.)* **Which of the two lenses has a higher magnification?** *(The lens closer to the eye)* **What do you do if the image you see in a microscope is blurry?** *(You move the lenses closer or farther from the object and from each other.)*

Design and Build a Microscope

Problem
How can you design and build a compound microscope?

Design Skills
building a prototype, evaluating design constraints

Materials
- book
- 2 dual magnifying glasses, each with one high-power and one low-power lens
- metric ruler
- 2 cardboard tubes from paper towels, or black construction paper
- tape

Procedure

PART 1 Research and Investigate

1. Work with a partner. Using only your eyes, examine words in a book. Then use the high-power lens to examine the same words. In your notebook, contrast what you saw with and without the magnifying lens.
2. Hold the high-power lens about 5–6 cm above the words in the book. When you look at the words through the lens, they will look blurry.
3. Keep the high-power lens about 5–6 cm above the words. Hold the low-power lens above the high-power lens, as shown in the photograph on the right.
4. Move the low-power lens up and down until the image is in focus and upside down. (*Hint:* You may have to move the high-power lens up or down slightly too.)
5. Once the image is in focus, experiment with raising and lowering both lenses. Your goal is to produce the highest magnification while keeping the image in clear focus.
6. When the image is in focus at the position of highest magnification, have your lab partner measure and record the distance between the book and the high-power lens. Your lab partner should also measure and record the distance between the two lenses.
7. Write a description of how the magnified words viewed through two lenses compares with the words seen without magnification.

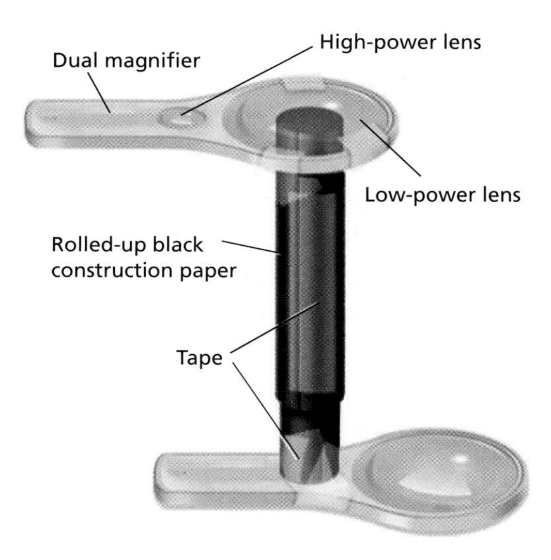

PART 2 Design and Build

8. Based on what you learned in Part 1, work with a partner to design your own two-lens (compound) microscope. Your microscope should
   - consist of one high-power lens and one low-power lens, each attached to a tube of paper or rolled-up cardboard
   - allow one tube to fit snugly inside the other tube so the distance between the two lenses can be easily adjusted
   - focus to produce a clear, enlarged, upside-down image of the object
   - be made from dual magnifying glasses, cardboard tubes, and tape
9. Sketch your design on a sheet of paper. Obtain your teacher's approval for your design. Then construct your microscope.

PART 3 Evaluate and Redesign

10. Test your microscope by examining printed words or a printed photograph. Then, examine other objects such as a leaf or your skin. Record your observations. Did your microscope meet the criteria listed in Step 8?
11. Examine microscopes made by other students. Based on your tests and your examination of other microscopes, list ways you could improve your microscope.

Analyze and Conclude

1. **Observing** Compare the images you observed using one lens with the image from two lenses.
2. **Evaluating** When you used two lenses, how did moving the top lens up and down affect the image? What was the effect of moving the bottom lens up and down?
3. **Building a Prototype** Describe how you built your microscope and explain why you built it that way.
4. **Evaluating the Impact on Society** Describe some of the ways that microscopes have aided scientists in their work.

Communicate

Imagine it is 1675. Write an explanation that will convince scientists to use your new microscope rather than the single-lens variety used by Leeuwenhoek.

Troubleshooting the Experiment

Remind students to write down all of their observations and to record which lenses they used and in which combinations they used them.

Expected Outcome

The image is blurry and inverted with the high-power lens a few centimeters above the print. When the low-power lens is placed near the print, the image appears in focus and inverted. Holding the high-power lens still and moving the low-power lens upward increases the magnification, causing the print to appear larger. Holding the low-power lens still and moving the high-power lens closer to the print increases the magnification, causing the print to appear larger until you get very close to the page. At that point the image is smaller and no longer inverted. The distances measured will depend on the lenses used.

Analyze and Conclude

1. Images obtained with two lenses were magnified more.

2. Moving the top lens up increased the magnification, while moving the bottom lens down increased magnification.

3. Each lens was attached to a cardboard tube. One tube was then inserted in the other so that the lenses could be moved closer to or farther from one another.

4. Answers might note that increasing magnifications have enabled scientists to make detailed examinations of the structures of cells.

Extend the Inquiry

Communicate Explanations should note that the total magnification of a compound microscope is the product of the magnifying power of each lens; therefore, compound microscopes have greater magnifying power than most single-lens microscopes.

Section 2 Looking Inside Cells

Objectives

After this lesson, students will be able to

C.1.2.1 Identify the role of the cell wall and the cell membrane in the cell.

C.1.2.2 Describe the functions of cell organelles.

C.1.2.3 Explain how cells are organized in many-celled organisms.

C.1.2.4 Tell how bacterial cells differ from plant and animal cells.

Target Reading Skill

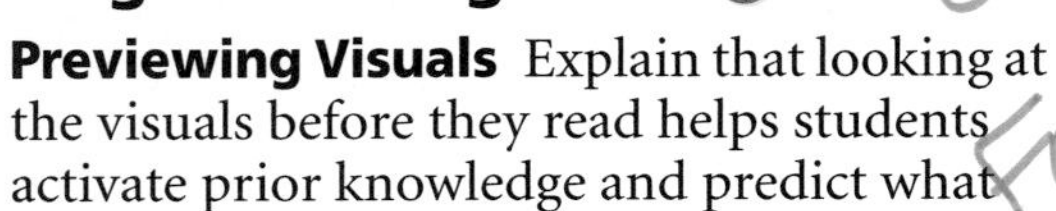

Previewing Visuals Explain that looking at the visuals before they read helps students activate prior knowledge and predict what they are about to read.

Answers

Possible questions and answers: **How are animal cells different from plants cells?** *(Plants cells have a cell wall and chloroplasts, which animal cells do not have.)* **What do mitochondria do?** *(Mitochondria convert energy in food molecules to energy the cell can use.)*

All in One Teaching Resources

- Transparency C3

Preteach

Build Background Knowledge L1

Division of Labor

Introduce students to the division of labor among structures in cells by relating it to the division of labor in a community. Ask: **How are jobs in a town divided up among people?** *(Possible answers: Shopkeepers supply food, police officers enforce laws, and the mayor and city council members make decisions.)* **Why is it effective to divide the labor in this way?** *(By dividing labor, people can become specialized at their work and do it more effectively.)* Point out that, like a town and its people, cells have a division of labor among their structures.

Section 2 Looking Inside Cells

Reading Preview

Key Concepts

- What role do the cell wall and cell membrane play in the cell?
- What are the functions of cell organelles?
- How are cells organized in many-celled organisms?
- How do bacterial cells differ from plant and animal cells?

Key Terms

- organelle
- cell wall
- cell membrane
- nucleus
- cytoplasm
- mitochondria
- endoplasmic reticulum
- ribosome
- Golgi body
- chloroplast
- vacuole
- lysosome

Target Reading Skill

Previewing Visuals Before you read, preview Figure 12. Then write two questions that you have about the illustrations in a graphic organizer like the one below. As you read, answer your questions.

Plant and Animal Cells

Plant and Animal Cells
Q. How are animal cells different from plant cells?
A.
Q.

Lab zone Discover Activity

How Large Are Cells?

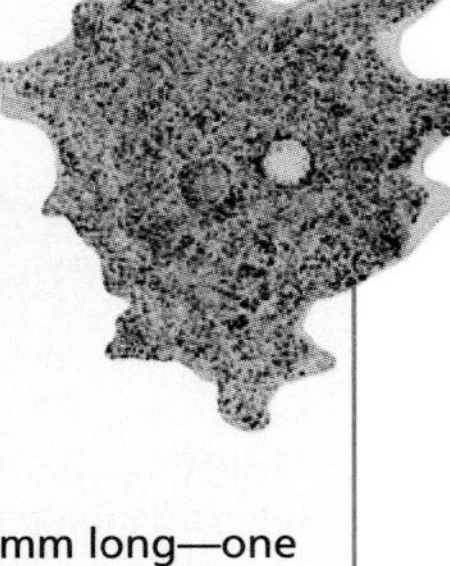

1. Look at the organism in the photo. The organism is an amoeba (uh MEE buh), a large single-celled organism. This type of amoeba is about 1 mm long.
2. Multiply your height in meters by 1,000 to get your height in millimeters. How many amoebas would you have to stack end-to-end to equal your height?
3. Many of the cells in your body are about 0.01 mm long—one hundredth the size of an amoeba. How many body cells would you have to stack end-to-end to equal your height?

Think It Over

Inferring Look at a metric ruler to see how small 1 mm is. Now imagine a distance one one-hundredth as long, or 0.01 mm. Why can't you see your body's cells without the aid of a microscope?

Nasturtiums brighten up many gardens with green leaves and colorful flowers. How do nasturtiums carry out all the functions necessary to stay alive? To answer this question, you are about to take an imaginary journey. You will travel inside a nasturtium leaf, visiting its tiny cells. You will observe some of the structures found in plant cells. You will also learn some differences between plant and animal cells.

As you will discover on your journey, there are even smaller structures inside a cell. These tiny cell structures, called **organelles,** carry out specific functions within the cell. Just as your stomach, lungs, and heart have different functions in your body, each organelle has a different function within the cell. Now it's time to hop aboard your imaginary ship and sail into a typical plant cell.

Nasturtiums ►

Lab zone Discover Activity

Skills Focus Inferring L1

Materials calculator, metric ruler

Time 10 minutes

Tips If students do not know their height in meters, have partners measure each other's height with a metric ruler.

Expected Outcome A student who is 1.5 m tall would be the same height as a stack of 1,500 amoebas. The same student would be 150,000 body cells tall.

Think It Over You cannot see body cells without a microscope because they are too small.

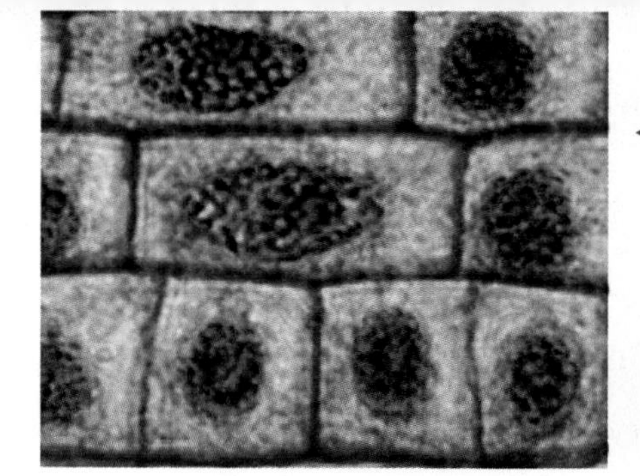

◀ Onion root cells

Paramecium ▼

Enter the Cell

Your ship doesn't have an easy time getting inside the cell. It has to pass through the cell wall and the cell membrane.

Cell Wall As you travel through the plant cell, refer to Figure 12. First, you must slip through the cell wall. The **cell wall** is a rigid layer of nonliving material that surrounds the cells of plants and some other organisms. The cells of animals, in contrast, do not have cell walls. **A plant's cell wall helps to protect and support the cell.** The cell wall is made mostly of a strong material called cellulose. Although the cell wall is tough, many materials, including water and oxygen, can pass through easily.

Cell Membrane After you sail through the cell wall, the next barrier you must cross is the **cell membrane**. All cells have cell membranes. In cells with cell walls, the cell membrane is located just inside the cell wall. In other cells, the cell membrane forms the outside boundary that separates the cell from its environment.

The cell membrane controls what substances come into and out of a cell. Everything the cell needs, from food to oxygen, enters the cell through the cell membrane. Fortunately, your ship can slip through, too. Harmful waste products leave the cell through the cell membrane. For a cell to survive, the cell membrane must allow these materials to pass in and out. In addition, the cell membrane prevents harmful materials from entering the cell. In a sense, the cell membrane is like a window screen. The screen allows air to enter and leave a room, but it keeps insects out.

Reading Checkpoint What is the function of the cell wall?

FIGURE 8
Cell Wall and Cell Membrane
The onion root cells have both a cell wall and a cell membrane. The single-celled paramecium has only a cell membrane.
Interpreting Photographs *What shape do the cell walls give to the onion root cells?*

Instruct

Enter the Cell

Teach Key Concepts L2

Cell Wall and Cell Membrane

Focus Point out that when Hooke observed cork cells, what he saw was the cell wall.

Teach Have students locate the cell wall in Figure 8. Ask: **What is the function of the cell wall?** *(It helps protect and support the cell.)* Have students locate the cell membrane. Ask: **What is the function of the cell membrane?** *(It controls what substances come into and out of a cell.)* **Which two structures do plants have?** *(Both)* **Animal cells?** *(Only cell membranes, not cell walls)*

Apply Point out that cells with cell walls also have a cell membrane. Ask: **Why does a cell with a cell wall need a cell membrane?** *(The cell wall separates the cell from the outside environment, but it cannot control all substances that come into and out of the cell.)* **learning modality: visual**

Independent Practice L2

All in One Teaching Resources

- Guided Reading and Study Worksheet: *Looking Inside Cells*

Student Edition on Audio CD

Differentiated Instruction

English Learners/Beginning L1
Vocabulary: Science Glossary Have students find the terms *cell wall* and *cell membrane* in the text as you read aloud. Use Figure 8 to describe the meanings of the terms. Have students write the meanings in their science glossaries. Then have students draw and label diagrams of the structures. **learning modality: verbal**

English Learners/Intermediate L2
Vocabulary: Science Glossary Have students expand on the *Beginning* activity and add the other key terms to their science glossaries as they read the section. Have students draw structures designated by the terms and write a sentence about each term in their own words. **learning modality: verbal**

Monitor Progress L2

Oral Presentation Call on students to identify differences and similarities between cell walls and cell membranes.

Answers
Figure 8 Rectangular

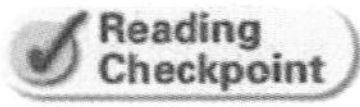

To help protect and support the cell

Sail on to the Nucleus

Teach Key Concepts

L1

Functions of the Nucleus

Focus Have students locate the nucleus in Figure 9. Point out the membrane around it, called the nuclear envelope.

Teach Ask: **What is the function of the nucleus?** *(The nucleus directs all of the cell's activities.)* **What keeps material in the nucleus from spilling out?** *(The nucleus is surrounded by the nuclear envelope.)* **How does the nucleus "know" how to direct the cell?** *(Thin strands of chromatin in the nucleus contain genetic material, the instructions for directing the cell's functions.)* **What is the nucleolus?** *(It is where organelles that make proteins are produced.)*

Apply Ask: **How is the nucleus like the manager of a company?** *(The nucleus directs functions of the cell, just as a manager directs functions of a company.)* **learning modality: verbal**

Address Misconceptions

L1

Cells Have the Same Genetic Material

Focus Students may think that different types of cells within an organism contain different genetic material.

Teach Point out to students that exactly the same genetic material is found in every cell of an organism. Different cells in their bodies, such as skin cells and blood cells, look and function differently because they respond to different genetic instructions. Ask: **How is a cookbook like the genetic code?** *(The same cookbook can be used by different cooks to make different recipes. Different cells contain a copy of the same cookbook or genetic material, yet the cells look and function differently because they follow different recipes.)*

Apply Remind students that Virchow proposed that all cells come from cells. Explain that cells get their genetic material from the cell they came from, and an organism grows as cells divide to make new cells. This explains why all cells in an organism have the same genetic material. **learning modality: verbal**

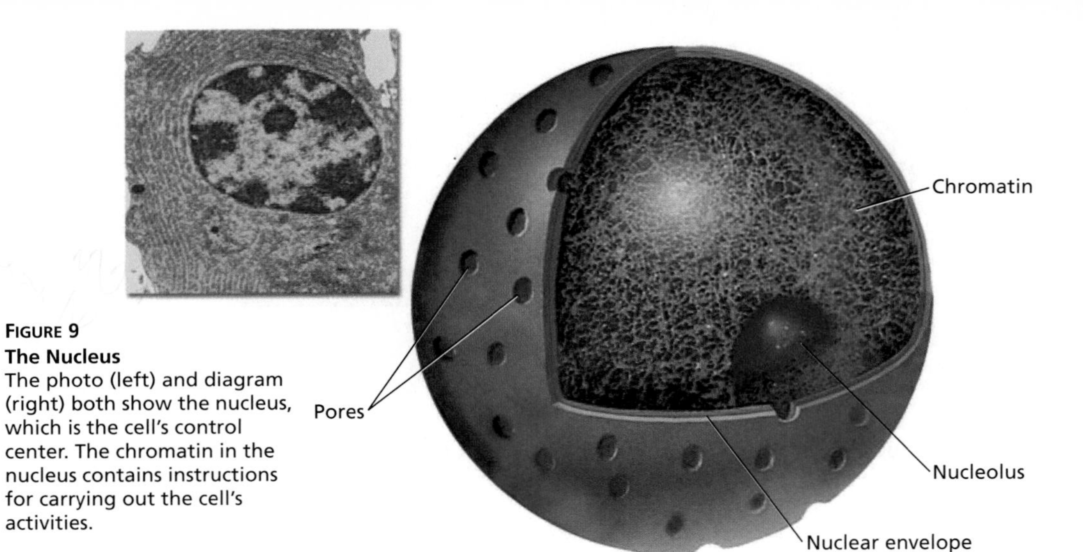

FIGURE 9
The Nucleus
The photo (left) and diagram (right) both show the nucleus, which is the cell's control center. The chromatin in the nucleus contains instructions for carrying out the cell's activities.

Sail on to the Nucleus

As you sail inside the cell, a large, oval structure comes into view. This structure, called the **nucleus** (NOO klee us), acts as the "brain" of the cell. **You can think of the nucleus as the cell's control center, directing all of the cell's activities.**

Nuclear Envelope Notice in Figure 9 that the nucleus is surrounded by a membrane called the nuclear envelope. Just as a mailing envelope protects the letter inside it, the nuclear envelope protects the nucleus. Materials pass in and out of the nucleus through pores in the nuclear envelope. So aim for that pore just ahead and carefully glide into the nucleus.

Chromatin You might wonder how the nucleus "knows" how to direct the cell. The answer lies in those thin strands floating directly ahead in the nucleus. These strands, called chromatin, contain genetic material, the instructions for directing the cell's functions. For example, the instructions in the chromatin ensure that leaf cells grow and divide to form more leaf cells.

Nucleolus As you prepare to leave the nucleus, you spot a small object floating by. This structure, a nucleolus, is where ribosomes are made. Ribosomes are the organelles where proteins are produced. Proteins are important chemicals in cells.

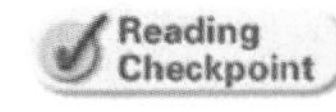

Where in the nucleus is genetic material found?

Lab zone Try This Activity

Gelatin Cell

Make your own model of a cell.

1. Dissolve a packet of colorless gelatin in warm water. Pour the gelatin into a rectangular pan (for a plant cell) or a round pan (for an animal cell).
2. Choose different materials that resemble each of the cell structures found in the cell you are modeling. Insert these materials into the gelatin before it begins to solidify.

Making Models On a sheet of paper, develop a key that identifies each cell structure in your model. Describe the function of each structure.

Lab zone Try This Activity

Skills Focus Making models

L2

Materials packet of colorless gelatin, warm water, stirrer, craft materials, rectangular or round pan

Time 10 min one day; 10 min the next

Tips Use warm, not hot, water. Students should stir the gelatin until it dissolves completely and chill it for up to an hour before adding the cell structures.

Extend Challenge students to model an animal cell with gelatin in a resealable plastic bag. Ask: **What does the bag represent?** *(The cell membrane)* **Why is this a better model for an animal cell than a pan?** *(There is no "cell wall" to support the cell and make it rigid.)* **learning modality: kinesthetic**

FIGURE 10
Mitochondrion
The mitochondria produce most of the cell's energy. **Inferring** *In what types of cells would you expect to find a lot of mitochondria?*

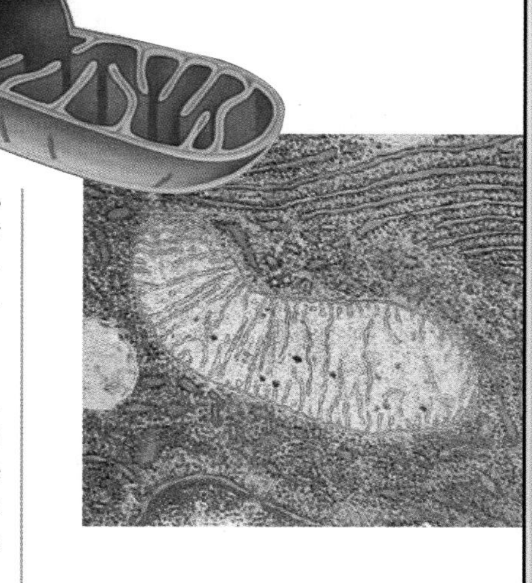

Organelles in the Cytoplasm

As you leave the nucleus, you find yourself in the **cytoplasm,** the region between the cell membrane and the nucleus. Your ship floats in a clear, thick, gel-like fluid. The fluid in the cytoplasm is constantly moving, so your ship does not need to propel itself. Many cell organelles are found in the cytoplasm.

Mitochondria Suddenly, rod-shaped structures loom ahead. These organelles are **mitochondria** (my tuh KAHN dree uh) (singular *mitochondrion*). **Mitochondria are known as the "powerhouses" of the cell because they convert energy in food molecules to energy the cell can use to carry out its functions.** Figure 10 shows a mitochondrion up close.

Endoplasmic Reticulum As you sail farther into the cytoplasm, you find yourself in a maze of passageways called the **endoplasmic reticulum** (en duh PLAZ mik rih TIK yuh lum). **The endoplasmic reticulum's passageways carry proteins and other materials from one part of the cell to another.**

Ribosomes Attached to some surfaces of the endoplasmic reticulum are small, grainlike bodies called **ribosomes.** Other ribosomes float in the cytoplasm. **Ribosomes function as factories to produce proteins.** Some newly made proteins are released through the wall of the endoplasmic reticulum. From the interior of the endoplasmic reticulum, the proteins will be transported to the Golgi bodies.

FIGURE 11
Endoplasmic Reticulum
The endoplasmic reticulum is similar to the system of hallways in a building. Proteins and other materials move throughout the cell by way of the endoplasmic reticulum. The spots on this organelle are ribosomes, which produce proteins.

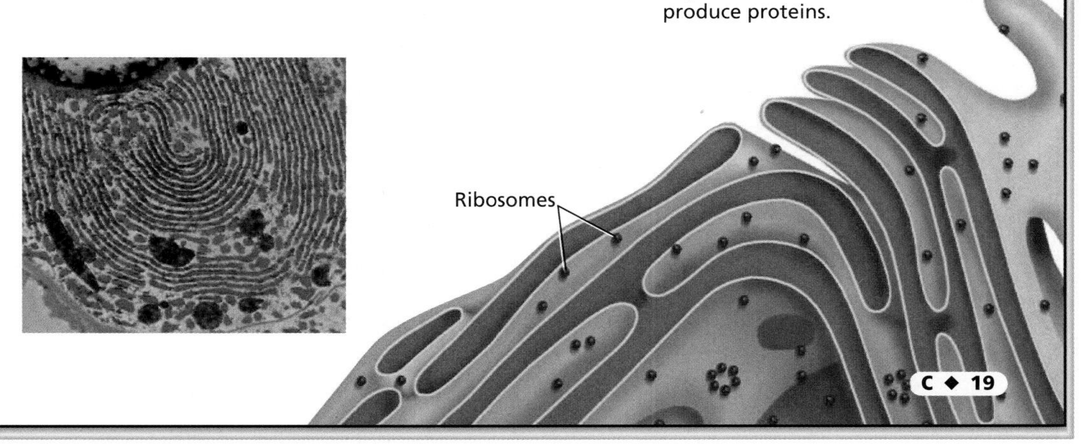

Differentiated Instruction

Gifted and Talented L3
Modeling Organelles Encourage students who are interested in drama to work together to write a short play based on the analogy of the cell as a factory. Students can make signs that identify the organelles they represent. Encourage them to use any other suitable props they wish. Remind them to give their play a storyline and to include as many organelles as possible. Give them time to plan and prepare their play, then present it to the class. **learning modality: kinesthetic**

Organelles in the Cytoplasm

Teach Key Concepts L2

Functions of Organelles

Focus Remind students that organelles work together just as machine parts do.

Teach As you discuss each organelle, refer students to the respective figures in this section. Ask: **How do ribosomes, Golgi bodies, and the endoplasmic reticulum work together?** *(Ribosomes make proteins that are released through the endoplasmic reticulum and moved to the Golgi bodies. Golgi bodies move materials around and outside the cell.)* **How do chloroplasts, mitochondria, lysosomes, and vacuoles work together in a plant cell?** *(Chloroplasts capture the sun's energy and use it to make food for the cell. Mitochondria convert energy in food to energy the cell can use. Lysosomes break down materials, including food particles. Vacuoles store food and other materials the cell needs.)*

Apply Ask: **Why are chloroplasts found only in plant cells?** *(Only plants have the ability to capture energy from sunlight and make food.)* **learning modality: logical/mathematical**

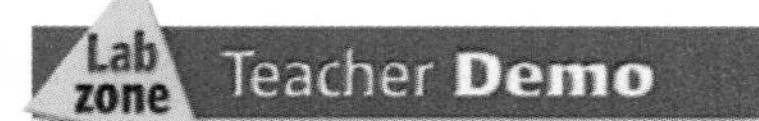

Lab zone Teacher Demo L1

The Effect of Water in Plant Vacuoles

Materials water, wilted houseplant

Time 5 minutes at the beginning of class; 5 minutes at the end of class

Focus Review the definition of vacuole.

Teach At the beginning of class, show students a wilted coleus or impatiens. Water the plant thoroughly.

Apply Ask: **Why is the plant no longer wilted?** *(Its vacuoles have filled up with water.)* **learning modality: visual**

Monitor Progress L2

Skills Check Have each student create a table listing at least five organelles in the cell and summarizing their functions.

Answer

Figure 10 Muscle cells and other active cells

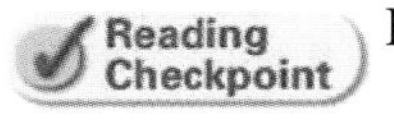

Reading Checkpoint In strands called chromatin

Use Visuals: Figure 12 L2

Comparing Plant and Animal Cells

Focus Point out that some cell structures are defined on only one drawing because they are much the same in both plant cells and animal cells.

Teach Help students organize the material in the figure by creating a table on the board titled "Comparison of Plant and Animal Cells." For headings, use *Similarities* and *Differences,* and for rows use *Plants* and *Animals*. Encourage students to examine the diagrams and other information in the figure to help fill in the cells of the table. Complete the table as students volunteer their ideas. When the table is finished, you may want to have students copy it in a notebook and refer to it as they study this section.

Apply Ask: **Which organelles are found only in plant cells? Which are found in both plant and animal cells?** *(Except for cell walls and chloroplasts, most organelles are found in both plant and animal cells.)* **learning modality: visual**

All in One Teaching Resources

- Transparencies C4, C5

Help Students Read L1

Relating Text and Visuals Have students compare the drawings on these pages with the descriptions of their functions in the passages Sail on to the Nucleus and Organelles in the Cytoplasm. Instruct students to go back and read about each organelle, then locate it on the drawing.

FIGURE 12
Plant and Animal Cells
These illustrations show typical structures found in plant and animal cells. **Comparing and Contrasting** *Identify one structure found in plant cells but not animal cells.*

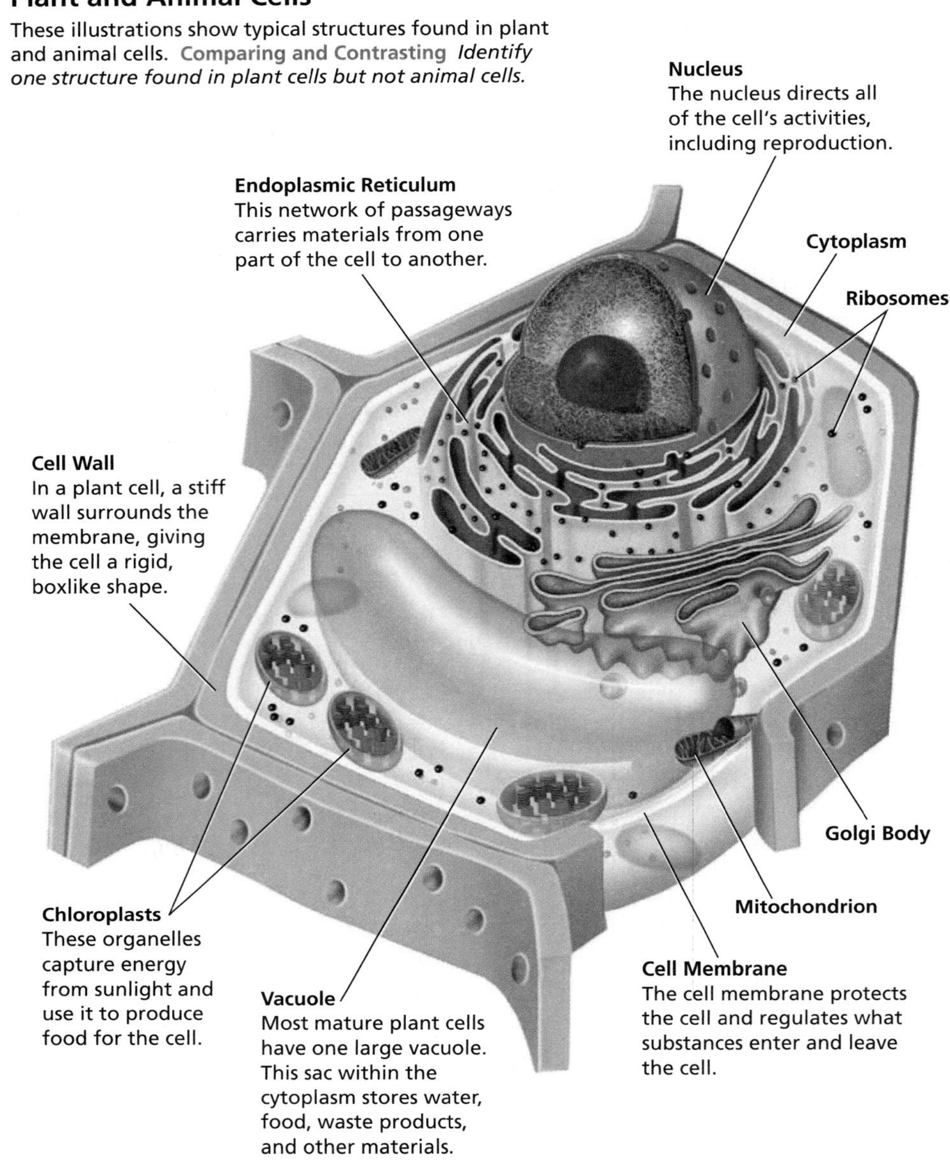

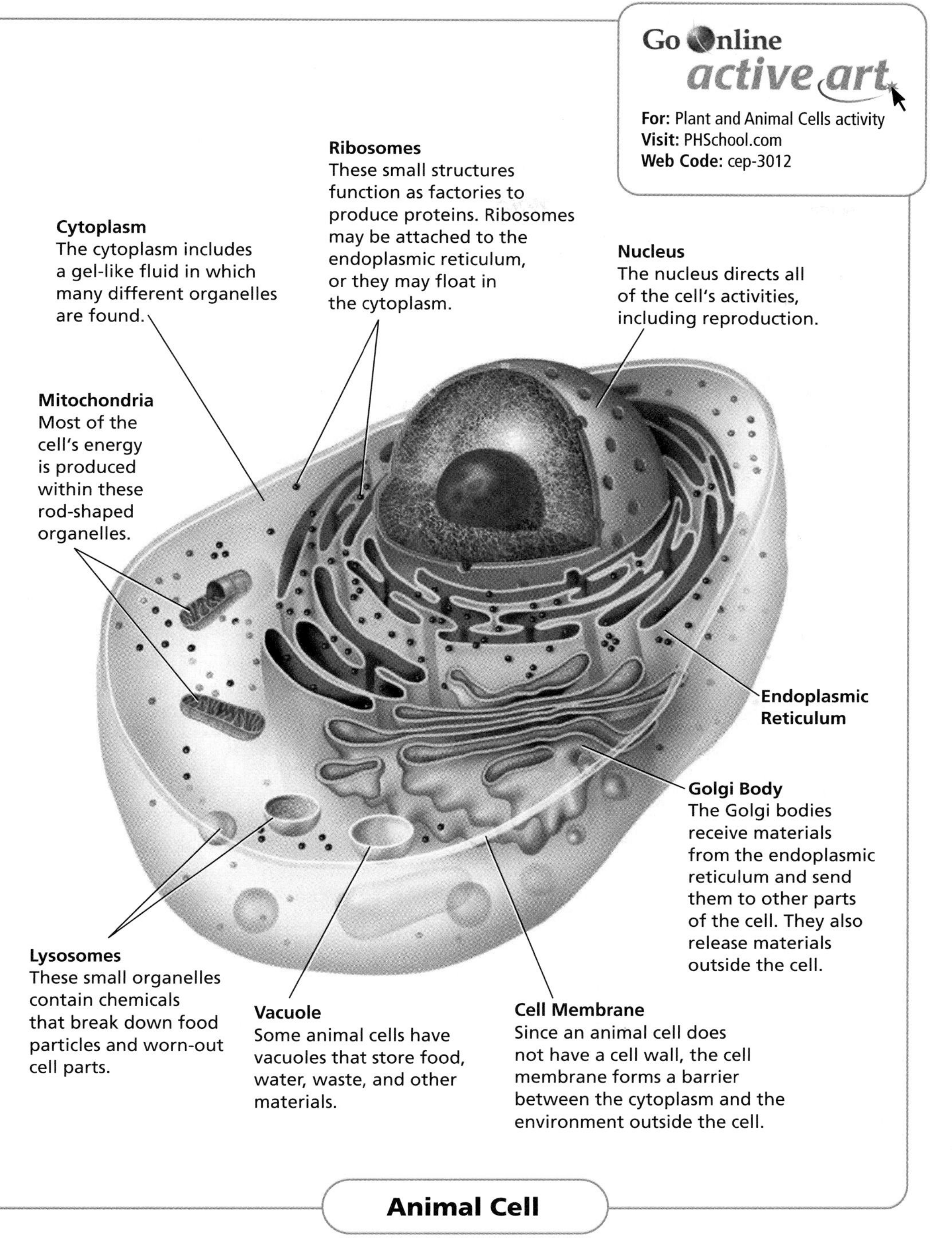

Animal Cell

For: Plant and Animal Cells activity
Visit: PHSchool.com
Web Code: cep-3012

Students can interact with the art of cells online.

Lab zone Teacher Demo

Comparing Slides to Illustrations L2

Materials microprojector, prepared slide of plant cells, prepared slide of animal cells, drawings of other types of cells (such as leaf and root cells for plants, and muscle and bone cells for animals)

Time 10 minutes

Focus Point out that the drawings of plant and animal cells shown on these pages are generalized representations of cells.

Teach Project the prepared slides, and have students relate the organelles they see to the illustrations. Encourage them to describe how the actual cells vary in shape and structure from the generalized cells in the text. Point out that cells have many different shapes and sizes. They also can vary in the specific organelles they contain.

Apply Ask: **Why do you think different cells look so different from one other?** *(Because they have different functions in the organism)* **learning modality: visual**

Differentiated Instruction

Special Needs L1

Making Flash Cards Have students use index cards to write the name of a cell structure on one side and the structure's function on the other side. Pair students and have them use their flash cards to quiz each other. **learning modality: verbal**

Less Proficient Readers L1

Identifying Organelles Make photocopies of the plant and animal cell illustrations in Figure 12. Blank out the labels but leave the taglines. As each organelle is studied and discussed, have students write in the labels. Give students extra copies for practice and as a study aid. **learning modality: visual**

Monitor Progress L2

Oral Presentation Call out the names of organelles, and have students tell what they do.

Answer

Figure 12 Either one: Cell walls, chloroplasts

Specialized Cells

Teach Key Concepts L2

How Cells Are Organized

Focus Point out the different shapes and functions of the cells in Figure 14.

Teach Ask: **What is a tissue?** *(A group of similar cells that work together to perform a specific function)* **What are different types of tissues working together called?** *(An organ)* **What is an organ system?** *(A group of organs that work together to perform a major function)*

Apply Blood is able to circulate through the human body because of the heart and blood vessels. Ask: **Is this an example of tissues, organs, or an organ system?** *(This is an organ system called the circulatory system. The heart and blood vessels are organs of this system.)* **learning modality: logical/ mathematical**

Use Visuals: Figure 14 L1

Focus Remind students that cells have different structures because of their functions.

Teach Ask students to compare the nerve cell and the red blood cells. *(The nerve cell has extensions, and the red blood cells look flattened or donut-shaped.)*

Apply Ask: **How do you think each cell's shape helps it do its job?** *(The extensions on nerve cells help them reach out and send messages to other cells; the flatness of red blood cells helps them squeeze through tiny blood vessels.)* **learning modality: visual**

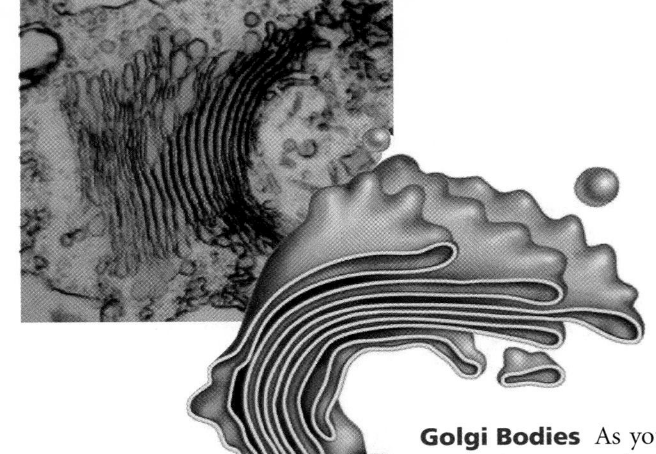

FIGURE 13
A Golgi Body
Golgi bodies are organelles that transport materials.

Golgi Bodies As you leave the endoplasmic reticulum, you see the structure shown in Figure 13. It looks like flattened sacs and tubes. This structure, called a **Golgi body,** can be thought of as the cell's mail room. **The Golgi bodies receive proteins and other newly formed materials from the endoplasmic reticulum, package them, and distribute them to other parts of the cell.** The Golgi bodies also release materials outside the cell.

Chloroplasts Have you noticed the many large green structures floating in the cytoplasm? Only the cells of plants and some other organisms have these green organelles called **chloroplasts. Chloroplasts capture energy from sunlight and use it to produce food for the cell.** Chloroplasts make leaves green.

Vacuoles Steer past the chloroplasts and head for that large, water-filled sac, called a **vacuole** (VAK yoo ohl), floating in the cytoplasm. **Vacuoles are the storage areas of cells.** Most plant cells have one large vacuole. Some animal cells do not have vacuoles; others do. Vacuoles store food and other materials needed by the cell. Vacuoles can also store waste products.

Lysosomes Your journey through the cell is almost over. Before you leave, take another look around you. If you carefully swing your ship around the vacuole, you may be lucky enough to see a **lysosome** (LY suh sohm). **Lysosomes are small, round structures containing chemicals that break down certain materials in the cell.** Some chemicals break down large food particles into smaller ones. Lysosomes also break down old cell parts and release the substances so they can be used again. In this sense, you can think of lysosomes as the cell's cleanup crew.

Lab zone Try This Activity

Comparing Cells

Observe the characteristics of plant and animal cells.

1. Obtain a prepared slide of plant cells from your teacher. Examine these cells under the low-power and high-power lenses of a microscope.
2. Draw a picture of what you see.
3. Repeat Steps 1 and 2 with a prepared slide of animal cells.

Observing How are plant and animal cells alike? How are they different?

Reading Checkpoint What organelle captures the energy of sunlight and uses it to make food for the cell?

Lab zone Try This Activity

Skills Focus Observing L2

Materials microscope, prepared slide of animal cells, prepared slide of plant cells

Time 15 minutes

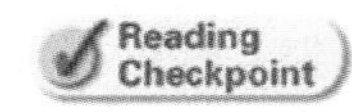

Tips Help students identify organelles by looking at Figure 12. Challenge students to locate the cell wall or cell membrane, nucleus, and other organelles on the slides.

Expected Outcome Only plant cells have cell walls and chloroplasts. Most other cell structures are found in both plant and animal cells.

Extend Encourage students to describe how the actual cells vary in shape and structure from the illustrations. **learning modality: visual**

Specialized Cells

Plants and animals (including yourself) contain many cells. In a many-celled organism, the cells are often quite different from each other and are specialized to perform specific functions. Contrast, for example, the nerve cell and red blood cells in Figure 14. Nerve cells are specialized to transmit information from one part of your body to another, and red blood cells carry oxygen throughout your body.

In many-celled organisms, cells are often organized into tissues, organs, and organ systems. A tissue is a group of similar cells that work together to perform a specific function. For example, your brain is made mostly of nervous tissue, which consists of nerve cells. An organ, such as your brain, is made of different kinds of tissues that function together. In addition to nervous tissue, the brain contains other kinds of tissue that support and protect it. Your brain is part of your nervous system, which is an organ system that directs body activities and processes. An organ system is a group of organs that work together to perform a major function.

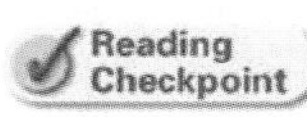

What is an organ system? Give an example.

Discovery Channel School

Cell Structure and Function

Video Preview
▶ Video Field Trip
Video Assessment

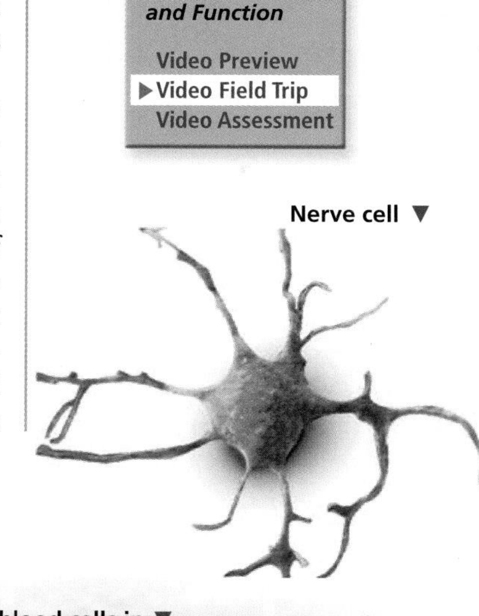

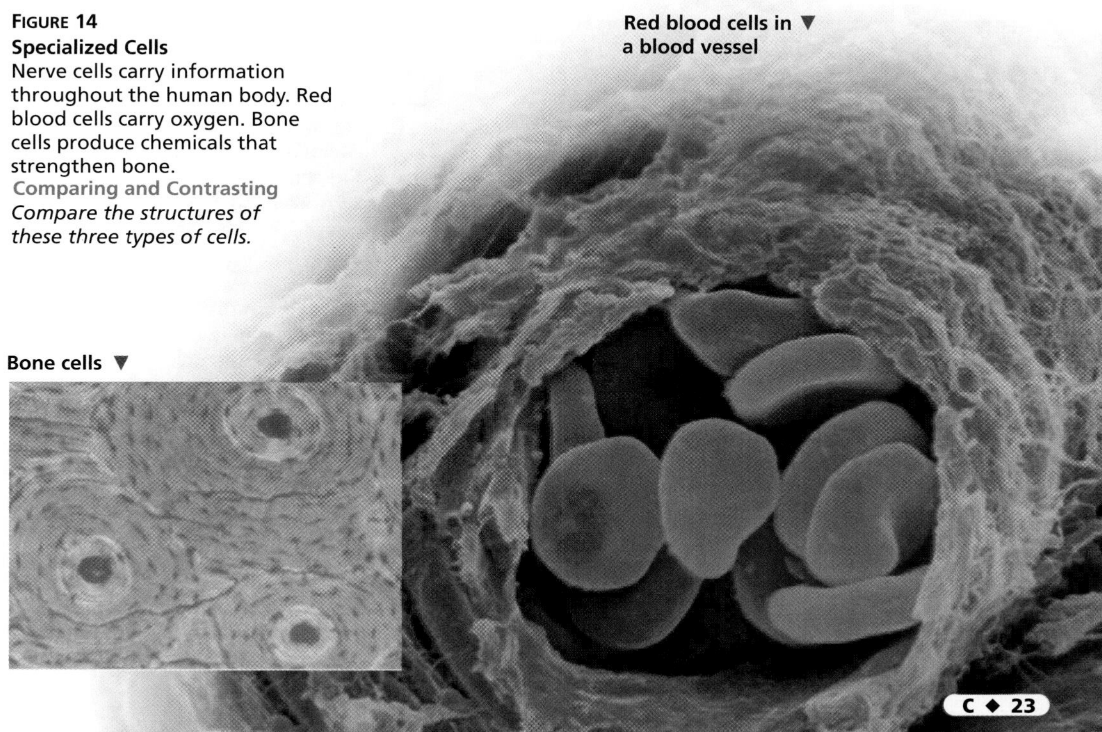

FIGURE 14
Specialized Cells
Nerve cells carry information throughout the human body. Red blood cells carry oxygen. Bone cells produce chemicals that strengthen bone.
Comparing and Contrasting *Compare the structures of these three types of cells.*

C ◆ 23

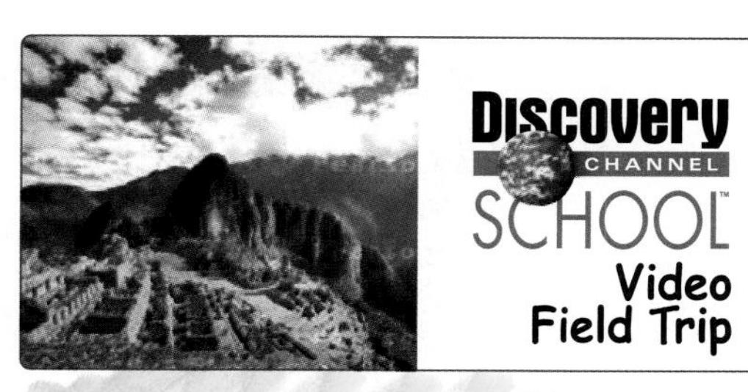

Cell Structure and Function

Show the Video Field Trip to let students learn about different kinds of cells.

Bacterial Cells

Teach Key Concepts

Examining Bacterial Cells L2

Focus Refer students to Figure 15.

Teach Ask students to locate the cell wall and the cell membrane. Ask: **Where is the genetic material?** *(In the cytoplasm)* **What organelles found in plant or animal cells do the bacterial cells appear to be lacking?** *(Possible answers include nucleus, mitochondria, chloroplasts, and endoplasmic reticulum)*

Apply Ask: **How does the location of the genetic material in the bacteria differ from its location in animal and plant cells?** *(In bacterial cells, the genetic material is located in the cytoplasm; in plant and animal cells, the genetic material is found in the nuclei.)* **learning modality: visual**

Monitor Progress L2

Answers

Figure 14 A nerve cell has long, thin projections. A red blood cell is shaped like a disk. Bone cells are round and surrounded by concentric circles.

Reading Checkpoint The chloroplast

Reading Checkpoint An organ system consists of a group of organs that work together to perform a major function. The nervous system is one example of an organ system.

Differentiated Instruction

English Learners/Beginning L1
Comprehension: Modified Cloze Give students a list of simple sentences that describe organelles, but leave the name of the organelle blank. For example, "______ are storage areas of cells." Provide students with a list of correct answers, and have them fill in each blank. Model how to do the first one. **learning modality: verbal**

English Learners/Intermediate L2
Comprehension: Modified Cloze Give students the cloze sentences described for the *Beginning* activity, but fill in incorrect answers and have students correct them. **learning modality: verbal**

Assess

Reviewing Key Concepts

1. a. The cell membrane separates a cell from its environment and controls what substances go into and come out of the cell. The cell wall protects and supports the cell. **b.** Strong **c.** Because cellulose is strong, the cell wall, which is made up of cellulose, can protect the cell and provide support.
2. a. The ribosomes produce proteins. The Golgi bodies distribute these proteins and other materials to different parts of the cell. **b.** The endoplasmic reticulum has many passageways that carry proteins and other materials from one part of the cell to another. **c.** The ribosomes make proteins. The endoplasmic reticulum carries the proteins to the Golgi bodies, which distribute them to other parts of the cell.
3. a. A tissue is a group of similar cells that work together to perform a specific function. An organ is a body structure made up of different kinds of tissues that function together. **b.** Cells make up tissues, which make up organs. **c.** An organ would have more kinds of specialized cells because it is made up of different tissues, each of which consists of the same type of cells.
4. a. In the cytoplasm **b.** A plant or animal cell's nucleus encloses chromatin that contains the cell's genetic material. A bacterial cell's genetic material is found in the cytoplasm.

Reteach L1

Bring in photographs of different types of cells. Ask students to classify them as plant, animal, or bacterial, and identify any visible organelles.

Performance Assessment L2

Have students draw a plant cell, animal cell, and bacterial cell and label their structures.

All in One Teaching Resources

- Section Summary: *Looking Inside Cells*
- Review and Reinforce: *Looking Inside Cells*
- Enrich: *Looking Inside Cells*

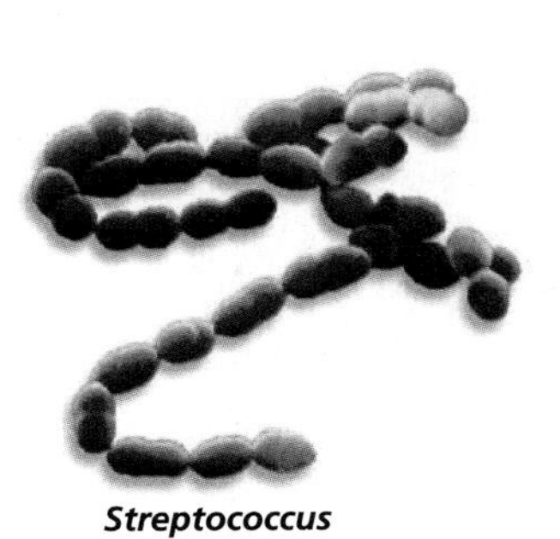

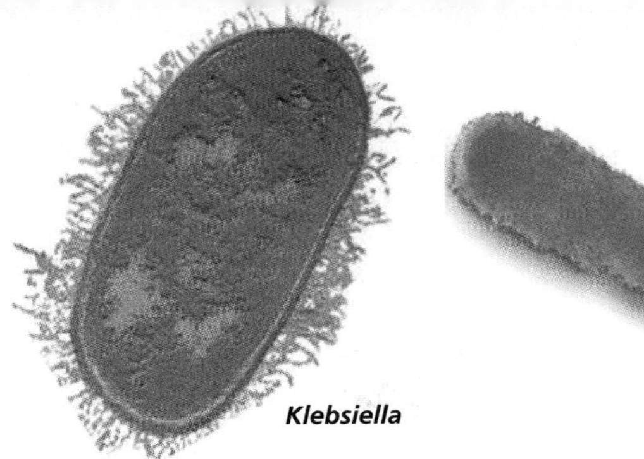

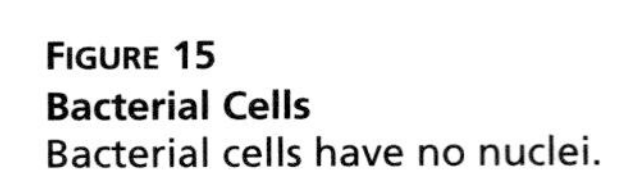

FIGURE 15
Bacterial Cells
Bacterial cells have no nuclei.

Bacterial Cells

The plant and animal cells that you just learned about are very different from the bacterial cells you see in Figure 15. First, bacterial cells are usually much smaller than plant or animal cells. A human skin cell, for example, is about ten times as large as an average bacterial cell. **While a bacterial cell does have a cell wall and a cell membrane, it does not contain a nucleus. The bacterial cell's genetic material, which looks like a thick, tangled string, is found in the cytoplasm.** Bacterial cells contain ribosomes, but none of the other organelles found in plant or animal cells.

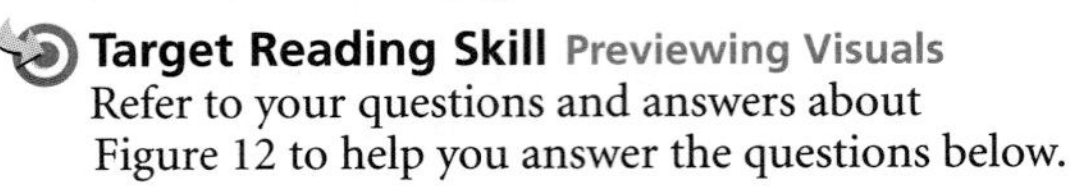

Section 2 Assessment

Target Reading Skill Previewing Visuals Refer to your questions and answers about Figure 12 to help you answer the questions below.

Reviewing Key Concepts

1. a. Comparing and Contrasting Compare the functions of the cell wall and the cell membrane.
   b. Describing What is a characteristic of cellulose?
   c. Inferring How does cellulose help with the functions of the cell wall?
2. a. Identifying Identify the functions of ribosomes and Golgi bodies.
   b. Describing Describe the characteristics of the endoplasmic reticulum.
   c. Applying Concepts How are the functions of ribosomes, Golgi bodies, and the endoplasmic reticulum related to one another?
3. a. Reviewing What is a tissue? What is an organ?
   b. Explaining What is the relationship among cells, tissues, and organs?
   c. Inferring Would a tissue or an organ have more kinds of specialized cells? Explain.
4. a. Reviewing Where is the genetic material in a bacterial cell?
   b. Comparing and Contrasting Contrast the location of genetic material in bacterial cells to its location in plant and animal cells.

Writing in Science

Writing a Description Write a paragraph describing a typical animal cell. Your paragraph should include all the structures generally found in animal cells and a brief explanation of the functions of those structures.

Lab zone Chapter Project

Keep Students on Track At this point, students will soak their eggs for one or two days in water, then in water with food coloring, then in salt water, and finally in another liquid of their choice. They will still rinse the eggs, and measure and record the circumference every day.

Writing in Science

Writing Mode Description

Scoring Rubric

4 Includes descriptions of structures and explains their functions; goes beyond requirements in some way, for example, explaining how organelles work together
3 Includes all criteria, but does not go beyond requirements
2 Includes very brief description
1 Includes inaccurate or incomplete information

Section 3

Integrating Chemistry

Chemical Compounds in Cells

Reading Preview

Key Concepts

- What are elements and compounds?
- What are the main kinds of organic molecules in living things?
- How is water important to the function of cells?

Key Terms

- element • compound
- carbohydrate • lipid
- protein • amino acid
- enzyme • nucleic acid
- DNA • RNA

Target Reading Skill

Comparing and Contrasting
As you read, compare and contrast carbohydrates, lipids, and proteins in a table like the one below.

Type of Compound	Elements	Functions
Carbo-hydrate	Carbon, hydrogen, oxygen	
Lipid		
Protein		

Lab zone Discover Activity

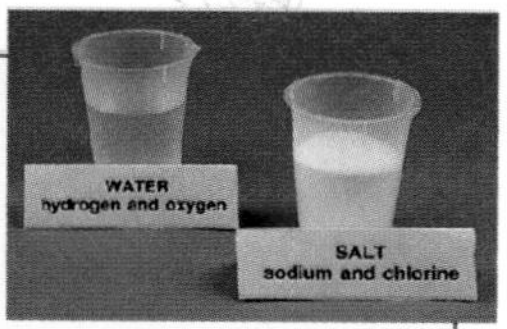

What Is a Compound?

1. Your teacher will provide you with containers filled with various substances. All of the substances are chemical compounds.
2. Examine each substance. Read the label on each container to learn what each substance is made of.

Think It Over
Forming Operational Definitions Write a definition of what you think a chemical compound is.

Watch out—you are surrounded by particles that you can't see! Air is made up of millions of tiny particles. They bump into your skin, hide in the folds of your clothes, and whoosh into your nose every time you take a breath. In fact, you and the world around you, including the cells in your body, are composed of tiny particles. Some of these particles are elements, and others are compounds.

Elements and Compounds

You may not realize it, but air is a mixture of gases. These gases include both elements and compounds. Three gases in the air are oxygen, nitrogen, and carbon dioxide.

Elements Oxygen and nitrogen are examples of **elements. An element is any substance that cannot be broken down into simpler substances.** The smallest unit of an element is called an atom. An element is made up of only one kind of atom. The elements found in living things include carbon, hydrogen, oxygen, nitrogen, phosphorus, and sulfur.

FIGURE 16
An Element
Sulfur is an element. In its pure form, it sometimes forms crystals.

Lab zone Discover Activity

Skills Focus Forming operational definitions L2

Materials Labeled containers of chemical compounds such as baking soda, chalk, salt, and zinc oxide sun block

Time 10 minutes

Tips Label the compounds with their common and chemical names (sodium bicarbonate for baking soda, calcium carbonate for chalk, sodium chloride for salt, zinc oxide for sun block).

Expected Outcome Students will discover that all the compounds consist of two or more elements.

Think It Over Students may say that a chemical compound is something that is made up of more than one substance.

Section 3

Chemical Compounds in Cells

Objectives

After this lesson, students will be able to

C.1.3.1 Define elements and compounds.

C.1.3.2 Identify the four main kinds of organic compounds in living things.

C.1.3.3 Explain how water is important to the function of cells.

Target Reading Skill 

Comparing and Contrasting Explain that comparing and contrasting information shows how ideas, facts, and events are similar and different. The results of the comparison can have importance.

Answers

Possible answers:

- *Type of Compound:* Carbohydrate
- *Elements in It:* Carbon, hydrogen, oxygen
- *Its Functions:* Stores and provides energy and makes up cellular parts
- *Type of Compound:* Lipid
- *Elements in It:* Carbon, hydrogen, oxygen
- *Its Functions:* Stores energy
- *Type of Compound:* Protein
- *Elements in It:* Carbon, hydrogen, oxygen, nitrogen, and sometimes sulfur
- *Its Function:* Makes up much of the structure of cells and speeds up chemical reactions

All in One Teaching Resources

- Transparency C6

Preteach

Build Background Knowledge L1

Component Parts

Show students a jar with its lid on. Ask: **Can the lid be separated from the jar?** *(Yes)* Then remove the lid and put it alongside the jar. Ask: **Can the jar be easily divided into two or more parts?** *(No)* **What about the lid?** *(No)* Tell students that the jar and the lid by themselves are something like elements, and the jar with the lid attached is something like a compound. Tell students that they will learn about elements and compounds in this section.

Instruct

For: Links on proteins
Visit: www.SciLinks.org
Web Code: scn-0313

Download a worksheet to guide students' review of proteins.

Elements and Compounds

Teach Key Concepts L2

Elements, Compounds, and Water

Focus Write H_2O on the board. Explain that it is the chemical formula for water.

Teach Ask: **Which is water—an element or a compound?** *(Compound)* **Why?** *(It contains two elements—oxygen and water—that are combined chemically.)* **Why is water so important to living things?** *(Because most chemical reactions in living things couldn't take place without water; water also helps cells retain their size and shape and helps stabilize temperature.)* **How are organic compounds different from inorganic compounds?** *(Organic compounds contain carbon.)*

Apply Ask students to look at the chemical formula for water. Point out that the symbol *H* represents hydrogen and *O* represents oxygen. Ask: **What do you think this formula tells you about water?** As a hint, suggest that students look at the structure of water in the illustration. *(A water molecule has two hydrogen atoms and one oxygen atom.)* **learning modality: visual**

Independent Practice L2

All in One Teaching Resources

- Guided Reading and Study Worksheet: *Chemical Compounds in Cells*
- Transparency C7

Student Edition on Audio CD

For: Links on proteins
Visit: www.SciLinks.org
Web Code: scn-0313

Compounds Carbon dioxide is a **compound** made up of the elements carbon and oxygen. **When two or more elements combine chemically, they form a compound.** Most elements in living things occur in the form of compounds.

The smallest unit of many compounds is called a molecule. A molecule of carbon dioxide consists of one carbon atom and two oxygen atoms. Water is another compound. Each water molecule is made up of two hydrogen atoms and one oxygen atom. In Figure 17, notice the diagrams of carbon dioxide and water molecules.

Organic and Inorganic Compounds Many of the compounds found in living things contain the element carbon. Most compounds that contain carbon are called organic compounds. **Some important groups of organic compounds found in living things are carbohydrates, lipids, proteins, and nucleic acids.** As you may know, many of these compounds are found in the foods you eat. This is not surprising, since the foods you eat come from living things.

Compounds that don't contain the element carbon are called inorganic compounds. Water and sodium chloride, or table salt, are familiar examples of inorganic compounds. Organisms contain many inorganic compounds as well as organic compounds.

Reading Checkpoint How are inorganic compounds different from organic compounds?

FIGURE 17
Molecules and Compounds
Carbon dioxide, which is found in the gas bubbles, is a chemical compound. So is water.
Applying Concepts *What is a compound?*

Carbohydrates

A **carbohydrate** is an energy-rich organic compound made of the elements carbon, hydrogen, and oxygen. Sugars and starches are examples of carbohydrates.

Sugars are produced during the food-making process that takes place in plants. Foods such as fruits and some vegetables have a high sugar content. Sugar molecules can combine, forming large molecules called starches, or complex carbohydrates. Plant cells store excess energy in molecules of starch. Many foods that come from plants contain starch. These foods include potatoes, pasta, rice, and bread. When you eat these foods, your body breaks down the starch into glucose, a sugar that your cells can use to produce energy.

Carbohydrates are important components of some cell parts. For example, the cellulose found in the cell walls of plants is a type of carbohydrate. Carbohydrates are also found in cell membranes.

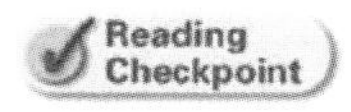
What is the difference between sugar and starch?

FIGURE 18
Starch
These potatoes contain a large amount of starch. Starch is a carbohydrate. The blue grains in the close-up are starch granules in a potato. The grains have been colored blue to make them easier to see.

Lipids

Have you ever seen a cook trim the fat from a piece of meat before cooking it? The cook is trimming away a lipid. Fats, oils, and waxes are all lipids. Like carbohydrates, **lipids** are energy-rich organic compounds made of carbon, hydrogen, and oxygen. Lipids contain even more energy than carbohydrates. Cells store energy in lipids for later use. For example, during winter, a dormant bear lives on the energy stored in fat within its cells. In addition, cell membranes are made mainly of lipids.

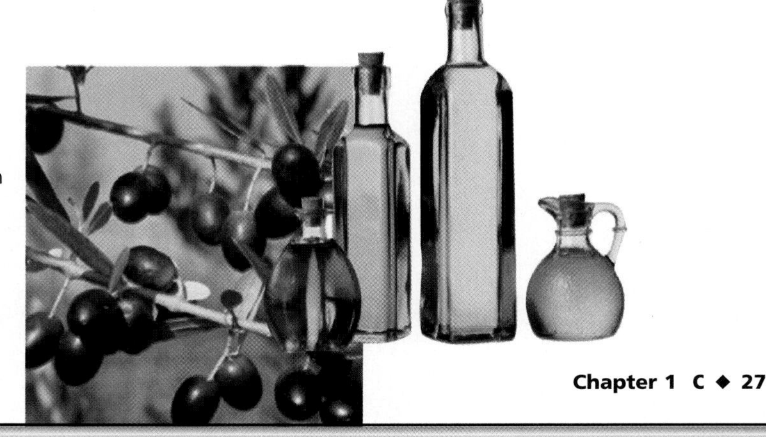

FIGURE 19
Lipids
Olive oil, which comes from olives such as those shown here, is made mostly of lipids.
Making Generalizations *What elements are lipids composed of?*

Carbohydrates

Teach Key Concepts L2

The Role of Carbohydrates

Focus Review the definition of *carbohydrate.*

Teach Ask: **What are the functions of carbohydrates?** *(To store and produce energy and to make up some cell parts)*

Apply Ask students to name foods that are carbohydrates. **learning modality: verbal**

Lipids

Teach Key Concepts L2

The Role of Lipids

Focus Review the definition of *lipid.*

Teach Ask: **How do living things use lipids?** *(They use some of the energy contained in lipids and store some energy in lipids for later use.)*

Apply Ask students to name foods that contain lipids. **learning modality: verbal**

Detecting Starch L2

Materials dropper, iodine solution, soda crackers, bread, granulated sugar

Time 10 minutes

Focus Tell students that iodine darkens in the presence of starch.

Teach Add three drops of iodine to each sample. Only the sugar will not darken.

Apply Ask students to find out why the iodine changes color when combining with starch. **learning modality: visual**

Differentiated Instruction

Special Needs L1
Modeling Elements and Compounds
Use colored beads or blocks and glue to model elements and compounds and to help students distinguish between the two. Point out the illustration of a water molecule. Explain that it consists of two atoms of hydrogen, which is an element, and one atom of oxygen, which is an element. To demonstrate this, use two beads of one color to represent hydrogen and another bead of a different color to represent oxygen. First, focus attention on these "elements" as separate entities. Then glue the three element-beads together to represent a water molecule. Explain that the glue represents chemical bonds. Then help students repeat the modeling procedure for carbon dioxide. **learning modality: kinesthetic**

Monitor Progress L2

Writing Have students describe how the body uses carbohydrates and fats.

Answers

Figure 17 A chemical combination of two or more elements

Figure 19 Carbon, hydrogen and oxygen

 Organic compounds contain carbon; inorganic compounds do not usually contain carbon.

 Sugar molecules combine to form starch.

Proteins

Teach Key Concepts

L2

The Role of Proteins

Focus Point out that proteins make up much of the structure of cells.

Teach Ask: **What elements make up proteins?** *(Carbon, hydrogen, oxygen, nitrogen, and sometimes sulfur)* **What kinds of molecules make up proteins?** *(Amino acids)* **How are proteins used in living things?** *(Proteins form parts of cell membranes and organelles. Proteins known as enzymes speed up many chemical reactions necessary for life.)*

Apply Ask: **What foods that you have eaten today contain proteins?** *(Sample answer: meat, eggs, fish, nuts, and beans.)* **learning modality: verbal**

Modeling Enzymes

L1

Materials hot plate, 1 package of pudding (not instant), water, spoon

Time 10 minutes

Focus Review the definition of enzyme.

Teach Prepare the pudding according to the package directions. Heat until it thickens. Ask: **What happened to the pudding?** *(It thickened.)* **How long would it have taken the pudding to thicken without heating it?** *(Much longer, perhaps not at all)* **How is the heat like an enzyme?** *(Both speed up chemical reactions.)*

Apply Explain that thrombin is an enzyme in blood that helps blood clot after an injury. Have students infer what would happen if thrombin were missing from blood. *(The blood would clot slowly or not at all.)* **learning modality: visual**

Lab zone Try This Activity

What's That Taste?

Use this activity to discover one role that enzymes play in your body.

1. Put an unsalted soda cracker in your mouth. Chew it, but do not swallow. Note what the cracker tastes like.
2. Continue to chew the cracker for a few minutes, mixing it well with your saliva. Note how the taste of the cracker changes.

Inferring Soda crackers are made up mainly of starch, with little sugar. How can you account for the change in taste after you chewed the cracker for a few minutes?

Proteins

What do a bird's feathers, a spider's web, and your fingernails have in common? All of these substances are made mainly of proteins. **Proteins** are large organic molecules made of carbon, hydrogen, oxygen, nitrogen, and, in some cases, sulfur. Foods that are high in protein include meat, eggs, fish, nuts, and beans.

Structure of Proteins Protein molecules are made up of smaller molecules called **amino acids.** Although there are only 20 common amino acids, cells can combine them in different ways to form thousands of different proteins. The kinds of amino acids and the order in which they link together determine the type of protein that forms. You can think of the 20 amino acids as being like the 26 letters of the alphabet. Those 26 letters can form thousands of words. The letters you use and their order determine the words you form. Even a change in one letter, for example, from *rice* to *mice*, creates a new word. Similarly, a change in the type or order of amino acids can result in a different protein.

Functions of Proteins Much of the structure of cells is made up of proteins. Proteins form parts of cell membranes. Proteins also make up many of the organelles within the cell.

The proteins known as enzymes perform important functions in the chemical reactions that take place in cells. An **enzyme** is a type of protein that speeds up a chemical reaction in a living thing. Without enzymes, many chemical reactions that are necessary for life would either take too long or not occur at all. For example, enzymes in your saliva speed up the digestion of food by breaking down starches into sugars in your mouth.

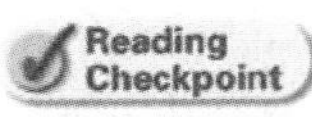

What is the role of enzymes in cells?

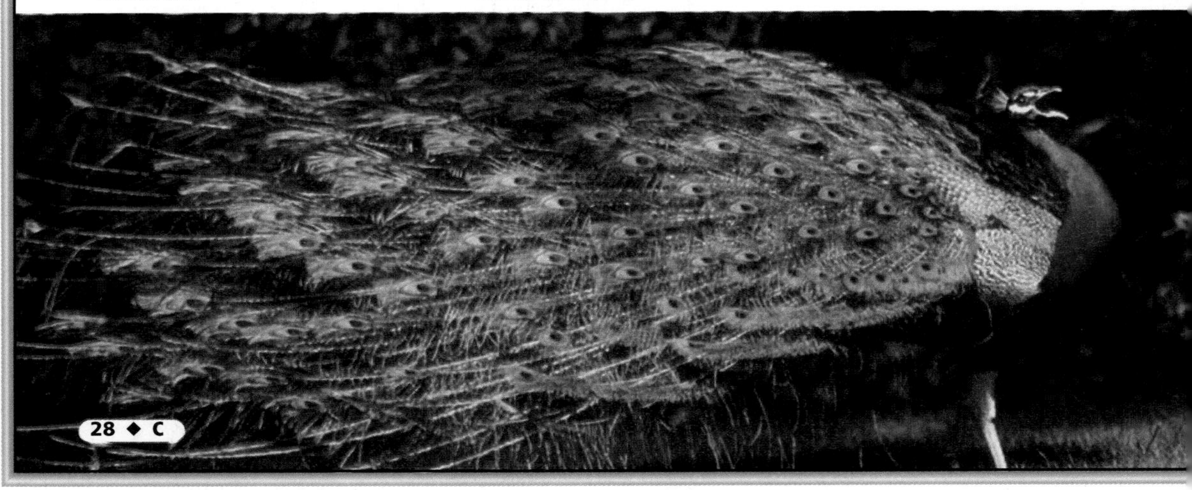

FIGURE 20
Feathers Made of Protein
The feathers of this peacock are made mainly of protein.
Applying Concepts *What smaller molecules make up protein molecules?*

Lab zone Try This Activity

Skills Focus Inferring

L1

Materials unsalted soda cracker

Time 5 minutes

Tips CAUTION: *Students with food allergies to ingredients in the cracker should be exempted from this activity.*

Expected Outcome After students have chewed the cracker for a minute or two, it should start to taste slightly sweet. Enzymes in saliva help break down the cracker's starch into sugar.

Extend Ask: **How can you tell that a food is high in sugar?** *(It tastes sweet.)* **learning modality: kinesthetic**

Nucleic Acids

Nucleic acids are very long organic molecules made of carbon, oxygen, hydrogen, nitrogen, and phosphorus. Nucleic acids contain the instructions that cells need to carry out all the functions of life.

There are two kinds of nucleic acids. Deoxyribonucleic acid (dee ahk see ry boh noo KLEE ik), or **DNA,** is the genetic material that carries information about an organism and is passed from parent to offspring. The information in DNA also directs all of the cell's functions. Most of the DNA in a cell is found in the chromatin in the nucleus. Ribonucleic acid (ry boh noo KLEE ik), or **RNA,** plays an important role in the production of proteins. RNA is found in the cytoplasm as well as in the nucleus.

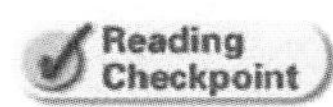
What are the two kinds of nucleic acids? What are their functions?

Math Analyzing Data

Compounds in Bacteria and Mammals

All cells contain carbohydrates, lipids, proteins, and nucleic acids, as well as water and other inorganic compounds. But do all cells contain the same percentages of these compounds? The graph compares the percentages of some kinds of compounds found in a bacterial cell and a cell from a mammal.

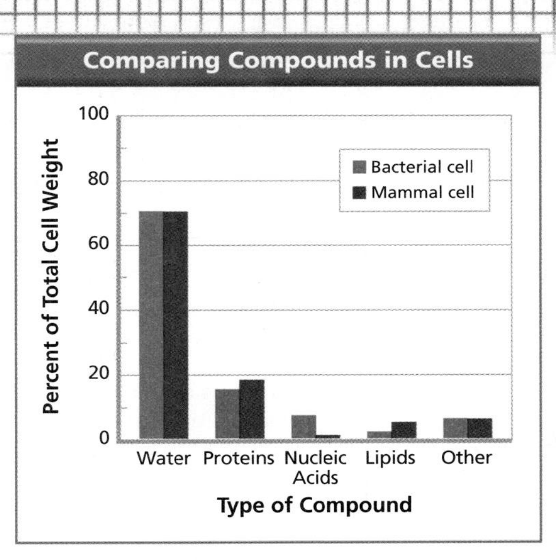

1. **Reading Graphs** What do the red bars represent? What do the blue bars represent?
2. **Interpreting Data** What percentage of a mammalian cell is made up of water? How does this compare to the percentage of water in a bacterial cell?
3. **Interpreting Data** Which kind of compound—proteins or nucleic acids—makes up the larger percentage of a mammalian cell?
4. **Drawing Conclusions** In general, how do a bacterial cell and a mammalian cell compare in their chemical composition?

Nucleic Acids

Teach Key Concepts L2

The Roles of DNA and RNA

Focus Remind students that the nucleus directs all the activities of animal and plant cells.

Teach Ask: **What is DNA?** *(The genetic material that carries information about an organism and that is passed from parent to offspring)* **What does RNA do?** *(It plays an important role in the production of proteins.)* **Why are nucleic acids important to all cells in the body?** *(They contain instructions that cells need to carry out all the functions of life.)*

Apply Ask: **How is RNA related to the structure of an organism?** *(RNA is important in the production of proteins, which make up much of the structure of cells.)* **learning modality: verbal**

Math Analyzing Data

Math Skill Making and interpreting graphs

Focus Point out that bar graphs are often used to compare different values.

Teach Show students how to use their finger or the eraser end of a pencil to estimate percent values between 60% and 80%.

Answers

1. Percentage of cell weight in bacterial cells; percentage in mammal cells
2. About 70%; they are the same.
3. Proteins
4. They are similar, though mammalian cells have a lower percentage of nucleic acids, and bacterial cells have lower percentages of lipids and proteins.

Differentiated Instruction

Gifted and Talented L3

Planning a Balanced Diet Have students use nutritional references or access the Internet to find the percentages of carbohydrates, lipids, and proteins recommended by nutritionists for a balanced diet. Challenge them to put together some healthful meals for teens. Check that students access reliable sources, such as the U.S. Department of Agriculture and the American Dietetic Association. **learning modality: verbal**

Less Proficient Readers L1

Making Concept Maps As students read through this section, help them make a concept map of the four groups of organic compounds found in living things. They can attach bubbles for structure, functions, and examples. **learning modality: visual**

Monitor Progress L2

Skills Check Have students compare and contrast DNA and RNA.

Answers

Figure 20 Amino acids

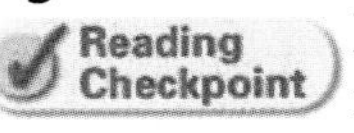
Enzymes speed up chemical reactions that take place in cells.

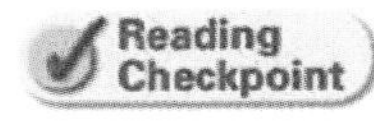
DNA and RNA. DNA is the genetic material, and RNA is important in protein synthesis.

Water and Living Things

Teach Key Concepts L2

The Many Roles of Water

Focus Tell students that people can live only a few days without water.

Teach Ask: **Why is water important to living things?** *(Water dissolves substances involved in chemical reactions in living things and takes part in many chemical reactions. It helps cells keep their size and shape, keeps the temperature of cells stable, and carries substances into and out of cells.)*

Apply Have students calculate how many kilograms of water their body contains. **learning modality: logical/mathematical**

Monitor Progress L2

Answers

Figure 21 It helps keep the temperature of body cells from changing rapidly.

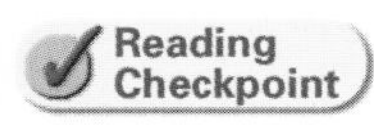

Water

Assess

Reviewing Key Concepts

1. a. Any substance that cannot be broken down into simpler substances **b.** A compound can be broken down into two or more elements. **c.** A compound; it is made of the two elements nitrogen and hydrogen.
2. a. Carbohydrates, proteins, lipids, and nucleic acids **b.** Proteins and nucleic acids **c.** It could be a carbohydrate, but not a protein. All proteins contain nitrogen.
3. a. Water helps cells keep their size and shape, helps keep the temperature of cells stable, and helps carry substances into and out of cells. **b.** Chemical reactions could not take place, so enzymes could not function.

Reteach L1

Help students compare and contrast the four main types of organic compounds.

All in One Teaching Resources

- Section Summary: *Chemical Compounds in Cells*
- Review and Reinforce: *Chemical Compounds in Cells*
- Enrich: *Chemical Compounds in Cells*

Water and Living Things

Did you know that water makes up about two thirds of your body? Water plays many important roles in cells. For example, most chemical reactions in cells involve substances that are dissolved in water. Also, water molecules themselves take part in many chemical reactions in cells. **Most chemical reactions within cells could not take place without water.**

Water also helps cells keep their size and shape. In fact, a cell without water would be like a balloon without air. In addition, because water changes temperature slowly, it helps keep the temperature of cells from changing rapidly. In the next section, you'll learn about the role that water plays in carrying substances into and out of cells.

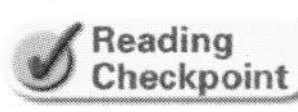

What compound is needed for most chemical reactions to take place in cells?

FIGURE 21
Mostly Water
About two-thirds of the human body is water.
Relating Cause and Effect *How does water help regulate body temperature?*

Section 3 Assessment

Target Reading Skill

Comparing and Contrasting Use the information in your table to help you answer the questions below.

Reviewing Key Concepts

1. a. **Defining** What is an element?
   b. **Comparing and Contrasting** How is a compound different from an element?
   c. **Classifying** A molecule of ammonia consists of one atom of nitrogen and three atoms of hydrogen. Is ammonia an element or a compound? Explain.
2. a. **Reviewing** What are four types of organic molecules found in living things?
   b. **Classifying** Which of the four types of organic molecules contain the element nitrogen?
   c. **Inferring** An organic compound contains only the elements carbon, hydrogen, and oxygen. Could this compound be a carbohydrate? Could it be a protein? Explain.
3. a. **Reviewing** What three important functions does water perform in cells?
   b. **Relating Cause and Effect** Suppose a cell is seriously deprived of water. How might this lack of water affect the cell's enzymes? Explain.

Lab zone At-Home Activity

Compounds in Food With family members, look at the "Nutrition Facts" labels on a variety of food products. Identify foods that contain large amounts of the following organic compounds: carbohydrates, proteins, and fats. Discuss with your family what elements make up each of these compounds and what roles they play in cells and in your body.

Lab zone At-Home Activity

Compounds in Food L2 Before students perform the activity at home, allow class time for them to review the composition and function of the organic compounds. Bring in some empty food containers with labels to model how to find the information.

Lab zone **Consumer Lab**

Which Foods Are Fat-Free?

Problem

Some people want to limit their intake of fats, or lipids. How can you determine whether information about fats on a food label is accurate?

Skills Focus

interpreting data, inferring

Materials

- 5 different snack dips in their containers, including nutrition labels
- 5 fat-testing strips with color key
- permanent marker
- 5 cotton swabs
- 5 small squares of paper towel

Procedure 

1. Copy the data table on a sheet of paper. Record the brand names of the five snack dips in the table. **CAUTION:** *Do not taste the dips at any time.*
2. Examine the nutrition label on the container of each dip. Record the percentage of the Daily Value (% DV) of fat that the dip contains.
3. Look at other information on the container to see whether the dip is labeled "fat-free." Record this information in the table.
4. Obtain five fat-testing strips. Label each strip with the name of one of the dips.
5. Use a cotton swab to smear a bit of one dip onto the test square of the corresponding testing strip. After 30 seconds, gently wipe the dip from the strip with a paper towel.
6. To determine whether the sample contains fat, compare the test square with the color key. Record your observation in the table.
7. Repeat Steps 5–6 for each of the sample dips.

Analyze and Conclude

1. **Observing** According to the information on the containers, which dips had 0% fat? Which dips were labeled "fat-free"?
2. **Interpreting Data** Did the result shown on the test square always agree with the information on the dip's container?
3. **Inferring** Based on your results, what can you conclude about the accuracy of labels indicating that foods are fat-free?
4. **Communicating** Write a report for consumers that summarizes your results. Summarize the processes you used.

Design an Experiment

Protein test strips indicate *how much* protein is present in a food sample. Design an experiment to rank five food samples in the order of least protein to most protein. *Obtain your teacher's permission before carrying out your investigation.*

Data Table

Name of Dip	Percent Fat (% Daily Value)	Labeled Fat-Free?	Result of Test

Analyze and Conclude

1. Results will vary. Sometimes a "fat-free" sample will produce a positive result.
2. Answers will vary. The test does not indicate the amount of fat, only the presence or absence of fat. Intermediate results (dark pink) indicate a moderate level of fat.
3. Students will probably say that labels are generally accurate.
4. The report should include the methods used, the limitations of the test, and an explanation to consumers of the meaning of "fat free."

Extend Inquiry

Design an Experiment Designs should include methods for controlling variables such as the amount of the food and the time before reading the result.

L2

Which Foods Are Fat-Free?

Prepare for Inquiry

Skills Objectives

Students will be able to

- organize and interpret results on the published values of nutritional labels
- infer the amount of fat present in the samples

Prep Time 20 minutes

Class Time 30 minutes

All in One Teaching Resources

- Lab Worksheet: *Which Foods Are Fat-Free?*

Advance Planning

Suggested foods are mayonnaise, butter, sour cream, olive oil, fat-free sour cream, cream cheese, light cream cheese, and fat-free liquid creamer.

Safety

Warn students to be careful when using the scissors and not to eat any of the foods. Review the safety guidelines in Appendix A.

Guide Inquiry

Introduce the Procedure

Show students how to interpret a food label. Explain that a serving that contains less than 0.5 g of fat/serving is considered "fat free."

Troubleshooting

- These test strips sometimes show false negative results with certain types of fats and those with an acidic pH (for example, vinegar in salad dressing).
- The age of the testing strip may affect its ability to change color.
- Some foods take longer than others to show a positive result.

Expected Outcome

Most foods with greater than 50% fat will show positive results. Some false negatives may occur.

Section 4 The Cell in Its Environment

Objectives

After this lesson, students will be able to

C.1.4.1 Describe how most small molecules cross the cell membrane.

C.1.4.2 Explain why osmosis is important to cells.

C.1.4.3 Tell the difference between passive transport and active transport.

Target Reading Skill

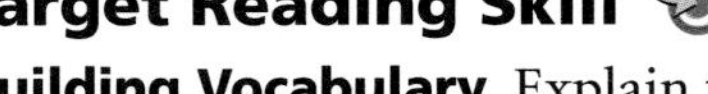

Building Vocabulary Explain that knowing the definitions of key terms helps students understand what they read.

Answers

Have students write what they know about each Key Term before reading the definitions in the section. Explain that connecting what they already know about Key Terms helps them to remember the terms. As they read each passage that contains Key Terms, remind them to write the definitions in their own words.

Preteach

Build Background Knowledge L1

Comparing a Membrane to a Sieve

Ask: **Why might you use a sieve or colander?** *(Possible answers: Strain lumps out of gravy or drain vegetables or pasta.)* **What do these things have in common?** *(They use a filter to separate large from small particles or solids from liquids.)* Tell students that the cell membrane also acts like a filter. It allows some substances, but not others, to pass in and out of the cell.

Section 4 The Cell in Its Environment

Reading Preview

Key Concepts

- How do most small molecules cross the cell membrane?
- Why is osmosis important to cells?
- What is the difference between passive transport and active transport?

Key Terms

- selectively permeable
- diffusion
- osmosis
- passive transport
- active transport

Target Reading Skill

Building Vocabulary

A definition states the meaning of a word or phrase. After you read the section, reread the paragraphs that contain definitions of Key Terms. Use all the information you have learned to write a definition of each Key Term in your own words.

Lab zone Discover Activity

How Do Molecules Move?

1. Stand with your classmates in locations that are evenly spaced throughout the classroom.
2. Your teacher will spray an air freshener into the room. When you first smell the air freshener, raise your hand.
3. Note how long it takes for other students to smell the scent.

Think It Over

Developing Hypotheses How was each student's distance from the teacher related to when he or she smelled the air freshener? Develop a hypothesis about why this pattern occurred.

As darkness fell, the knight urged his horse toward the castle. The weary knight longed for the safety of the castle, with its thick walls of stone and strong metal gates. The castle's gatekeeper opened the gates and slowly lowered the drawbridge. The horse clopped across the bridge, and the knight sighed with relief. Home at last!

Like ancient castles, cells have structures that protect their contents from the world outside. All cells are surrounded by a cell membrane that separates the cell from the outside environment. The cell membrane is **selectively permeable,** which means that some substances can pass through the membrane while others cannot.

Lab zone Discover Activity

Skills Focus Developing hypotheses L1

Materials air freshener spray

Time 5 minutes

Tips Spray the air freshener up or down rather than in the direction of students.

Expected Outcome The spray will diffuse evenly throughout the classroom, reaching students at the same distance from the source at about the same time.

Think It Over The farther each student is from the teacher, the longer it takes for the student to smell the air freshener. Students may hypothesize that particles in the spray moved from an area of higher concentration to an area of lower concentration.

Cells, like castles, must let things enter and leave. Cells must let in needed materials, such as oxygen and food molecules. In contrast, waste materials must move out of cells. Oxygen, food molecules, and waste products all must pass through the cell membrane.

Diffusion

Substances that can move into and out of a cell do so by one of three methods: diffusion, osmosis, or active transport. **Diffusion is the main method by which small molecules move across the cell membrane. Diffusion** (dih FYOO zhun) is the process by which molecules move from an area of higher concentration to an area of lower concentration. The concentration of a substance is the amount of the substance in a given volume. For example, suppose you dissolve 1 gram of sugar in 1 liter of water. The concentration of the sugar solution is 1 gram per liter.

If you did the Discover activity, you observed diffusion in action. The area where the air freshener was sprayed had many molecules of freshener. The molecules gradually moved from this area of higher concentration to the other parts of the classroom, where there were fewer molecules of freshener—and thus a lower concentration.

What Causes Diffusion? Molecules are always moving. As they move, the molecules bump into one another. The more molecules there are in an area, the more collisions there will be. Collisions cause molecules to push away from one another. Over time, the molecules of a substance will continue to spread out. Eventually, they will be spread evenly throughout the area.

Ratios

The concentration of a solution can be expressed as a ratio. A ratio compares two numbers. It tells you how much you have of one item in comparison to another. For example, suppose you dissolve 5 g of sugar in 1 L of water. You can express the concentration of the solution in ratio form as 5 g : 1 L, or 5 g/L.

Practice Problem Suppose you dissolve 7 g of salt in 1 L of water. Express the concentration of the solution as a ratio.

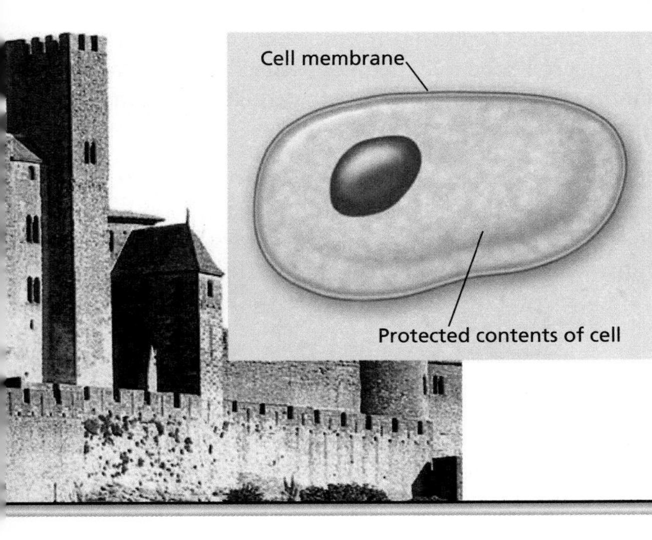

FIGURE 22
A Selective Barrier
The walls of a castle protected the inhabitants within, and the castle gatekeeper allowed only certain people to pass through. Similarly, the cell membrane protects the contents of the cell and helps control the materials that enter and leave.

Differentiated Instruction

Less Proficient Readers — L1

Making a Chart Have students make a chart with three headings: *Diffusion, Osmosis,* and *Active Transport.* As they read the section, have students write notes about each process in the chart, paying attention to the relationships among the three topics. **learning modality: visual**

Gifted and Talented — L3

Extending the Topic Ask students what happens in a cell once the concentrations of molecules inside and outside the cell are equal. Have students research the concept of dynamic equilibrium. *(Molecules continue to move into and out of a cell, but the numbers entering and leaving are approximately equal.)* **learning modality: logical/mathematical**

Instruct

Diffusion

Teach Key Concepts — L2

Diffusion Across a Cell Membrane

Focus Remind students that all cells have a cell membrane.

Teach Ask: **What is the main way small molecules move across the cell membrane?** *(Diffusion)* **In what direction do molecules move during diffusion?** *(Molecules move from an area of higher concentration to an area of lower concentration.)*

Apply Ask: **Suppose a permeable membrane separates sugar solutions with concentrations of 5 g/L and 7 g/L. Which way will the sugar diffuse across the membrane?** *(The salt will diffuse from the side that has 7 g/L to the side that has 5 g/L.)* **learning modality: logical/mathematical**

All in One Teaching Resources
- Transparency C8

Math Skills

Math Skill Ratios

Focus Remind students that ratios can compare parts to a whole.

Teach Point out that concentrations that are written in fraction form often express the ratio of the mass of the solute to the volume of the solvent.

Answer
7 g : 1 L or 7 g/L

Independent Practice

All in One Teaching Resources
- Guided Reading and Study Worksheet: *The Cell in Its Environment*

Student Edition on Audio CD

Monitor Progress — L2

Drawing Have students make a drawing that explains diffusion. Students can save their drawings in their portfolios.

For: More on cellular transport
Visit: PHSchool.com
Web Code: ced-3014

Students can review cellular transport in an online activity.

Help Students Read

L2

Outlining This section provides students with an excellent opportunity to practice outlining skills. Tell students to write the heads and subheads, leaving room between each one. As they read, they can list details under each subhead.

Observing Diffusion

Materials cornstarch, 2 cups, iodine, plastic dropper, resealable plastic bag, tablespoon, water

Time 10 minutes

Focus Remind students that iodine turns purple in the presence of starch.

Teach Explain that iodine molecules are small enough to move through plastic, but starch molecules are too large. Have students stir a tablespoon of cornstarch into half a cup of water and pour the mixture into a plastic bag. Seal the bag, rinse it, and place it in a clean cup half full of water. Add 20 drops of iodine to the water in the cup. Later, observe the cup and its contents. Ask: **Why did the water in the bag turn purple?** *(Iodine molecules passed through the plastic into the bag and interacted with the starch.)* **Why didn't the water in the cup turn purple?** *(The starch molecules were too big to pass through the bag.)*

Apply Ask: **How is this activity a model for a cell?** *(The bag is like a cell membrane.)* **learning modality: visual**

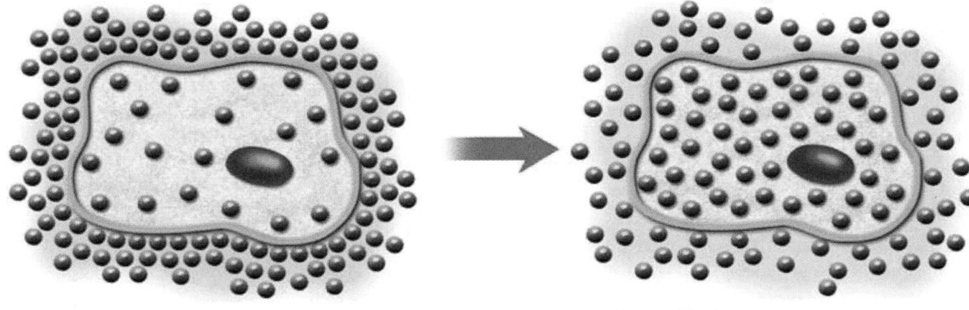

Before Diffusion
There is a higher concentration of oxygen molecules outside the cell than inside the cell.

After Diffusion
The concentration of oxygen molecules is the same outside and inside the cell.

FIGURE 23
Diffusion in Action
Molecules move by diffusion from an area of higher concentration to an area of lower concentration.
Predicting *What would happen if the concentration of oxygen molecules outside the cell was lower than inside the cell?*

Diffusion of Oxygen Have you ever used a microscope to observe one-celled organisms in pond water? These organisms obtain the oxygen they need to survive from the water around them. Luckily for them, there are many more molecules of oxygen in the water outside the cell than there are inside the cell. In other words, there is a higher concentration of oxygen molecules in the water than inside the cell. Remember that the cell membrane is permeable to oxygen molecules. The oxygen molecules diffuse from the area of higher concentration—the pond water—through the cell membrane to the area of lower concentration—the inside of the cell.

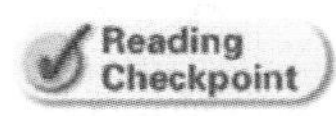

By what process do small molecules move into cells?

Osmosis

Like oxygen, water passes easily into and out of cells through the cell membrane. **Osmosis** is the diffusion of water molecules through a selectively permeable membrane. **Because cells cannot function properly without adequate water, many cellular processes depend on osmosis.**

Osmosis and Diffusion Remember that molecules tend to move from an area of higher concentration to an area of lower concentration. In osmosis, water molecules move by diffusion from an area where they are highly concentrated through the cell membrane to an area where they are less concentrated.

Go Online PHSchool.com
For: More on cellular transport
Visit: PHSchool.com
Web Code: ced-3014

Effects of Osmosis Osmosis can have important consequences for the cell. Look at Figure 24 to see the effect of osmosis on cells. In Figure 24A, a red blood cell is bathed in a solution in which the concentration of water is the same as it is inside the cell. This is the normal shape of a red blood cell.

Contrast this shape to the cell in Figure 24B. The red blood cell is floating in water that contains a lot of salt. The concentration of water molecules outside the cell is lower than the concentration of water molecules inside the cell. This difference in concentration occurs because the salt takes up space in the salt water. Therefore, there are fewer water molecules in the salt water outside the cell compared to the water inside the cell. As a result, water moves out of the cell by osmosis. When water moves out, cells shrink.

In Figure 24C, the red blood cell is floating in water that contains a very small amount of salt. The water inside the cell contains more salt than the solution outside the cell. Thus, the concentration of water outside the cell is greater than it is inside the cell. The water moves into the cell, causing it to swell.

Reading Checkpoint How is osmosis related to diffusion?

Lab zone Try This Activity

Diffusion in Action

Here's how you can observe the effects of diffusion.

1. Fill a small, clear plastic cup with cold water. Place the cup on the table and allow it to sit until there is no movement in the water.
2. Use a plastic dropper to add one large drop of food coloring to the water.
3. Observe the water every minute. Note any changes that take place. Continue to observe until you can no longer see any changes.

Inferring What role did diffusion play in the changes you observed?

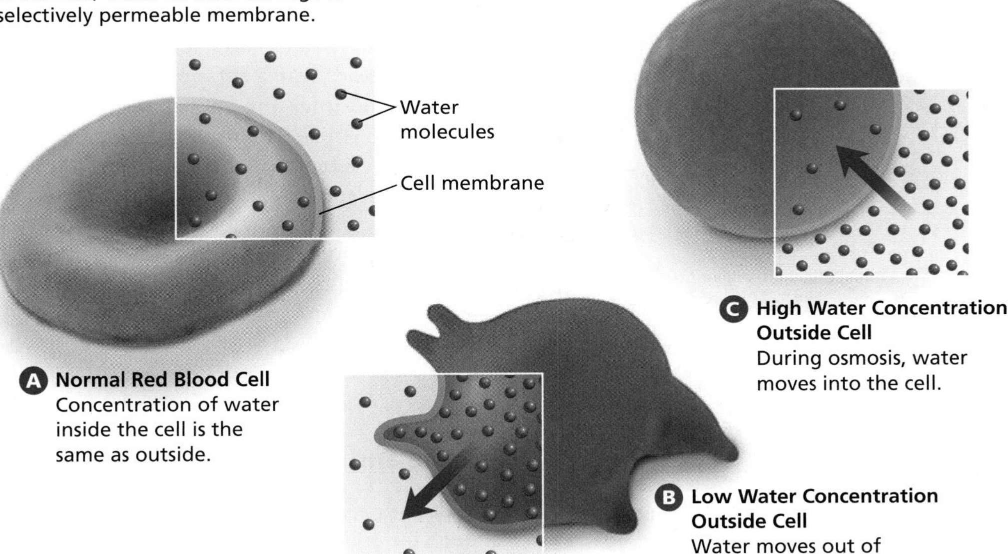

FIGURE 24
Effects of Osmosis on Cells
In osmosis, water diffuses through a selectively permeable membrane.

A Normal Red Blood Cell Concentration of water inside the cell is the same as outside.

B Low Water Concentration Outside Cell Water moves out of the cell during osmosis.

C High Water Concentration Outside Cell During osmosis, water moves into the cell.

Osmosis

Teach Key Concepts L2

The Importance of Osmosis

Focus Point out that one of the substances that must move across a cell membrane is water.

Teach Ask: **What is osmosis?** *(The diffusion of water molecules through a selectively permeable membrane)* **Why is it important?** *(Cells cannot function properly without adequate water.)* Refer students to the illustration showing the effects of osmosis. Ask a student volunteer to read the passage Effects of Osmosis while the class follows by examining the visuals. Then ask: **Is the cell in A gaining or losing water?** *(Neither—the concentration is equal inside and outside.)* **In B, which side of the cell has a higher concentration of water molecules?** *(Inside the cell)* **What might eventually happen to the cell in C?** *(The cell might eventually burst as it continued to fill with more water.)*

Apply Ask: **Why can't people drink large amounts of salt water?** *(The salt water causes water to move out of body cells.)* **learning modality: logical/mathematical**

All in One Teaching Resources

- Transparency C9

Lab zone Try This Activity

Skills Focus Inferring L1

Materials cold water; food coloring; small, clear plastic cup; plastic dropper

Time 10 minutes

Expected Outcome The large drop of food coloring will diffuse throughout the water in the cup, causing the water to become evenly shaded.

Extend Have students predict how changing the parameters of the experiment would affect the outcome. Ask: **How would the results of the activity be different if you were to use a larger amount of water?** *(Diffusion would take longer; the water would turn a lighter shade.)* Allow students to test their predictions. **learning modality: logical/mathematical**

Monitor Progress L2

Skills Check Have students compare and contrast diffusion and osmosis.

Answers

Figure 23 Oxygen molecules inside would diffuse out of the cell.

Reading Checkpoint Diffusion

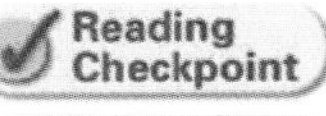
Reading Checkpoint Diffusion is the process by which small molecules move from an area of higher concentration to an area of lower concentration; osmosis is the diffusion of water molecules through a selectively permeable membrane.

Active Transport

Teach Key Concepts L2

Comparing Active and Passive Transport

Focus Have students think about the words *active, passive,* and *transport.* Ask: **What are some ways you have heard all or parts of these words used?** *(Possible answers are* activity, passive smoke, *and* transportation.*)*

Teach Refer students to the diagram of passive and active transport. Ask: **What are two different types of passive transport?** *(Diffusion and osmosis)* **What is different about the movement of molecules using active transport?** *(It requires cellular energy, while passive transport does not.)* **When would active transport be used?** *(When a cell needs to take in a substance that is in a higher concentration inside the cell than outside)* **Which method of active transport is shown in the illustration?** *(Transport proteins in the cell membrane pick up molecules outside the cell and carry them in.)* **What other method is used in active transport?** *(The cell membrane engulfs a particle, then pinches off and forms a vacuole within the cell.)*

Apply Have students draw a Venn diagram that relates active and passive transport. *(Diagrams should show that active transport requires cellular energy and passive transport does not. The overlap area should indicate that in both processes, materials move in and out of cells.)* **learning modality: visual**

All in One Teaching Resources

- Transparency C10

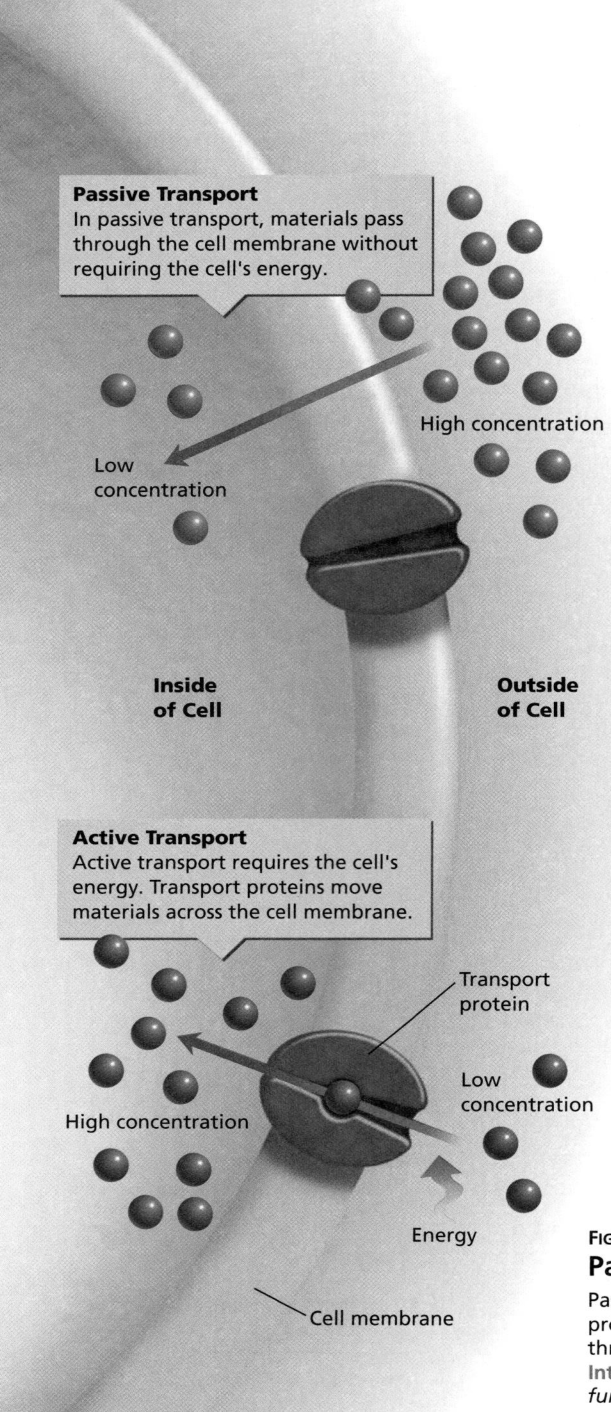

Active Transport

If you have ever ridden a bicycle down a long hill, you know that it doesn't take any of your energy to go fast. But you do have to use some of your energy to pedal back up the hill. For a cell, moving materials through the cell membrane by diffusion and osmosis is like cycling downhill. These processes do not require the cell to use its own energy. The movement of dissolved materials through a cell membrane without using cellular energy is called **passive transport.**

What if a cell needs to take in a substance that is present in a higher concentration inside the cell than outside? The cell would have to move the molecules in the opposite direction than they naturally move by diffusion. Cells can do this, but they have to use energy—just as you would use energy to pedal back up the hill. **Active transport** is the movement of materials through a cell membrane using cellular energy. **Active transport requires the cell to use its own energy, while passive transport does not.**

Transport Proteins Cells have several ways of moving materials by active transport. In one method, transport proteins in the cell membrane "pick up" molecules outside the cell and carry them in, using energy. Figure 25 illustrates this process. Transport proteins also carry molecules out of cells in a similar way. Some substances that are carried into and out of cells in this way include calcium, potassium, and sodium.

FIGURE 25
Passive and Active Transport
Passive and active transport are two processes by which materials pass through the cell membrane.
Interpreting Diagrams *What is the function of a transport protein?*

Differentiated Instruction

Special Needs L1

Modeling Active and Passive Transport Provide students with a small board, stack of books, and a toy car. Help pairs of students to model active and passive transport, or model for them. *(The most likely way is to make an inclined plane with the board and books, and then to roll the toy car down the ramp to simulate passive transport and push it up the ramp to simulate active transport.)* Ask: **Why do you need to supply energy to move the toy car up the ramp?** *(To overcome the force of gravity)* Ask: **Why is energy needed to actively transport some substances into the cell?** *(To move the substances from an area of lower to an area of higher concentration)* **learning modality: kinesthetic**

Transport by Engulfing Figure 26 shows another method of active transport. First, the cell membrane surrounds and engulfs, or encloses, a particle. Once the particle is engulfed, the cell membrane wraps around the particle and forms a vacuole within the cell. The cell must use energy in this process.

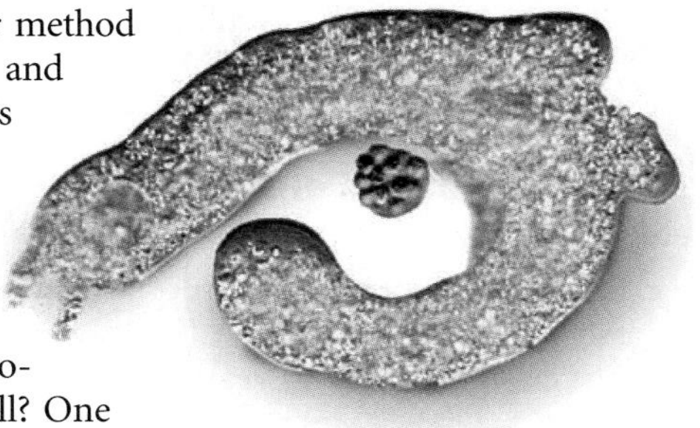

FIGURE 26
Amoeba Engulfing Food
This single-celled amoeba is surrounding a smaller organism. The amoeba will engulf the organism and use it for food. Engulfing is a form of active transport.

Why Cells Are Small As you know, most cells are so small that you cannot see them without a microscope. Have you ever wondered why cells are so small? One reason is related to how materials move into and out of cells.

As a cell's size increases, more of its cytoplasm is located farther from the cell membrane. Once a molecule enters a cell, it is carried to its destination by a stream of moving cytoplasm, somewhat like the way currents in the ocean move a raft. But in a very large cell, the streams of cytoplasm must travel farther to bring materials to all parts of the cell. It would take much longer for a molecule to reach the center of a very large cell than it would in a small cell. Likewise, it would take a long time for wastes to be removed. If a cell grew too large, it could not function well enough to survive.

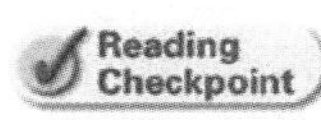

What prevents cells from growing very large?

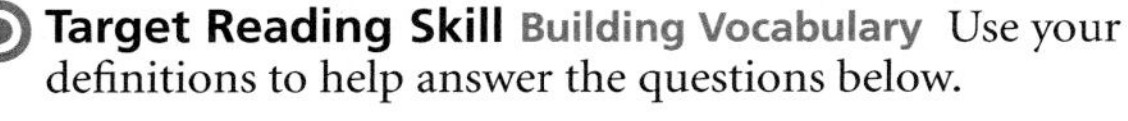

Section 4 Assessment

Target Reading Skill Building Vocabulary Use your definitions to help answer the questions below.

Reviewing Key Concepts

1. a. **Defining** What is diffusion?
   b. **Relating Cause and Effect** Use diffusion to explain what happens when you drop a sugar cube into a mug of hot tea.
2. a. **Defining** What is osmosis?
   b. **Describing** Describe how water molecules move through the cell membrane during osmosis.
   c. **Applying Concepts** A selectively permeable membrane separates solutions A and B. The concentration of water molecules in Solution B is higher than that in Solution A. Describe how the water molecules will move.
3. a. **Comparing and Contrasting** How is active transport different from passive transport?
   b. **Reviewing** What are transport proteins?
   c. **Explaining** Explain why transport proteins require energy to function in active transport.

Math Practice

A scientist dissolves 60 g of sugar in 3 L of water.

4. **Calculating a Concentration** Calculate the concentration of the solution in grams per liter.
5. **Ratios** Express the concentration as a ratio.

Lab zone Chapter Project

Keep Students on Track Encourage students to think about how their eggs have changed and how different substances affected the eggs. Have them make graphs that show their eggs' changing circumferences on one axis and the dates they were measured on the other, and indicate on their graphs what liquid the eggs were soaking in each day.

Monitor Progress L2

Answers

Figure 25 A transport protein picks up molecules outside the cell and brings them into the cell, or carries them out in a similar way.

Reading Checkpoint If cells were very large, they could not function because it would take too long for molecules entering the cell to reach the center of the cell and for wastes to be removed.

Assess

Reviewing Key Concepts

1. a. The process by which molecules move from an area of higher concentration to an area of lower concentration **b.** The sugar molecules dissolve and move from the area near the cube, where the sugar concentration is high, to the rest of the tea, where the concentration is lower.
2. a. The diffusion of water molecules through a selectively permeable membrane **b.** Water molecules move from the side of the cell membrane with a higher concentration of water to the side with a lower concentration of water. **c.** Water molecules move by osmosis from B to A.
3. a. Active transport requires cellular energy; passive transport does not. **b.** Proteins in the cell membrane that carry molecules from outside the cell to inside using energy **c.** Because they are moving molecules from an area of lower concentration to an area of higher concentration.

Math Practice

4. 20 g/L **5.** 60 g : 3 L or 20 g : 1 L

Reteach L1

Have students summarize the three ways substances can move into and out of a cell and tell whether each requires the cell to use energy.

All in One Teaching Resources

- Section Summary: *The Cell in Its Environment*
- Review and Reinforce: *The Cell in Its Environment*
- Enrich: *The Cell in Its Environment*

Study Guide

- Complete student edition
- Section and chapter self-assessments
- Assessment reports for teachers

Help Students Read L2

Building Vocabulary

Word Origins Explain that the term *mitochondrion* comes from the Greek root *chondros,* which means "granule."

Paraphrasing Ask students to look up the words *active, passive,* and *transport*. Then have them use these definitions to paraphrase the meanings of the terms *passive transport* and *active transport* in the context of cells. *(*Active *means characterized by energetic activity.* Passive *means inactive or not participating.* Transport *means to carry from one place to another. In* active transport, *cells use energy to carry substances from one place to another. In* passive transport, *cells do not need to actively participate in the carrying of substances from one place to another.)*

Connecting Concepts

Concept Maps Help students develop one way to show how the information in this chapter is related. Cells, the basic units of structure and function in living things, contain structures that help the cell perform its specific tasks within the organism and that require particular chemical compounds to function and grow. Have students brainstorm to identify the Key Concepts, Key Terms, details, and examples, and then write each one on a sticky note and attach it at random to chart paper or to the board.

Tell students that this concept map will be organized in hierarchical order and to begin at the top with the Key Concepts. Ask students these questions to guide them to categorize the information on the stickies: **What is the cell theory? What are the different structures found in cells and their functions? What chemical compounds are found in cells, and how are they useful? What methods do cells use to move substances into and out of cells?**

Prompt students by using connecting words or phrases, such as "can contain," "whose function is," and "allow the cell to," to indicate the basis for the organization of the map. The phrases should form a sentence between or among a set of concepts.

Answer Accept logical presentations by students.

All in One Teaching Resources

- Key Terms Review: *Cell Structure and Function*
- Connecting Concepts: *Cell Structure and Function*

Chapter 1 Study Guide

1 Discovering Cells

Key Concepts

- Cells are the basic units of structure and function in living things.
- The invention of the microscope enabled people to discover and learn about cells.
- The cell theory states the following: All living things are composed of cells. Cells are the basic units of structure and function in living things. All cells are produced from other cells.
- The lenses in light microscopes magnify an object by bending the light that passes through them.
- Electron microscopes use a beam of electrons instead of light to produce a magnified image.

Key Terms

cell
microscope
cell theory

2 Looking Inside Cells

Key Concepts

- A plant's cell wall protects and supports the cell.
- The cell membrane controls what substances come into and out of a cell.
- The nucleus directs the cell's activities.
- Mitochondria convert energy in food molecules to energy the cell can use.
- The endoplasmic reticulum carries materials throughout the cell.
- Ribosomes produce proteins.
- The Golgi bodies receive materials, package them, and distribute them.
- Chloroplasts capture energy from sunlight and use it to produce food for the cell.
- Vacuoles are the storage areas of cells.
- Lysosomes contain chemicals that break down certain materials in the cell.
- In many-celled organisms, cells are often organized into tissues, organs, and organ systems.
- A bacterial cell has a cell wall and cell membrane, but no nucleus. Its genetic material is found in the cytoplasm.

Key Terms

organelle
cell wall
cell membrane
nucleus
cytoplasm
mitochondria
endoplasmic reticulum
ribosome
Golgi body
chloroplast
vacuole
lysosome

3 Chemical Compounds in Cells

Key Concepts

- An element is any substance that cannot be broken down into simpler substances.
- When two or more elements combine chemically, they form a compound.
- Important groups of organic compounds found in living things are carbohydrates, proteins, lipids, and nucleic acids.
- Without water, most chemical reactions within cells could not take place.

Key Terms

element
compound
carbohydrate
protein
amino acid
enzyme
lipid
nucleic acid
DNA
RNA

4 The Cell in Its Environment

Key Concepts

- Diffusion is the main method by which small molecules move across the cell membrane.
- Osmosis is important to cells because cells cannot function properly without adequate water.
- Active transport requires the cell to use energy, while passive transport does not.

Key Terms

selectively permeable
diffusion
osmosis
passive transport
active transport

Review and Assessment

Go Online PHSchool.com
For: Self-Assessment
Visit: PHSchool.com
Web Code: cea-3010

Organizing Information

Concept Mapping Copy the concept map. Then complete the map to show the types of organic compounds. (For more about Concept Mapping, see the Skills Handbook.)

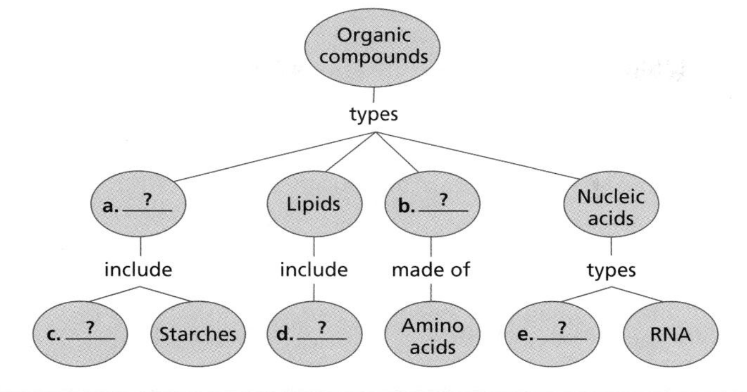

Reviewing Key Terms

Choose the letter of the best answer.

1. All living things are composed of
   a. blood.
   b. chloroplasts.
   c. vacuoles.
   d. cells.
2. In plant and animal cells, the control center of the cell is the
   a. chloroplast.
   b. cytoplasm.
   c. nucleus.
   d. Golgi body.
3. A storage compartment of the cell is the
   a. cell wall.
   b. lysosome.
   c. endoplasmic reticulum.
   d. vacuole.
4. Starch is an example of a
   a. nucleic acid.
   b. protein.
   c. lipid.
   d. carbohydrate.
5. The process by which water moves across a cell membrane is called
   a. osmosis.
   b. active transport.
   c. organelle.
   d. resolution.

If the statement is true, write *true*. If it is false, change the underlined word or words to make the statement true.

6. Cells were discovered using electron microscopes.
7. Ribosomes produce proteins.
8. The cells of plants and animals lack nuclei.
9. Both DNA and RNA are proteins.
10. The cell membrane is selectively permeable.

Writing in Science

Dialogue A dialogue is a conversation. Write a dialogue that might have taken place between Schleiden and Schwann. The scientists should discuss their observations and conclusions.

Cell Structure and Function
Video Preview
Video Field Trip
▶ Video Assessment

Review and Assessment

Organizing Information

Concept Map

a. Carbohydrates
b. Proteins
c. Sugars
d. Fats, oils, and waxes
e. DNA

Reviewing Key Terms

1. d **2.** c **3.** d **4.** d **5.** a
6. light
7. true
8. bacteria
9. nucleic acids
10. true

Writing in Science

Writing Skill Dialogue

Scoring Rubric

4 Includes a dialogue that goes beyond requirements, for example, describing the structures of animal and plant cells
3 Includes criteria but does not go beyond requirements
2 Includes factual information that is not written in dialogue form
1 Includes inaccurate information

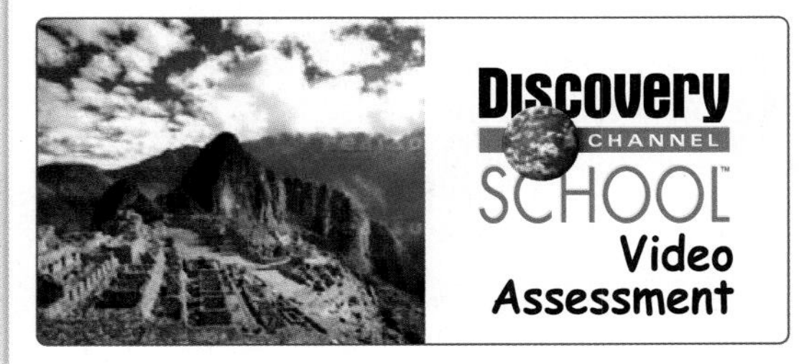

Cell Structure and Function

Show the Video Assessment to review chapter content and as a prompt for the writing assignment.

Go Online PHSchool.com
For: Self-Assessment
Visit: PHSchool.com
Web Code: cea-3010

Students can take a practice test online that is automatically scored.

All in One Teaching Resources

- Transparency C11
- Chapter Test
- Performance Assessment Teacher Notes
- Performance Assessment Student Worksheet
- Performance Assessment Scoring Rubric

***ExamView®* Computer Test Bank CD-ROM**

Checking Concepts

11. The microscope allowed scientists to observe the cells that make up living things. Over the years, they discovered that all living things are made up of cells.

12. The cell wall helps to protect and support the cell in plants and some other organisms.

13. An element is any substance that cannot be broken down into simpler substances. A compound is made up of two or more elements.

14. Enzymes speed up chemical reactions in living things. Without enzymes, many of the chemical reactions that are necessary for life would either take too long or not occur at all.

15. DNA is the genetic material that carries information about an organism and is passed from parent to offspring. The information also directs all of the cell's functions. RNA plays an important role in the production of proteins.

16. Water dissolves substances involved in chemical reactions in living things and takes part in many chemical reactions. It helps cells keep their size and shape, keeps the temperature of cells stable, and carries substances into and out of cells.

17. Diffusion is the process by which molecules move from an area of higher concentration to an area of lower concentration. Diffusion helps the cell take in the substances it needs and get rid of those it does not need.

18. As a cell size increases, more of its cytoplasm is located farther away from the cell membrane. The farther away the cytoplasm is from the cell membrane, the longer it takes substances to reach the cytoplasm. A smaller cell can function better than a larger cell because it can move needed materials and wastes to and from all parts of its cytoplasm more quickly.

Review and Assessment

Checking Concepts

11. What role did the microscope play in the development of the cell theory?

12. Describe the function of the cell wall.

13. Explain the difference between elements and compounds.

14. How are enzymes important to living things?

15. What are the functions of DNA and RNA?

16. Why is water important in the cell?

17. What is diffusion? What function does diffusion have in the cell?

18. Explain the relationship between cell size and the movement of materials into and out of cells.

Thinking Critically

19. Applying Concepts Do the cells below come from a plant or an animal? Explain your answer.

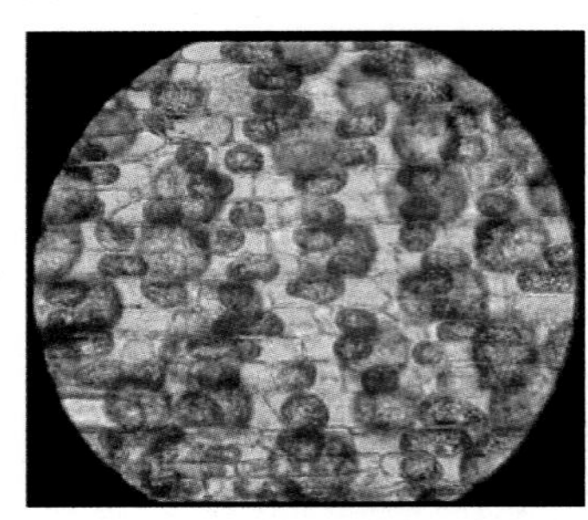

20. Comparing and Contrasting How are plant and animal cells similar? How are they different? To answer these questions, make a list of the different organelles in each cell. Explain how each organelle is vital to the life and function of a plant or animal.

21. Predicting Suppose a cell did not have a supply of amino acids and could not produce them. What effect might this have on the cell?

22. Comparing and Contrasting Explain how active transport is different from osmosis.

Math Practice

23. Ratios A solution consists of 24 g of table salt dissolved in 2 L of water. Express the concentration of salt in the form of a ratio.

Applying Skills

Use the diagrams to answer Questions 24–26.

A scientist watered the plant in Figure A with salt water. After 30 minutes, the plant looked as you see it in Figure B.

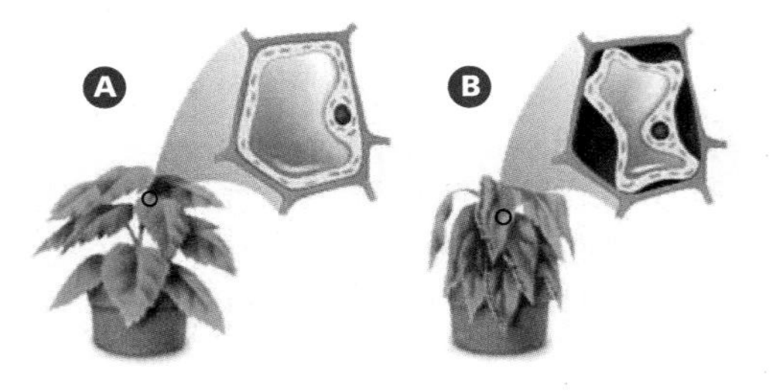

24. Observing How did the plant cells change after the plant was watered?

25. Inferring Describe a process that would lead to the changes in the plant cells.

26. Developing Hypotheses Suppose the scientist were to water the plant in B with fresh (unsalted) water. Develop a hypothesis about what would happen to the plant. Explain your hypothesis.

Lab zone Chapter Project

Performance Assessment Bring in your egg, graph, and any diagrams you made. As a class, discuss your results and conclusions. Then, as a group, try to answer these questions: What happened to the eggshell? What process took place at each stage of the experiment?

Lab zone Chapter Project

L3

Performance Assessment Have students display their eggs and share their graphs and diagrams showing how the size of their egg changed and what it was soaking in each day. Guide the class discussion so that students come to the conclusion that the eggshell dissolved in the vinegar, and that the egg increased and decreased in size because of osmosis.

Reflect and Record Encourage students to reflect on what they learned from this "egg-speriment." The most surprising part may have been how the texture of the egg changed. Most students probably began to understand what was happening to the egg when they read about osmosis. Students may say that if they did the project over, they would test a greater variety of liquids.

Standardized Test Prep

Test-Taking Tip

Measuring

In some multiple-choice questions, selecting the right units of measurement may help you find the correct answer choice or eliminate one or more answer choices. You often can eliminate answers because the measurements are much too large or small. For example, in the sample question below, three of the answer choices are much too large. Only one choice is a reasonable measurement for the total length of 100 cells. Read the question, and determine which choice is correct.

Sample Question

Cells are very small. If 100 skin cells were lined up in a row, their total length would probably measure about

A 1 cm.
B 100 cm.
C 1 mm.
D 100 mm.

Answer

Answer choice **C** is correct. Answer choices **A, B,** and **D** are much too large.

Choose the letter of the best answer.

1. A reasonable estimate for the size of a cell's nucleus is
A 0.003 mm.
B 3 mm.
C 0.003 m.
D 3 m.

2. A compound microscope has two lenses. One lens has a magnification of 15 and the other lens has a magnification of 40. What is the total magnification of the microscope?
F 55
G 150
H 25
J 600

3. A tissue in an animal produces and releases chemicals that are used by cells throughout the animal's body. Cells in that tissue probably have a larger than normal number of
A lysosomes.
B mitochondria.
C Golgi bodies.
D nuclei.

Use the diagram below and your knowledge of science to answer Questions 4 and 5.

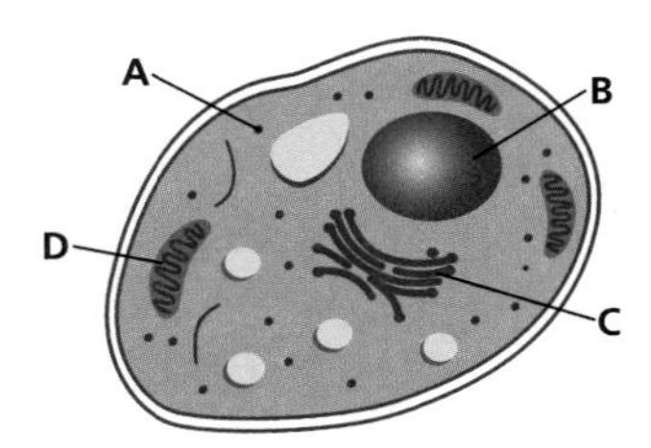

4. Which organelle contains instructions for directing the cell's functions?
F A
G B
H C
J D

5. In which organelle is food energy converted to energy that the cell can use?
A A
B B
C C
D D

Constructed Response

6. Describe the structure of proteins, and explain how proteins play an important role in the cell.

Standardized Test Prep

1. A **2.** J **3.** C **4.** G **5.** D

6. Protein molecules are made up of smaller molecules called amino acids, which combine in different ways to form thousands of different proteins. Proteins form much of the structure of cells, such as cell membranes and many organelles. Proteins known as enzymes speed up chemical reactions that are necessary for life.

Thinking Critically

19. From a plant; the cell has chloroplasts and rigid, rectangular cell walls.

20. They both have the same types of organelles except that plant cells have cell walls and chloroplasts, and animal cells do not. Nucleus—directs all of the cell's activities, including reproduction; mitochondria—produce energy for plant and animal cells; endoplasmic reticulum—provides an internal transport system for plant and animal cells; ribosomes—produce proteins in plant and animal cells; Golgi bodies—package and distribute protein made in plant and animal cells; chloroplasts—make food in plant cells; vacuoles—provide storage areas in plant and some animal cells; lysosomes—contain chemicals that break down food particles in plant and animal cells

21. The cell would not be able to make proteins. Proteins make up many parts of the cell, and some proteins act as enzymes, which speed up chemical reactions in the cell. Without proteins, the cell would be missing important structures and would not be able to carry out many of its functions. The cell would likely die.

22. Active transport and osmosis are both ways that molecules cross cell membranes, but osmosis is a passive form of transport that requires no cellular energy, whereas active transport requires energy to take place. In addition, osmosis refers specifically to the transfer of water across the cell membrane, whereas active transport involves other kinds of molecules.

Math Practice

23. 24 g/2 L or 12 g/1 L or 12 g : 1 L

Applying Skills

24. The plant cells got smaller.

25. Osmosis, or movement of water by diffusion, would lead to the changes in the plant cells. In B, water has moved out of the cell by osmosis.

26. Sample answer: If the plant in B were to be watered with fresh water, it would return to its original size because it would gain water by osmosis.

Chapter at a Glance

Chapter Project *Shine On!*

Technology | **Local Standards**

All in One Teaching Resources
- Chapter Project Teacher Notes, pp. 102–103
- Chapter Project Student Overview, pp. 104–105
- Chapter Project Student Worksheets, pp. 106–107
- Chapter Project Scoring Rubric, p. 108

Technology: Discovery Channel School Video Preview

Photosynthesis

2–3 periods
1–1 1/2 blocks

C.2.1.1 Explain how the sun supplies living things with the energy they need.
C.2.1.2 Describe what happens during the process of photosynthesis.

Respiration

2–3 periods
1–1 1/2 blocks

C.2.2.1 Describe the events that occur during respiration.
C.2.2.2 Tell what fermentation is.

Cell Division

3–4 periods
1 1/2–2 blocks

C.2.3.1 Identify the events that take place during the three stages of the cell cycle.
C.2.3.2 Explain how the structure of DNA helps account for the way in which DNA copies itself.

Section 4

Cancer

2–3 periods
1–1 1/2 blocks

C.2.4.1 Explain how cancer is related to the cell cycle.
C.2.4.2 Describe how cancer can be treated and prevented.

Video Field Trip

Review and Assessment

All in One Teaching Resources
- Key Terms Review, p. 142
- Transparency C23
- Performance Assessment Teacher Notes, p. 151
- Performance Assessment Scoring Rubric, p. 152
- Performance Assessment Student Worksheet, p. 153
- Chapter Test, pp. 154–157

Video Assessment

Go Online PHSchool.com

Test Preparation

Chapter Activities Planner

For more activities

Student Edition	Inquiry	Time	Materials	Skills	Resources
Chapter Project, p. 43	Open-Ended	3 weeks	All in One **Teaching Resources,** Support, p. 102	Designing an experiment, observing, measuring, making and interpreting graphs, drawing conclusions	**Lab zone Easy Planner** All in One **Teaching Resource** Support, pp. 102–103
Section 1					
Discover Activity, p. 44	Directed	5 minutes	solar-powered calculator that does not use batteries	Inferring	**Lab zone Easy Planner**
Try This Activity, p. 47	Guided	20 minutes	coffee filter, scissors, leaf, metric ruler, dime, rubbing alcohol, plastic cup	Inferring	**Lab zone Easy Planner**
Section 2					
Discover Activity, p. 49	Directed	20 minutes	2 test tubes with stoppers, warm water, 5 mL sugar, test tube rack, 1.0 mL dried yeast, 2 straws	Observing	**Lab zone Easy Planner**
Skills Activity, p. 50	Guided	5 minutes	none	Predicting	**Lab zone Easy Planner**
Design Your Own Lab, p. 54	Open-Ended	30 minutes	2 250-mL beakers or plastic cups, 30 mL bromthymol blue (0.1% solution), 2 straws, watch with second hand or stopwatch, 25-mL graduated cylinder, paper towels	Predicting, controlling variables	**Lab zone Easy Planner** All in One **Teaching Resource** Design Your Own Lab: *Exhaling Carbon Dioxide*, pp. 123–124
Section 3					
Discover Activity, p. 55	Guided	15 minutes	plastic dropper, yeast culture, stained microscope slide, coverslip, microscope	Developing hypotheses	**Lab zone Easy Planner**
Try This Activity, p. 56	Guided	10 minutes	construction paper, different colored pipe cleaners	Making models	**Lab zone Easy Planner**
Skills Lab, p. 63	Directed	40 minutes	microscope, colored pencils, calculator (optional), prepared slides of onion root tip cells undergoing cell division	Observing, calculating	**Lab zone Easy Planner** All in One **Teaching Resource** Skills Lab: *Multiplying by Dividing,* pp. 133–134
Section 4					
Discover Activity, p. 64	Directed	15 minutes	masking tape, meter stick	Predicting	**Lab zone Easy Planner**

Section 1 Photosynthesis

 *2–3 periods, 1–1 1/2 blocks*

ABILITY LEVELS
- L1 Basic to Average
- L2 For All Students
- L3 Average to Advanced

Objectives

C.2.1.1 Explain how the sun supplies living things with the energy they need.
C.2.1.2 Describe what happens during the process of photosynthesis.

Key Terms

• photosynthesis • autotroph • heterotroph • pigment • chlorophyll • stomata

Local Standards

Preteach

Build Background Knowledge

Invite students to share what they know about the role of light in caring for houseplants.

 *Where Does the Energy Come From?* L1

Targeted Print and Technology Resources

 **Teaching Resources**
- L2 Reading Strategy Transparency C12: Sequencing

PresentationExpress™ CD-ROM

Instruct

Sources of Energy Compare and contrast how autotrophs and heterotrophs receive energy from the sun directly and indirectly.

The Two Stages of Photosynthesis Use a diagram to examine what happens during photosynthesis.

Targeted Print and Technology Resources

 **Teaching Resources**
- L2 Guided Reading, pp. 111–113
- L2 Transparencies C13, C14

PHSchool.com Web Code: cep-1042

Student Edition on Audio CD

Assess

Section Assessment Questions

Have students use their completed flowcharts that sequence photosynthesis to help them answer the questions.

Reteach

Use a diagram to review what happens during photosynthesis.

Targeted Print and Technology Resources

Teaching Resources
- Section Summary, p. 110
- L1 Review and Reinforce, p. 114
- L3 Enrich, p. 115

Section 2 Respiration

 *2–3 periods, 1–1 1/2 blocks*

ABILITY LEVELS
- L1 Basic to Average
- L2 For All Students
- L3 Average to Advanced

Objectives

C.2.2.1 Describe the events that occur during respiration.
C.2.2.2 Tell what fermentation is.

Local Standards

Key Terms

• respiration • fermentation

Preteach

Build Background Knowledge

Relate students' knowledge of combustion to the concept of respiration.

 *What Is a Product of Respiration?* 

Targeted Print and Technology Resources

All in One Teaching Resources
- L2 Reading Strategy Transparency C15: Using Prior Knowledge

 **PresentationExpress™ CD-ROM**

Instruct

What Is Respiration? Analyze the two stages of respiration and the events that occur in each.

Fermentation Describe fermentation and its products, and relate it to the familiar situation of exercising.

 *Exhaling Carbon Dioxide* 

Targeted Print and Technology Resources

All in One Teaching Resources
- L2 Guided Reading, pp. 118–120
- L2 Transparencies C16, C17
- L2 Design Your Own Lab: *Exhaling Carbon Dioxide,* pp. 123–124

Lab Activity Video
Design Your Own Lab: *Exhaling Carbon Dioxide*

www.SciLinks.org Web Code: scn-0322

 **Student Edition on Audio CD**

Assess

Section Assessment Questions

Have students use their completed graphic organizer about respiration to answer the questions.

Reteach

Have students make flowcharts to show what occurs during respiration and fermentation.

Targeted Print and Technology Resources

All in One Teaching Resources
- Section Summary, p. 117
- L1 Review and Reinforce, p. 121
- L3 Enrich, p. 122

Section 3 Cell Division

 *3–4 periods, 1 1/2–2 blocks*

ABILITY LEVELS
- L1 Basic to Average
- L2 For All Students
- L3 Average to Advanced

Objectives

C.2.3.1 Identify the events that take place during the three stages of the cell cycle.

C.2.3.2 Explain how the structure of DNA helps account for the way in which DNA copies itself.

Local Standards

Key Terms

• cell cycle • interphase • replication • mitosis • chromosome • cytokinesis

Preteach

Build Background Knowledge

Elicit the stages of the human life cycle, and relate that cycle to the cell cycle.

 *What Are the Yeast Cells Doing?* L1

Targeted Print and Technology Resources

All in One Teaching Resources
- L2 Reading Strategy Transparency C18: Sequencing

 **PresentationExpress™ CD-ROM**

Instruct

Stage 1: Interphase Identify the events that occur during interphase, and lead students to infer the role of DNA replication.

Stage 2: Mitosis Examine how the cell's genetic material changes during mitosis.

Stage 3: Cytokinesis Discuss what happens during cytokinesis, and compare and contrast the process in plant and animal cells.

Structure and Replication of DNA Use diagrams of the structure of DNA to discuss how DNA replicates.

 *Multiplying by Dividing* L2

Targeted Print and Technology Resources

All in One Teaching Resources
- L2 Guided Reading, pp. 127–130
- L2 Transparencies C19, C20, C21
- L2 Skills Lab: *Multiplying by Dividing,* pp. 133–134

Lab Activity Video
Skills Lab: *Multiplying by Dividing*

PHSchool.com Web Code: cep-3023

Student Edition on Audio CD

Assess

Section Assessment Questions

Have students use their diagrams showing the sequence in the cell cycle to help them answer the questions.

Reteach

Have students sketch the stages of the cell cycle and exchange with partners to identify each stage.

Targeted Print and Technology Resources

All in One Teaching Resources
- Section Summary, p. 126
- L1 Review and Reinforce, p. 131
- L3 Enrich, p. 132

Section 4 Cancer

2–3 periods, 1–1 1/2 block

ABILITY LEVELS
- L1 Basic to Average
- L2 For All Students
- L3 Average to Advanced

Objectives

C.2.4.1 Explain how cancer is related to the cell cycle.
C.2.4.2 Describe how cancer can be treated and prevented.

Key Terms

• cancer • mutation • tumor • chemotherapy

Local Standards

Preteach

Build Background Knowledge

Assess students' current knowledge of how cancer is caused, treated, and prevented.

What Happens When There Are Too Many Cells?

Targeted Print and Technology Resources

All in One Teaching Resources
- L2 Reading Strategy Transparency C22: Previewing Visuals

PresentationExpress™ CD-ROM

Instruct

What Is Cancer? Relate the behavior of cancer cells to the cell cycle, and discuss how cancer begins and spreads.

Treating and Preventing Cancer Ask questions to help students discuss cancer treatments and prevention, and to apply their knowledge by identifying ways to reduce the risk of skin cancer.

Targeted Print and Technology Resources

All in One Teaching Resources
- L2 Guided Reading, pp. 137–139

Discovery Channel School
Video Field Trip

www.SciLinks.org Web Code: scn-0324
PHSchool.com Web Code: ceh-3020

Student Edμition on Audio CD

Assess

Section Assessment Questions

Have students use their Previewing Visuals graphic organizers to answer the questions.

Reteach

Use a diagram to review how cancer begins and how it spreads.

Targeted Print and Technology Resources

All in One Teaching Resources
- Section Summary, p. 136
- L1 Review and Reinforce, p. 140
- L3 Enrich, p. 141

Chapter 2 Content Refresher

For: Professional development support
Visit: www.SciLinks.org/PDLinks
Web Code: scf-0320

Professional Development

Section 1 Photosynthesis

Chlorophyll and the Absorption of Light The light that we see consists of a mixture of different wavelengths. If light passes through a prism, the waves are separated according to length and produce a spectrum of different colors, such as the one in the graph below.

The pigment chlorophyll absorbs some, but not all, of the wavelengths of light. There are two main types of chlorophyll—chlorophyll *a* and chlorophyll *b*. The graph shows the percentage of different wavelengths absorbed by chlorophyll *a*. Notice that the highest percentage of absorption occurs in the purple/blue and orange/red areas of the spectrum. In contrast, almost no light is absorbed in the green area of the spectrum. This general pattern is also true for the absorption of light by chlorophyll *b*.

Address Misconceptions

Some students may think that soil provides plants with food. However, plants do not take in food; they produce all of their food through photosynthesis. From soil, plants obtain water—one of the raw materials for *making* food—and minerals, which are needed for growth and development. For a strategy for overcoming this misconception, see **Address Misconceptions** in the section *Photosynthesis*.

Chlorophyll makes chloroplasts—and leaves—look green because it reflects green light rather than absorbing it. It is the light reflected by leaves that reaches people's eyes.

Light is a form of energy. When chlorophyll absorbs light, energy is transferred to electrons in the chlorophyll. These "energized" electrons provide the energy for photosynthesis.

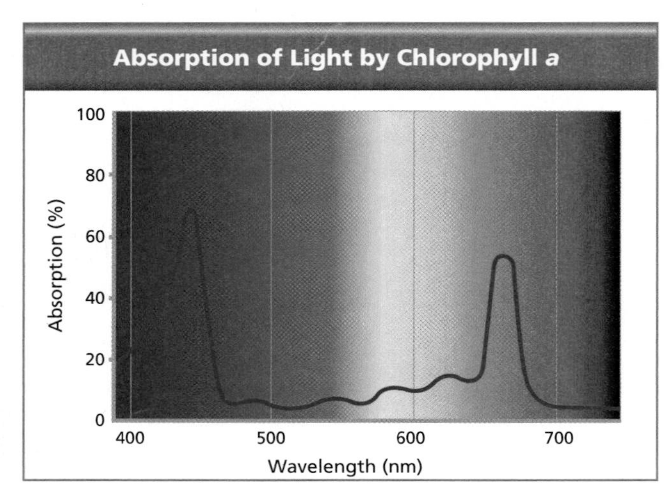

Section 2 Respiration

A Form of Combustion Respiration is often compared to combustion because both processes involve the breakdown of molecules in the presence of oxygen to produce energy and carbon dioxide. However, respiration is a much slower, more controlled process than combustion. If respiration is like carrying a bundle down five flights of stairs, combustion is like dropping it from a fifth-story window.

The discovery of the nature of cellular respiration is attributed jointly to the French chemist Antoine Laurent Lavoisier and the French physicist, mathematician, and astronomer Pierre Laplace. In 1780 they published the results of their experiments showing that animal respiration is a form of combustion.

Energy and ATP Adenosine triphosphate, or ATP, is one of the main chemical compounds that release energy in organisms. The energy released by ATP powers processes such as active transport, muscle contraction, and the synthesis of DNA molecules.

During cellular respiration, cells use the energy stored in food molecules to produce ATP. For each molecule of glucose that undergoes the chemical reactions of cellular respiration, 36 molecules of ATP are formed. The stage of respiration that does not take place in a mitochondrion, which is called glycolysis, produces a net of only 2 ATP molecules. Oxygen is not required for the production of those two molecules. In contrast, the stage of respiration that takes place in the mitochondrion requires oxygen. The reactions that take place within a mitochondrion generate the remaining 34 molecules of ATP.

Section 3 Cell Division

Discovery of Chromosomes With the development of dyes for staining microscope specimens in the 1800s, scientists could see organelles in the nucleus and learn the details of mitosis. Some of the dyes stained the granular material in the nucleus, so it was given the name *chromatin,* from the Greek word *chroma,* meaning "color." With the dye, chromatin could be seen condensing into rodlike structures during cell division. These rodlike structures were called chromosomes, or "colored bodies" (the Greek word *soma* means "body.")

DNA Replication In most eukaryotic cells—that is, cells with nuclei and other membrane-bound organelles—the replication of a DNA molecule does not start at one end and finish at the other end. Instead, replication occurs simultaneously at many sites along the molecule. At each replication site, the two DNA strands separate. The opening that forms between the two strands, which is called a bubble, can be compared to the opening produced in a resealable plastic bag when the bag is opened in the middle of the "zipper" rather than at either end. The points at which the strands separate are called replication forks.

The process of DNA replication is facilitated by many different enzymes as well as other types of protein molecules. Protein molecules called single-strand binding proteins hold the original DNA strands apart. An enzyme called DNA polymerase links individual nucleotides in a chain, one by one, to form the new DNA strand. DNA polymerase also "proofreads" each new nucleotide as it is added to the strand, making sure that the new nucleotide correctly pairs with the corresponding nucleotide on the original strand. If a nucleotide is incorrect, DNA polymerase removes it.

DNA Replication Bubble

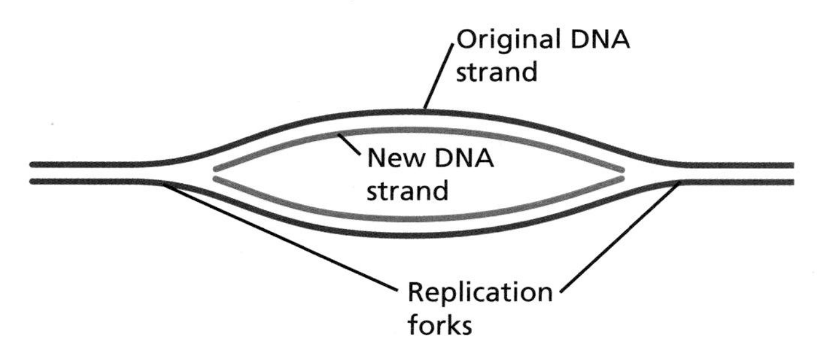

Section 4 Cancer

Second Leading Cause of Death in the U.S. More than 1,500 people die of cancer each day in the United States. Cancer is second only to heart disease as a leading cause of death in this country, killing one out of every four Americans. About eight million Americans alive today now have or have had cancer. For men in the United States, there is a one in two lifetime risk of developing cancer. For women, the risk is one in three.

After almost 20 years of rising cancer rates, the rate of new cancer cases among Americans finally started to decline in the early 1990s. The rates declined for most ages, both sexes, and most racial and ethnic groups. The only exceptions were African American males and Asian and Pacific Islander females. The main forms of cancer that declined were lung and prostate cancers in males and colorectal cancers in both males and females. The decline in these and some other cancers may be due to decreased tobacco use, better screening to detect and treat precancerous conditions, and, possibly, improved diet. Despite the good news, not all types of cancer are decreasing. Some types of cancer, including melanoma and non-Hodgkin's lymphoma, occur more often now than they did in the past.

Help Students Read

Visualizing

Forming Mental Pictures

Strategy Help students understand and recall complex text by forming mental pictures as they read. In some cases, images in the text can aid students in visualizing; in other cases, students must rely solely on verbal descriptions. Choose several paragraphs from this chapter. Include at least one paragraph that has an accompanying figure and at least one paragraph that is not illustrated.

Example

1. Have students keep their books closed. Tell them to listen while you read and to visualize, or form mental pictures of, each object or action you read about.
2. Read a paragraph aloud, pausing frequently to demonstrate, by thinking aloud, how to visualize each thing described.
3. Tell students to continue visualizing. Slowly and clearly, read on. Then, select a logical stopping point, and discuss with students the images they visualized.
4. If there is an accompanying figure, have students open to it and see how it compares with their visualizing. Point out that visuals in the text help readers picture what they are reading.
5. Have students work with partners to practice by taking turns reading and visualizing aloud. Tell them to expand on visuals that appear in the text and to describe their own mental images of ideas or events that are not shown in visuals.

- Complete student edition
- Video and audio
- Simulations and activities
- Section and chapter reviews

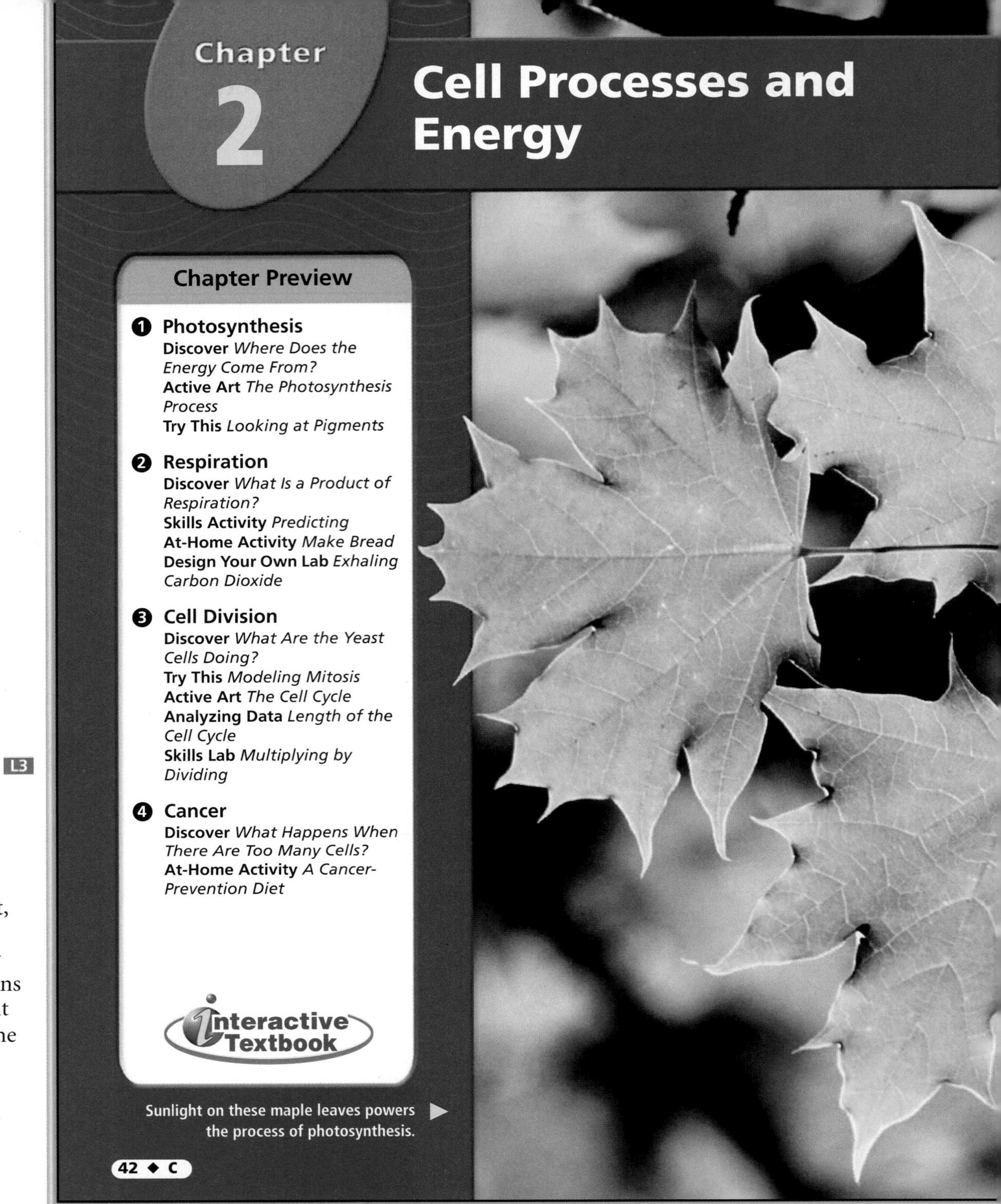

Chapter 2

Cell Processes and Energy

Chapter Preview

1. **Photosynthesis**
   Discover *Where Does the Energy Come From?*
   Active Art *The Photosynthesis Process*
   Try This *Looking at Pigments*
2. **Respiration**
   Discover *What Is a Product of Respiration?*
   Skills Activity *Predicting*
   At-Home Activity *Make Bread*
   Design Your Own Lab *Exhaling Carbon Dioxide*
3. **Cell Division**
   Discover *What Are the Yeast Cells Doing?*
   Try This *Modeling Mitosis*
   Active Art *The Cell Cycle*
   Analyzing Data *Length of the Cell Cycle*
   Skills Lab *Multiplying by Dividing*
4. **Cancer**
   Discover *What Happens When There Are Too Many Cells?*
   At-Home Activity *A Cancer-Prevention Diet*

Interactive Textbook

Sunlight on these maple leaves powers the process of photosynthesis. ▶

42 ◆ C

L3

Objectives

This project will give students an opportunity to learn how plants use sunlight to make food in the process of photosynthesis. After this Chapter Project, students will be able to

- design a controlled experiment to grow plants under different lighting conditions while keeping other conditions constant
- observe, measure, and record data on the health and growth of the plants
- graph the data and draw conclusions about the effect of light on plant health and growth

Skills Focus

Designing an experiment, observing, measuring, making and interpreting graphs, drawing conclusions

Project Time Line 3 weeks

All in One Teaching Resources

- Chapter Project Teacher Notes
- Chapter Project Overview
- Chapter Project Worksheet 1
- Chapter Project Worksheet 2
- Chapter Project Scoring Rubric

Developing a Plan

During the first week, students will read and discuss the project, assemble into their groups, write an experimental plan, and begin setting up their experiment. Students continue to measure and record data during the next three weeks. Set aside time at the end of three weeks for students to prepare and deliver their presentations.

Possible Materials

- Provide rapidly growing plants (such as bean seedlings), watering cans, water, and metric rulers.
- Students may achieve different lighting conditions by placing the plants in different areas of the room, or by using plant lights on timers or colored cellophane paper.

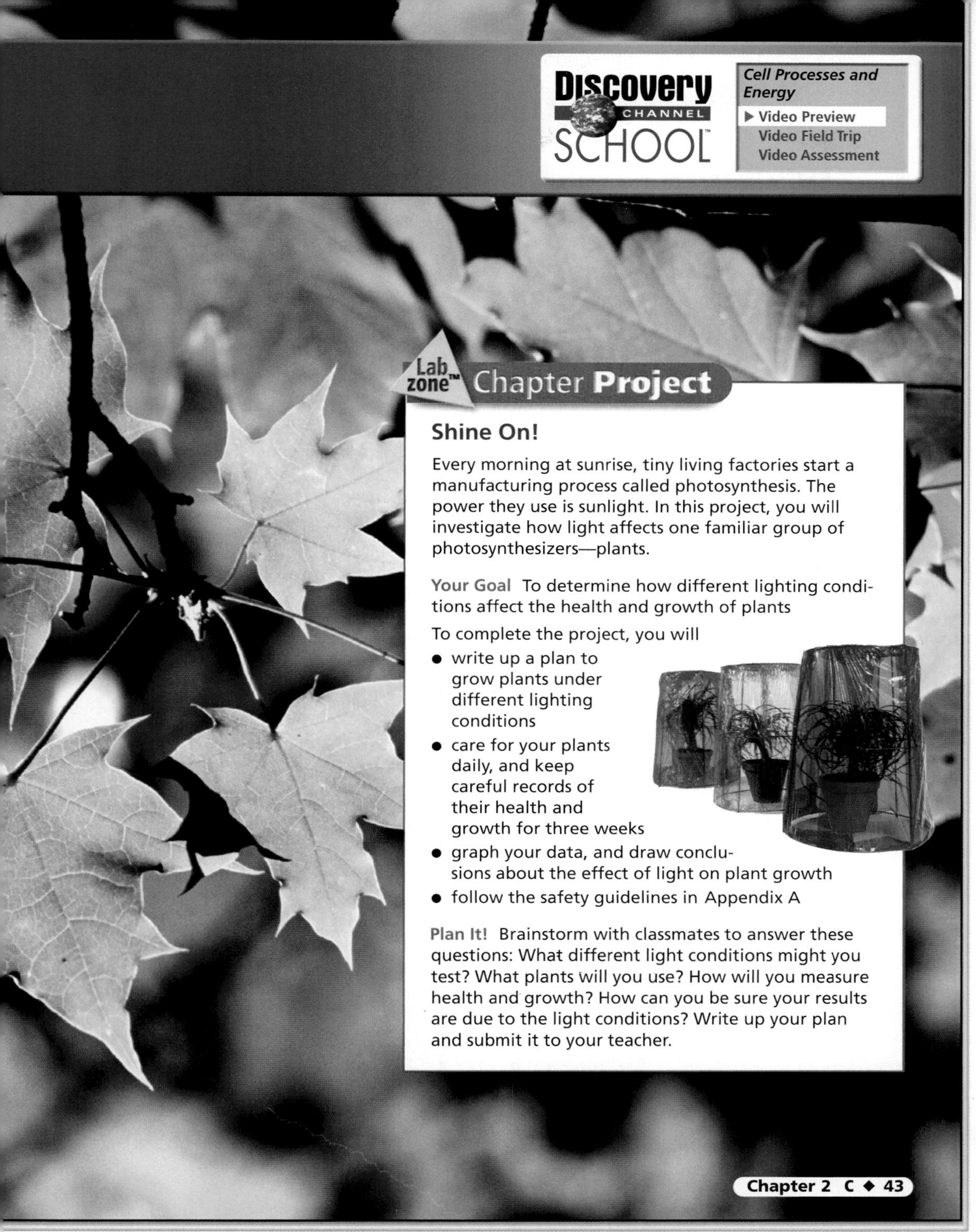

Lab zone™ Chapter Project

Shine On!

Every morning at sunrise, tiny living factories start a manufacturing process called photosynthesis. The power they use is sunlight. In this project, you will investigate how light affects one familiar group of photosynthesizers—plants.

Your Goal To determine how different lighting conditions affect the health and growth of plants

To complete the project, you will

- write up a plan to grow plants under different lighting conditions
- care for your plants daily, and keep careful records of their health and growth for three weeks
- graph your data, and draw conclusions about the effect of light on plant growth
- follow the safety guidelines in Appendix A

Plan It! Brainstorm with classmates to answer these questions: What different light conditions might you test? What plants will you use? How will you measure health and growth? How can you be sure your results are due to the light conditions? Write up your plan and submit it to your teacher.

Cell Processes and Energy

Show the Video Preview to introduce the video topic and the topic of the cell cycle.

Suggested Shortcut

Individual students can grow the plants at home to reduce the amount of class time and classroom space needed to care for and measure the plants.

Launching the Project

Ask: **What do plants need to grow?** *(Possible answers include soil, minerals, water, and light.)* Emphasize the importance of light to plant growth. Point out that plants need light to make food, which in turn provides them with the energy they need for growth and all other life processes. Ask: **What do you predict would happen to a plant that did not receive any light?** *(Possible answer: The plant would not be able to make food, so it probably would die.)*

Performance Assessment

The Chapter Project Scoring Rubric will help you evaluate how well students complete the Chapter Project. You may want to share the scoring rubric with your students so they are clear about what will be expected of them. Students will be assessed on

Portfolio

- their experimental design and how well they control variables
- their record of observations and measurements of plant health and growth
- their graphs of the data and their conclusions about the effect of light on plant health and growth
- their group participation, if they worked in groups

Section 1 Photosynthesis

Objectives
After this lesson, students will be able to
C.2.1.1 Explain how the sun supplies living things with the energy they need.
C.2.1.2 Describe what happens during the process of photosynthesis.

Target Reading Skill 

Sequencing Explain that organizing information from beginning to end helps students understand a step-by-step process.

Answer
One possible way to complete the flowchart is to place the following sentence in the third bar: Cells use the energy to produce sugars and oxygen from water and carbon dioxide.

All in One Teaching Resources
- Transparency C12

Preteach

Build Background Knowledge L1

Care of Houseplants
Ask: **How many of you have houseplants in your home?** Most will probably say they do. **Where are houseplants usually placed?** *(Near a window or under plant lights)* **What happens if a houseplant doesn't get enough light?** *(They lose their leaves, turn yellow, and may die.)* **Why do plants need light?** Some students may know that plants use light energy to make food. Accept all responses without comment at this time.

Section 1 Photosynthesis

Reading Preview

Key Concepts
- How does the sun supply living things with the energy they need?
- What happens during the process of photosynthesis?

Key Terms
- photosynthesis
- autotroph
- heterotroph
- pigment
- chlorophyll
- stomata

Target Reading Skill
Sequencing A sequence is the order in which the steps in a process occur. As you read, create a flowchart that shows the steps in photosynthesis. Put each step in a separate box in the flowchart in the order in which it occurs.

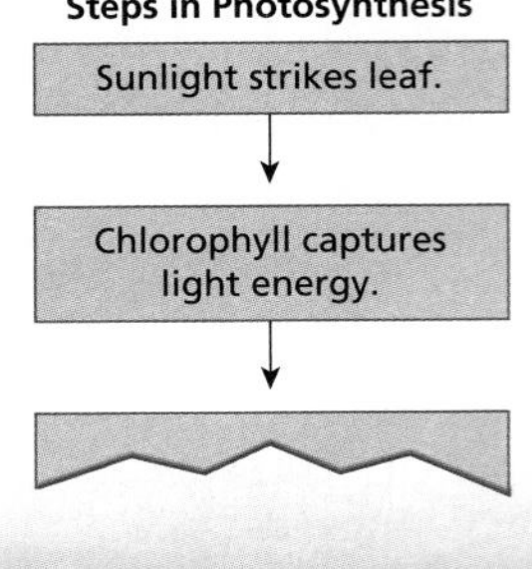

Lab zone Discover Activity

Where Does the Energy Come From?
1. Obtain a solar-powered calculator that does not use batteries. Place the calculator in direct light.
2. Cover the solar cells with your finger. Note how your action affects the number display.
3. Uncover the solar cells. What happens to the number display?
4. Now cover all but one of the solar cells. How does that affect the number display?

Think It Over
Inferring From your observations, what can you infer about the energy that powers the calculator?

On a plain in Africa, a herd of zebras peacefully eat the grass. But watch out—the zebras' grazing will soon be harshly interrupted. A group of lions is about to attack the herd. The lions will kill one of the zebras and eat it.

Both the zebras and the lions use the food they eat to obtain energy. Every living thing needs energy. All cells need energy to carry out their functions, such as making proteins and transporting substances into and out of the cell. The zebra's meat supplies the lion's cells with the energy they need, just as the grass provides the zebra's cells with energy. But plants and certain other organisms, such as algae and some bacteria, obtain their energy in a different way. These organisms use the energy in sunlight to make their own food.

Lab zone Discover Activity

Skills Focus Inferring L1

Materials solar-powered calculator that does not use batteries

Time 5 minutes

Tips If necessary, show students where the solar cells are located on the calculator.

Expected Outcome When all the solar cells are covered, the number display should go blank. When all but one of the solar cells are covered, the number display should flicker and fade.

Think It Over Energy to power the calculator comes from sunlight.

The sun is the source of energy for most living things.

Plants such as grass use energy from the sun to make their own food.

The zebra obtains energy by eating grass.

The lion obtains energy by feeding on the zebra.

FIGURE 1
Energy From the Sun
The sun supplies energy for most living things, directly or indirectly.
Relating Cause and Effect *How does sunlight provide food for the zebra?*

Sources of Energy

The process by which a cell captures energy in sunlight and uses it to make food is called **photosynthesis** (foh toh SIN thuh sis). The term *photosynthesis* comes from the Greek words *photo*, which means "light," and *synthesis*, which means "putting together."

Nearly all living things obtain energy either directly or indirectly from the energy of sunlight captured during photosynthesis. Grass obtains energy directly from sunlight, because it makes its own food during photosynthesis. When the zebra eats the grass, it gets energy that has been stored in the grass. Similarly, the lion obtains energy stored in the zebra. The zebra and lion both obtain the sun's energy indirectly, from the energy that the grass obtained through photosynthesis.

Plants manufacture their own food through the process of photosynthesis. An organism that makes its own food is called an **autotroph** (AWT oh trahf). An organism that cannot make its own food, including animals such as the zebra and the lion, is called a **heterotroph** (HET ur oh trahf). Many heterotrophs obtain food by eating other organisms. Some heterotrophs, such as fungi, absorb their food from other organisms.

Reading Checkpoint What are autotrophs?

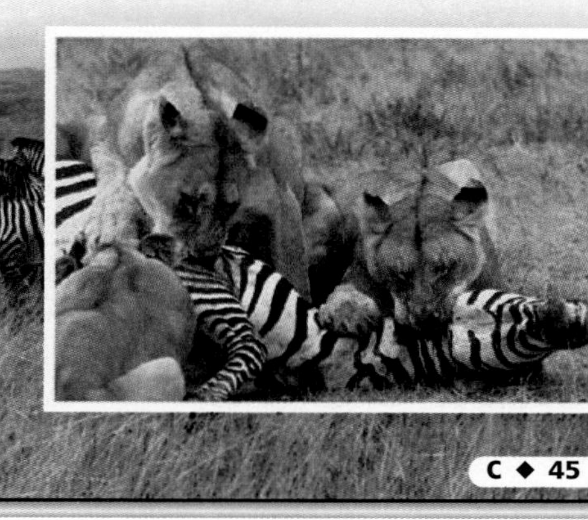

FIGURE 2
Autotrophs and Heterotrophs
Grass, which makes its own food during photosynthesis, is an autotroph. Zebras and lions are heterotrophs, because they cannot make their own food.

Instruct

Sources of Energy

Teach Key Concepts L2

Photosynthesis and Food Chains

Focus Tell students that light energy from the sun is changed into chemical energy that is stored in food.

Teach Ask: **How do autotrophs get their food?** *(They make their own food using sunlight and photosynthesis.)* **How does the sun supply heterotrophs with energy?** *(Heterotrophs get energy by eating plants or other animals that eat plants. The plants get their energy from sunlight, so heterotrophs get their energy from sunlight indirectly.)*

Apply Ask: **Why are autotrophs sometimes referred to as producers and heterotrophs as consumers?** *(Autotrophs produce, or make food. Heterotrophs consume, or eat the food; they cannot make the food.)* **learning modality: verbal**

All in One Teaching Resources
- Transparency C13

Independent Practice L2

All in One Teaching Resources
- Guided Reading and Study Worksheet: *Photosynthesis*

Student Edition on Audio CD

Differentiated Instruction

Special Needs L1

Understanding Visuals Ask: **How are each of the organisms pictured at the top of the page related to one another?** *(Each organism relies on the organism or energy source to its left to meet its energy needs.)* Point out that the drawings of the organisms are set in circles shaped like the cogs of a machine. Explain that each cog in a machine depends on the one next to it in order to turn and allow the machine to function. If possible, show part of an actual mechanical device that has gears. **Why do you think the artist chose to show each organism in a cog?** *(Like cogs in a machine, the organisms depend on one another to function.)* **learning modality: visual**

Monitor Progress L2

Oral Presentation Call on students to identify several organisms that are autotrophs and some that are heterotrophs.

Answers

Figure 1 The zebra eats grass, which uses energy from sunlight to make its own food.

Reading Checkpoint Organisms that make their own food

The Two Stages of Photosynthesis

For: The Photosynthesis Process
Visit: PHSchool.com
Web Code: cep-1042

Students can interact with the art of photosynthesis online.

Help Students Read

L2

Visualizing Refer to the Content Refresher for guidelines on visualizing. Have students close their eyes and form mental pictures as you slowly read aloud The Two Stages of Photosynthesis. Ask them to think about the role of the different parts of a plant. Then have students look at Figure 3 and see how it compares with their visualizing. Point out that visualizing text helps readers understand what they are reading.

Teach Key Concepts

L2

What Happens During Photosynthesis

Focus Refer students to Figure 3.

Teach Ask: **What are the two stages of photosynthesis?** *(Capturing the sun's energy and producing sugars)* **What is the energy captured in the first stage used for?** *(To produce sugars in the second stage)* **What pigment in chloroplasts absorbs light?** *(Chlorophyll)* **How is chlorophyll like a solar cell?** *(Both chlorophyll and solar cells absorb light energy and use it to power a process.)* **What happens in the second stage?** *(Water and carbon dioxide combine chemically to form sugars, and oxygen is released.)* **How are roots and stomata important for photosynthesis?** *(Roots take up water, and stomata take in carbon dioxide, both of which are needed for photosynthesis.)*

Apply Explain that not all the oxygen produced in photosynthesis is released from the plant. Plants use some of the oxygen to break down the sugar molecules they need for their own energy needs. **learning modality: visual**

All in One Teaching Resources

- Transparency C14

For: The Photosynthesis Process
Visit: PHSchool.com
Web Code: cep-1042

The Two Stages of Photosynthesis

Photosynthesis is a complex process. **During photosynthesis, plants and some other organisms use energy from the sun to convert carbon dioxide and water into oxygen and sugars.** The process of photosynthesis is shown in Figure 3. You can think of photosynthesis as taking place in two stages: capturing the sun's energy and producing sugars. You're probably familiar with many two-stage processes. To make a cake, for example, the first stage is to combine the ingredients to make the batter. The second stage is to bake the batter. To get the desired result—the cake—both stages must occur in the correct order.

Stage 1: Capturing the Sun's Energy The first stage of photosynthesis involves capturing the energy in sunlight. In plants, this energy-capturing process occurs mostly in the leaves. Recall that chloroplasts are green organelles inside plant cells. The green color comes from **pigments,** colored chemical compounds that absorb light. The main photosynthetic pigment in chloroplasts is **chlorophyll.**

Chlorophyll functions in a manner similar to that of the solar "cells" in a solar-powered calculator. Solar cells capture the energy in light and use it to power the calculator. Similarly, chlorophyll captures light energy and uses it to power the second stage of photosynthesis.

FIGURE 3
Two Stages of Photosynthesis
Photosynthesis has two stages, as shown in the diagram. Interpreting Diagrams *Which stage requires light?*

Differentiated Instruction

Gifted and Talented

L3

Researching Light and Chlorophyll
Help students integrate science concepts by having them research the nature of light, reflection, and absorption. Ask: **Why is chlorophyll green? What does chlorophyll's color have to do with the kind of light that plants grow best in?** *(Visible light consists of all colors of light, including red, blue, and green light. Chlorophyll is green because it reflects green light. Red and blue light is absorbed by chlorophyll and used to power photosynthesis. Because chlorophyll does not absorb green light very well, green light does not help power photosynthesis. Red and blue light is best for growing plants.)* **learning modality: logical/mathematical**

Stage 2: Using Energy to Make Food In the next stage of photosynthesis, the cell uses the captured energy to produce sugars. The cell needs two raw materials for this stage: water (H_2O) and carbon dioxide (CO_2). In plants, the roots absorb water from the soil. The water then moves up through the plant's stem to the leaves. Carbon dioxide is one of the gases in the air. Carbon dioxide enters the plant through small openings on the undersides of the leaves called **stomata** (STOH muh tuh) (singular *stoma*). Once in the leaves, the water and carbon dioxide move into the chloroplasts.

Inside the chloroplasts, the water and carbon dioxide undergo a complex series of chemical reactions. The reactions are powered by the energy captured in the first stage. These reactions produce chemicals as products. One product is a sugar that has six carbon atoms. Six-carbon sugars have the chemical formula $C_6H_{12}O_6$. Recall that sugars are a type of carbohydrate. Cells can use the energy in the sugar to carry out important cell functions.

The other product of photosynthesis is oxygen (O_2), which exits the leaf through the stomata. In fact, almost all the oxygen in Earth's atmosphere was produced by living things through the process of photosynthesis.

Reading Checkpoint **What makes plants green?**

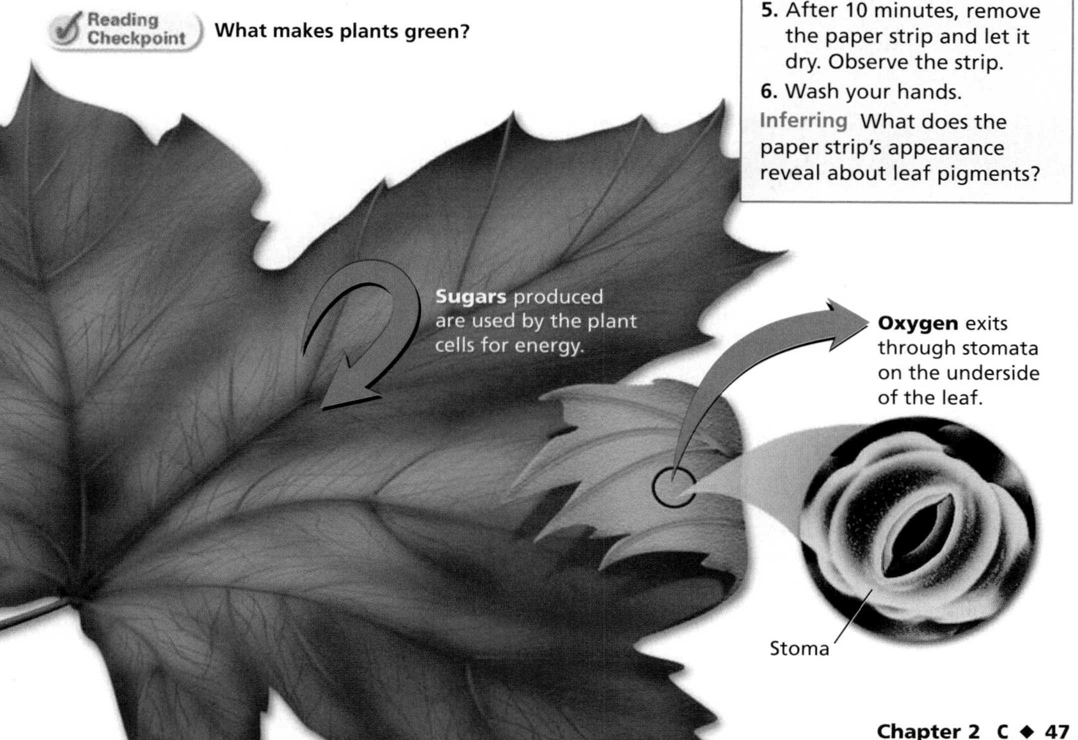

Lab zone Try This **Activity**

Looking at Pigments

You can observe the pigments in a leaf.

1. Cut a strip 5 cm by 20 cm out of a paper coffee filter.
2. Place a leaf on top of the paper strip, about 2 cm from the bottom.
3. Roll the edge of a dime over a section of the leaf, leaving a narrow band of color on the paper strip.
4. Pour rubbing alcohol into a plastic cup to a depth of 1 cm. Stand the paper strip in the cup so the color band is about 1 cm above the alcohol. Hook the other end of the strip over the top of the cup.
5. After 10 minutes, remove the paper strip and let it dry. Observe the strip.
6. Wash your hands.

Inferring What does the paper strip's appearance reveal about leaf pigments?

Lab zone Build **Inquiry** L2

Observing Stomata

Materials forceps, lettuce leaf, water, microscope slide, coverslip, microscope

Time 15 minutes

Focus Review the function of stomata.

Teach Have students use forceps to gently pull away a small piece of the thin membrane on the underside of a lettuce leaf, then make a slide and sketch the structures they see. Call their attention to the sausage-shaped guard cells on either side of each stoma, and ask: **What role do you think the guard cells play?** *(They regulate what enters the stomata.)*

Apply Tell students that stomata are not open all the time. Ask: **When do you think the stomata are usually open?** *(During the day when light energy is available for photosynthesis)* **learning modality: visual**

Address Misconceptions L2

The Role of Soil in Photosynthesis

Focus Some students may think that soil provides plants with food.

Teach Explain that soil provides one of the raw materials for plants to make food—water. However, plants produce their own food from water plus carbon dioxide and the energy from sunlight; plants do not "take in" food.

Apply Tell students that hydroponics means growing plants in water, without soil. As long as plants are provided with the minerals they need and the materials for making their own food, they do not have to be grown in soil. **learning modality: logical/mathematical**

Lab zone Try This **Activity**

Skills Focus Inferring L2

Materials coffee filter, scissors, leaf, metric ruler, dime, rubbing alcohol, plastic cup

Time 20 minutes

Tips **CAUTION:** *Do not use plants that may cause allergic reactions. Warn students not to taste or inhale the alcohol. Make sure no open flames are present.*
A geranium works well.

Expected Outcome Alcohol dissolves plant pigments and carries them up the paper strip. The paper's appearance reveals that leaves contain several pigments.

Extend Ask: **In the fall, when chlorophyll decreases in some plants, why do leaves change color?** *(As chlorophyll decreases, other pigments that were hidden by the green chlorophyll can then be seen.)* **learning modality: kinesthetic**

Monitor Progress L2

Skills Check Have students make a flowchart to show what happens during photosynthesis.

Answers

Figure 3 Stage 1

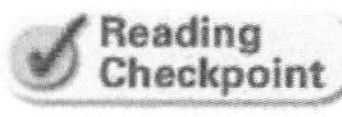

Chloroplasts contain the green pigment chlorophyll.

Monitor Progress L2

Answer

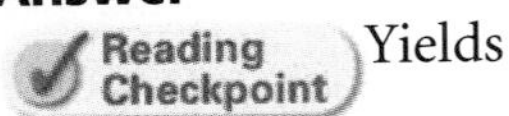
Yields

Assess

Reviewing Key Concepts

1. a. All living things are made up of cells, which need energy to carry out their functions. **b.** They trap energy from sunlight in the process of photosynthesis. **c.** The leaf has stored food that the plant made using energy from the sun in the process of photosynthesis.

2. a. 6 CO_2 (carbon dioxide) + 6 H_2O (water) + (light energy) → $C_6H_{12}O_6$ (a sugar) + 6 O_2 (oxygen) **b.** Carbon dioxide, water, and light energy; sugar and oxygen **c.** A plant would likely produce more oxygen on a sunny day, because there would be more sunlight available to the plant for photosynthesis.

Reteach L1

Use Figure 3 to review what happens during photosynthesis. Have students identify how the figure relates to the equation for photosynthesis.

Performance Assessment L2

Writing Have students explain how life on Earth depends on the sun.

All in One Teaching Resources

- Section Summary: *Photosynthesis*
- Review and Reinforce: *Photosynthesis*
- Enrich: *Photosynthesis*

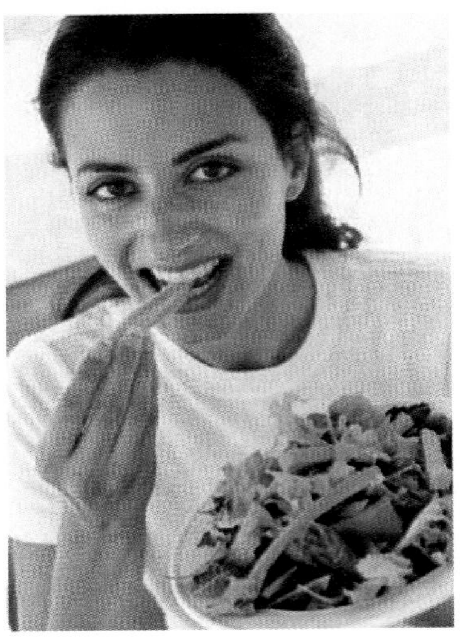

FIGURE 4
Stored energy
When you eat a carrot, you obtain energy stored during photosynthesis.

The Photosynthesis Equation The events of photosynthesis can be summed up by the following chemical equation:

$$6\,CO_2 + 6\,H_2O \xrightarrow{\text{light energy}} C_6H_{12}O_6 + 6\,O_2$$

carbon dioxide + water → a sugar + oxygen

Notice that the raw materials—six molecules of carbon dioxide and six molecules of water—are on the left side of the equation. The products—one molecule of a sugar and six molecules of oxygen—are on the right side of the equation. An arrow, which you can read as "yields," connects the raw materials to the products. Light energy, which is necessary for the chemical reaction to occur, is written above the arrow.

What happens to the sugar produced in photosynthesis? Plant cells use some of the sugar for food. The cells break down the sugar molecules to release the energy they contain. This energy can then be used to carry out the plant's functions. Some sugar molecules are converted into other compounds, such as cellulose. Other sugar molecules may be stored in the plant's cells for later use. When you eat food from plants, such as potatoes or carrots, you are eating the plant's stored energy.

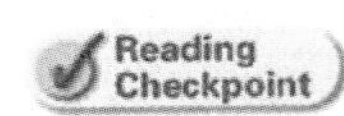
In the photosynthesis equation, what does the arrow mean?

Section 1 Assessment

Target Reading Skill Sequencing Use your flowchart about photosynthesis to help answer Question 2.

Reviewing Key Concepts

1. a. Reviewing Why do living things need energy?
   b. Explaining How do plants obtain energy?
   c. Applying Concepts An insect eats a leaf. Explain how the insect depends on the sun for energy.
2. a. Reviewing What chemical equation sums up the events of photosynthesis?
   b. Comparing and Contrasting What are the substances needed for photosynthesis? What substances are produced during photosynthesis?
   c. Making Generalizations Would you expect a plant to produce more oxygen on a cloudy day or a sunny day? Explain.

Writing in Science

Job Qualifications When people apply for jobs, they often must complete a job application form in which they describe their qualifications for a job. Suppose that you are a leaf, and that you are applying for a job in a photosynthesis factory. Write a paragraph in which you summarize your qualifications for the job of photosynthesis. Your paragraph should include the following words: *chloroplasts, chlorophyll, light, energy, water, carbon dioxide,* and *stomata.*

Lab zone Chapter Project

Keep Students on Track Have students make any necessary revisions to their experimental plans. Make sure students are exposing their plants to different lighting conditions and are controlling all other variables. Check that students have a data table ready to record observations and measurements.

Writing in Science

Writing Mode Description

Scoring Rubric

4 Includes complete description of the stages of photosynthesis written from the point of view of a leaf; description is lively and engaging
3 Includes all criteria, but description is uninteresting
2 Includes incomplete description
1 Includes inaccurate description

Section 2

Respiration

Reading Preview

Key Concepts

- What events occur during respiration?
- What is fermentation?

Key Terms

- respiration
- fermentation

Target Reading Skill

Using Prior Knowledge Your prior knowledge is what you already know before you read about a topic. Before you read, write a definition of respiration in a graphic organizer like the one below. As you read, revise your definition based on what you learn.

What You Know
1. Definition of respiration:

What You Learned
1.

Lab zone Discover Activity

What Is a Product of Respiration?

1. Put on your goggles. Fill two test tubes half full of warm water. Add 5 mL of sugar to one of the test tubes. Put the tubes in a test-tube rack.
2. Add 0.5 mL of dried yeast (a single-celled organism) to each tube. Stir the contents of each tube with a straw. Place a stopper snugly in the top of each tube.
3. Observe any changes that occur in the two test tubes over the next 10 to 15 minutes.

Think It Over

Observing What changes occurred in each test tube? How can you account for any differences that you observed?

You and your friend have been hiking all morning. You look for a flat rock to sit on, so you can eat the lunch you packed. The steepest part of the trail is ahead. You'll need a lot of energy to get to the top of the mountain. That energy will come from food.

Before food can provide your body with energy, it must pass through your digestive system. There, the food is broken down into small molecules. These small molecules can then pass out of the digestive system and into your bloodstream. Next, the molecules travel through the bloodstream to the cells of your body. Inside the cells, the energy in the molecules is released. In this section, you'll learn how your body's cells obtain energy from the food you eat.

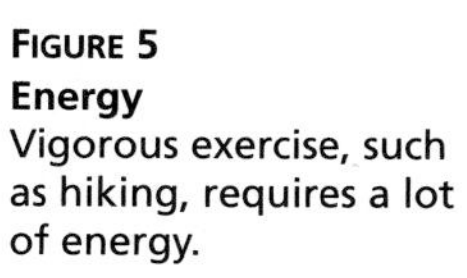

FIGURE 5
Energy
Vigorous exercise, such as hiking, requires a lot of energy.

Lab zone Discover Activity

Skills Focus Observing L1

Materials 2 test tubes with stoppers, warm water, 5 mL sugar, test tube rack, 1.0 mL dried yeast, 2 straws

Time 20 minutes

Tips CAUTION: *Advise students to handle the test tubes with care.* If possible, use fast-acting yeast, which you can purchase at a food store. The water should be warm, but not hot.

Expected Outcome Students will observe bubbles in the sugar water but none in the plain water.

Think It Over The bubbles in the test tube containing the sugar are due to some process involving the yeast and the sugar.

Section 2

Respiration

Objectives

After this lesson, students will be able to

C.2.2.1 Describe the events that occur during respiration.

C.2.2.2 Tell what fermentation is.

Target Reading Skill

Using Prior Knowledge Explain that prior knowledge helps students connect what they already know to what they read.

Possible Answers

What You Know

The definition of respiration is breathing in oxygen by an organism.

What You Learned

Respiration also means the process in which cells break down simple food molecules such as sugar and release the energy they contain.

All in One Teaching Resources

- Transparency C15

Preteach

Build Background Knowledge L1

Combustion and Respiration

Ask: **What does a fire need to burn?** *(Fuel and oxygen)* **What is released when fuel is burned?** *(Energy in the form of heat and light)* Tell students that a similar chemical process, called respiration, "burns" food molecules in cells. Like combustion, respiration uses fuel and oxygen to produce energy. The fuel comes from food, and the energy is used for cellular functions.

Instruct

What Is Respiration?

Teach Key Concepts L2

Events During Respiration

Focus Remind students that the food they eat must be broken down to release the energy it contains.

Teach Ask: **What is the process called that releases energy from food?** *(Respiration)* **Why is respiration important to cells?** *(It provides cells with the energy they need to carry out their functions.)* **What happens in the first stage of respiration?** *(Glucose is broken down into smaller molecules and a small amount of energy is released.)* **What happens in the second stage of respiration?** *(The smaller molecules are broken down into even smaller molecules and a large amount of energy is released.)*

Apply Ask: **Why do you think that muscle cells have many mitochondria?** *(The second stage of respiration, which produces lots of energy, takes place in the mitochondria. The large numbers of mitochondria in muscle cells supply a great amount of energy for movement.)* **learning modality: verbal**

All in One Teaching Resources

- Transparency C16

Independent Practice L2

All in One Teaching Resources

- Guided Reading and Study Worksheet: *Respiration*

 **Student Edition on Audio CD**

FIGURE 6
Energy From Respiration
All organisms need energy to live. The leopard frog uses energy to leap great distances. Although the mushrooms don't move, they still need energy to grow and reproduce.

What Is Respiration?

After you eat a meal, your body converts some of the food into glucose, a type of sugar. **Respiration** is the process by which cells obtain energy from glucose. **During respiration, cells break down simple food molecules such as sugar and release the energy they contain.** Because living things need a continuous supply of energy, the cells of all living things carry out respiration continuously. Plant cells, as well as animal cells, respire.

Storing and Releasing Energy Energy stored in cells is something like money you put in a savings account in a bank. When you want to buy something, you withdraw some of the money. Cells store and use energy in a similar way. During photosynthesis, plants capture the energy from sunlight and "save" it in the form of carbohydrates, including sugars and starches. Similarly, when you eat a meal, you add to your body's energy savings account. When cells need energy, they "withdraw" it by breaking down the carbohydrates in the process of respiration.

Breathing and Respiration The term *respiration* has two meanings. You have probably used it to mean "breathing," that is, moving air in and out of your lungs. To avoid confusion, the respiration process that takes place inside cells is sometimes called cellular respiration. The two meanings of the term *respiration* do point out a connection, however. Breathing brings oxygen, which is usually necessary for cellular respiration, into your lungs.

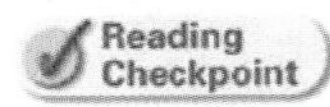 **Reading Checkpoint** What is respiration?

Lab zone Skills Activity

Predicting

During the winter months, some animals go into a state called hibernation. During hibernation, an animal does not eat and its body activities are greatly reduced. Predict what will happen to an animal's rate of cellular respiration when the animal goes into hibernation. Explain your prediction.

50 ◆ C

Lab zone Skills Activity

Skills Focus Predicting L3

Time 5 minutes

Tips Remind students that cells need energy to carry out the many activities performed by the body.

Expected Outcome Students will predict that the rate of cellular respiration will decrease when the animal goes into hibernation because the animal's body no longer needs to carry out many of the activities that require energy.

Extend Point out that many plants lose their leaves in winter. Ask: **Why would plants need to use stored energy during the winter?** *(When plants lose their leaves, they cannot photosynthesize.)* **learning modality: logical/mathematical**

The Two Stages of Respiration Like photosynthesis, respiration is a two-stage process. The first stage takes place in the cytoplasm of the organism's cells. There, molecules of glucose are broken down into smaller molecules. Oxygen is not involved, and only a small amount of energy is released.

The second stage of respiration takes place in the mitochondria. There, the small molecules are broken down into even smaller molecules. These chemical reactions require oxygen, and they release a great deal of energy. This is why the mitochondria are sometimes called the "powerhouses" of the cell.

Trace the steps in the breakdown of glucose in Figure 7. Note that energy is released in both stages. Two other products of respiration are carbon dioxide and water. These products diffuse out of the cell. In most animals, the carbon dioxide and some water leave the body during exhalation, or breathing out. Thus, when you breathe in, you take in oxygen—a raw material for respiration. When you breathe out, you release carbon dioxide and water—products of respiration.

The Respiration Equation Although respiration occurs in a series of complex steps, the overall process can be summarized in the following equation:

$$\underset{\text{sugar}}{C_6H_{12}O_6} + \underset{\text{oxygen}}{6\,O_2} \longrightarrow \underset{\text{carbon dioxide}}{6\,CO_2} + \underset{\text{water}}{6\,H_2O} + \text{energy}$$

Notice that the raw materials for respiration are sugar and oxygen. Plants and other organisms that undergo photosynthesis make their own sugar. The glucose in the cells of animals and other organisms comes from the food they consume. The oxygen used in respiration comes from the air or water surrounding the organism.

FIGURE 7
Two Stages of Respiration
Respiration, like photosynthesis, takes place in two stages.
Interpreting Diagrams *In which stage of respiration is oxygen used?*

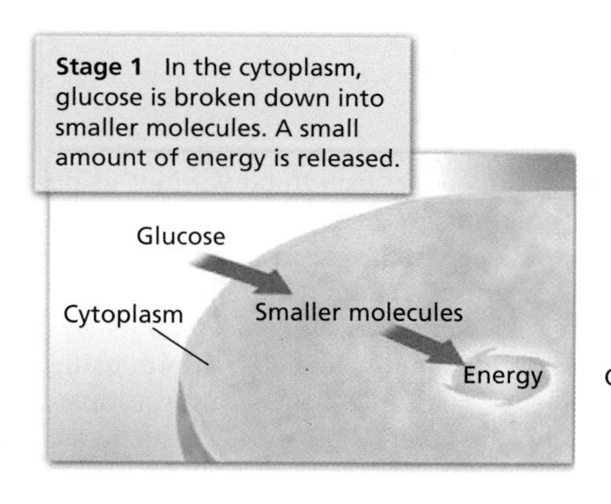

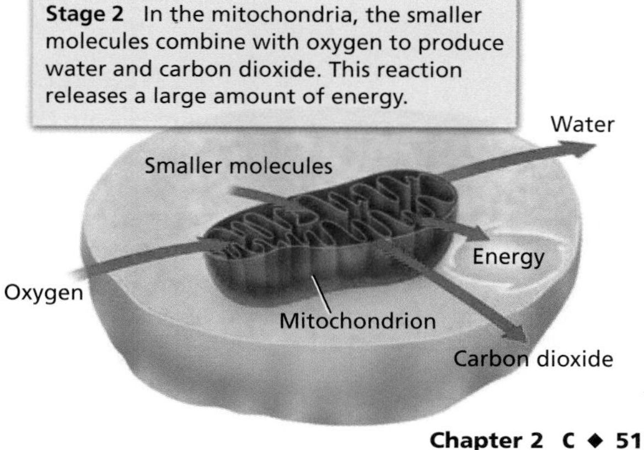

Measuring Carbon Dioxide L1

Materials 100 mL tap water, flask, phenolphthalein, 0.4% sodium hydroxide solution, 2 plastic droppers

Time 20 minutes

Focus Tell students that the carbon dioxide in exhaled breath can be measured.

Teach Breathe for one minute into a flask containing the water. Add five drops of phenolphthalein to the water, and then add the sodium hydroxide solution, drop by drop, until the water turns light pink. Explain that the more sodium hydroxide that is needed to turn the water pink, the greater the concentration of carbon dioxide.

Apply Ask students to infer how exercise affects the amount of carbon dioxide in exhaled breath. *(The amount would be greater because more respiration is needed to provide energy for the activity.)* **learning modality: visual**

Use Visuals: Figure 7 L2

Focus Remind students that respiration occurs in plant and animal cells.

Teach Ask students to locate where the first stage of respiration takes place. *(Cytoplasm)* Ask: **What happens in the cytoplasm?** *(Glucose is broken down.)* Have students locate the mitochondrion in the cell. Ask: **Do you think plants have mitochondria?** *(Yes, because they need to break down energy for their functions.)* **In which stage is oxygen involved?** *(The second stage, in the mitochondrion)* **How do most animals get rid of carbon dioxide?** *(They breathe it out.)*

Apply Ask: **How do plants get rid of carbon dioxide and water vapor?** *(Through their stomata)* **learning modality: visual**

All in One Teaching Resources

- Transparency C17

Differentiated Instruction

Less Proficient Readers L1

Comparing Breathing and Cellular Respiration Make a copy of What Is Respiration? and have students read and highlight phrases that will help to answer the following questions: **How are breathing and cellular respiration similar?** *(Both involve using or taking in oxygen and releasing carbon dioxide and water.)* **How are breathing and cellular respiration different?** *(Breathing takes place in the lungs and provides the body with oxygen, whereas cellular respiration takes place inside cells and provides the cells with energy.)* **learning modality: verbal**

Monitor Progress L2

Skills Check Have students create a compare and contrast table of the two stages of cellular respiration.

Answer

Figure 7 The second stage

Reading Checkpoint The process by which cells obtain energy from glucose

For: Links on cellular respiration
Visit: www.SciLinks.org
Web Code: scn-0322

Download a worksheet to guide students' review of cellular respiration.

Fermentation

Teach Key Concepts L2

Obtaining Energy Without Oxygen

Focus Tell students that some organisms, such as yeasts, are able to release energy without oxygen.

Teach Ask: **What is the process in which energy is released without using oxygen?** *(Fermentation)* **What are the products of alcoholic fermentation?** *(Alcohol, carbon dioxide, and energy)* **What is a product of lactic-acid fermentation?** *(Lactic acid)* **When might your body release energy using fermentation?** *(If you are exercising so hard or long that your muscle cells cannot take up oxygen faster than it is being used)*

Apply Ask students to compare and contrast fermentation and respiration. *(Both produce energy. Respiration uses oxygen and produces more energy, while fermentation does not use oxygen and produces less energy.)* **learning modality: verbal**

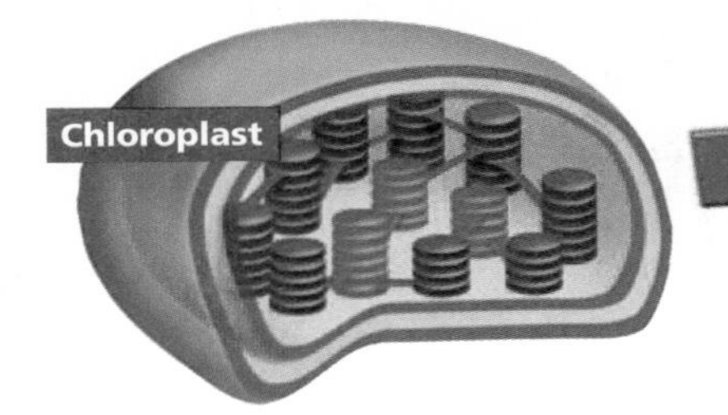

Photosynthesis
During photosynthesis, plants use carbon dioxide and release oxygen.

$$6\ CO_2 + 6\ H_2O \longrightarrow C_6H_{12}O_6 + 6\ O_2$$

Respiration
During respiration, organisms use oxygen and release carbon dioxide.

$$C_6H_{12}O_6 + 6\ O_2 \longrightarrow 6\ CO_2 + 6\ H_2O$$

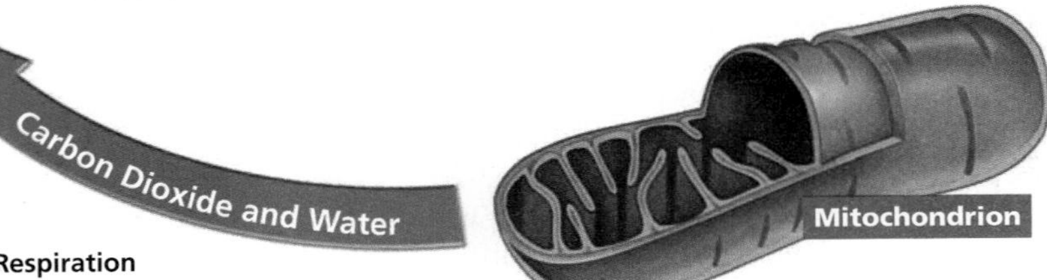

FIGURE 8
Photosynthesis and Respiration
You can think of photosynthesis and respiration as opposite processes.
Comparing and Contrasting
Which process uses oxygen? Which uses carbon dioxide?

Comparing Photosynthesis and Respiration Can you notice anything familiar about the equation for respiration? You are quite right if you said it is the opposite of the equation for photosynthesis. This is an important point. During photosynthesis, carbon dioxide and water are used to produce sugars and oxygen. During respiration, the sugar glucose and oxygen are used to produce carbon dioxide and water. Photosynthesis and respiration can be thought of as opposite processes.

Together, these two processes form a cycle that keeps the levels of oxygen and carbon dioxide fairly constant in Earth's atmosphere. As you can see in Figure 8, living things use both gases over and over again.

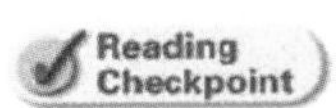

Which process—photosynthesis or respiration—produces water?

Fermentation

Some cells are able to obtain energy from food without using oxygen. For example, some single-celled organisms live where there is no oxygen, such as deep in the ocean or in the mud of lakes or swamps. These organisms obtain their energy through **fermentation,** an energy-releasing process that does not require oxygen. **Fermentation provides energy for cells without using oxygen.** The amount of energy released from each sugar molecule during fermentation, however, is much lower than the amount released during respiration.

For: Links on cellular respiration
Visit: www.SciLinks.org
Web Code: scn-0322

52 ◆ C

Differentiated Instruction

English Learners/Beginning L1
Comprehension: Ask Questions Write the chemical equations for photosynthesis and respiration on the board. Read the equations aloud, pointing to the chemical symbols and labels. Ask students questions such as: **What is one product of respiration? What do plants use to make food?** Have students answer orally. Then help them to write the answers. **learning modality: visual**

English Learners/Intermediate L2
Comprehension: Ask Questions Have students do the *Beginning* activity. Then, ask questions that cannot be answered directly from the equation, such as: **What part of the equation represents what you breathe out? learning modality: visual**

Alcoholic Fermentation One type of fermentation occurs when yeast and some other single-celled organisms break down sugars. This process is sometimes called alcoholic fermentation because alcohol is one of the products. The other products are carbon dioxide and a small amount of energy.

The products of alcoholic fermentation are important to bakers and brewers. The carbon dioxide produced by yeast creates air pockets in bread dough, causing it to rise. Carbon dioxide is also the source of bubbles in alcoholic drinks such as beer and sparkling wine.

Lactic Acid Fermentation Another type of fermentation takes place at times in your body. You've probably felt its effects. Think of a time when you ran as fast as you could for as long as you could. Your leg muscles were pushing hard against the ground, and you were breathing quickly.

No matter how hard you breathed, your muscle cells used up the oxygen faster than it could be replaced. Because your cells lacked oxygen, fermentation occurred. The fermentation supplied your cells with energy. One product of this type of fermentation is an acid known as lactic acid. When lactic acid builds up, you feel a painful sensation in your muscles. Your muscles feel weak and sore.

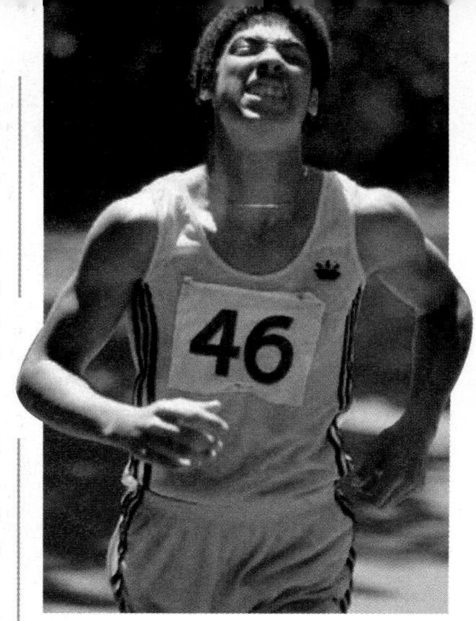

FIGURE 9
Lactic Acid Fermentation
When an athlete's muscles run out of oxygen, lactic acid fermentation supplies the cells with energy.

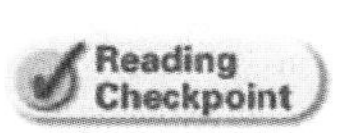
Which kind of fermentation is important to bakers?

Section 2 Assessment

Target Reading Skill
Using Prior Knowledge Review your graphic organizer about respiration. List two things that you learned about respiration.

Reviewing Key Concepts

1. a. **Reviewing** What happens during respiration?
   b. **Reviewing** What is the equation for respiration?
   c. **Comparing and Contrasting** Compare the equations for respiration and photosynthesis.
   d. **Relating Cause and Effect** Explain why cellular respiration adds carbon dioxide to the atmosphere, but photosynthesis does not.
2. a. **Identifying** What is the process in which cells obtain energy without using oxygen?
   b. **Inferring** How would athletes be affected if this process could not take place?
   c. **Predicting** Is this process more likely to occur during a short run or a long walk? Explain your answer.

Lab zone At-Home Activity

Make Bread With an adult family member, follow a recipe in a cookbook to make a loaf of bread using yeast. Explain to your family what causes the dough to rise. After you bake the bread, observe a slice and look for evidence that fermentation occurred.

Lab zone At-Home Activity

Make Bread L2 Students will explain that yeast cells use the sugar in the dough for alcoholic fermentation, which releases carbon dioxide. The carbon dioxide, in turn, causes the dough to rise and small holes to form in the baked bread.

Monitor Progress L2

Answers

Figure 8 Respiration uses oxygen. Photosynthesis uses carbon dioxide.

 Respiration

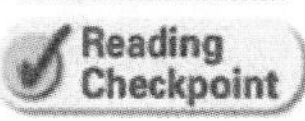 Alcoholic fermentation

Assess

Reviewing Key Concepts

1. a. Cells break down simple food molecules such as sugar and release the energy they contain. **b.** $C_6H_{12}O_6$ (sugar) + 6 O_2 (oxygen) → 6 CO_2 (carbon dioxide) + 6 H_2O (water) + energy **c.** Both involve the same chemical compounds, but they are reverse processes. **d.** Cellular respiration produces carbon dioxide, while photosynthesis uses up carbon dioxide.
2. a. Fermentation **b.** If an athlete's muscles ran out of oxygen and fermentation did not occur, the athlete would not be able to continue the activity. **c.** Fermentation is more likely to take place during a short, fast run than in a long, less intense walk. For the short run, the athlete is pushing the muscles hard to run very fast, so the muscles will use up oxygen sooner.

Reteach L1

As a class, make flowcharts showing what happens during respiration and fermentation.

Performance Assessment L2

Writing Have students describe how plants maintain the level of oxygen in the atmosphere.

All in One Teaching Resources

- Section Summary: *Respiration*
- Review and Reinforce: *Respiration*
- Enrich: *Respiration*

Lab zone Design Your Own Lab

Exhaling Carbon Dioxide 

Prepare for Inquiry

Skills Objectives

Students will be able to
- predict the outcome of their experiment
- control variables

Class Time 30 minutes

All in One Teaching Resources
- Lab Worksheet: *Exhaling Carbon Dioxide*

Safety

    Make sure students know how to blow into the straw without sucking solution back into their mouths. Use a clean straw for each student. **CAUTION:** *Excuse students with health problems from physical activity.* Review the safety guidelines in Appendix A.

Guide Inquiry

Introduce the Procedure

Demonstrate the proper procedure for blowing into the solution without sucking solution back through the straw. Explain that bromthymol blue is an indicator solution (a solution that changes color) that can test for the presence of carbon dioxide.

Analyze and Conclude

1. Between 25 and 45 seconds

2. Exercising decreased the amount of time required for the solution to change color.

3. More carbon dioxide is produced during exercise. If students predicted that the amount of time would decrease after exercise, their predictions were accurate.

4. Possible answers: Volume of bromthymol blue solution; force used to exhale through the straw; type, intensity, and length of exercise; amount of time between the end of exercising and start of exhaling through the straw

5. Paragraphs will explain that increased cellular respiration results in an increased output of carbon dioxide.

Lab zone Design Your Own Lab

Exhaling Carbon Dioxide

Problem

Is there a relationship between exercise and the amount of carbon dioxide you exhale?

Skills Focus

predicting, controlling variables

Materials

- 2 250-mL beakers
- bromthymol blue solution (0.1% solution), 30 mL
- 2 straws
- stopwatch or watch with second hand
- graduated cylinder, 25 mL
- paper towels

Procedure  

PART 1 Testing for Carbon Dioxide

1. Label one beaker "Beaker 1" and the other beaker "Beaker 2." Beaker 1 will be the control in the experiment.
2. Bromthymol blue can be used to test for the presence of carbon dioxide. To see how this works, fill each beaker with 15 mL of bromthymol solution. **CAUTION:** *Bromthymol blue can stain skin and clothing. Avoid spilling or splashing it on yourself.*
3. Note and record the color of the solution in both beakers.
4. Place a straw in Beaker 2. Gently blow through the straw into the solution until the solution changes color. **CAUTION:** *Use the straw to breathe out only. Do not suck the solution back through the straw.* Your partner should begin timing when you first blow through the straw and stop as soon as the solution changes color. Record the time that has elapsed.

PART 2 Exercise and Carbon Dioxide

5. In Part 1 you timed the change of color without exercising first. Predict how long it would take the solution to change color if you conduct the test after you exercise. Design an experiment to test your prediction. Be sure to include a plan for recording your results and steps to review your results.
6. Write down the steps of your experiment and get your teacher's approval. Then, conduct your experiment. **CAUTION:** *Do not over-exert yourself. If you have a medical condition that limits your ability to exercise, do not take part in the exercise portion of this experiment.*

Analyze and Conclude

1. Measuring How long did it take for the solution to change color the first time you did the test (without exercising)?
2. Drawing Conclusions How did exercising affect the amount of time it took for the solution to change color?
3. Predicting What was your prediction in Step 5 based upon? Was your prediction accurate?
4. Controlling Variables In Part 2, what variables did you need to control? Explain how you controlled those variables.
5. Communicating Write a paragraph that relates the results of your experiment to the process of cellular respiration. Be sure to explain how increased cellular activity affects carbon dioxide output.

More to Explore

Some plants grow in water. If you added bromthymol blue to the water, do you think it would turn color? *(Hint:* What might happen to the carbon dioxide that the plants produce during respiration?)

Extend Inquiry

More to Explore

The bromthymol blue probably would not change color, because the plants use up carbon dioxide during photosynthesis.

Section 3

Cell Division

Reading Preview

Key Concepts

- What events take place during the three stages of the cell cycle?
- How does the structure of DNA help account for the way in which DNA copies itself?

Key Terms

- cell cycle
- interphase
- replication
- mitosis
- chromosome
- cytokinesis

Target Reading Skill

Sequencing As you read, make a cycle diagram that shows the events in the cell cycle, including the phases of mitosis. Write each event in a separate circle.

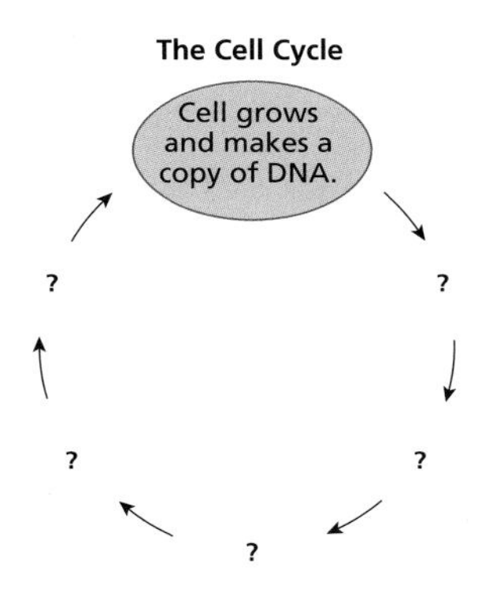

Lab zone Discover Activity

What Are the Yeast Cells Doing?

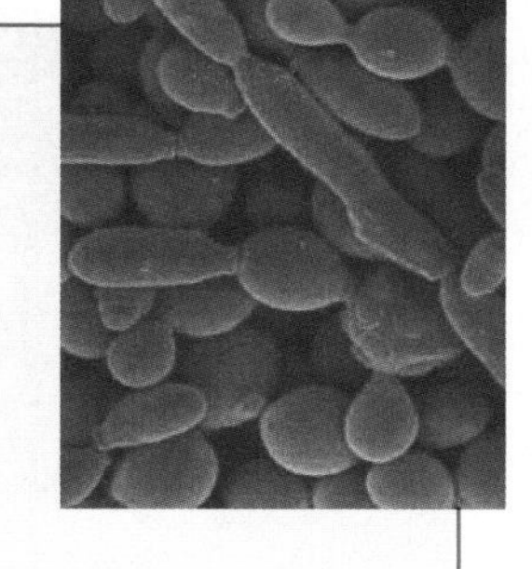

1. Use a plastic dropper to transfer some yeast cells from a yeast culture to a microscope slide. Your teacher has prepared the slide by drying methylene blue stain onto it. Add a coverslip and place the slide under a microscope.
2. Examine the cells on the slide. Use low power first, then high power. Look for what appears to be two cells attached to each other. One cell may be larger than the other. Draw what you see.

Think It Over

Developing Hypotheses What process do you think the "double cells" are undergoing? Develop a hypothesis that might explain what you see.

In the early autumn, many local fairs run pumpkin contests. Proud growers enter their largest pumpkins, hoping to win a prize. The pumpkin below has a mass greater than 600 kilograms! This giant pumpkin began as a small flower. How did the pumpkin grow so big?

A pumpkin grows in size by increasing both the size and the number of its cells. A single cell grows and then divides, forming two cells. Then two cells grow and divide, forming four, and so on. This process of cell growth and division does not occur only in pumpkins, though. In fact, many cells in your body are dividing as you read this page.

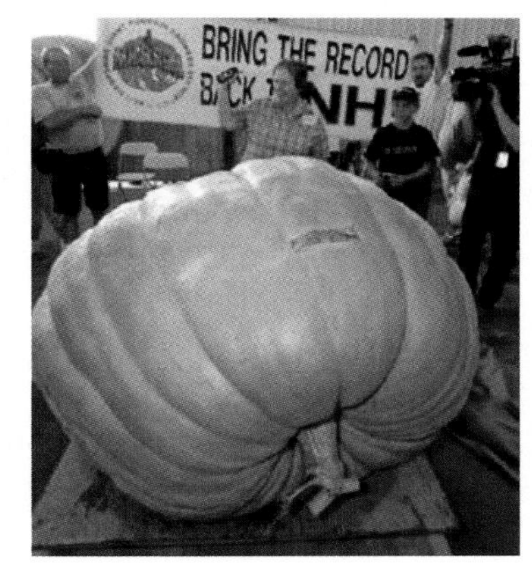

Prize-winning pumpkin ▲

Lab zone Discover Activity

Skills Focus Developing hypotheses L1

Materials plastic dropper, yeast culture, stained microscope slide, coverslip, microscope

Time 15 minutes

Tips **CAUTION:** *Students must handle the glass and microscope carefully.* Prepare culture by stirring dry yeast and sugar into warm water. Stain each slide with a drop of methylene blue, and let it dry. Or use prepared slides.

Expected Outcome Students will observe yeast cells budding.

Think It Over Students may say that the cells are dividing, and hypothesize that yeast cells split in two to reproduce.

Section 3

Cell Division

Objectives

After this lesson, students will be able to

C.2.3.1 Identify the events that take place during the three stages of the cell cycle.

C.2.3.2 Explain how the structure of DNA helps account for the way in which DNA copies itself.

Target Reading Skill 

Sequencing Explain that organizing information in sequence helps students understand a step-by-step process.

Answers

One possible way to complete the graphic organizer:

The Cell Cycle

1. Cell grows, makes a copy of DNA.
2. Chromosomes and spindle fibers form; nuclear envelope breaks down.
3. Chromosomes line up across the center and attach to a spindle fiber.
4. Centromeres split; chromatids separate and move to opposite ends.
5. Chromosomes stretch out; new nuclear envelope forms around chromosomes.
6. Cell pinches in two; each daughter cell has same number of identical chromosomes.

All in One Teaching Resources

- Transparency C18

Preteach

Build Background Knowledge 

Comparing Different Cycles

Ask: **What are the stages that people go through during their life, starting with infancy and ending with old age?** Students are likely to name or describe the additional stages of childhood, adolescence, and adulthood. Point out that cells, like people, undergo a life cycle, called the cell cycle. During the stages of the cell cycle, cells grow and mature. But unlike the human life cycle, the cell cycle starts over when the cell divides.

Instruct

Stage 1: Interphase

Teach Key Concepts L2

Events in Interphase

Focus Remind students that living things grow by producing more cells rather than the cells becoming larger.

Teach Ask: **What is the cell cycle?** *(The regular sequence of growth and division that cells undergo)* **What are daughter cells?** *(The cells that result when a cell divides)* **What happens during interphase?** *(The cell grows, makes a copy of its DNA, and prepares to divide into two cells.)* **In what process does the cell make a copy of the DNA?** *(Replication)* **How does the cell prepare for cell division?** *(It produces structures that it will use to divide.)*

Apply Ask students to infer what would happen if cell division occurred without DNA replication occurring first. Ask: **How would this affect the daughter cells?** *(Each daughter cell would have only half the DNA of the parent cell and would be unable to direct all cell activities. The cells probably would not survive.)* **learning modality: logical/mathematical**

Independent Practice L2

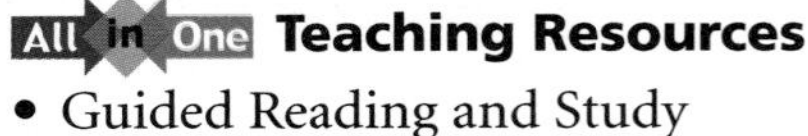

All in One **Teaching Resources**

- Guided Reading and Study Worksheet: *Cell Division*

Student Edition on Audio CD

Help Students Read L1

Outlining Instruct students to outline this section, writing the subheads and leaving room between each one. As students read, they can list details under each subhead.

Stage 1: Interphase

How do little pigs get to be big pigs? Their cells grow and divide, over and over. The regular sequence of growth and division that cells undergo is known as the **cell cycle.** During the cell cycle, a cell grows, prepares for division, and divides into two new cells, which are called "daughter cells." Each of the daughter cells then begins the cell cycle again. You can see details of the cell cycle in Figure 12. Notice that the cell cycle is divided into three main stages: interphase, mitosis, and cytokinesis.

The first stage of the cell cycle is called **interphase.** Interphase is the period before cell division. **During interphase, the cell grows, makes a copy of its DNA, and prepares to divide into two cells.**

Growing During the first part of interphase, the cell grows to its full size and produces structures it needs. For example, the cell makes new ribosomes and produces enzymes. Copies are made of both mitochondria and chloroplasts.

Copying DNA In the next part of interphase, the cell makes an exact copy of the DNA in its nucleus in a process called **replication.** Recall that DNA is found in the chromatin in the nucleus. DNA holds all the information that the cell needs to carry out its functions. Replication of DNA is very important, since each daughter cell must have a complete set of DNA to survive. At the end of DNA replication, the cell contains two identical sets of DNA. You will learn the details of DNA replication later in this section.

Preparing for Division Once the DNA has replicated, preparation for cell division begins. The cell produces structures that it will use to divide into two new cells. At the end of interphase, the cell is ready to divide.

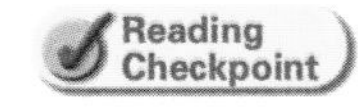

Reading Checkpoint **What is replication?**

Lab zone Try This Activity

Modeling Mitosis

Refer to Figure 12 as you carry out this activity.

1. Construct a model of a cell that has four chromosomes. Use a piece of construction paper to represent the cell. Use different-colored pipe cleaners to represent the chromosomes. Make sure that the chromosomes look like double rods.
2. Position the chromosomes in the cell where they would be during prophase.
3. Repeat Step 2 for metaphase, anaphase, and telophase.

Making Models How did the model help you understand the events of mitosis?

Lab zone Try This Activity

Skills Focus Making models L1

Materials construction paper, different colored pipe cleaners

Time 10 minutes

Expected Outcome Prophase: Join pipe cleaners in each pair at center. Cluster paired pipe cleaners. Metaphase: Align paired pipe cleaners across center. Anaphase: Separate pipe cleaners in each pair and move them toward opposite ends. Telophase: Move separated pipe cleaners to opposite ends. The model helps students see mitosis as a continuous process.

Extend Ask: **How could you show the next stage of the cell cycle?** *(Cut the paper into two halves and place half the pipe cleaners on each piece to model cytokinesis.)* **learning modality: kinesthetic**

Stage 2: Mitosis

Once interphase is complete, the second stage of the cell cycle begins. **Mitosis** (my TOH sis) is the stage during which the cell's nucleus divides into two new nuclei. **During mitosis, one copy of the DNA is distributed into each of the two daughter cells.**

Scientists divide mitosis into four parts, or phases: prophase, metaphase, anaphase, and telophase. During prophase, the threadlike chromatin in the nucleus condenses to form double-rod structures called **chromosomes.** Each chromosome has two rods because the cell's DNA has replicated, and each rod in a chromosome is an exact copy of the other. Each identical rod in a chromosome is called a chromatid. Notice in Figure 11 that the two chromatids are held together by a structure called a centromere.

As the cell progresses through metaphase, anaphase, and telophase, the chromatids separate from each other and move to opposite ends of the cell. Then two nuclei form around the new chromosomes at the two ends of the cell.

FIGURE 10
Bigger Pig, More Cells
The mother pig has more cells in her body than her small piglets.

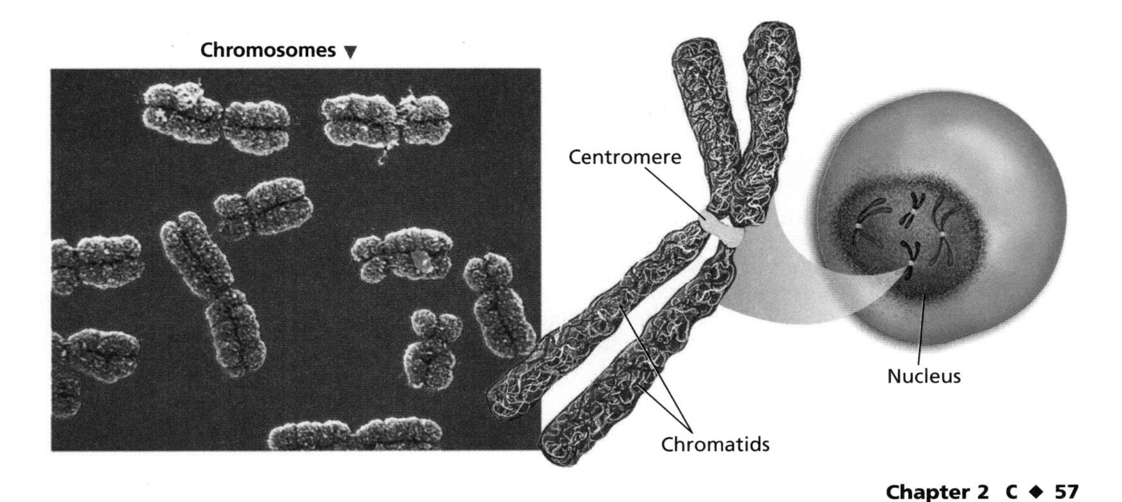

FIGURE 11
Chromosomes
During mitosis, the chromatin condenses to form chromosomes. Each chromosome consists of two identical strands, or chromatids.
Applying Concepts *During which phase of mitosis do the chromosomes form?*

Stage 2: Mitosis

Teach Key Concepts L2

Events in Mitosis

Focus Review with students that interphase prepares the cell to divide.

Teach Ask: **What happens during mitosis?** *(One copy of the DNA is distributed into each of the two daughter cells.)* **What two-rod structures contain the cell's DNA?** *(Chromosomes)* **What is each rod called?** *(Chromatid)* **What are the stages of mitosis?** *(Prophase, metaphase, anaphase, telophase)*

Apply Explain that there is no chemical difference between chromosomes and chromatids except that the chromatids are always double structures (DNA replicas) fastened together at their centromeres. **learning modality: verbal**

L2

Calculating Numbers of Cells

Materials calculator

Time 5 minutes

Focus Ask students to predict how many cell divisions it takes to produce 1,000 cells, starting with one cell.

Teach Students will find that 1,024 cells result after only ten divisions. *(2, 4, 8, 16, 32, 64, 128, 256, 512, 1024)* Ask: **With each division, how does the number of cells change?** *(It doubles.)*

Apply Ask: **Do you think all human cells divide at the same rate throughout life? Explain.** *(No; some cells would divide faster in children and teens than in adults because people are growing.)* **learning modality: logical/mathematical**

Differentiated Instruction

Special Needs L1

Relating Interphase and Mitosis to the Human Life Cycle Explain that interphase in the cell cycle is like childhood and adolescence in the human life cycle. During these times, a person grows and matures. During interphase, a cell grows to its full size. Emphasize that the cell does not divide during interphase. Ask: **What stage in the human life cycle might mitosis represent?** *(Adulthood, because humans reproduce in this stage. During mitosis, the nucleus divides to form new cells.)* **learning modality: verbal**

Monitor Progress L2

Drawing Have students draw and label what happens during interphase. Students can save their drawings in their portfolios.

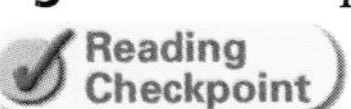

Answers

Figure 11 Prophase

Reading Checkpoint The process in which the cell makes a copy of DNA in its nucleus

Use Visuals: Figure 12 L2

Visualizing the Cell Cycle

Focus Point out that the cell cycle shown is moving clockwise and that the photographs show actual cells.

Teach Ask: **Where is the chromatin in the interphase stage?** *(In the nucleus)* Point out that, in prophase, each pair of chromatids consists of the original DNA of the parent cell plus a copy of the DNA, which is made during interphase. Have students trace the movement of chromosomes through the cycle. Ask: **When are the chromosomes completely separated in their own nuclear envelope?** *(During telophase)*

Apply Ask: **How does the genetic material of each of the daughter cells in the cytokinesis stage compare to the genetic material of the cell shown in prophase?** *(The cell in prophase has condensed genetic material.)* **learning modality: visual**

All in One Teaching Resources

- Transparency C19

L2

Modeling the Cell Cycle

Materials poster board, colored markers, index cards, dice, small objects such as colored erasers or game tokens

Time 20 minutes

Focus Challenge students to create a board game that models the cell cycle.

Teach Divide the class into groups and provide game materials. To get from "start" to "finish" on the game board, players must advance through each stage of the cell cycle by correctly answering questions about that stage.

Apply Ask a student volunteer to compile all questions into a list that all students can use as a study guide. **learning modality: kinesthetic**

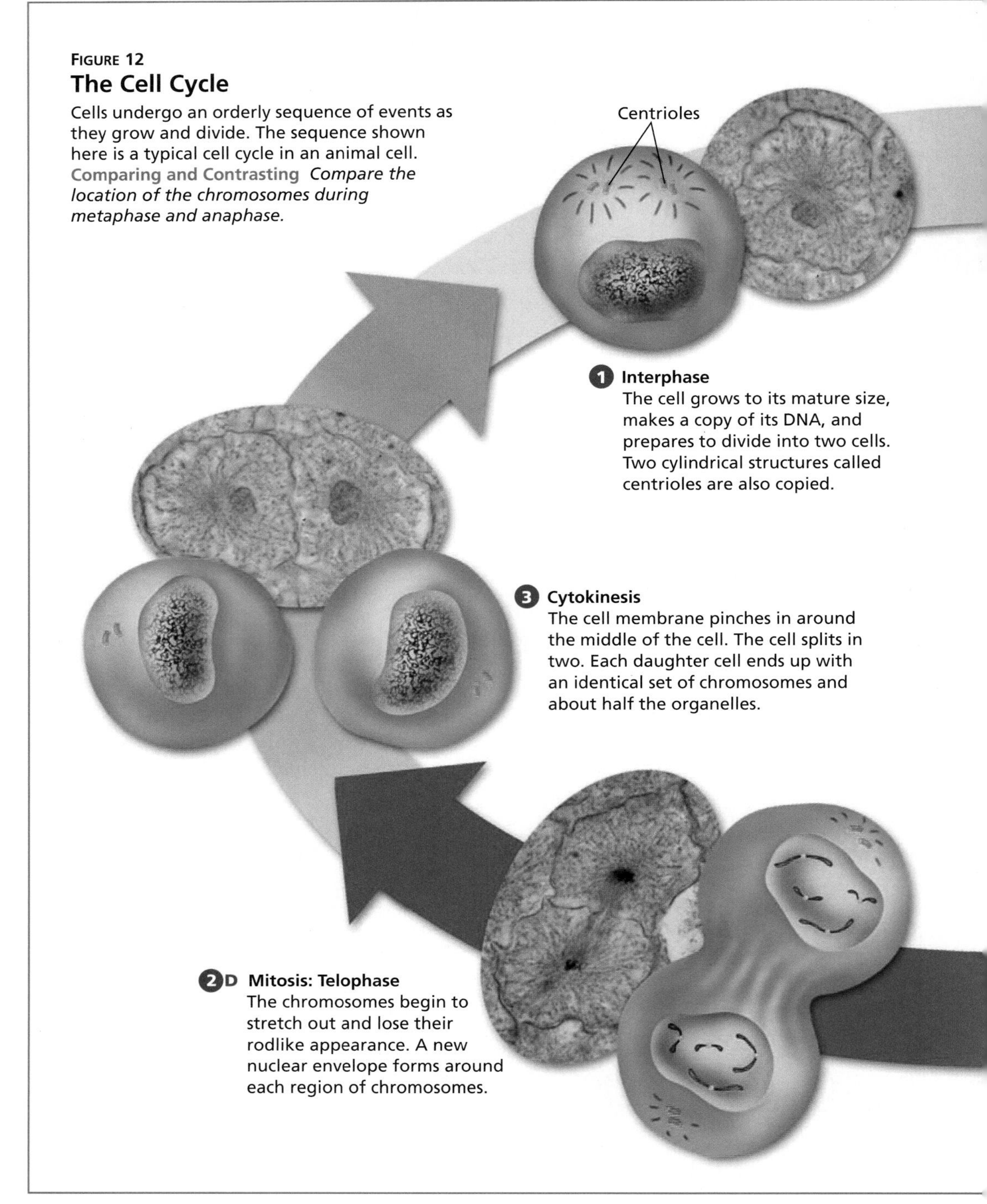

FIGURE 12
The Cell Cycle
Cells undergo an orderly sequence of events as they grow and divide. The sequence shown here is a typical cell cycle in an animal cell.
Comparing and Contrasting *Compare the location of the chromosomes during metaphase and anaphase.*

Centrioles

1 Interphase
The cell grows to its mature size, makes a copy of its DNA, and prepares to divide into two cells. Two cylindrical structures called centrioles are also copied.

3 Cytokinesis
The cell membrane pinches in around the middle of the cell. The cell splits in two. Each daughter cell ends up with an identical set of chromosomes and about half the organelles.

2D Mitosis: Telophase
The chromosomes begin to stretch out and lose their rodlike appearance. A new nuclear envelope forms around each region of chromosomes.

58 ◆ C

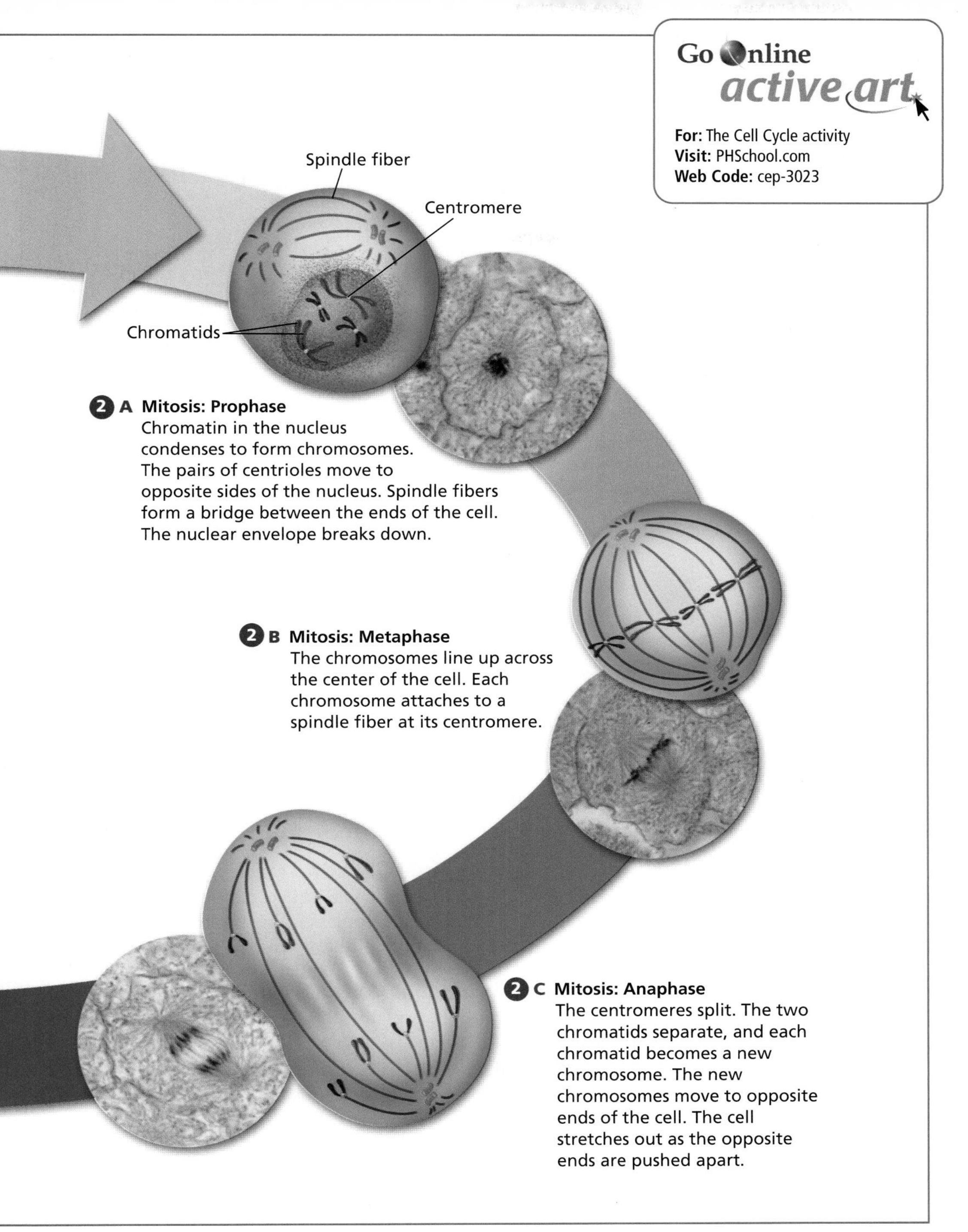

2 A Mitosis: Prophase
Chromatin in the nucleus condenses to form chromosomes. The pairs of centrioles move to opposite sides of the nucleus. Spindle fibers form a bridge between the ends of the cell. The nuclear envelope breaks down.

2 B Mitosis: Metaphase
The chromosomes line up across the center of the cell. Each chromosome attaches to a spindle fiber at its centromere.

2 C Mitosis: Anaphase
The centromeres split. The two chromatids separate, and each chromatid becomes a new chromosome. The new chromosomes move to opposite ends of the cell. The cell stretches out as the opposite ends are pushed apart.

For: The Cell Cycle activity
Visit: PHSchool.com
Web Code: cep-3023

Students can interact with the art of mitosis online.

L1

Modeling Mitosis

Materials construction paper, colored markers, tape or safety pins

Time 15 minutes

Focus Review the four parts of mitosis.

Teach Challenge the class to describe how to make a human model of the nucleus to show how mitosis occurs. *(To start out, a few pairs of students, representing paired chromatids, might stand face to face and join hands, while the other students, representing the nuclear envelope, join hands in a circle around them.)* Have students make and wear signs that show which part of the nucleus they represent, then move in ways to model the parts.

Apply Ask students to model the chromatin inside the nucleus during the other stages of the cell cycle. *(The formerly paired students might stand at random inside the "nuclear envelope" and no longer hold hands.)*
learning modality: kinesthetic

Differentiated Instruction

English Learners/Beginning L1
Comprehension: Word-Part Analysis Pair students with English-proficient students. To help them identify and remember the stages and parts, explain the prefixes *inter-*, *meta-*, *ana-*, *telo-*, and *cyto-*, and then describe how those prefixes relate to each stage or part.
learning modality: verbal

English Learners/Intermediate L2
Comprehension: Link to Visual Make copies of Figure 12, and cut out each step showing the cells and the caption. Have students place the steps in order and write a sentence about each step to summarize what is happening.
learning modality: visual

Monitor Progress L2

Writing Have students list in chronological order the major events that occur during mitosis and describe each event in their own words. Students may place their lists in their portfolios.

Portfolio

Answer
Figure 12 The chromosomes are lined up across the center of the cell during metaphase, while they are moving to the opposite ends of the cell during anaphase.

Math Analyzing Data

Math Skill Interpreting graphs

Focus Remind students that the sections of a circle graph show portions of a whole.

Teach Ask: **What does the circle represent?** *(The time it takes a human liver cell to go through the entire cell cycle)* **Which parts of the circle are included in interphase?** *(Growth, DNA replication, and Preparation for division)* **Which stages of the cell cycle does cell division include?** *(Mitosis and cytokinesis)*

Answers

1. The longest curved arrow represents the cell's interphase; the shortest represents cytokinesis; and the middle one represents mitosis.
2. Interphase
3. 10 hours
4. Interphase

Stage 3: Cytokinesis

Teach Key Concepts L2

The Cell Divides

Focus Review that during mitosis the nucleus of a cell divides, but the cell is still one cell.

Teach Ask: **What happens during cytokinesis?** *(The cytoplasm divides, distributing the organelles into each of the two new cells.)* **What happens during cytokinesis of animal cells?** *(The cell membrane squeezes together around the middle of the cell.)* **Plant cells?** *(A cell plate forms across the middle of the cell and gradually develops into new cell membranes, and new cell walls form around the cell membranes.)*

Apply Explain that there are many variations of the basic pattern of cytokinesis. For example, yeast cells divide, though not equally. A small daughter cell, or bud, pinches off of the parent cell. The bud then grows into a full-sized yeast cell. **learning modality: verbal**

Math Analyzing Data

Length of the Cell Cycle

How long does it take for a cell to go through one cell cycle? It all depends on the cell. A human liver cell, for example, completes one cell cycle in about 22 hours, as shown in the graph. Study the graph and then answer the following questions.

1. **Reading Graphs** What do the three curved arrows outside the circle represent?
2. **Reading Graphs** In what stage of the cell cycle is the wedge representing growth?
3. **Interpreting Data** In human liver cells, how long does it take DNA replication to occur?
4. **Drawing Conclusions** In human liver cells, what stage in the cell cycle takes the longest time?

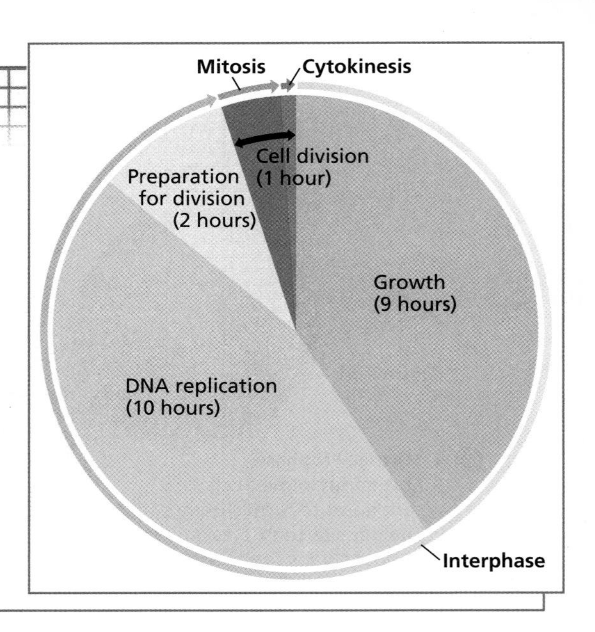

Stage 3: Cytokinesis

The final stage of the cell cycle, which is called **cytokinesis** (sy toh kih NEE sis), completes the process of cell division. **During cytokinesis, the cytoplasm divides. The organelles are distributed into each of the two new cells.** Cytokinesis usually starts at about the same time as telophase. When cytokinesis is complete, two new cells, or daughter cells, have formed. Each daughter cell has the same number of chromosomes as the original parent cell. At the end of cytokinesis, each cell enters interphase, and the cycle begins again.

Cytokinesis in Animal Cells During cytokinesis in animal cells, the cell membrane squeezes together around the middle of the cell. The cytoplasm pinches into two cells. Each daughter cell gets about half of the organelles.

Cytokinesis in Plant Cells Cytokinesis is somewhat different in plant cells. A plant cell's rigid cell wall cannot squeeze together in the same way that a cell membrane can. Instead, a structure called a cell plate forms across the middle of the cell. The cell plate gradually develops into new cell membranes between the two daughter cells. New cell walls then form around the cell membranes.

During what phase of mitosis does cytokinesis begin?

FIGURE 13
Cytokinesis in Plant Cells
During cytokinesis in plant cells, a cell plate forms between the two new nuclei.

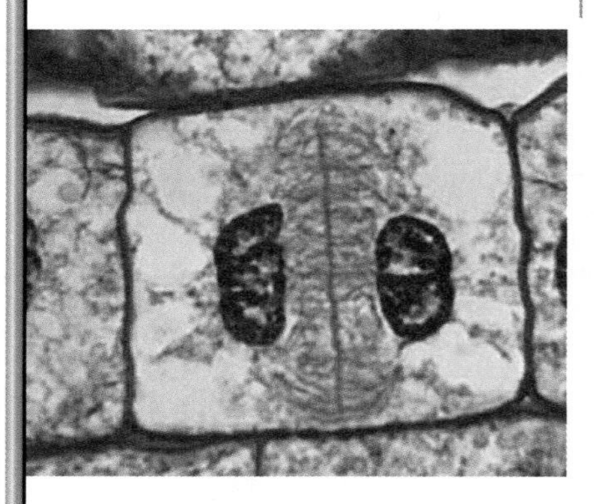

60 ◆ C

Structure and Replication of DNA

DNA replication ensures that each daughter cell will have the genetic information it needs to carry out its activities. Before scientists could understand how DNA replicates, they had to know its structure. In 1952, Rosalind Franklin used an X-ray method to photograph DNA molecules. Her photographs helped James Watson and Francis Crick figure out the structure of DNA in 1953.

The Structure of DNA Notice in Figure 14 that a DNA molecule looks like a twisted ladder, or spiral staircase. The two sides of the DNA ladder are made up of molecules of a sugar called deoxyribose, alternating with molecules known as phosphates.

Each rung is made up of a pair of molecules called nitrogen bases. Nitrogen bases are molecules that contain the element nitrogen and other elements. DNA has four kinds of nitrogen bases: adenine (AD uh neen), thymine (THY meen), guanine (GWAH neen), and cytosine (SY tuh seen). The capital letters A, T, G, and C are used to represent the four bases.

The bases on one side of the ladder pair with the bases on the other side. Adenine (A) only pairs with thymine (T), while guanine (G) only pairs with cytosine (C). This pairing pattern is the key to understanding how DNA replication occurs.

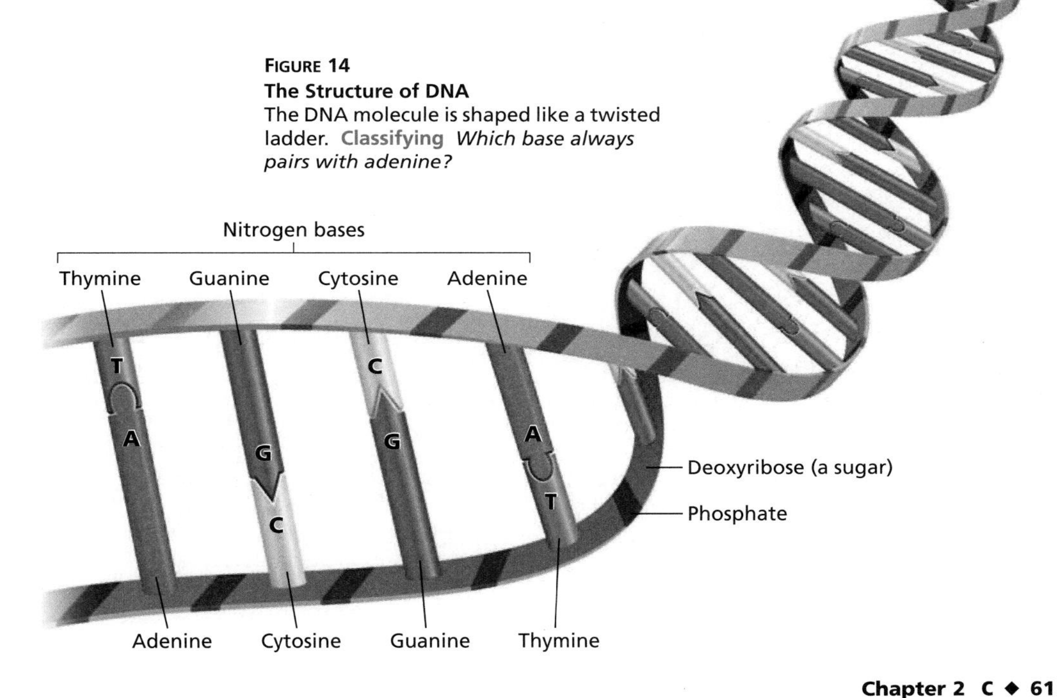

FIGURE 14
The Structure of DNA
The DNA molecule is shaped like a twisted ladder. **Classifying** *Which base always pairs with adenine?*

Differentiated Instruction

Less Proficient Readers L1

Organizing Information Urge students to create flash cards for the stages of the cell cycle and the phases of mitosis. Suggest that they write the name of each stage or phase on one side of an index card, and describe it in their own words on the other side. After students have finished making their flash cards, check to see that they have included all the stages of the cell cycle and all the phases of mitosis. Also make sure that students have correctly described each stage or phase. Encourage pairs of students of quiz each other using their flash cards. **learning modality: verbal**

Structure and Replication of DNA

Teach Key Concepts L2

How DNA Copies Itself

Focus Review with students that DNA is replicated during interphase.

Teach Refer students to Figure 14. Ask: **What do you notice about the nitrogen bases?** *(The same ones always pair. Adenine pairs with thymine, and guanine pairs with cytosine.)* **How does this pairing determine how DNA replication occurs?** *(The order of the bases in each new DNA molecule exactly matches the order of the bases in the original DNA molecule.)* **What happens in DNA replication?** *(The two strands in one molecule separate, and then new nitrogen bases pair up with each strand to form two molecules of DNA.)*

Apply Ask: **If you had one strand of DNA, could you make a molecule with it?** *(Yes; the rules of base pairing would allow you to reconstruct the base sequence of the other strand to make a complete molecule.)* **learning modality: logical/mathematical**

All in One **Teaching Resources**

- Transparencies C20, C21

Modeling DNA Molecules L2

Materials toothpicks, white and colored miniature marshmallows

Time 15 minutes

Focus Review how nitrogen bases pair in a DNA molecule.

Teach Have students make a three-dimensional model of a DNA molecule.

Apply Have students use their models to demonstrate how a molecule of DNA is replicated. **learning modality: kinesthetic**

Monitor Progress 

Writing Have students explain why the pairing of nitrogen bases is the key to understanding DNA replication.

Answers

Figure 14 Thymine

Telophase

Monitor Progress ______ L2

Answer

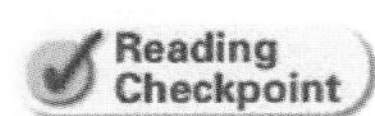
Cytosine

Assess

Reviewing Key Concepts

1. a. Interphase, mitosis, and cytokinesis
b. In prophase, the chromatin condenses to form chromosomes. In metaphase, the chromosomes line up across the center of the cell and attach to the spindle fibers. In anaphase, the chromatids separate, and each moves to an opposite end of the cell. In telophase, the chromosomes begin to stretch out and lose their rodlike appearance.
c. The chromosomes move along the spindle fibers to the ends of the cell.
2. a. Adenine, thymine, cytosine, and guanine **b.** Adenine pairs with thymine, and cytosine pairs with guanine. **c.** TCTAAG

Reteach L1

Have students make sketches of each stage of the cell cycle on separate pieces of paper. Then have them shuffle their drawings and exchange with a partner to place in the correct order and identify each stage.

Performance Assessment L2

Skills Check Have students create a concept map that includes the following terms: *DNA structure, phosphate molecules, sugar molecules, nitrogen bases, adenine, thymine, guanine,* and *cytosine.*

All in One Teaching Resources

- Section Summary: *Cell Division*
- Review and Reinforce: *Cell Division*
- Enrich: *Cell Division*

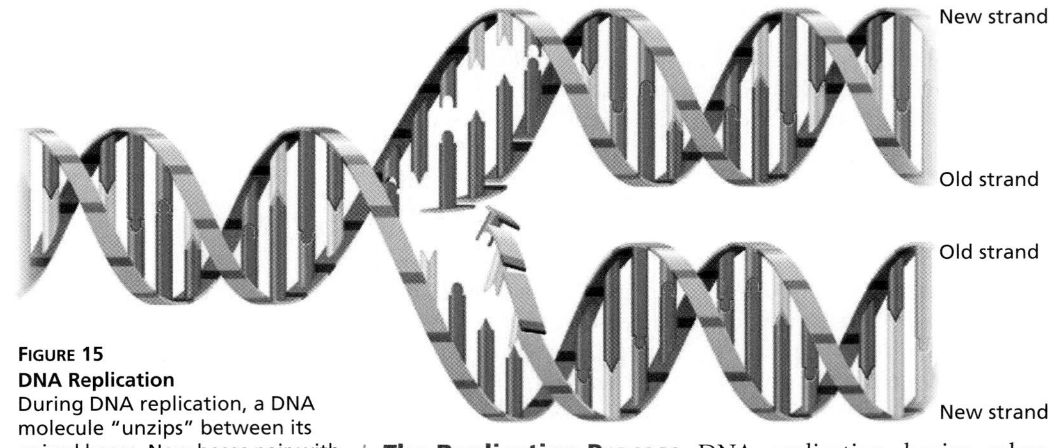

FIGURE 15
DNA Replication
During DNA replication, a DNA molecule "unzips" between its paired bases. New bases pair with the bases on each old strand. As a result, two identical DNA strands form.

The Replication Process DNA replication begins when the two sides of the DNA molecule unwind and separate, somewhat like a zipper unzipping. As you can see in Figure 15, the molecule separates between the paired nitrogen bases.

Next, nitrogen bases that are floating in the nucleus pair up with the bases on each half of the DNA molecule. **Because of the way in which the nitrogen bases pair with one another, the order of the bases in each new DNA molecule exactly matches the order in the original DNA molecule.** Adenine always pairs with thymine, while guanine always pairs with cytosine. Once the new bases are attached, two new DNA molecules are formed.

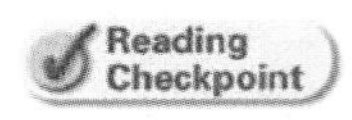
During DNA replication, which base pairs with guanine?

Section 3 Assessment

Target Reading Skill Sequencing Your cycle diagram will help you answer Question 1.

Reviewing Key Concepts

1. a. Reviewing What are the three stages of the cell cycle?
   b. Summarizing Summarize what happens to chromosomes during the stage of the cell cycle in which the nucleus divides. Include the terms *prophase, metaphase, anaphase,* and *telophase.*
   c. Interpreting Diagrams Look at Figure 12. What is the role of spindle fibers during cell division?
2. a. Listing List the nitrogen bases in DNA.
   b. Describing Describe how the nitrogen bases pair in a DNA molecule.
   c. Inferring One section of a strand of DNA has the base sequence AGATTC. What is the base sequence on the other strand?

Writing in Science

Writing Instructions Imagine that you work in a factory where cells are manufactured. Write instructions for newly forming cells on how to carry out cytokinesis. Provide instructions for both plant and animal cells.

Lab zone Chapter Project

Keep Students on Track Make sure students are making and recording daily measurements for at least two weeks. Check that students are doing their best to control variables. Suggest that students make drawings of the plants at different stages and include in their observations the number and length of stems, and the number, size, color, and firmness of the leaves.

Writing in Science

Writing Mode Exposition (how to)

Scoring Rubric

4 Includes complete description of the steps in cytokinesis for plant and animal cells and is written as instructions to the cells
3 Includes all criteria, but is not written to the cells
2 Includes incomplete description
1 Includes inaccuracies

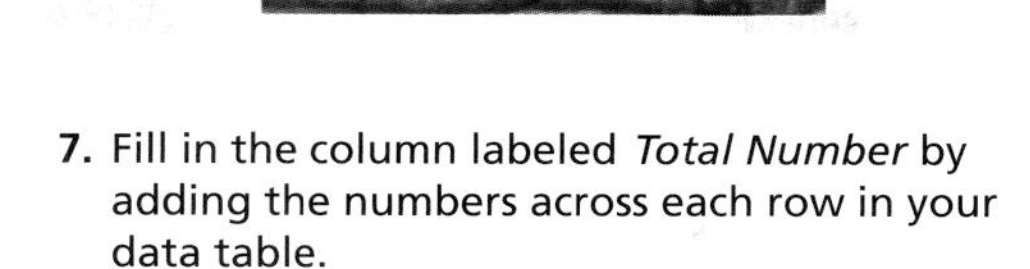

Lab zone Skills Lab

Multiplying by Dividing

Problem
How long do the stages of the cell cycle take?

Skills Focus
observing, calculating

Materials
- microscope
- colored pencils
- calculator (optional)
- prepared slides of onion root tip cells undergoing cell division

Procedure 

1. Place the slide on the stage of a microscope. Use low power to locate a cell in interphase. Then switch to high power, and make a labeled drawing of the cell. **CAUTION:** *Slides and coverslips break easily. Do not allow the objective to touch the slide. If the slide breaks, notify your teacher. Do not touch broken glass.*
2. Repeat Step 1 to find cells in prophase, metaphase, anaphase, and telophase. Then copy the data table into your notebook.
3. Return to low power. Find an area of the slide with many cells undergoing cell division. Switch to the magnification that lets you see about 50 cells at once (for example, 100 ×).
4. Examine the cells row by row, and count the cells that are in interphase. Record that number in the data table under *First Sample*.
5. Examine the cells row by row four more times to count the cells in prophase, metaphase, anaphase, and telophase. Record the results.
6. Move to a new area on the slide. Repeat Steps 3–5 and record your counts in the column labeled *Second Sample*.
7. Fill in the column labeled *Total Number* by adding the numbers across each row in your data table.
8. Add the totals for the five stages to find the total number of cells counted.

Analyze and Conclude

1. **Observing** Which stage of the cell cycle did you observe most often?
2. **Calculating** The cell cycle for onion root tips takes about 720 minutes (12 hours). Use your data and the formula below to find the number of minutes each stage takes.

$$\text{Time for each stage} = \frac{\text{Number of cells at each stage}}{\text{Total number of cells counted}} \times 720 \text{ min}$$

3. **Communicating** Use the data to compare the amount of time spent in mitosis with the total time for the whole cell cycle. Write your answer in the form of a paragraph.

More to Explore
Examine prepared slides of animal cells undergoing cell division. Use drawings and descriptions to compare plant and animal mitosis.

Data Table

Stage of Cell Cycle	First Sample	Second Sample	Total Number
Interphase			
Mitosis:			
Prophase			
Metaphase			
Anaphase			
Telophase			
Total number of cells counted			

Lab zone Skills Lab L2

Multiplying by Dividing

Prepare for Inquiry

Key Concept
Mitosis occurs quickly, and cells spend most of their time in interphase.

Skills Objectives
Students will be able to
- observe cells in different stages of the cell cycle
- calculate the amount of time cells spend in each stage of the cell cycle

Class Time 40 minutes

All in One Teaching Resources
- Lab Worksheet: *Multiplying by Dividing*

Safety
Remind students to handle slides and coverslips carefully. Review the safety guidelines in Appendix A.

Guide Inquiry

Expected Outcome
Most of the cells students count should be in the interphase stage of the cell cycle, but errors in counting and differences in samples may give varying results.

Analyze and Conclude
1. The most likely answer is interphase.
2. Answers will vary depending on students' data. Answers for the sample data are: Interphase, 641 minutes; prophase, 50 minutes; metaphase, 14 minutes; anaphase, 7 minutes; telophase, 7 minutes.
3. Based on the sample data, the amount of time spent in mitosis is 11%. Students' answers will vary.

Extend Inquiry

More to Explore
Interphase and mitosis are very similar in plant and animal cells, except that the centrioles appear during prophase in animal cells. Challenge students to predict whether animal or plant cells spend a longer time in mitosis. Then have them design an experiment to test their prediction.

Sample Data Table

Stages of Cell Cycle	First Sample	Second Sample	Total Number
Interphase	43	46	89
Mitosis: Prophase	3	4	7
Metaphase	1	1	2
Anaphase	1	0	1
Telophase	0	1	1
Total number of cells counted			100

Section 4

Cancer

Objectives

After this lesson, students will be able to

C.2.4.1 Explain how cancer is related to the cell cycle.

C.2.4.2 Describe how cancer can be treated and prevented.

Target Reading Skill 

Previewing Visuals Explain that looking at the visuals before they read helps students activate prior knowledge and predict what they are about to read.

Answers

Possible questions and answers:

What is a tumor? *(A mass of abnormal cells that develops when cancerous cells divide and grow uncontrollably)* **How does cancer spread?** *(Some of the tumor cells can break off and enter the bloodstream.)*

All in One Teaching Resources

- Transparency C22

Preteach

Build Background Knowledge 

Causes and Treatments of Cancer

Ask: **What is cancer?** *(Possible answer: A disease that often kills people.)* **What causes cancer?** *(Possible answer: Genes, diet, smoking, environment, or similar factors.)* Accept any reasonable answers. **How can cancer be treated?** *(Possible answer: Surgery and drugs.)* **How can the risk of cancer be reduced?** *(Possible answer: By not smoking or by eating a healthy diet.)* Tell students they will learn about the causes, treatment, and prevention of cancer in this section.

Section 4

Integrating Health

Cancer

Reading Preview

Key Concepts

- How is cancer related to the cell cycle?
- What are some ways that cancer can be treated?

Key Terms

- cancer
- mutation
- tumor
- chemotherapy

Target Reading Skill

Previewing Visuals When you preview, you look ahead at the material to be read. Preview Figure 17. Then write two questions that you have in a graphic organizer like the one below. As you read, answer your questions.

How Cancer Spreads
Q. What is a tumor?
A.
Q.

Lab zone Discover Activity

What Happens When There Are Too Many Cells?

1. Use tape to mark off a 1 m × 1 m square on the floor. The square represents an area inside the human body. Have two students stand in the square to represent cells.
2. Suppose each cell divides every 30 seconds, and then one cell dies. With a group of students, model this situation. After 30 seconds, two new students should enter the square and one student should leave the square.
3. Model another round of cell division by having three new students enter the square while one student leaves. Continue this process until no more students can fit in the square.

Think It Over

Predicting Use this activity to predict what would happen if some cells in a person's body divided faster than they should.

If you go outside on a clear night in spring, you may be able to see the constellation, or group of stars, called Cancer. The word *cancer* means "crab" in Latin, the language of the ancient Romans. According to an ancient Roman myth, the goddess Juno sent a giant crab to help kill the hero Hercules. Instead, Hercules crushed the crab with his foot. Juno then put the crab in the sky in the form of a constellation.

Today the word *cancer* still names the constellation, but it also names a disease. As the mythological crab threatened Hercules, the disease called cancer threatens human health. But doctors and scientists are making progress in treating and preventing cancer. As Hercules conquered the monster called Cancer, perhaps one day scientists will conquer the disease.

The constellation Cancer ▶

Lab zone Discover Activity

Skills Focus Predicting L1

Materials masking tape, meter stick

Time 15 minutes

Tips Use another method of marking off a square if your school does not allow tape to be placed on hard-surfaced floors. Make sure students understand that each time one student leaves the square, two more students should enter. Ask a volunteer to keep track of the time.

Expected Outcome The square fills up quickly with students as the "cells" divide.

Think It Over Students may predict that part of the body would grow too fast and crowd other parts, perhaps causing damage or disease.

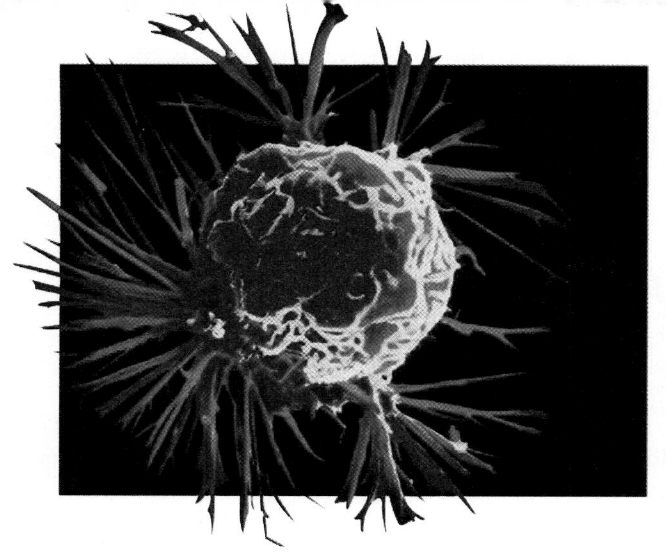

FIGURE 16
A Breast Cancer Cell
A cancer tumor begins as a single cell. A mutation in the cell's DNA disrupts the normal cell cycle.
Relating Cause and Effect *How does the cell behave as a result of the mutation?*

What Is Cancer?

Cancer is a disease in which cells grow and divide uncontrollably, damaging the parts of the body around them. Cancer is something like weeds in a garden. Weeds can overrun the garden plants, robbing them of the space, sunlight, and water they need. Similarly, cancer cells can overrun normal cells.

Cancer is actually not just one disease. In fact, there are more than 100 types of cancer. Cancer can occur in almost any part of the body. Cancers are often named by the place in the body where they begin. For example, lung cancer begins in the tissues of the lungs. In the United States today, lung cancer is the leading cause of cancer deaths among both men and women.

How Cancer Begins Scientists think that cancer begins when something damages a portion of the DNA in a chromosome. The damage causes a change in the DNA called a **mutation.** DNA contains all the instructions necessary for life. Damage to the DNA can cause cells to function abnormally.

Normally, the cells in one part of the body live in harmony with the cells around them. Cells that go through the cell cycle divide in a controlled way. **Cancer begins when mutations disrupt the normal cell cycle, causing cells to divide in an uncontrolled way.** Without the normal controls on the cell cycle, the cells grow too large and divide too often.

At first, one cell develops in an abnormal way. As the cell divides over and over, the repeated divisions produce more and more abnormal cells. In time, these cells form a tumor. A **tumor** is a mass of abnormal cells that develops when cancerous cells divide and grow uncontrollably.

Instruct

Cell Processes and Energy

Show the Video Field Trip to let students explore the relationship between the cell cycle and cancer.

What Is Cancer?

Help Students Read L1

KWL Have students make a chart with three columns titled What I Know, What I Want to Know, and What I Learned. In the first column, students recall what they know about cancer. They fill out the second column before they read. They complete the third column after reading.

Teach Key Concepts L2

Cancer and the Cell Cycle

Focus Review the definition of cancer.

Teach Ask: **How does cancer begin?** *(When mutations disrupt the normal cell cycle)* **What changes occur in the normal cell cycle?** *(The cells grow too large and divide too often.)*

Apply Ask students why the first sign of cancer may occur in an organ in which it did not begin. *(Some cancer cells might break off from the original site, enter the bloodstream, and cause a tumor in another area.)* **learning modality: logical/mathematical**

Independent Practice L2

All in One Teaching Resources

- Guided Reading and Study Worksheet: *Cancer*

Student Edition on Audio CD

Monitor Progress L2

Oral Presentation Call on students to explain how cancer begins and spreads.

Answer

Figure 16 The cell divides uncontrollably.

Differentiated Instruction

Gifted and Talented L3

Using Community Resources Have small groups of students make posters to educate students in your school about cancer prevention. Encourage them to focus on the most common causes of cancer, such as tobacco and ultraviolet radiation. Suggest that students access the Web sites of the American Cancer Society or the Centers for Disease Control and Prevention for information. Students can display their posters throughout their school or community. **learning modality: visual**

For: Links on cancer
Visit: www.SciLinks.org
Web Code: scn-0324

Download a worksheet that will guide students review of Internet resources on cancer.

Treating and Preventing Cancer

Teach Key Concepts

L2

Treatment and Prevention Methods

Focus Tell students that most cases of cancer can be treated and prevented.

Teach Ask: **What are three ways in which cancer can be treated?** *(Surgery, radiation, and drugs that destroy cancer cells)* **How is surgery used to treat cancer?** *(Surgery is used to remove a cancerous tumor.)* **How is radiation used to treat cancer?** *(Radiation is used to destroy fast-growing cancer cells.)* **What do you call the use of drugs to treat a disease such as cancer?** *(Chemotherapy)* **What are three ways in which cancer can be prevented?** *(Avoiding smoking, eating a healthful diet, and protecting the skin from ultraviolet light)* **What kind of cancer does smoking often lead to?** *(Lung cancer)* **What type of diet can lead to cancer?** *(A diet high in fatty foods, such as fatty meats and fried foods)*

Apply Ask: **What are ways to protect your skin from ultraviolet radiation?** *(Limit your exposure by staying in the shade, avoid tanning beds, wear protective clothing, and use sunscreen.)* **learning modality: verbal**

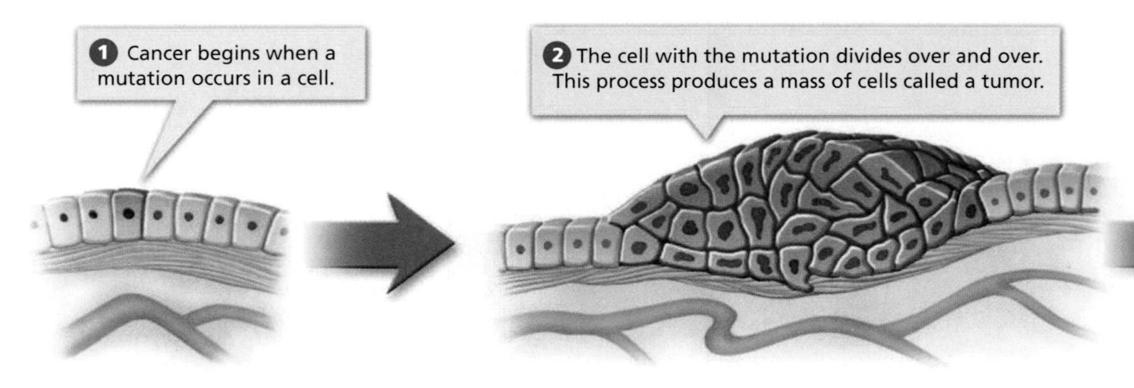

FIGURE 17
How Cancer Spreads
A cancerous tumor is a mass of cells that divide uncontrollably.
Interpreting Diagrams *How can cancer spread from one part of the body to another?*

How Cancer Spreads Figure 17 shows how a tumor forms. Tumors often take years to grow to a noticeable size. During that time, the cells become more and more abnormal as they continue to divide. Some of the cancerous cells may break off the tumor and enter the bloodstream. In this way, the cancer can spread to other areas of the body.

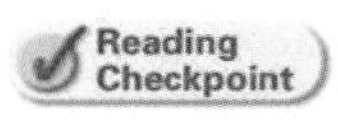

Reading Checkpoint **What is the first step that leads to the development of a tumor?**

Treating and Preventing Cancer

Scientists are making progress in the battle against cancer. Treatments offer hope for cancer patients. In addition, people can take steps that help prevent the disease.

Treating Cancer If a person is diagnosed with cancer, there are a variety of treatments. **There are three common ways to treat cancer: surgery, radiation, and drugs that destroy the cancer cells.**

When a cancer is detected before it has spread to other parts of the body, surgery is usually the best treatment. If doctors can completely remove the cancerous tumor, a person may be cured. If, however, the cancer has spread or if the tumor cannot be removed, doctors may use radiation. Radiation consists of beams of high-energy waves. Fast-growing cancer cells are more likely than normal cells to be destroyed by radiation.

Chemotherapy is another form of cancer treatment. **Chemotherapy** is the use of drugs to treat a disease. Cancer-treatment drugs are carried throughout the body by the bloodstream. These drugs kill cancer cells or slow their growth.

Scientists continue to look for new ways to treat cancer. If scientists can discover how the cell cycle is controlled, they may find ways to stop cancer cells from multiplying.

For: Links on cancer
Visit: www.SciLinks.org
Web Code: scn-0324

3 Cancer cells break off from the main tumor. The cells enter the bloodstream and spread throughout the body.

Preventing Cancer People can reduce their chances of developing cancer by avoiding smoking, eating a healthful diet, and protecting their skin from bright sunlight. When people repeatedly inhale tobacco smoke, lung cancer and other forms of cancer may result. Unhealthful diets may lead to almost as many cancer deaths as does tobacco. A diet high in fatty foods, such as fatty meats and fried foods, is especially harmful. Eating a lot of fruits and vegetables may help lower the risk for some types of cancer.

Most skin cancers are caused by the ultraviolet light in sunlight. If people limit their exposure to bright sunlight, they can reduce their risk of getting skin cancer.

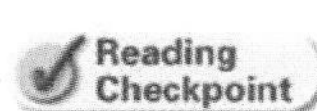
How can exposure to bright sunlight lead to cancer?

Section 4 Assessment

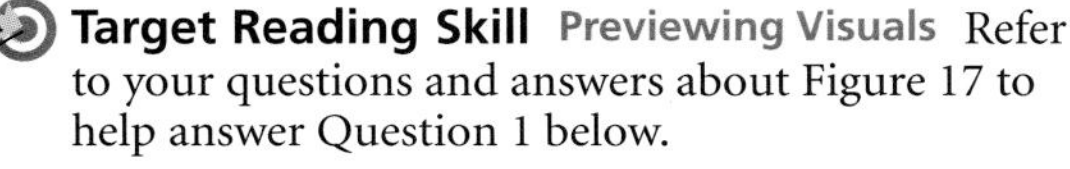

Target Reading Skill **Previewing Visuals** Refer to your questions and answers about Figure 17 to help answer Question 1 below.

Reviewing Key Concepts

1. a. **Defining** What is cancer?
   b. **Comparing and Contrasting** How are cancer cells different from normal cells?
   c. **Relating Cause and Effect** What is the relationship between cancer and DNA?
2. a. **Identifying** Identify the three ways in which cancer is treated.
   b. **Explaining** Which method is almost always a part of the treatment for very small tumors that have not spread to other parts of the body? Explain why this method is chosen.
   c. **Inferring** Why is a combination of methods typically used to treat cancer that has spread beyond the original tumor?

Lab zone At-Home Activity

A Cancer-Prevention Diet With your family, discuss what cancer is and how it spreads. Then explain that a diet that is low in fat can help prevent some forms of cancer. Work with members of your family to plan some low-fat meals. You might find new recipes for low-fat foods and prepare them together.

Lab zone Build Inquiry L2

Contrasting Rates of Cell Division

Materials calculator

Time 5 minutes

Focus Remind students that uncontrolled cell division can lead to a tumor.

Teach Have students calculate the number of cell divisions and cells if cells divide every 30 minutes for 10 hours *(20 divisions, 1,048,576 cells)* and every 2 hours for 10 hours *(5 divisions, 32 cells)*.

Apply Ask: **How do your results relate to how a tumor forms?** *(Cancer cells divide very rapidly, forming a mass of cells called a tumor.)* **learning modality: logical/ mathematical**

Monitor Progress L2

Answers

Figure 17 Cancer cells can break off a tumor and enter the bloodstream.

A mutation

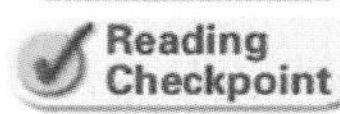
The ultraviolet light in sunlight can cause cancer.

Assess

Reviewing Key Concepts

1. a. A disease in which cells grow and divide uncontrollably, damaging parts of the body around them **b.** Cancer cells grow too large and divide too often. **c.** The DNA in cancer cells is damaged.

2. a. Surgery, radiation, and drugs **b.** Surgery, because if the doctors can completely remove the cancerous cells, the person may be cured of the disease **c.** The chance of getting rid of the cancer cells is greater if it is attacked by more than one method.

Reteach L1

Use Figure 17 to review how cancer begins and spreads throughout the body.

All in One Teaching Resources

- Section Summary: *Cancer*
- Review and Reinforce: *Cancer*
- Enrich: *Cancer*

Lab zone At-Home Activity

A Cancer-Prevention Diet L1

Suggest that students write down what they want to explain to their families. The American Heart Association, the American Cancer Association, and the American Diabetes Association can provide many suggestions for low-fat meals. Encourage students to share some recipes with the class.

Lab zone Chapter Project

Keep Students on Track Instruct students to examine the data they have collected, such as growth in height or number of leaves, and prepare graphs. Other observations, such as leaf color or shape, might be presented in drawings. Ask students to prepare a brief summary that describes their experimental plan and their results. Tell students to save their plants for their presentation.

Science and Society

When Should New Medicines Be Made Available?

Key Concept
It is sometimes difficult to find a balance between making a new medication available too soon and testing it for too long.

Build Background Knowledge
The Benefits of Pharmaceutical Drugs
Have students think about the benefits of medications available both over the counter and through prescription. Ask: **Name some examples of medications.** *(Aspirin, cough medicine, antibiotics, asthma medicine)* **How do medications benefit people?** *(In some cases they provide relief from minor illnesses such as allergies or sore throats. Other medicines are life-saving or allow people to lead a productive life.)* **What are side effects?** *(Side effects are unwanted results from taking a medication.)* **Give some examples of possible side effects from taking medication.** *(Upset stomach, rash, dizziness, allergic reaction, feeling drowsy or tired)*

Introduce the Debate
Ask: **What are the benefits of thoroughly testing a drug before it is approved for widespread use?** *(The complete effects of the drug are known. It is known how effectively the drug works, what dosage is most effective, and what immediate and long-term side effects may occur.)* **What are some disadvantages of a lengthy test period before a drug is approved for widespread use?** *(People who could benefit from the medication may die before it is made available.)*

Science and **Society**

When Should New Medicines Be Made Available?

A woman is seriously ill with cancer. She has read about a new drug that shows promise in treating the type of cancer she has. The woman asks her doctor for the medicine. The doctor, however, tells her that she cannot have the drug. The new medicine is still being tested, and it has not yet been approved for use. When the cancer patient hears this news, she feels angry and helpless.

The Issues

Why Does Drug Approval Take So Long?
Before a new medicine becomes available, it must undergo extensive testing. The testing of new medicines is regulated by the Food and Drug Administration, or FDA, which is an agency of the United States government. The FDA tries to balance two important needs. First, sick people need to have the best treatments available, including promising new drugs. Second, patients need to be protected from drugs that do not work or are harmful.

It takes several years of testing for a new drug to be approved. The lengthy testing process is designed to ensure that the new medicine works, and that it is safe. Scientists begin by using chemical tests and computer programs to determine the drug's characteristics. Then the drug is tested on animals to see whether it is safe and effective. Next, the drug is extensively tested on human volunteers. If the results of the tests on human volunteers are good, the drug becomes available to patients who may benefit from it.

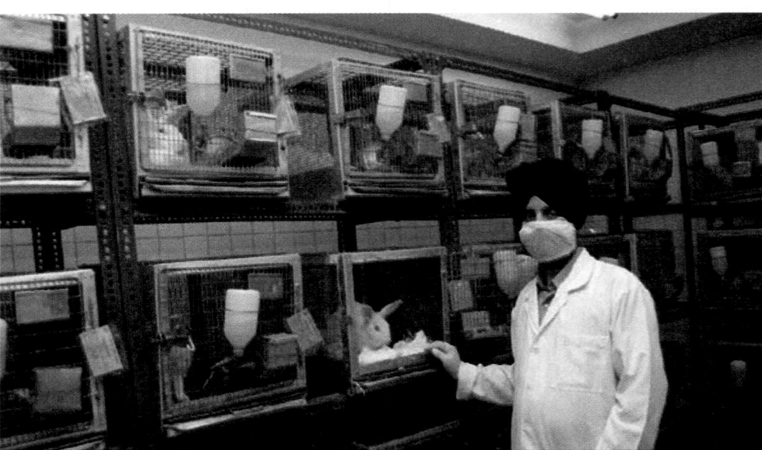

Testing for Safety and Effectiveness
To ensure that new medicines are safe and effective, they are tested on animals before being tested on humans.

Background

Facts and Figures The Center for Drug Evaluation and Research (CDER) is the branch of the FDA that evaluates new drugs for consumer use. The CDER approves prescription drugs, generic drugs, and over-the-counter drugs. The CDER does not develop, produce, or test drugs. A drug manufacturer turns in a complete report about the drug and the studies that have been done on it. The CDER reviews the report and determines the safety of the drug, weighing the benefits of the drug against any known risks or side effects. If a drug is found to have unexpected risks or to be unsafe after its approval, the CDER can amend the information presented on the label or remove the drug from the market.

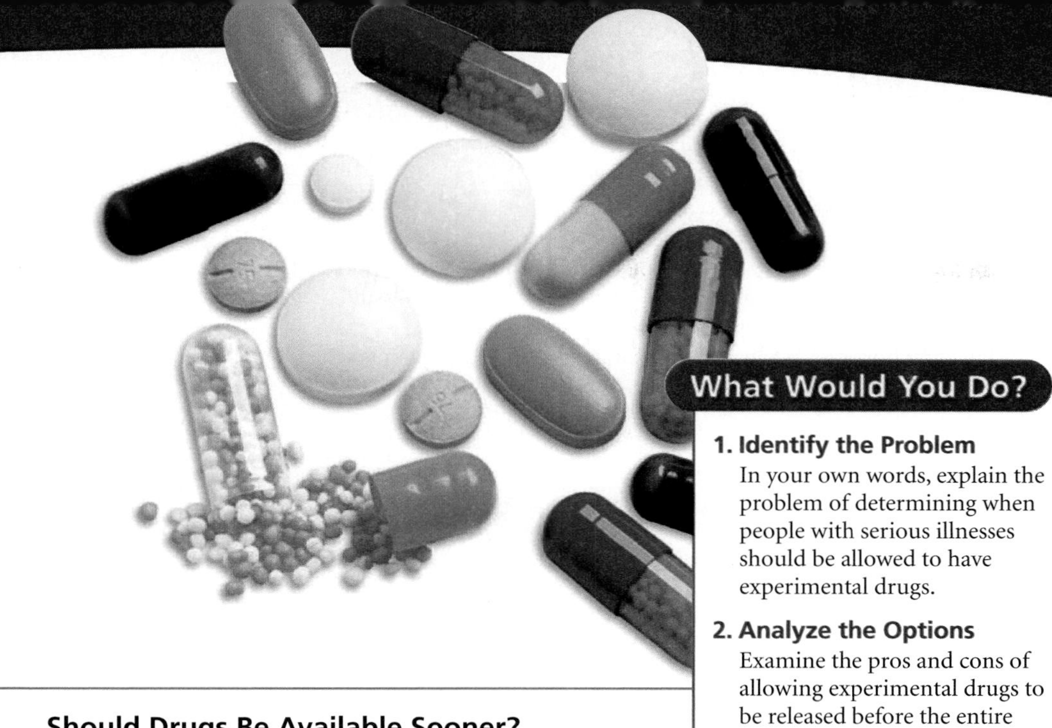

What Would You Do?

1. Identify the Problem
In your own words, explain the problem of determining when people with serious illnesses should be allowed to have experimental drugs.

2. Analyze the Options
Examine the pros and cons of allowing experimental drugs to be released before the entire testing process is complete. List the possible benefits of releasing a drug early. Also identify the risks that patients take when they use medicines that have not been fully tested.

3. Find a Solution
Suppose a patient has heard about a promising new drug that has been approved without the full testing procedure. To take this drug, the patient must stop using a standard treatment that may be safer but less effective. Write a conversation between a doctor and the patient in which they discuss the pros and cons of the new drug.

For: More on new medicines
Visit: PHSchool.com
Web Code: ceh-3020

Should Drugs Be Available Sooner?

While a new drug is being tested, the only patients who can get the drug are the volunteers who take part in the tests. Other patients—even those who are very sick—do not usually have access to the drug. However, in rare cases, if a new medicine shows special promise in fighting a life-threatening disease, such as AIDS or cancer, the FDA may make it available sooner than usual.

Risks of Making Drugs Available Too Soon

Some people are critical of the FDA's efforts to make new drugs available more quickly. Early-approval drugs have not undergone the extensive testing required for most drugs. Therefore, the effectiveness of the drugs has not been fully demonstrated.

In addition, long-term use of the drugs may have harmful side effects. For example, long-term use of some drugs can increase the risk that people will develop harmful conditions or diseases, such as some types of cancer. Long-term side effects cannot usually be detected without years of testing.

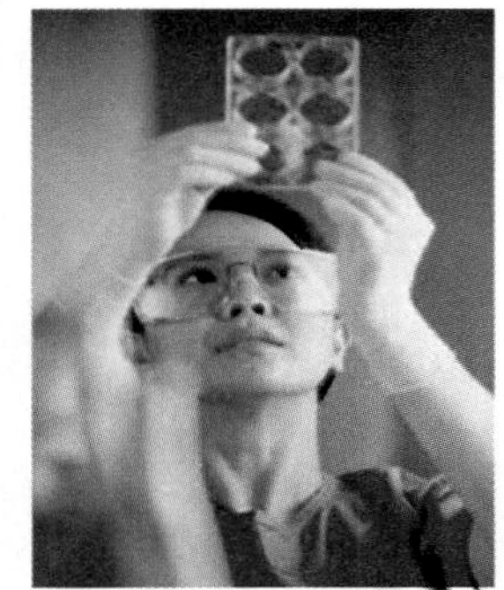

Facilitate the Debate

- Have students participate in a mock hospital meeting in which a doctor is trying to get approval from an FDA representative to have her patient test a new, unapproved drug that shows promise of a cure. Students can role-play the patient, the doctor, the FDA representative, the hospital administrators, and a representative from a health insurance company. Have students consider the benefits and risks of taking the unapproved drug.
- After the debate, ask student groups to create a pamphlet that includes information about both sides of the argument about the use of experimental drugs.

What Would You Do?

1. People who take experimental drugs are putting themselves at risk of negative side effects from the drug. The drug may not be effective against the disease.
2. The benefits of releasing a drug early are that people who are seriously ill may benefit from the drug. The risks include not knowing whether the drug will be effective and not knowing the immediate or long-term side effects of the drug.
3. Students responses will vary but should include the idea that, although the patient may benefit from the drug, the side effects are unknown.

For: More on new medications
Visit: PHSchool.com
Web Code: ceh-3020

Students can research this issue online.

Extend

Encourage students to research more information about drug testing on the FDA Web site. How are drugs tested? What has to happen for a drug to be approved for widespread use? How can a person become part of a clinical trial for a new drug?

- Complete student edition
- Section and chapter self-assessments
- Assessment reports for teachers

Help Students Read

Building Vocabulary

Word-Part Analysis Explain that the term *chlorophyll* comes from the Greek words *khloros,* which means "green" and *phullon,* which means "leaf." The term *autotroph* comes from the Greek words *autos,* meaning "self," and *trophe,* meaning "food." *Heteros* means "other." Ask students to relate these word parts to key terms. *(Chlorophyll is found in green leaves. An autotroph makes food for itself. A heterotroph gets food from others.)*

Vocabulary Knowledge Rating Chart Have students construct a chart with four columns: *Term, Can Define or Use It, Have Heard or Seen It,* and *Don't Know.* Students can copy the vocabulary terms for this chapter under Column 1, then place a check mark under one of the other columns for each term. If students did not check the *Can Define or Use It* column, have them reread passages with those terms.

Connecting Concepts

Concept Maps Help students develop one way to show how the information in this chapter is related. Cells require energy, which they manufacture and release in the processes of photosynthesis and respiration, and grow and reproduce in a sequence called the cell cycle, which can be disrupted by mutations and result in cancer. Have students brainstorm to identify the Key Concepts, Key Terms, details, and examples, and then write each one on a sticky note and attach it at random on chart paper or on the board.

Chapter 2 Study Guide

1 Photosynthesis

Key Concepts

- Nearly all living things obtain energy either directly or indirectly from the energy of sunlight captured during photosynthesis.
- During photosynthesis, plants and some other organisms use energy from the sun to convert carbon dioxide and water into oxygen and sugars.
- The equation for photosynthesis is
  $6\,CO_2 + 6\,H_2O \longrightarrow C_6H_{12}O_6 + 6\,O_2$.

Key Terms

photosynthesis
autotroph
heterotroph
pigment
chlorophyll
stomata

2 Respiration

Key Concepts

- During respiration, cells break down simple food molecules such as sugar and release the energy they contain.
- The respiration equation is
  $C_6H_{12}O_6 + 6\,O_2 \longrightarrow 6\,CO_2 + 6\,H_2O + \text{energy}$.
- Fermentation provides energy for cells without using oxygen.

Key Terms

respiration
fermentation

3 Cell Division

Key Concepts

- During interphase, the cell grows, makes a copy of its DNA, and prepares to divide into two cells.
- During mitosis, one copy of the DNA is distributed into each of the two daughter cells.
- During cytokinesis, the cytoplasm divides. The organelles are distributed into each of the two new cells.
- Because of the way in which the nitrogen bases pair with one another, the order of the bases in each new DNA molecule exactly matches the order in the original DNA molecule.

Key Terms

cell cycle
interphase
replication
mitosis
chromosome
cytokinesis

4 Cancer

Key Concepts

- Cancer begins when mutations disrupt the normal cell cycle, causing cells to divide in an uncontrolled way.
- There are three common ways to treat cancer: surgery, radiation, and drugs that destroy the cancer cells.

Key Terms

cancer
mutation
tumor
chemotherapy

Tell students that this concept map will be organized in hierarchical order and to begin at the top with the Key Concepts. Ask students these questions to guide them to categorize the information on the stickies: **What is photosynthesis? What is respiration, and how is it related to photosynthesis? What are the stages of the cell cycle? How does cancer begin?**

Prompt students by using connecting words or phrases, such as "is the opposite of," "includes," and "is related to," to indicate the basis for the organization of the map. The phrases should form a sentence between or among a set of concepts.

Answer Accept logical presentations by students.

All in One Teaching Resources

- Key Terms Review: *Cell Processes and Energy*
- Connecting Concepts: *Cell Processes and Energy*

Review and Assessment

For: Self-Assessment
Visit: PHSchool.com
Web Code: cea-3020

Organizing Information

Comparing and Contrasting
Copy the compare/contrast table about photosynthesis and respiration. Complete the table to compare these processes. (For more information on compare/contrast tables, see the Skills Handbook.)

Comparing Photosynthesis and Respiration

Feature	Photosynthesis	Respiration
Raw materials	Water and carbon dioxide	a. ___?___
Products	b. ___?___	c. ___?___
Is energy released?	d. ___?___	Yes

Reviewing Key Terms

Choose the letter of the best answer.

1. The organelle in which photosynthesis takes place is the
   a. mitochondrion.
   b. chloroplast.
   c. chlorophyll.
   d. nucleus.
2. What process produces carbon dioxide?
   a. photosynthesis
   b. replication
   c. mutation
   d. respiration
3. The process in which a cell makes an exact copy of its DNA is called
   a. fermentation.
   b. respiration.
   c. replication.
   d. reproduction.
4. What happens during cytokinesis?
   a. A spindle forms.
   b. Chloroplasts release energy.
   c. The cytoplasm divides.
   d. Chromosomes divide.
5. A mass of cancer cells is called a
   a. tumor.
   b. chromosome.
   c. mutation.
   d. mitochondrion.

If the statement is true, write *true*. If it is false, change the underlined word or words to make the statement true.

6. An organism that makes its own food is <u>an autotroph</u> .
7. During <u>respiration</u>, most energy is released in the mitochondria.
8. An energy-releasing process that does not require oxygen is <u>replication</u>.
9. The stage of the cell cycle when DNA replication occurs is called <u>telophase</u>.
10. <u>Uncontrolled</u> cell division is a characteristic of cancer.

Writing in Science

Brochure Suppose you are a volunteer who works with cancer patients. Write a brochure that could be given to cancer patients and their families. The brochure should explain what cancer is and how it is treated.

Cell Processes and Energy
Video Preview
Video Field Trip
▶ Video Assessment

Review and Assessment

Organizing Information
a. Oxygen and sugars
b. Oxygen and sugars
c. Water and carbon dioxide
d. No

Reviewing Key Terms
1. b **2.** d **3.** c **4.** c **5.** a
6. true
7. true
8. fermentation
9. interphase
10. true

Writing in Science

Writing Mode Explanation
Scoring Rubric
4 Includes complete and accurate information with many details; writing is clear and organized
3 Includes all criteria but fewer details
2 Includes all criteria but writing is disorganized
1 Includes inaccurate or incomplete information

Cell Processes and Energy

Show the Video Assessment to review chapter content and as a prompt for the writing assignment.

Go Online PHSchool.com
For: Self-Assessment
Visit: PHSchool.com
Web Code: cea-3020

Students can take a practice test online that is automatically scored.

All in One Teaching Resources
- Transparency C23
- Chapter Test
- Performance Assessment Teacher Notes
- Performance Assessment Student Worksheet
- Performance Assessment Scoring Rubric

***ExamView®* Computer Test Bank CD-ROM**

Checking Concepts

11. During photosynthesis, energy from sunlight is changed into chemical energy, which is used to convert carbon dioxide and water into oxygen and sugars.

12. Photosynthesis requires carbon dioxide and water. The products are oxygen and sugars.

13. Organisms need to carry out respiration to provide energy for cell processes.

14. During interphase, the cell grows, DNA is replicated, and the cell prepares to divide.

15. During interphase, exact copies of the DNA are made. During mitosis, the DNA and cell organelles are divided equally between the daughter cells.

16. Cancer usually begins with a mutation, or a change in the DNA. Mutations disturb the normal cell cycle.

17. Ultraviolet light in sunlight can cause skin cancer. Protective clothing and sunscreen can block ultraviolet light.

Review and Assessment

Checking Concepts

11. Briefly explain what happens to energy from the sun during photosynthesis.

12. What are the raw materials needed for photosynthesis? What are the products?

13. Why do organisms need to carry out the process of respiration?

14. Describe what happens during interphase.

15. How do the events in the cell cycle ensure that the genetic information in the daughter cells will be identical to that of the parent cell?

16. Describe how cancer usually begins to develop in the body.

17. Explain why it is important for people to wear protective clothing or use sunscreen when they are outdoors in bright sunlight.

Thinking Critically

18. **Predicting** Suppose a volcano threw so much ash into the air that it blocked most of the sunlight that usually strikes Earth. How might this affect the ability of animals to obtain the energy they need to live?

19. **Comparing and Contrasting** Explain the relationship between the processes of breathing and cellular respiration.

20. **Relating Cause and Effect** Do plant cells need to carry out respiration? Explain.

21. **Inferring** The diagram below shows part of one strand of a DNA molecule. What would the bases on the other strand be?

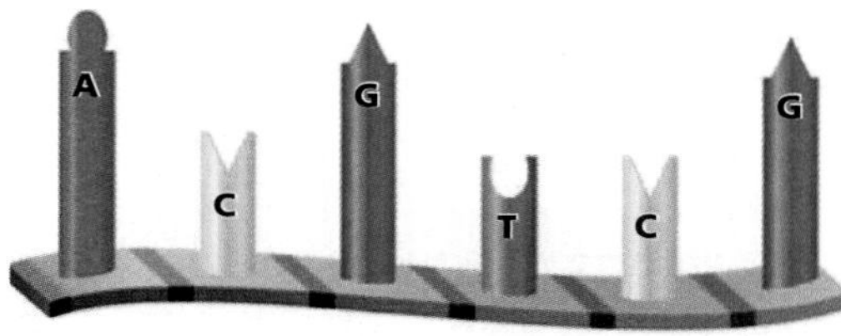

22. **Making Judgments** What information could you give someone to persuade him or her not to start smoking?

Applying Skills

Use the table below to answer Questions 23–26.

Percentages of Nitrogen Bases in the DNA of Various Organisms

Nitrogen Base	Human	Wheat	*E. coli* Bacterium
Adenine	30%	27%	24%
Guanine	20%	23%	26%
Thymine	30%	27%	24%
Cytosine	20%	23%	26%

23. **Graphing** For each organism, draw a bar graph to show the percentages of each nitrogen base in its DNA.

24. **Interpreting Data** What is the relationship between the amounts of adenine and thymine in the DNA of each organism? What is the relationship between the amounts of guanine and cytosine?

25. **Inferring** Based on your answer to Question 24, what can you infer about the structure of DNA in these three organisms?

26. **Applying Concepts** Suppose cytosine made up 28% of the nitrogen bases in an organism. What percentage of the organism's nitrogen bases should be thymine? Explain.

Lab zone Chapter Project

Performance Assessment Bring in your plants, recorded observations, and graphs to share with the class. Be prepared to describe your experimental plan and explain your results. How well did you follow your experimental plan? What did you learn about photosynthesis and light from the experiment you performed?

Lab zone Chapter Project

L3

Performance Assessment Advise students to describe how they varied lighting conditions and controlled other variables, as well as how they assessed plant health and growth. One learning outcome is that plants cannot carry out normal photosynthesis without adequate light.

Reflect and Record Students may not have varied the lighting conditions enough to affect plant growth. In another study, students might vary the color of light plants receive.

Standardized Test Prep

Test-Taking Tip

Interpreting Data

Before you answer a question about a data table, read the title of the table to see what type of data it contains. For example, the title of the table that follows Question 2 tells you that the data show how temperature affects the length of the cell cycle. Next, read the titles of the columns and rows. Do not spend time trying to analyze all the data, because you may not need total understanding to answer the question.

Sample Question

The data in the table show that

A cells divide faster when the temperature is decreased.
B cells divide faster when the temperature is increased.
C the length of the cell cycle is not affected by temperature.
D the length of the cell cycle is inherited.

Answer

The general trend of the data show that the cell cycle decreases in length as the temperature increases, so **B** is the correct answer and **A** is incorrect. Answer choice **C** is incorrect because the table shows that temperature affects cell cycle length. The data in the table do not deal with inheritance, so **D** is incorrect.

Choose the letter of the best answer.

1. Which statement best describes chromosomes?
A They carry out respiration.
B They consist mostly of the pigment chlorophyll.
C Their structure is visible only during interphase.
D They consist of tightly coiled strands of DNA and proteins.

2. A scientist performed an experiment to determine the effect of temperature on the length of the cell cycle. On the basis of the data in the table below, how long would you expect the cell cycle to be at 5°C ?
F less than 13.3 hours
G more than 54.6 hours
H between 29.8 and 54.6 hours
J about 20 hours

Effect of Temperature on Length of Onion Cell Cycle

Temperature (°C)	Length of Cell Cycle (hours)
10	54.6
15	29.8
20	18.8
25	13.3

3. Which of the following statements is true?
A Plants cannot respire because they have no mitochondria.
B Photosynthesis produces energy.
C Animals cannot photosynthesize.
D Only plants photosynthesize and only animals respire.

4. Which of the following nitrogen base pairs can be found in DNA?
F A-G
G T-C
H G-T
J A-T

Constructed Response

5. Explain the relationship between cell division and cancer. How do scientists believe cancer starts? What causes a tumor to form?

Standardized Test Practice

1. D **2.** G **3.** C **4.** J

5. Possible answer: Cancer is a disease in which cells grow and divide uncontrollably, so cancer involves an abnormal rate of cell division. Cancer begins with a mutation, when DNA is damaged. The mutation causes the cell to divide in an uncontrolled way. A tumor forms when an abnormal cell multiplies, forming a mass of abnormal cells.

Thinking Critically

18. The ash from the volcano would block the sun and prevent plants from using its energy to make food. Plants would die out, and the animals and other organisms that get their energy from plants would die out as well.

19. Breathing brings oxygen into the body for respiration. Cellular respiration uses the oxygen to break down food and provide energy for the body's needs.

20. Yes, plants need to carry out respiration to get the energy they need for their cell processes. Photosynthesis provides sugars, which are used in respiration to generate energy.

21. The bases on the other strand would be TGCAGC.

22. You could explain how smoking is related to lung cancer and other types of cancer.

Applying Skills

23. The bars in the graph should correspond to the percentages in the table. There should be four bars for each organism.

24. The percents of adenine and thymine are equal. The percents of guanine and cytosine also are equal.

25. Sample: In all of the organisms, adenine is paired with thymine and guanine is paired with cytosine.

26. The percentage of cytosine must equal the percentage of guanine, so together, they equal 56%. The percentages of all four must add up to 100%. The percentages of thymine and adenine must be half of the remaining bases, or 44%. Therefore, the percentage of nitrogen bases that are thymine would be 22%.

Chapter at a Glance

PRENTICE HALL TeacherEXPRESS™ Plan • Teach • Assess

Technology | **Local Standards**

All in the Family

All in One Teaching Resources
- Chapter Project Teacher Notes, pp. 166–167
- Chapter Project Student Overview, pp. 168–169
- Chapter Project Student Worksheets, pp. 170–171
- Chapter Project Scoring Rubric, p. 172

Discovery Channel School Video Preview

Mendel's Work

2–3 periods
1–1 1/2 blocks

C3.1.1 Describe the results of Mendel's experiments.
C3.1.2 Identify what controls the inheritance of traits in organisms.

Probability and Heredity

2–3 periods
1–1 1/2 blocks

C3.2.1 Define probability and describe how it helps explain the results of genetic crosses.
C3.2.2 Explain what is meant by genotype and phenotype.
C3.2.3 Tell what codominance is.

The Cell and Inheritance

2–3 periods
1–1 1/2 blocks

C3.3.1 Describe the role chromosomes play in inheritance.
C3.3.2 Identify the events that occur during meiosis.
C3.3.3 Explain the relationship between chromosomes and genes.

The DNA Connection

2–3 periods
1–1 1/2 blocks

C3.4.1 Explain what forms the genetic code.
C3.4.2 Describe how a cell produces proteins.
C3.4.3 Identify how mutations can affect an organism.

Video Field Trip

Review and Assessment

All in One Teaching Resources
- Key Terms Review, p. 207
- Transparency C32
- Performance Assessment Teacher Notes, p. 214
- Performance Assessment Scoring Rubric, p. 215
- Performance Assessment Student Worksheets, p. 216
- Chapter Test, pp. 217–220

Video Assesment

Test Preparation

Test Preparation Blackline Masters

Chapter Activities Planner

Student Edition	Inquiry	Time	Materials	Skills	Resources
Chapter Project, p. 75	Open-Ended	2 to 3 weeks	All in One **Teaching Resources,** p. 166	Making models, inferring, predicting, communicating	**Lab zone Easy Planner** All in One **Teaching Resources,** Support pp. 166–167
Section 1					
Discover Activity, p. 76	Guided	10 minutes	none	Inferring	**Lab zone Easy Planner**
Skills Activity, p. 80	Guided	5 minutes	none	Predicting	**Lab zone Easy Planner**
Skills Lab, pp. 82–83	Directed	40 minutes	mirror (optional)	Developing hypotheses, observing, interpreting data	**Lab zone Easy Planner** All in One **Teaching Resources,** Skills Lab: *Take a Class Survey,* pp. 180–182
Section 2					
Discover Activity, p. 84	Directed	15 minutes	coin	Predicting	**Lab zone Easy Planner**
Try This Activity, p. 86	Directed	15 minutes	2 coins, masking tape, scissors	Interpreting data	**Lab zone Easy Planner**
Skills Lab, pp. 90–91	Guided	40 minutes	2 small paper bags, marking pen, 3 blue marbles, 3 white marbles	Making models, interpreting data, predicting	**Lab zone Easy Planner** All in One **Teaching Resources,** Skills Lab: *Make the Right Call!,* pp. 190–192
Section 3					
Discover Activity, p. 92	Directed	10 minutes	4 craft sticks, 3 pieces of paper, marking pen	Making models	**Lab zone Easy Planner**
Section 4					
Discover Activity, p. 97	Guided	15 minutes	none	Forming operational definitions	**Lab zone Easy Planner**
Skills Activity, p. 99	Guided	5 minutes	none	Drawing conclusions	**Lab zone Easy Planner**

Section 1 Mendel's Work

 *2–3 periods, 1–1 1/2 blocks*

ABILITY LEVELS
- L1 Basic to Average
- L2 For All Students
- L3 Average to Advanced

Local Standards

Objectives

C.3.1.1 Describe the results of Mendel's experiments.

C.3.1.2 Identify what controls the inheritance of traits in organisms.

Key Terms

• heredity • trait • genetics • fertilization • purebred • gene • alleles
• dominant allele • recessive allele • hybrid

Preteach

Build Background Knowledge

Invite students to share observations about the physical similarities and differences among family members.

 *What Does the Father Look Like?* 

Targeted Print and Technology Resources

- L2 Reading Strategy Transparency C24: Outlining

 **PresentationExpress™ CD-ROM**

Instruct

Mendel's Experiments Discuss the results of Mendel's experiments.

Dominant and Recessive Alleles Ask leading questions to identify the role of genes in inheritance.

 *Take a Class Survey* 

Targeted Print and Technology Resources

All in One Teaching Resources

- L2 Guided Reading, pp. 175–177
- L2 Transparency C25
- L2 Skills Lab: *Take a Class Survey,* pp. 180–182

Skills Lab: *Take a Class Survey*

PHSchool.com Web Code: ced-3031

Student Edition on Audio CD

Assess

Section Assessment Questions

Have students use their completed outlines of the section to help them answer the questions.

Reteach

As a class, construct the crosses for the F_1 and F_2 generation for a particular trait.

Targeted Print and Technology Resources

All in One Teaching Resources

- Section Summary, p. 174
- L1 Review and Reinforce, p. 178
- L3 Enrich, p. 179

Section 2 Probability and Heredity

2–3 periods, 1–1 1/2 blocks

ABILITY LEVELS
- L1 Basic to Average
- L2 For All Students
- L3 Average to Advanced

Objectives

C.3.2.1 Define probability and describe how it helps explain the results of genetic crosses.

C.3.2.2 Explain what is meant by genotype and phenotype.

C.3.2.3 Tell what codominance is.

Key Terms

• probability • Punnett square • phenotype • genotype • homozygous
• heterozygous • codominance

Local Standards

Preteach

Build Background Knowledge

Invite students to describe situations in which they have used a coin toss to decide an issue.

Discover Activity *What's the Chance?*  L1

Targeted Print and Technology Resources

All in One Teaching Resources
- L2 Reading Strategy: Building Vocabulary

PresentationExpress™ CD-ROM

Instruct

Principles of Probability Define probability and apply it to a coin toss.

Probability and Genetics Use diagrams to explain how Punnett squares use probability to predict the results of genetic crosses.

Phenotypes and Genotypes Define phenotype and genotype, and apply to an example.

Codominance Define codominance and contrast it to complete dominance by creating patterns.

Skills Lab *Make the Right Call!* L2

Targeted Print and Technology Resources

All in One Teaching Resources
- L2 Guided Reading, pp. 185–187
- L2 Skills Lab: *Make the Right Call!* pp. 190–192
- L2 Transparency C26

Lab Activity Video/DVD
Skills Lab: *Make the Right Call!*

www.SciLinks.org Web Code: scn-0332

Student Edition on Audio CD

Assess

Section Assessment Questions

Have students use their definitions to answer the questions.

Reteach

Use Punnett squares to review the principles of probability.

Targeted Print and Technology Resources

All in One Teaching Resources
- Section Summary, p. 184
- L1 Review and Reinforce, p. 188
- L3 Enrich, p. 189

ABILITY LEVELS
L1 Basic to Average
L2 For All Students
L3 Average to Advanced

Section 3 The Cell and Inheritance

2–3 periods, 1–1 1/2 blocks

Local Standards

Objectives

C.3.3.1 Describe the role chromosomes play in inheritance.
C.3.3.2 Identify the events that occur during meiosis.
C.3.3.3 Explain the relationship between chromosomes and genes.

Key Term

- meiosis

Preteach

Build Background Knowledge

Have students predict the location of hereditary factors in the cell.

 *Which Chromosome Is Which?* L2

Targeted Print and Technology Resources

All in One Teaching Resources

L2 Reading Strategy Transparency C27: Identifying Supporting Evidence

PresentationExpress™ CD-ROM

Instruct

Chromosomes and Inheritance Explain the chromosomal theory of inheritance.

Meiosis Use a labeled diagram to describe how cells divide in each stage of meiosis.

A Lineup of Genes Use a diagram to explain how chromosomes and genes are related.

Targeted Print and Technology Resources

All in One Teaching Resources

L2 Guided Reading, pp. 195–196
L2 Transparency C28

www.SciLinks.org Web Code: scn-0333

Student Edition on Audio CD

Assess

Section Assessment Questions

Have students use their graphic organizers with evidence that chromosomes play a role in inheritance to help them answer the questions.

Reteach

Have students sketch the stages of meiosis, exchange with a partner, and put the sketches in order.

Targeted Print and Technology Resources

All in One Teaching Resources

- Section Summary, p. 194

L1 Review and Reinforce, p. 197
L3 Enrich, p. 198

Section 4 The DNA Connection

2–3 periods, 1–1 1/2 blocks

ABILITY LEVELS
- L1 Basic to Average
- L2 For All Students
- L3 Average to Advanced

Objectives

C.3.4.1 Explain what forms the genetic code.
C.3.4.2 Describe how a cell produces proteins.
C.3.4.3 Identify how mutations can affect an organism.

Key Terms

• messenger RNA • transfer RNA

Local Standards

Preteach

Build Background Knowledge

Ask students to recall what they have learned about inheritance, DNA, and cell division, and to predict how genes determine traits.

Can You Crack the Code? 

Targeted Print and Technology Resources

All in One Teaching Resources
- L2 Reading Strategy Transparency C29: Sequencing

 **PresentationExpress™ CD-ROM**

Instruct

The Genetic Code Ask students questions to help them understand that genes carry genetic codes for making proteins.

How Cells Make Proteins Guide a discussion on how cells produce proteins.

Mutations Have students analyze how mutations occur and apply that knowledge by making models.

Targeted Print and Technology Resources

All in One Teaching Resources
- L2 Guided Reading, pp. 201–204
- L2 Transparencies C30, C31

PHSchool.com Web Code: cep-3034

Video Field Trip

Student Edition on Audio CD

Assess

Section Assessment Questions

Have students use their flowcharts sequencing the steps in protein synthesis to answer the questions.

Reteach

Use diagrams to summarize the structure of DNA and how cells make proteins.

Targeted Print and Technology Resources

All in One Teaching Resources
- Section Summary, p. 200
- L1 Review and Reinforce, p. 205
- L3 Enrich, p. 206

Chapter 3 Content Refresher

Section 1 Mendel's Work

The Law of Segregation As the textbook indicates, when Mendel saw the recessive short-stem trait reappear in the F_2 generation of pea plants, he suspected that each trait was controlled by two factors, now called alleles, one coming from each parent. He also thought that some alleles are dominant and others are recessive.

Mendel then reasoned that the each tall F_2 pea plant must have one of two allele combinations, *TT* or *Tt*. Mendel's next cross was inspired. He carefully self-pollinated each tall F_2 plant to produce an F_3 generation. Mendel predicted that if he was right about genes being paired and how they were passed along, some F_2 tall plants, when self-pollinated, should produce some short plants in the F_3 generation. Sure enough, a portion of the F_3 offspring were short.

Mendel's final conclusions, later formally codified into Mendel's First Law, or The Law of Segregation and Dominance, were as follows.

a. Each of the selected garden pea traits is controlled by a pair of alleles.
b. For each trait, an offspring receives one allele from one parent and one allele from the other.
c. The chance of offspring receiving one or the other allele from each pair is equal.
d. The expression of a dominant trait requires only one dominant allele; the expression of a recessive trait requires two recessive alleles.

Before Mendel, no plant breeder had even come close to understanding these basic principles of heredity. His conclusions qualify for the status of scientific law because after 150 years of testing, they are known to apply dependably to all sexually reproducing organisms, including humans.

Section 2 Probability and Heredity

Reginald C. Punnett The Punnett square was devised in the early 1900s by the English geneticist Reginald C. Punnett. Punnett studied at the University of Cambridge under the biologist William Bateson. Bateson had recognized that the results of his breeding experiments were perfectly explained by Mendel's principles. Bateson and Punnett were among the first to show that Mendel's principles were also applied to animals. Punnett wrote the first textbook on the subject of Mendel's principles of genetics, called *Mendelism,* in 1905.

Incomplete Dominance Incomplete dominance is a pattern of inheritance in which neither allele is fully dominant. This is different from codominance, in which both alleles are fully expressed, resulting in organisms that display the characteristics of both parents. Incomplete dominance results in organisms that have an intermediate phenotype. For example, in four o'clock flowers, a cross between a homozygous red-flowered plant and a homozygous white flowered plant produces F_1 offspring with pink flowers. When the F_1 offspring are crossed, the F_2 offspring are in a ratio of 1 red : 2 pink : 1 white.

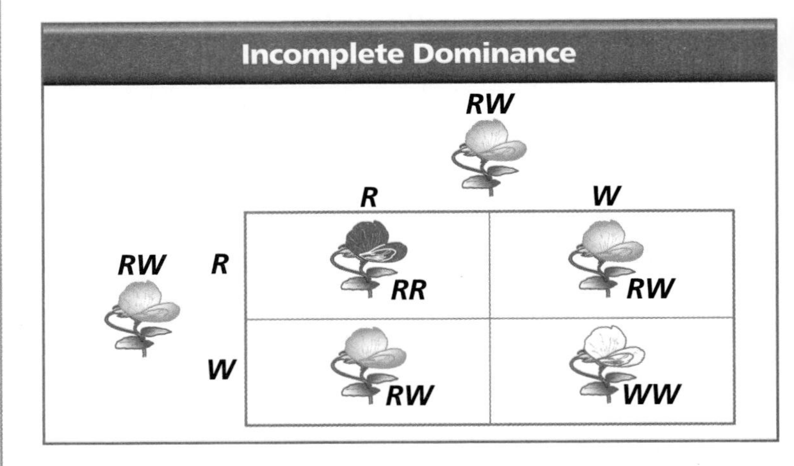

Section 3 The Cell and Inheritance

Crossing Over Before the first division of meiosis occurs, an important event, called crossing over, takes place. In crossing over, corresponding segments of chromosome pairs are exchanged, as shown in the illustration on the following page. In effect, the organism's maternal and paternal chromosomes exchange some alleles, producing some chromosomes that are genetically different from those of either parent of the organism. This increases the genetic diversity of a species.

Crossing over occurs randomly, but the farther apart genes are located on their chromosomes, the more often crossing over will occur between them. Geneticists use this principle to map the location of genes on chromosomes.

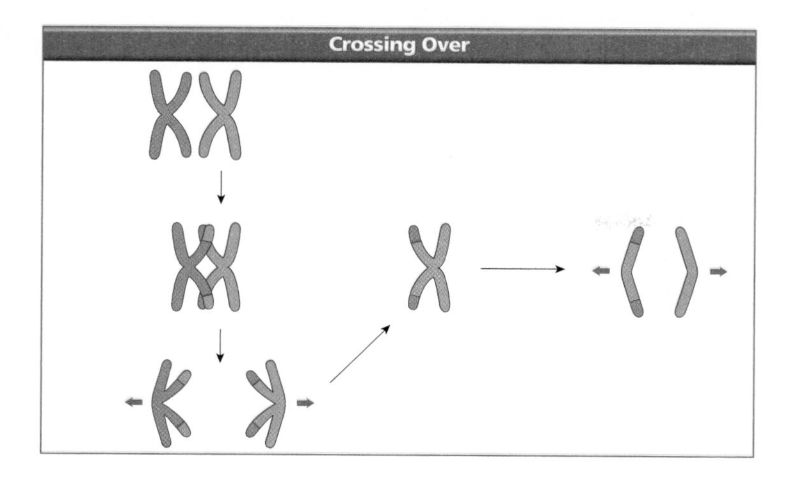

Section 4 The DNA Connection

Transcription and Translation Transcription is the process by which RNA is produced using a single-stranded DNA template. Messenger RNA, transfer RNA, and ribosomal RNA are all transcribed in the nuclei of eukaryotic cells and then pass into the cytoplasm. Ribosomal RNA and proteins make up the structures of ribosomes, the organelles where proteins are made.

Translation is the production of proteins on the ribosomes. Often, several ribosomes are attached to the same messenger RNA molecule. The ribosome holds both the messenger RNA with its genetic information and the transfer RNAs with their attached amino acids in position to allow a specific protein chain to form.

Mutations in DNA Different types of changes in the base sequence of DNA affect the organism in different ways. A frameshift mutation occurs when a base is inserted or deleted from a gene. To understand what happens to a gene that has undergone a frameshift mutation, consider the following sentence:

THE DOG WAS TOO FAT.

Note that each word in the sentence consists of three letters; this is similar to the code in DNA, in which a three-base sequence codes for an amino acid. If one letter in the sentence above, the E, is lost, the sentence might be read as follows:

THD OGW AST OOF AT.

As you can see, the sentence no longer makes sense. Similarly, when one base is lost from a gene or added to it, the gene's code may no longer function normally. The result of a frameshift mutation may be a nonfunctional protein.

Sometimes one base is substituted for another. This kind of mutation affects only one codon, which has variable effects on the protein product. Sometimes it has no effect because most amino acids are encoded by more than one codon. The protein may have a reduced function because one amino acid is substituted for the correct one. Other times the protein will not work at all, either because the codon has been changed to a stop codon or the amino acid that is substituted completely changes the nature of the protein.

Address Misconceptions

Some students may think that mutations can only be harmful to organisms. However, some mutations can be harmless or even helpful to an organism. For a strategy for helping to overcome this misconception, see **Address Misconceptions** in the section The DNA Connection.

Help Students Read

Think Aloud

Verbalize Thought Processes While Reading

Strategy Model processes that students can use to build meaning, self-correct, and monitor their own comprehension. Choose part of a section for this chapter, and preview it. As you do so, imagine that you are reading these paragraphs for the first time, just as your students will be. Make a copy of the section, and on it write comments and questions that you can use as "think-aloud" models.

Example

1. Read several paragraphs aloud and have your students follow along silently. Have them listen to how you pause to check your own comprehension and to determine meaning at trouble spots. You might model some of the following strategies aloud as you read:
- Make a prediction, then revise or verify it.
- Describe mental pictures as they form.
- Connect new information with prior knowledge or related ideas; share an analogy.
- Verbalize confusing points and work out steps to clarify their meanings; adjust your reading pace if needed.

2. Select a logical stopping point. Distribute copies of the annotated section you prepared earlier.

3. Then, have students read the next paragraph silently and apply similar strategies internally. Afterward, ask students to share the strategies they used. Repeat this step several times.

- Complete student edition
- Video and audio
- Simulations and activities
- Section and chapter reviews

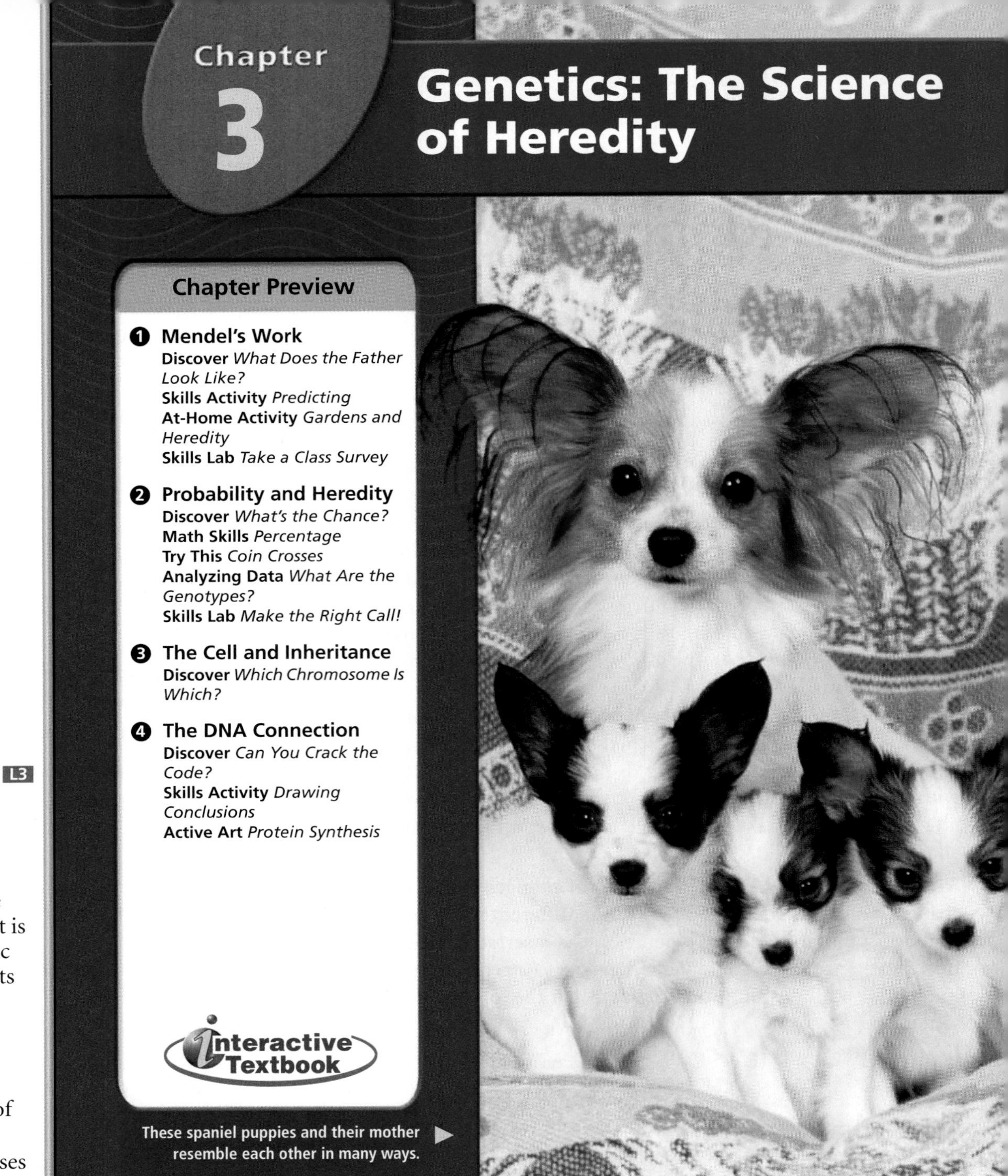

These spaniel puppies and their mother resemble each other in many ways.

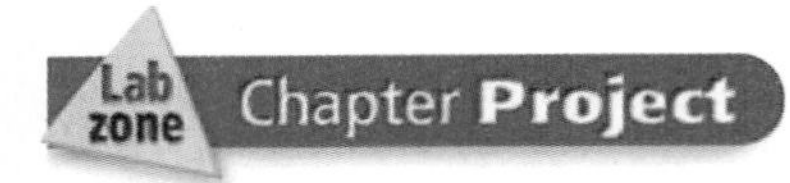

L3

Objectives

This project will give students an opportunity to create a family of "paper pets" based on phenotypes they have selected. Students will learn how traits are passed from parent to offspring and how it is possible to predict the outcomes of genetic crosses. After this Chapter Project, students will be able to

- model the inheritance of traits using a paper pet
- infer their pets' genotypes
- predict the genotypes and phenotypes of their pets' offspring
- communicate the results of genetic crosses in a class presentation

Skills Focus

Making models, inferring, predicting, communicating

Project Time Line 2 to 3 weeks

All in One Teaching Resources

- Chapter Project Teacher Notes
- Chapter Project Overview
- Chapter Project Worksheet 1
- Chapter Project Worksheet 2
- Chapter Project Scoring Rubric

Developing a Plan

Discuss the project with students and the materials they will need. Once they have created their pets, allow class time for students to set up crosses with another pet. Each pair can simply assume that one of their pets is female and the other is male. Then have students work with partners to determine the results of the crosses between their pets and create the offspring. Provide class time for students to prepare displays.

Possible Materials

- Students need blue or yellow construction paper for the pet's body, scissors, colored pencils, glue, markers, and posterboard.
- Encourage students to decorate their pets with additional materials that you provide or students bring from home, such as glitter, beads, feathers, sequins, yarn, and buttons.

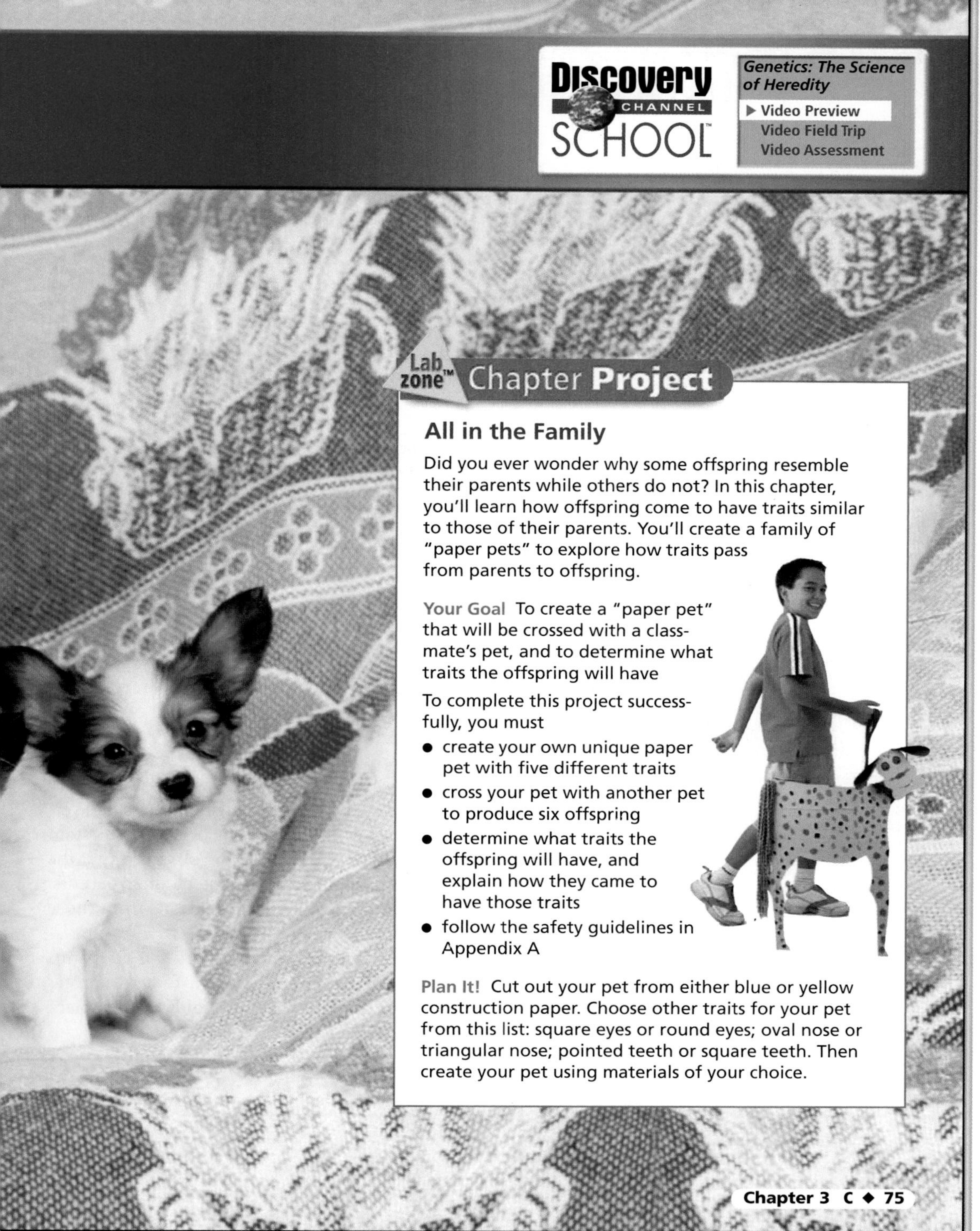

Chapter Project

All in the Family

Did you ever wonder why some offspring resemble their parents while others do not? In this chapter, you'll learn how offspring come to have traits similar to those of their parents. You'll create a family of "paper pets" to explore how traits pass from parents to offspring.

Your Goal To create a "paper pet" that will be crossed with a classmate's pet, and to determine what traits the offspring will have

To complete this project successfully, you must

- create your own unique paper pet with five different traits
- cross your pet with another pet to produce six offspring
- determine what traits the offspring will have, and explain how they came to have those traits
- follow the safety guidelines in Appendix A

Plan It! Cut out your pet from either blue or yellow construction paper. Choose other traits for your pet from this list: square eyes or round eyes; oval nose or triangular nose; pointed teeth or square teeth. Then create your pet using materials of your choice.

Genetics: The Science of Heredity

Show the Video Preview to introduce the topic of genetics.

Possible Shortcuts

You can simplify this project by having students record the phenotype and genotype of their pets on paper. Student pairs can set up Punnett squares for the crosses without making paper models of the pet parents and offspring.

Launching the Project

Invite students to look at the Chapter Opener photo. Ask: **How are these puppies similar to one other and to their mother? How are they different?** *(Accept all answers. Most students will describe similarities in the shape of the nose and ears and differences in color.)* Encourage students to offer explanations for these similarities and differences.

Performance Assessment

The Chapter Project Scoring Rubric will help you evaluate how well students complete the Chapter Project. You may want to share the scoring rubric with your students so they are clear about what will be expected of them. Students will be assessed on

- how neatly and creatively they design their paper pets
- how accurately they identify the phenotypes and genotypes of their pets and their offspring
- how effectively they design their display and explain it to the class

Section 1

Mendel's Work

Objectives

After this lesson, students will be able to

C.3.1.1 Describe the results of Mendel's experiments.

C.3.1.2 Identify what controls the inheritance of traits in organisms.

Target Reading Skill 

Outlining Explain that using an outline format helps students organize information by main topic, subtopic, and details.

Answer

Check students' outlines to make sure they include significant details. The beginning of the outlines should resemble the following:

I. Mendel's Experiments
  A. Crossing Pea Plants
    1. crossed plants with contrasting traits
    2. used only purebred plants

All in One Teaching Resources

- Transparency C24

Preteach

Build Background Knowledge L1

Family Resemblances

Invite students to share observations they have made about the physical similarities and differences among family members. Ask: **Have you ever wondered why some family members look very similar while others look very different?** *(Many students will have considered this in one way or another.)* Encourage students to share their ideas about the inheritance of traits in families. Be alert for misconceptions students might have, and address these throughout the section.

Section 1

Mendel's Work

Reading Preview

Key Concepts

- What were the results of Mendel's experiments, or crosses?
- What controls the inheritance of traits in organisms?

Key Terms

- heredity • trait • genetics
- fertilization • purebred • gene
- alleles • dominant allele
- recessive allele • hybrid

Target Reading Skill

Outlining As you read, make an outline about Mendel's work. Use the red headings for the main ideas and the blue headings for the supporting ideas.

Mendel's Work

I. Mendel's experiments
  A. Crossing pea plants
  B.
  C.

Lab zone Discover Activity

What Does the Father Look Like?

1. Observe the colors of the kitten in the photo. Record the kitten's coat colors and pattern. Include as many details as you can.
2. Observe the mother cat in the photo. Record her coat color and pattern.

Think It Over

Inferring Based on your observations, describe what you think the kitten's father might look like. Identify the evidence on which you based your inference.

In the mid nineteenth century, a priest named Gregor Mendel tended a garden in a central European monastery. Mendel's experiments in that peaceful garden would one day revolutionize the study of heredity. **Heredity** is the passing of physical characteristics from parents to offspring.

Mendel wondered why different pea plants had different characteristics. Some pea plants grew tall, while others were short. Some plants produced green seeds, while others had yellow seeds. Each different form of a characteristic, such as stem height or seed color, is called a **trait.** Mendel observed that the pea plants' traits were often similar to those of their parents. Sometimes, however, the plants had different traits from those of their parents.

Mendel experimented with thousands of pea plants to understand the process of heredity. Today, Mendel's discoveries form the foundation of **genetics,** the scientific study of heredity.

Gregor Mendel ▶

Lab zone Discover Activity

Skills Focus Inferring L1

Time 10 minutes

Materials none

Expected Outcome The mother cat's coat is gray and has a tiger pattern. The kitten's coat is orange and has a tiger pattern.

Think It Over Students will probably infer that the father may have orange fur. They may infer that the kitten has inherited its color from the father.

Mendel's Experiments

Figure 1 shows a pea plant's flower. The flower's petals surround the pistil and the stamens. The pistil produces female sex cells, or eggs. The stamens produce pollen, which contains the male sex cells, or sperm. A new organism begins to form when egg and sperm join in the process called **fertilization.** Before fertilization can happen in pea plants, pollen must reach the pistil of a pea flower. This process is called pollination.

Pea plants are usually self-pollinating. In self-pollination, pollen from a flower lands on the pistil of the same flower. Mendel developed a method by which he cross-pollinated, or "crossed," pea plants. To cross two plants, he removed pollen from a flower on one plant. He then brushed the pollen onto a flower on a second plant.

Crossing Pea Plants Suppose you wanted to study the inheritance of traits in pea plants. What could you do? Mendel decided to cross plants with contrasting traits—for example, tall plants and short plants. He started his experiments with purebred plants. A **purebred** organism is the offspring of many generations that have the same trait. For example, purebred short pea plants always come from short parent plants.

FIGURE 1
Crossing Pea Plants
Gregor Mendel crossed pea plants that had different traits. The illustrations show how he did this. **Interpreting Diagrams** *How did Mendel prevent self-pollination?*

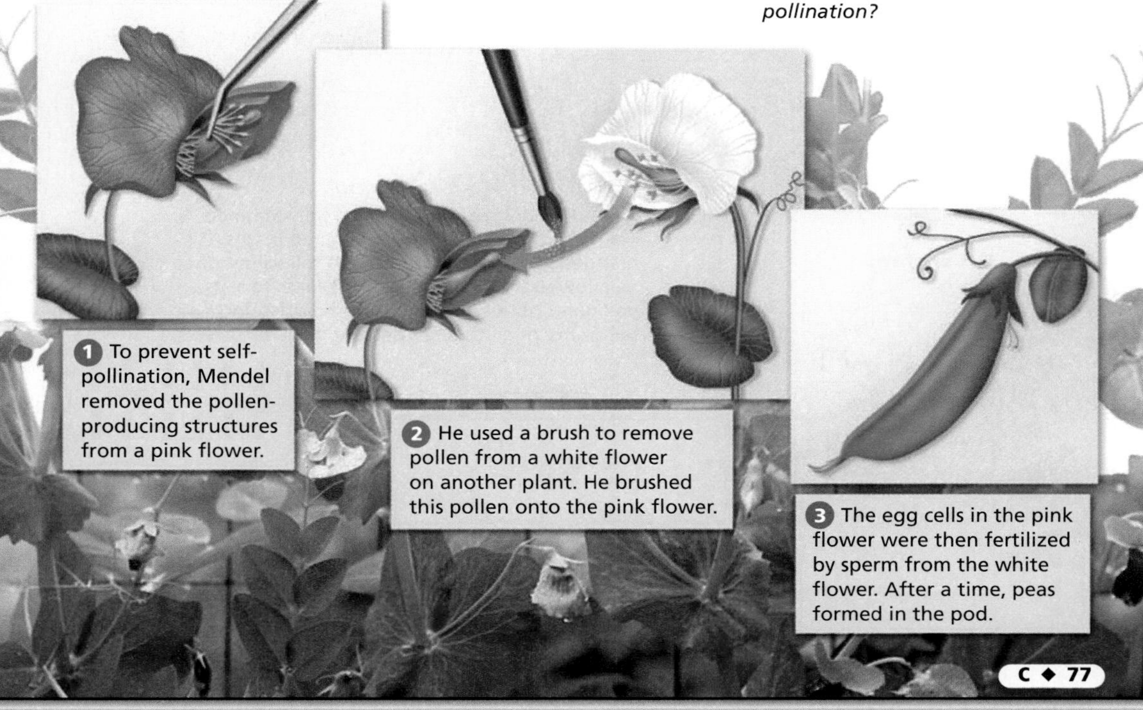

Instruct

Mendel's Experiments

Teach Key Concepts L2

Understanding Mendel's Crosses

Focus Tell students that every living thing has traits inherited from its parents. Until the work of Mendel, people did not understand how traits were passed from parents to offspring.

Teach Ask: **What is a purebred organism?** *(The offspring of many generations that have the same trait)* Ask: **What did Mendel find when he crossed purebred tall plants with purebred short plants?** *(The offspring were all tall.)* **When Mendel crossed the offspring, or F_1 generation, with one another, was the trait for shortness lost? Explain.** *(No; some of the offspring were tall, and some were short.)*

Apply Ask: **Are the plants in the F_1 generation purebred plants?** *(No; they were not all identical to the parent plants.)* **learning modality: visual**

Independent Practice L2

All in One Teaching Resources

- Guided Reading and Study Worksheet: *Mendel's Work*

Student Edition on Audio CD

Differentiated Instruction

English Learners/Beginning L1
Vocabulary: Prior Knowledge Write the word *trait* on the board, and say the word aloud. Show pictures of organisms in the text. Point to a few of them and say, for example, "This cat has the trait of black fur." Have students point to other traits. Then have them name the traits in Figure 3. **learning modality: visual**

English Learners/Intermediate L2
Vocabulary: Science Glossary Have students list and define the Key Terms in their science glossaries in English and in their native language, and include drawings. Students can add other terms to create a genetics dictionary, such as *factor, self-pollination,* and *cross.* **learning modality: verbal**

Monitor Progress L2

Writing Have students describe how fertilization takes place in a pea plant.

Answer
Figure 1 He removed the pollen-producing structures (stamens) from the flower.

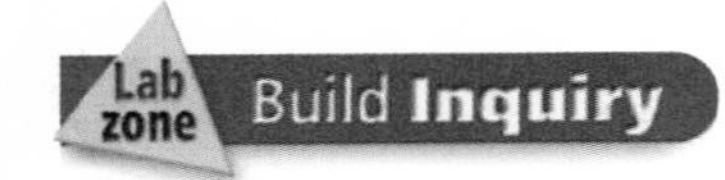

L2

Observing Pistils and Stamens

Materials tulip or lily flower, hand lens, small blunt-tipped scissors

Time 15 minutes

Focus Remind students that the pistil produces female sex cells and the stamens produce pollen, which contains male sex cells.

Teach Have students observe the intact flower with a hand lens, then snip apart the pistil and stamens with scissors and examine these parts individually. Ask students to draw a labeled diagram of the flower and its parts, and compare their diagrams with Figure 1.

Apply Ask: **Why are self-pollinating plants a better choice for studying inheritance?** *(Because it is easier to obtain purebreeding plants from them.)* **learning modality: kinesthetic**

Dominant and Recessive Alleles

Teach Key Concepts

L2

Factors That Control Inheritance

Focus Remind students that the trait of shortness did not disappear in the F_1 generation of pea plants.

Teach Explain that the factors that control traits exist in pairs. One factor can hide the other factor. Ask: **What are the factors that control inheritance of traits?** *(Genes)* **What are alleles?** *(The different forms of a gene.)* **What is a dominant allele?** *(An allele whose trait always shows up in the organism when it is present)* **What kind of allele can be hidden when a dominant allele is present?** *(A recessive allele)* **What kind of alleles does a hybrid organism have?** *(Both a dominant allele and a recessive allele)*

Apply Ask: **Why were purebred pea plants important for Mendel's experiments?** *(They have two identical alleles for a gene, so in a cross, each parent contributes one allele, making the inheritance pattern easier to detect.)* **learning modality: logical/mathematical**

The F_1 Offspring In one experiment, Mendel crossed purebred tall plants with purebred short plants. Scientists today call these parent plants the parental generation, or P generation. The offspring from this cross are the first filial (FIL ee ul) generation, or the F_1 generation. The word *filial* comes from *filia* and *filius*, the Latin words for "daughter" and "son."

In Figure 2, notice that all the offspring in the F_1 generation were tall. Even though one of the parent plants was short, none of the offspring were short. The shortness trait seemed to disappear!

The F_2 Offspring When the plants in the F_1 generation were full-grown, Mendel allowed them to self-pollinate. Surprisingly, the plants in the F_2 (second filial) generation were a mix of tall and short plants. The shortness trait had reappeared, even though none of the F_1 parent plants were short. Mendel counted the tall and short plants. About three fourths of the plants were tall, while one fourth were short.

Experiments With Other Traits Mendel also crossed pea plants with other contrasting traits. Compare the two forms of each trait in Figure 3. **In all of Mendel's crosses, only one form of the trait appeared in the F_1 generation. However, in the F_2 generation, the "lost" form of the trait always reappeared in about one fourth of the plants.**

Reading Checkpoint **What did Mendel observe about the F_2 plants?**

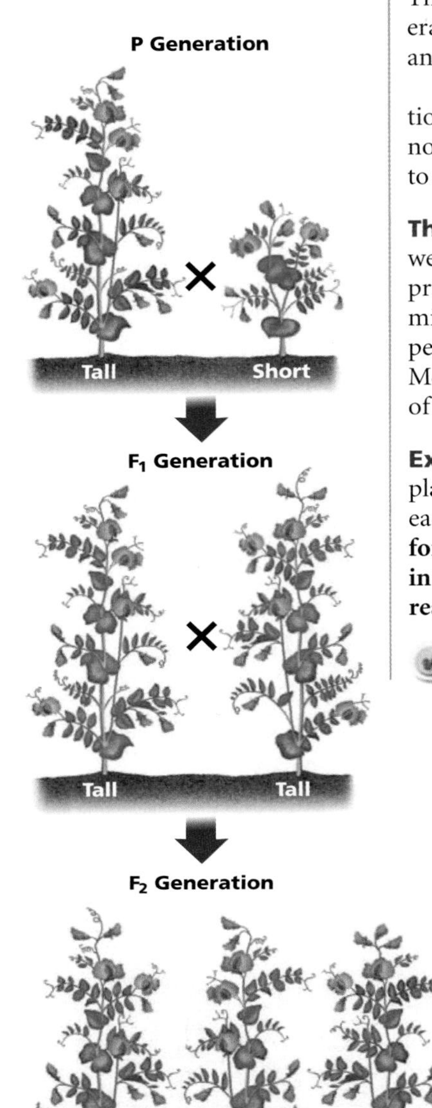

FIGURE 2
Results of a Cross
When Mendel crossed purebred tall-stemmed plants with purebred short-stemmed plants, the first-generation offspring all had tall stems. Then he allowed the first-generation plants to self-pollinate. About 75 percent of the offspring had tall stems, and about 25 percent had short stems.

Genetics of Pea Plants							
Traits	Seed Shape	Seed Color	Seed Coat Color	Pod Shape	Pod Color	Flower Position	Stem Height
Controlled by Dominant Allele	Round	Yellow	Gray	Smooth	Green	Side	Tall
Controlled by Recessive Allele	Wrinkled	Green	White	Pinched	Yellow	End	Short

Dominant and Recessive Alleles

Mendel reached several conclusions on the basis of his experimental results. He reasoned that individual factors, or sets of genetic "information," must control the inheritance of traits in peas. The factors that control each trait exist in pairs. The female parent contributes one factor, while the male parent contributes the other factor. Finally, one factor in a pair can mask, or hide, the other factor. The tallness factor, for example, masked the shortness factor.

Genes and Alleles Today, scientists use the word **gene** for the factors that control a trait. **Alleles** (uh LEELZ) are the different forms of a gene. The gene that controls stem height in peas, for example, has one allele for tall stems and one allele for short stems. Each pea plant inherits two alleles from its parents—one allele from the egg and the other from the sperm. A pea plant may inherit two alleles for tall stems, two alleles for short stems, or one of each.

An organism's traits are controlled by the alleles it inherits from its parents. Some alleles are dominant, while other alleles are recessive. A **dominant allele** is one whose trait always shows up in the organism when the allele is present. A **recessive allele,** on the other hand, is hidden whenever the dominant allele is present. A trait controlled by a recessive allele will only show up if the organism does not have the dominant allele. Figure 3 shows dominant and recessive alleles in Mendel's crosses.

FIGURE 3
Mendel studied several traits in pea plants.
Interpreting Diagrams *Is yellow seed color controlled by a dominant allele or a recessive allele?*

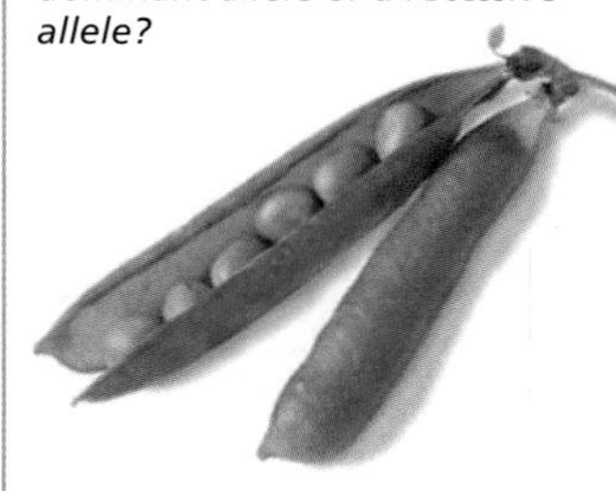

Use Visuals: Figure 3 L2

Pea Plant Crosses

Focus Remind students that the traits in pea plants have two distinct forms.

Teach Direct students' attention to the trait of seed shape. Ask: **What does it mean for this trait to be dominant?** *(If a plant has two alleles for round or one allele for round and one for wrinkled, you would get a pea plant that has a round seed shape.)*

Apply Have students choose a pea trait and use the symbols for alleles to diagram the crosses that Mendel made. **learning modality: visual**

All in One Teaching Resources

- Transparency C25

L3

Inferring the Parent Generation

Materials F_2 ear of corn with purple and yellow kernels (available from science supply companies)

Time 15 minutes

Focus Explain that the ears were produced by F_2 generation plants. The purple color is controlled by the dominant allele, and yellow is controlled by the recessive allele.

Teach Give each small group an ear of corn. Challenge them to trace the inheritance of the dominant and recessive alleles for kernel color by working backward from the F_2 ear to the F_1 cross and finally to the parental cross. *(F_1 parents: both purple (*—Pp; *P parents: one purple* —PP, *one yellow* —pp*)*

Apply Ask: ***What kind of corn can you conclude looks like what you normally eat?*** *(Yellow corn, which has two recessive alleles,* (pp)*)* **learning modality: logical/ mathematical**

Differentiated Instruction

Gifted and Talented L3

Describing the Scientific Method
Challenge students to create a poster on which they identify Mendel's question and hypothesis and outline his experimental design. Groups can also include a summary of their opinions about Mendel's procedures. **learning modality: visual**

Less Proficient Readers L1

Mapping Key Terms Help students make a concept map in which they show the relationships among the key terms in this section. Ask them to include the definitions on the map. You may wish to pair students with more proficient readers to construct the map. **learning modality: visual**

Monitor Progress L2

Skills Check Have students compare and contrast dominant and recessive alleles.

Answers

Figure 3 Dominant

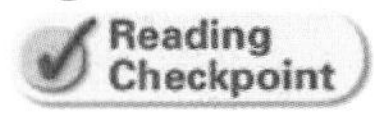

The "lost" form of the trait reappeared in about one-fourth of the plants.

Lab zone **Teacher Demo** L3

Observing Crosses in Fruit Flies

Materials 2 *Drosophila melanogaster* cultures—wild-type and ebony, culture vials and plugs, *Drosophila* media, nonether anesthesia kit, hand lens, paint brush, white index card, marking pen (Note: *Drosophila* cultures are available from science supply companies.)

Advance Preparation

Set up the parental cross about two weeks in advance by placing 2 to 3 ebony males with 2 to 3 wild-type virgin females in each of three vials. To collect virgin females, remove all adult flies from the culture vial. Then, within 4 to 6 hours, collect the newly emerged females. Females have pointed abdomens with stripes almost to the end. Males have rounded abdomens that are black at the end. Anesthetize flies to sort them and to set up the crosses. Place vials on their sides until the flies wake up. Remove parent flies from the vials when pupae begin to develop. When F_1 adults begin to emerge, remove the flies daily to prevent F_2 offspring from mixing with F_1 offspring. Dispose of flies in a jar of mineral oil. Empty this "morgue" into a garbage disposal.

Time 20 minutes

Focus Review that a recessive trait can show only if two recessive alleles for the trait are present in a gene.

Teach Anesthetize the parent flies and place them on index cards for students to examine. *CAUTION: Students should not work with anesthesia.* Ask: **How do these flies differ?** *(Ebony flies have darker bodies than wild-type flies.)* Challenge students to predict which trait is controlled by a dominant allele and which is controlled by a recessive allele. Then anesthetize the F_1 flies and place them on index cards for students to count. Ask: **Which trait is controlled by a dominant allele?** *(Lighter body color)* **How do you know?** *(None of the F_1 flies have ebony bodies.)* **What body color will F_2 flies have?** *(Some will have ebony bodies, but most will have lighter bodies.)*

Apply Ask students to use symbols for alleles to write out the cross that you have demonstrated and the cross that would produce an F_2 generation. **learning modality: logical/mathematical**

Lab zone **Skills Activity**

Predicting

In fruit flies, long wings are dominant over short wings. A scientist crossed a purebred long-winged male fruit fly with a purebred short-winged female. Predict the wing length of the F_1 offspring. If the scientist crossed a hybrid male F_1 fruit fly with a hybrid F_1 female, what would their offspring probably be like?

In pea plants, the allele for tall stems is dominant over the allele for short stems. Pea plants with one allele for tall stems and one allele for short stems will be tall. The allele for tall stems masks the allele for short stems. Only pea plants that inherit two recessive alleles for short stems will be short.

Alleles in Mendel's Crosses In Mendel's cross for stem height, the purebred tall plants in the P generation had two alleles for tall stems. The purebred short plants had two alleles for short stems. The F_1 plants each inherited an allele for tall stems from the tall parent and an allele for short stems from the short parent. Therefore, each F_1 plant had one allele for tall stems and one for short stems. The F_1 plants are called hybrids. A **hybrid** (HY brid) organism has two different alleles for a trait. All the F_1 plants are tall because the dominant allele for tall stems masks the recessive allele for short stems.

When Mendel crossed the F_1 plants, some of the offspring in the F_2 generation inherited two dominant alleles for tall stems. These plants were tall. Other F_2 plants inherited one dominant allele for tall stems and one recessive allele for short stems. These plants were also tall. The rest of the F_2 plants inherited two recessive alleles for short stems. These plants were short.

Symbols for Alleles Geneticists use letters to represent alleles. A dominant allele is represented by a capital letter. For example, the allele for tall stems is represented by *T*. A recessive allele is represented by the lowercase version of the letter. So, the allele for short stems would be represented by *t*. When a plant inherits two dominant alleles for tall stems, its alleles are written as *TT*. When a plant inherits two recessive alleles for short stems, its alleles are written as *tt*. When a plant inherits one allele for tall stems and one allele for short stems, its alleles are written as *Tt*.

FIGURE 4
Black Fur, White Fur
In rabbits, the allele for black fur is dominant over the allele for white fur. **Inferring** *What combination of alleles must the white rabbit have?*

Lab zone **Skills Activity**

Skills Focus Predicting L2

Materials none

Time 5 minutes

Tips Have students write out the crosses using *L* for the dominant allele and *l* for the recessive allele.

Expected Outcome The F_1 offspring will all have long wings. The F_2 generation will produce three fourths with long wings and one fourth with short wings.

Extend Have students determine what kind of cross would produce half the offspring with long wings and half with short wings. *(A hybrid fruit fly and a purebred short-winged fruit fly)* **learning modality: logical/mathematical**

Significance of Mendel's Contribution Mendel's discovery of genes and alleles eventually changed scientists' ideas about heredity. Before Mendel, most people thought that the traits of an individual organism were simply a blend of their parents' characteristics. According to this idea, if a tall plant and a short plant were crossed, the offspring would all have medium height.

However, when Mendel crossed purebred tall and purebred short pea plants, the offspring were all tall. Mendel's experiments demonstrated that parents' traits do not simply blend in the offspring. Instead, traits are determined by individual, separate alleles inherited from each parent. Some of these alleles, such as the allele for short height in pea plants, are recessive. If a trait is determined by a recessive allele, the trait can seem to disappear in the offspring.

Unfortunately, the importance of Mendel's discovery was not recognized during his lifetime. Then, in 1900, three different scientists rediscovered Mendel's work. These scientists quickly recognized the importance of Mendel's ideas. Because of his work, Mendel is often called the Father of Genetics.

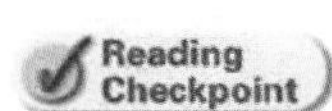
If an allele is represented by a capital letter, what does this indicate?

FIGURE 5
The Mendel Medal
Every year, to honor the memory of Gregor Mendel, an outstanding scientist is awarded the Mendel Medal.

Section 1 Assessment

Target Reading Skill Outlining Use the information in your outline about Mendel's work to help you answer the questions below.

Reviewing Key Concepts

1. a. Identifying In Mendel's cross for stem height, what contrasting traits did the pea plants in the P generation exhibit?
   b. Explaining What trait or traits did the plants in the F_1 generation exhibit? When you think of the traits of the parent plants, why is this result surprising?
   c. Comparing and Contrasting Contrast the offspring in the F_1 generation to the offspring in the F_2 generation. What did the differences in the F_1 and F_2 offspring show Mendel?
2. a. Defining What is a dominant allele? What is a recessive allele?
   b. Relating Cause and Effect Explain how dominant and recessive alleles for the trait of stem height determine whether a pea plant will be tall or short.
   c. Applying Concepts Can a short pea plant ever be a hybrid for the trait of stem height? Why or why not? As part of your explanation, write the letters that represent the alleles for stem height of a short pea plant.

Lab zone At-Home Activity

Gardens and Heredity Some gardeners save the seeds produced by flowers and plant them in the spring. If there are gardeners in your family, ask them how closely the plants that grow from these seeds resemble the parent plants. Are the offspring's traits ever different from those of the parents?

Monitor Progress L2

Answers

Figure 4 Two recessive alleles

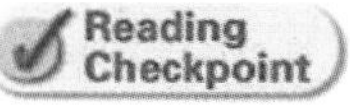
It is a dominant allele.

Assess

Reviewing Key Concepts

1. a. Tall and short **b.** All of the plants in the F_1 generation were tall. You might expect some of the offspring to be short like one of the parent plants. **c.** The F_2 generation was 75% tall and 25% short, while the F_1 generation was 100% tall. Individual factors, or sets of genetic information, must control the inheritance of traits in peas. These factors exist in pairs. Each parent contributes one factor. And one factor can hide another factor.

2. a. Dominant allele: an allele in which a trait always shows up when the allele is present; recessive allele: an allele in which a trait is masked whenever the dominant allele is present **b.** If the plant has two dominant alleles for stem height (*TT*), then it is tall. If the plant has two recessive alleles for stem height (*tt*), it is short. If the plant is a hybrid (*Tt*), it is tall. **c.** No, a short plant has two recessive alleles (*tt*); hybrids have two different alleles for a trait (*Tt*). A hybrid would appear tall because the tall allele is dominant. L1

Reteach

With the class, construct the crosses for the F_1 and F_2 generation for a particular trait. Identify the dominant and recessive alleles. L2

Performance Assessment

Writing Have students summarize Mendel's experiments and his conclusions about the inheritance of traits.

All in One Teaching Resources

- Section Summary: *Mendel's Work*
- Review and Reinforce: *Mendel's Work*
- Enrich: *Mendel's Work*

Lab zone At-Home Activity

Gardens and Heredity L1 Many seeds available in stores, such as foxgloves and lupines, are hybrids. Planting the seeds produced by the flowers of hybrid plants can result in offspring with traits that appear different from the original plants. Some plants will appear the same as the parent plants.

Lab zone Chapter Project

Keep Students on Track Check that students have constructed their paper pets and that students have correctly assigned pairs of alleles based on the traits they chose. The dominant alleles for the four traits are *B* (blue skin), *R* (round eyes), *T* (triangular nose), and *P* (pointed teeth). Make sure the numbers of male and female pets are equal.

Take a Class Survey L2

Prepare for Inquiry

Key Concept
Human traits are controlled by dominant and recessive alleles, causing many different combinations of traits among a group of people.

Skills Objectives
Students will be able to
- develop hypotheses about whether traits controlled by dominant alleles are more common than traits controlled by recessive alleles
- make observations and interpret data about certain traits controlled by dominant and recessive alleles in humans

Class Time 40 minutes

- Lab Worksheet: *Take a Class Survey*

Advance Planning
Gather mirrors, or invite students to bring some from home. You might wish to make photocopies of the circle chart and the data table.

Alternative Materials
If you do not have mirrors, students can observe one other.

Guide Inquiry

Invitation
Ask: **Why do you think people often look very similar to other family members, but also different?** *(Students should realize that children inherit both dominant and recessive alleles from each parent. The combination of these alleles determines the child's physical appearance.)*

Lab zone Skills Lab

For: Data sharing
Visit: PHSchool.com
Web Code: ced-3031

Take a Class Survey

Problem
Are traits controlled by dominant alleles more common than traits controlled by recessive alleles?

Skills Focus
developing hypotheses, interpreting data

Materials
- mirror (optional)

Procedure

PART 1 Dominant and Recessive Alleles

1. Write a hypothesis reflecting your ideas about the problem. Then copy the data table.
2. For each of the traits listed in the data table, work with a partner to determine which trait you have. Circle that trait in your data table.
3. Count the number of students in your class who have each trait. Record that number in your data table. Also record the total number of students.

PART 2 Are Your Traits Unique?

4. Look at the circle of traits on the opposite page. All the traits in your data table appear in the circle. Place the eraser end of your pencil on the trait in the small central circle that applies to you—either free ear lobes or attached ear lobes.
5. Look at the two traits touching the space your eraser is on. Move your eraser onto the next description that applies to you. Continue using your eraser to trace your traits until you reach a number on the outside rim of the circle. Share that number with your classmates.

Analyze and Conclude

1. **Observing** The traits listed under Trait 1 in the data table are controlled by dominant alleles. The traits listed under Trait 2 are controlled by recessive alleles. Which traits controlled by dominant alleles were shown by a majority of students? Which traits controlled by recessive alleles were shown by a majority of students?

Free ear lobe

Widow's peak

Cleft chin

Dimple

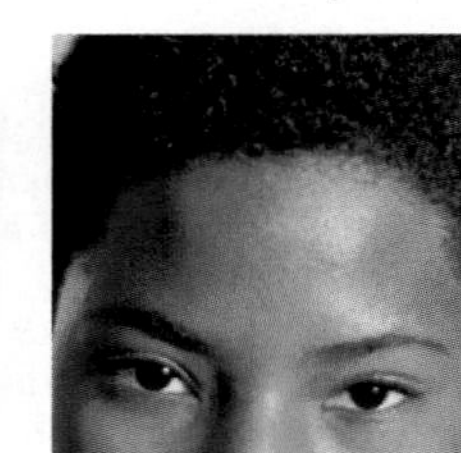
Attached ear lobe

No widow's peak

No cleft chin

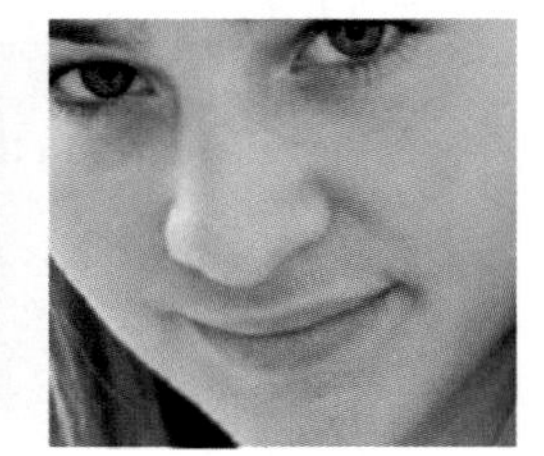
No dimple

82 ◆ C

Introduce the Procedure
- Have students read through the entire procedure. Then review with them what each trait looks like. Refer students to the photos in the text, or find examples of each trait among the class. Tell students that curly hair includes wavy hair or any hair that is not straight.
- Make sure students know how to use the circle of traits in Part 2. Point out how to use the color-coding, starting at the center of the circle.

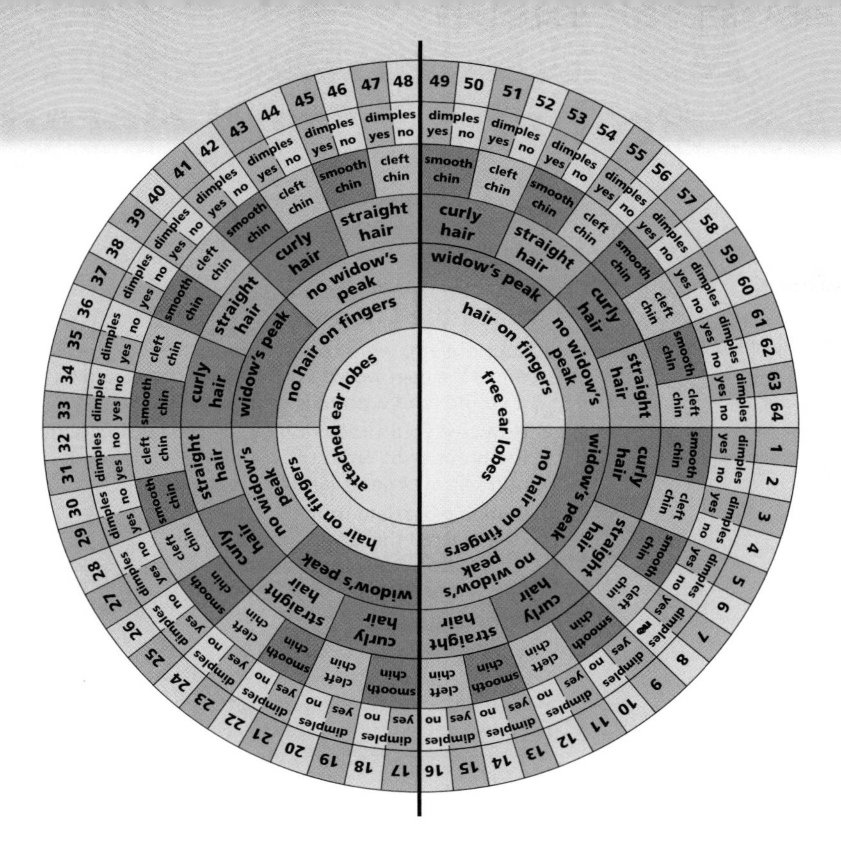

2. **Interpreting Data** How many students ended up on the same number on the circle of traits? How many students were the only ones to have their number? What do the results suggest about each person's combination of traits?
3. **Developing Hypotheses** Do your data support the hypothesis you proposed in Step 1? Write an answer with examples.

Design an Experiment

Do people who are related to each other show more genetic similarity than unrelated people? Write a hypothesis. Then design an experiment to test your hypothesis. *Obtain your teacher's permission before carrying out your investigation.*

Data Table				
Total Number of Students_________				
	Trait 1	Number	Trait 2	Number
A	Free ear lobes		Attached ear lobes	
B	Hair on fingers		No hair on fingers	
C	Widow's peak		No widow's peak	
D	Curly hair		Straight hair	
E	Cleft chin		Smooth chin	
F	Smile dimples		No smile dimples	

Troubleshooting the Experiment

- Monitor students as they work to make sure they correctly identify each trait.
- The class can record their results on a large data table on the chalkboard by writing their initials in the appropriate columns.

Expected Outcome

Students will show a great variation in traits. Few, if any, will have the same number on the circle of traits.

Analyze and Conclude

1. One trait controlled by a dominant allele that is usually more common is free earlobes. Some traits controlled by recessive alleles that are usually more common include smooth chin, straight hair, no widow's peak, and no mid-finger hair. However, any class's results may vary from the overall population patterns because of the small sample size.
2. Answers will vary, but usually few or no students have the same number when six traits are studied. The more traits that are considered, the smaller the chance that any two people in a class will have the same number. Even siblings, except identical twins, have different combinations of traits.
3. Answers will vary, but answers should include examples from the lab to explain that neither traits controlled by dominant alleles nor traits controlled by recessive alleles are automatically more common in a population.

Extend Inquiry

Design an Experiment Students' hypotheses will vary. *Possible hypothesis:* A group of related people will share more numbers on the circle of traits than a group of unrelated people. Student experiments can follow the same procedure as this lab, except students would observe the traits in people from a single family.

For: Data sharing
Visit: PHSchool.com
Web Code: ced-3031

Students can share data online.

Section 2

Probability and Heredity

Objectives

After this lesson, students will be able to

C.3.2.1 Define probability and describe how it helps explain the results of genetic crosses.

C.3.2.2 Explain what is meant by genotype and phenotype.

C.3.2.3 Tell what codominance is.

Target Reading Skill

Building Vocabulary Explain that knowing the definitions of key-concept words helps students understand what they read.

Answers

Call on volunteers to read their definitions aloud. Make sure that students have explained the definitions in their own words.

Preteach

Build Background Knowledge

L1

Coin Tosses and Probability

Invite students to describe situations in which they have used a coin toss to decide an issue. Ask: **Why did you toss a coin in these situations?** *(Possible answer: It was the fairest way to make a decision.)* **Why is a coin toss fair?** *(Each person has a 50–50 chance of winning.)*

For: Links on probability and genetics
Visit: www.SciLinks.org
Web Code: scn-0332

Download a worksheet to guide students' review of probability and genetics.

Section 2

Integrating Mathematics

Probability and Heredity

Reading Preview

Key Concepts

- What is probability and how does it help explain the results of genetic crosses?
- What is meant by genotype and phenotype?
- What is codominance?

Key Terms

- probability
- Punnett square
- phenotype
- genotype
- homozygous
- heterozygous
- codominance

Target Reading Skill

Building Vocabulary After you read the section, reread the paragraphs that contain definitions of Key Terms. Use all the information you have learned to write a definition of each Key Term in your own words.

For: Links on probability and genetics
Visit: www.SciLinks.org
Web Code: scn-0332

Lab zone Discover Activity

What's the Chance?

1. Suppose you were to toss a coin 20 times. Predict how many times the coin would land with heads up and how many times it would land with tails up.
2. Now test your prediction by tossing a coin 20 times. Record the number of times the coin lands with heads up and the number of times it lands with tails up.
3. Combine the data from the entire class. Record the total number of tosses, the number of heads, and the number of tails.

Think It Over

Predicting How did your results in Step 2 compare to your prediction? How can you account for any differences between your results and the class results?

On a brisk fall afternoon, the stands are packed with cheering football fans. Today is the big game between Riverton's North and South high schools, and it's almost time for the kickoff. Suddenly, the crowd becomes silent, as the referee is about to toss a coin. The outcome of the coin toss will decide which team kicks the ball and which receives it. The captain of the visiting North High team says "heads." If the coin lands with heads up, North High wins the toss and the right to decide whether to kick or receive the ball.

What is the chance that North High will win the coin toss? To answer this question, you need to understand the principles of probability.

Principles of Probability

If you did the Discover activity, you used the principles of **probability** to predict the results of a particular event. In this case, the event was the toss of a coin. **Probability is a number that describes how likely it is that an event will occur.**

Lab zone Discover Activity

Skills Focus Predicting

Materials coin

Time 15 minutes

Expected Outcome The outcome of the coin tosses will vary. The more data, the closer the outcome will be to the expected ratio of one "heads" to one "tails."

Think It Over For most students, their results were slightly different from their predictions. The combined class data should be closer to the expected ratio of one "heads" to one "tails." Students might infer that the difference is due to chance or that the more coin tosses they make, the closer they will come to the predicted outcome.

Mathematics of Probability Each time you toss a coin, there are two possible ways that the coin can land—heads up or tails up. Each of these two events is equally likely to occur. In mathematical terms, you can say that the probability that a tossed coin will land with heads up is 1 in 2. There is also a 1 in 2 probability that the coin will land with tails up. A 1 in 2 probability can also be expressed as the fraction $\frac{1}{2}$ or as a percent—50 percent.

The laws of probability predict what is likely to occur, not necessarily what will occur. If you tossed a coin 20 times, you might expect it to land with heads up 10 times and with tails up 10 times. However, you might not get these results. You might get 11 heads and 9 tails, or 8 heads and 12 tails. The more tosses you make, the closer your actual results will be to the results predicted by probability.

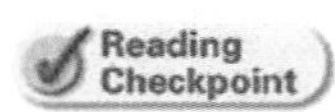

What is probability?

Independence of Events When you toss a coin more than once, the results of one toss do not affect the results of the next toss. Each event occurs independently. For example, suppose you toss a coin five times and it lands with heads up each time. What is the probability that it will land with heads up on the next toss? Because the coin landed heads up on the previous five tosses, you might think that it would be likely to land heads up on the next toss. However, this is not the case. The probability of the coin landing heads up on the next toss is still 1 in 2, or 50 percent. The results of the first five tosses do not affect the result of the sixth toss.

Math Skills

Percentage

One way you can express a probability is as a percentage. A percentage (%) is a number compared to 100. For example, 50% means 50 out of 100.

Suppose that 3 out of 5 tossed coins landed with heads up. Here's how you can calculate what percent of the coins landed with heads up.

1. Write the comparison as a fraction.
   $$3 \text{ out of } 5 = \frac{3}{5}$$
2. Multiply the fraction by 100% to express it as a percentage.
   $$\frac{3}{5} \times \frac{100\%}{1} = 60\%$$

Practice Problem Suppose 3 out of 12 coins landed with tails up. How can you express this as a percent?

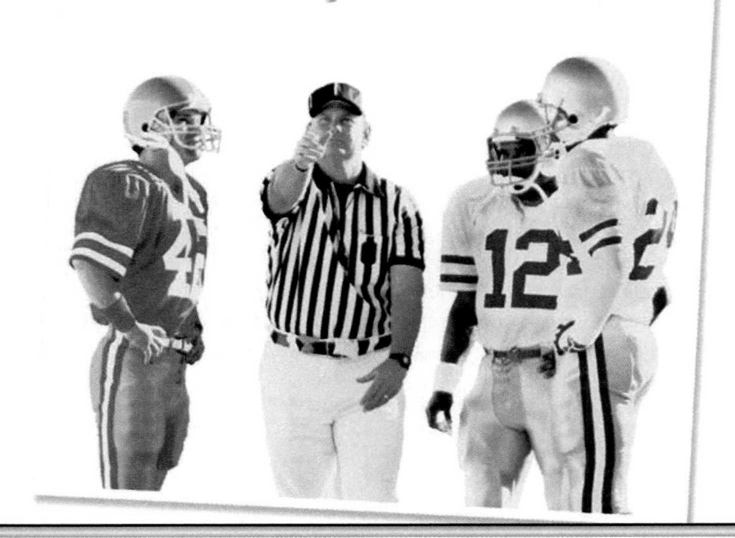

FIGURE 6
A Coin Toss
The result of a coin toss can be explained by probability.

Instruct

Principles of Probability

Teach Key Concepts L2

Understanding Probability

Focus Use the Discover activity to focus attention on probability.

Teach Explain that Mendel used the principles of probability to explain his results. Ask: **What is probability?** *(A number that describes how likely it is that on event will occur)* **Does probability predict what will definitely occur?** *(No; it predicts what is likely to occur.)*

Apply Ask: **What does probability predict is likely to occur if you toss a coin ten times?** *(The coin will land heads up 5 times and tails up 5 times.)* **learning modality: verbal**

Math Practice

Skills Focus Percentage

Focus Remind students that a percentage can be expressed as a fraction.

Teach Point out that 5 in the denominator is the total number of parts that make up 100%. Use 5 coins to demonstrate so that students can see that the total number is 5, not 8 (3 + 5). Show how 60% is 300% divided by 5%.

Answer
25%

Independent Practice L2

Teaching Resources

- Guided Reading and Study Worksheet: *Probability and Heredity*

Student Edition on Audio CD

Differentiated Instruction

Less Proficient Readers L1

Personalizing Study Aids Have students create flash cards for each of the Key Terms. One side will have the definition. The other side will have the word and mnemonic devices, pictures, or verbal clues that help in recalling the meaning of the term. For example, *genotype* and *genetics* begin with the same prefix, and *physical* and *phenotype* begin with *ph*. To remember the meaning of the term *Punnett square*, students might draw a Punnett square for a hybrid cross. **learning modality: verbal**

Monitor Progress L2

Oral Presentation Ask students to describe the principles of probability.

Answer

A number that describes how likely it is that an event will occur

Probability and Genetics

Help Students Read (L2)

Active Comprehension Read the first paragraph on this page. Ask: **What more would you like to know about probability and genetics?** Help students make connections between probability and their daily lives, such as weather forecasts. As students read the section, have them consider their questions. After reading, have students discuss the section, making sure each question is answered or that students know where to look for the answer.

Teach Key Concepts (L2)

Probability Explains Genetic Crosses

Focus Remind students that the outcome of tossing a coin is based on probability.

Teach Ask: **How is this similar to the outcome of a genetic cross?** *(The allele that each parent will pass on to its offspring is based on probability.)* **What tool can be used to predict the results of a cross?** *(A Punnett square, a chart that shows all the possible combinations of alleles that can result from a genetic cross)* Refer students to Figure 7, and have student volunteers read each step. Point out that combinations are simply pairings of the male and female alleles from a particular row and column.

Apply Challenge students to devise a Punnett square that illustrates the possible offspring in a cross between a purebred pea plant whose seeds have gray coats and a purebred pea plant whose seeds have white coats. Students can also make Punnett squares showing a cross between the hybrid offspring of the first cross. **learning modality: logical/mathematical**

All in One Teaching Resources

- Transparency C26

FIGURE 7

How to Make a Punnett Square

The diagrams show how to make a Punnett square. In this cross, both parents are heterozygous for the trait of seed shape. *R* represents the dominant round allele, and *r* represents the recessive wrinkled allele.

1. Start by drawing a box and dividing it into four squares.

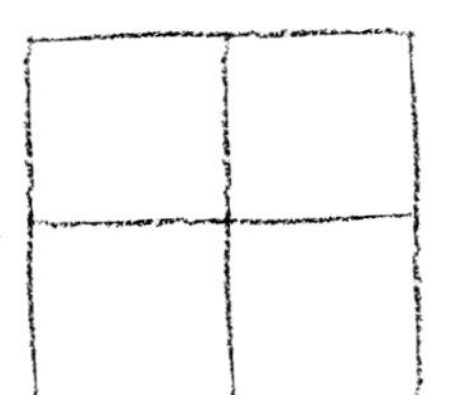

2. Write the male parent's alleles along the top of the square and the female parent's alleles along the left side.

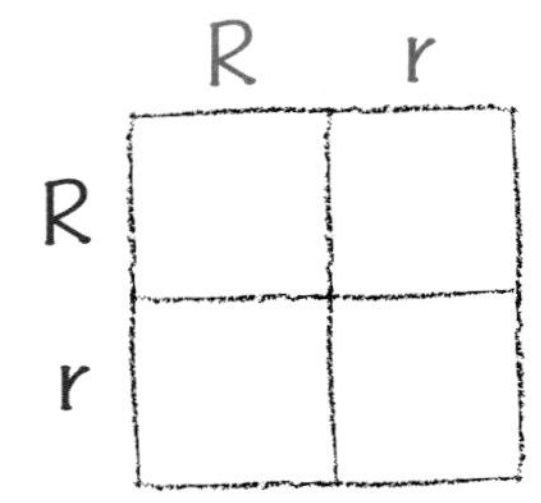

Probability and Genetics

How is probability related to genetics? To answer this question, think back to Mendel's experiments with peas. Remember that Mendel carefully counted the offspring from every cross that he carried out. When Mendel crossed two plants that were hybrid for stem height (*Tt*), three fourths of the F_1 plants had tall stems. One fourth of the plants had short stems.

Each time Mendel repeated the cross, he obtained similar results. Mendel realized that the mathematical principles of probability applied to his work. He could say that the probability of such a cross producing a tall plant was 3 in 4. The probability of producing a short plant was 1 in 4. Mendel was the first scientist to recognize that the principles of probability can be used to predict the results of genetic crosses.

Punnett Squares A tool that can help you understand how the laws of probability apply to genetics is called a Punnett square. A **Punnett square** is a chart that shows all the possible combinations of alleles that can result from a genetic cross. Geneticists use Punnett squares to show all the possible outcomes of a genetic cross, and to determine the probability of a particular outcome.

Figure 7 shows how to construct a Punnett square. In this case, the Punnett square shows a cross between two hybrid pea plants with round seeds (*Rr*). The allele for round seeds (*R*) is dominant over the allele for wrinkled seeds (*r*). Each parent can pass either of its alleles, *R* or *r*, to its offspring. The boxes in the Punnett square represent the possible combinations of alleles that the offspring can inherit.

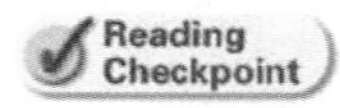

What is a Punnett square?

Lab zone Try This Activity

Coin Crosses

Here's how you can use coins to model Mendel's cross between two *Tt* pea plants.

1. Place a small piece of masking tape on each side of two coins.
2. Write a *T* (for tall) on one side of each coin and a *t* (for short) on the other.
3. Toss both coins together 20 times. Record the letter combinations that you obtain from each toss.

Interpreting Data How many of the offspring would be tall plants? (*Hint:* What different letter combinations would result in a tall plant?) How many would be short? Convert your results to percentages. Then compare your results to Mendel's.

Lab zone Try This Activity

Skills Focus Interpreting data (L1)

Materials 2 coins, masking tape, scissors

Time 15 minutes

Expected Outcome 5 *TT*, 10 *Tt*, 5 *tt*; All plants that are *TT* and *Tt* will be tall, approximately 15, or 75%. All *tt* plants will be short, approximately 5, or 25%. Some students might observe that their results are similar to Mendel's results.

Extend Let students toss both coins another 20 times and observe whether their percentages are closer to Mendel's results. **learning modality: logical/mathematical**

3 Copy the female parent's alleles into the boxes to their right.

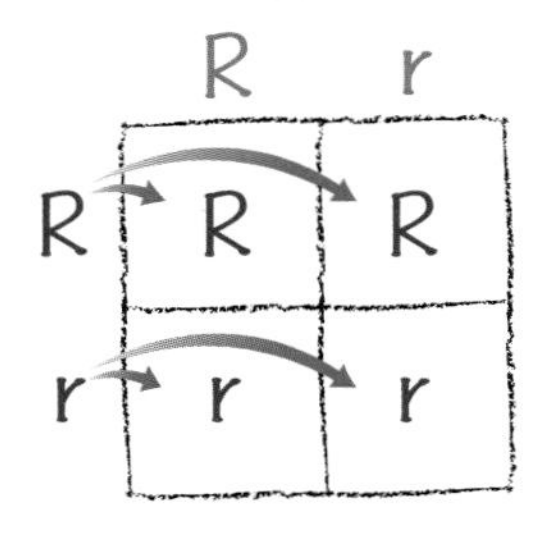

4 Copy the male parent's alleles into the boxes beneath them.

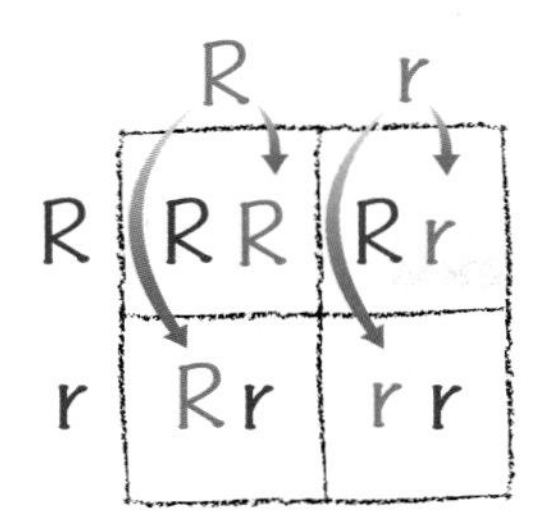

5 The completed Punnett square shows all the possible allele combinations in the offspring.

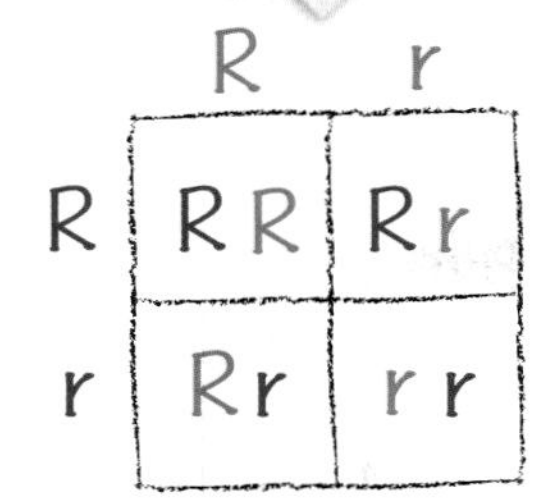

Using a Punnett Square You can use a Punnett square to calculate the probability that offspring with a certain combination of alleles will result. **In a genetic cross, the allele that each parent will pass on to its offspring is based on probability.** The completed Punnett square in Figure 7 shows four possible combinations of alleles. The probability that an offspring will be *RR* is 1 in 4, or 25 percent. The probability that an offspring will be *rr* is also 1 in 4, or 25 percent. Notice, however, that the *Rr* allele combination appears in two boxes in the Punnett square. This is because there are two possible ways in which this combination can occur. So the probability that an offspring will be *Rr* is 2 in 4, or 50 percent.

When Mendel crossed hybrid plants with round seeds, he discovered that about three fourths of the plants (75 percent) had round seeds. The remaining one fourth of the plants (25 percent) produced wrinkled seeds. Plants with the *RR* allele combination would produce round seeds. So too would those plants with the *Rr* allele combination. Remember that the dominant allele masks the recessive allele. Only those plants with the *rr* allele combination would have wrinkled seeds.

Predicting Probabilities You can use a Punnett square to predict probabilities. For example, Figure 8 shows a cross between a purebred black guinea pig and a purebred white guinea pig. The allele for black fur is dominant over the allele for white fur. Notice that only one allele combination is possible in the offspring—*Bb*. All of the offspring will inherit the dominant allele for black fur. Because of this, all of the offspring will have black fur. There is a 100 percent probability that the offspring will have black fur.

FIGURE 8
Guinea Pig Punnett Square
This Punnett square shows a cross between a black guinea pig (*BB*) and a white guinea pig (*bb*).
Calculating *What is the probability that an offspring will have white fur?*

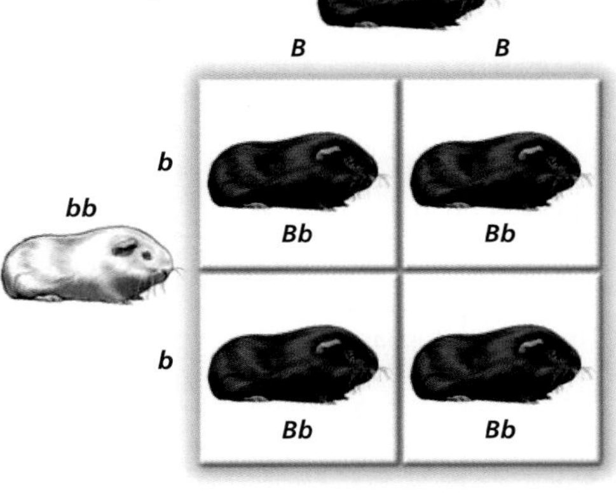

Use Visuals: Figure 8 L2

Interpreting Punnett Squares

Focus Remind students that a Punnett square identifies possible gene combinations.

Teach Have students identify the alleles that each parent could pass on to the offspring. (BB *and* bb) Walk through each column and row to make sure students understand how the alleles combine. Ask: **Why are all the offspring black?** *(Black is the dominant allele, and all the offspring have it.)*

Apply Ask: **What percent of the F_2 offspring are likely to be black?** *(75%)* **learning modality: visual**

L1

Observing Crosses in Tobacco Plants

Materials F_2 tobacco seeds that produce green (*GG, Gg*) and albino (*gg*) seedlings in a ratio of 3:1, seed starting soil, shallow pan, plastic wrap, water. Order the seeds from a science supply house, and plant them 7 to 14 days in advance, or as directed on the packet.

Time 15 minutes

Focus Explain that a cross between two hybrid green tobacco plants (*Gg* and *Gg*) produces both green and white offspring.

Teach Draw a Punnett square of this cross; 75% of the seedlings are likely to be green and 25% are likely to be white. Have students count the numbers of green and white seedlings from the F_2 seeds you planted and compare those numbers to the predictions.

Apply Ask students to explain why the numbers may not match. *(The Punnett square just predicts the probability. The actual combinations could be different.)* **learning modality: logical/mathematical**

Differentiated Instruction

Special Needs L1

Understanding Independence of Events Provide one student in a pair with four pipe cleaners of different lengths, but all the same color. Ask the student to hold them so that they all appear to be the same length. Ask: **What is the chance that the longest pipe cleaner will be chosen?** *(1 out of 4, or 25%)* Have the other student test this answer, and then replace the pipe cleaner. Ask if the probability is still 25% that the same pipe cleaner will be chosen if he or she draws again. *(Yes)* Explain that this models how events occur independently. Have students repeat this exercise as needed to understand the concept. **learning modality: kinesthetic**

Monitor Progress L2

Drawing Have students draw a Punnett square for a cross between any two hybrids (*Aa* × *Aa*) and include the probabilities of each offspring type.

Answers

Figure 8 0%

Reading Checkpoint A chart that shows all the possible combinations of alleles that can result from a genetic cross

Phenotypes and Genotypes

Teach Key Concepts

L2

Comparing Phenotype and Genotype

Focus Review that a hybrid has a recessive allele but shows the dominant trait.

Teach Ask: **What is a phenotype?** *(An organism's physical appearance)* **What is a genotype?** *(An organism's genetic makeup)* **What is the term used to describe an organism whose genotype consists of two identical alleles for a trait?** *(Homozygous)* **What term is used to describe an organism whose genotype consists of two different alleles for a trait?** *(Heterozygous)*

Apply Ask: **Why can you be certain of the genotype of an organism that shows a recessive trait?** *(It must have a homozygous recessive genotype, because the recessive allele is not hidden by a dominant allele.)* **learning modality: logical/mathematical**

Math Analyzing Data

Math Skill Making and interpreting graphs

Focus Point out that bar graphs are often used to compare different types of data.

Teach Ask: **What two types of data are being compared in the graph?** *(Numbers of plants with yellow seeds and with green seeds)*

Answers

1. 6,000 yellow; 2,000 green
2. 8,000; 75% have yellow peas and 25% have green peas.
3. Both parents probably had the genotype *Bb*.

Codominance

Teach Key Concepts

Focus Refer students to Figure 10.

Teach Ask: **Which alleles are expressed in these offspring?** *(Both)* **What is codominance?** *(In codominance, the alleles are neither dominant nor recessive.)*

Apply Have students create colored patterns comparing genotypes and phenotypes in simple dominance and in codominance. **learning modality: visual**

Math Analyzing Data

What Are the Genotypes?

Mendel allowed several F_1 pea plants with yellow seeds to self-pollinate. The graph shows the approximate numbers of the F_2 offspring with yellow seeds and with green seeds.

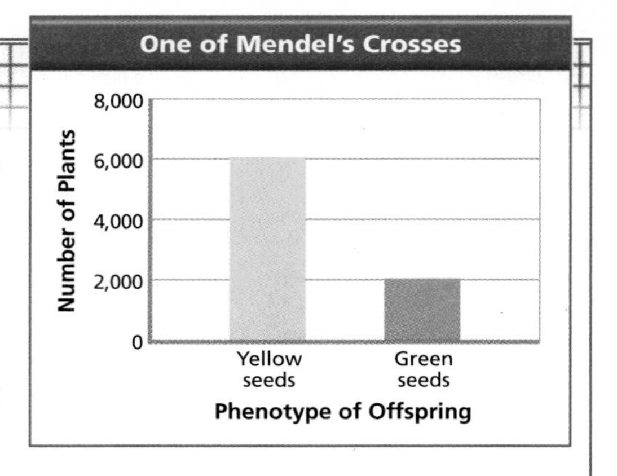

1. **Reading Graphs** How many F_2 offspring had yellow seeds? How many had green seeds?
2. **Calculating** Use the information in the graph to calculate the total number of offspring that resulted from this cross. Then calculate the percentage of the offspring with yellow peas, and the percentage with green peas.
3. **Inferring** Use the answers to Question 2 to infer the probable genotypes of the parent plants. (*Hint:* Construct Punnett squares with the possible genotypes of the parents.)

Phenotypes and Genotypes

Two useful terms that geneticists use are **phenotype** (FEE noh typ) and **genotype** (JEN uh typ). **An organism's phenotype is its physical appearance, or visible traits. An organism's genotype is its genetic makeup, or allele combinations.**

To understand the difference between phenotype and genotype, look at Figure 9. The allele for smooth pea pods (*S*) is dominant over the allele for pinched pea pods (*s*). All of the plants with at least one dominant allele have the same phenotype—they all produce smooth pods. However, the plants can have two different genotypes—*SS* or *Ss*. If you were to look at the plants with smooth pods, you would not be able to tell the difference between those with the *SS* genotype and those with the *Ss* genotype. The plants with pinched pods, on the other hand, would all have the same phenotype—pinched pods—as well as the same genotype—*ss*.

Geneticists use two additional terms to describe an organism's genotype. An organism that has two identical alleles for a trait is said to be **homozygous** (hoh moh ZY gus) for that trait. A smooth-pod plant that has the alleles *SS* and a pinched-pod plant with the alleles *ss* are both homozygous. An organism that has two different alleles for a trait is **heterozygous** (het ur oh ZY gus) for that trait. A smooth-pod plant with the alleles *Ss* is heterozygous. Mendel used the term *hybrid* to describe heterozygous pea plants.

SS *Ss* *ss*

Phenotypes and Genotypes

Phenotype	Genotype
Smooth pods	*SS*
Smooth pods	*Ss*
Pinched pods	*ss*

FIGURE 9
The phenotype of an organism is its physical appearance. Its genotype is its genetic makeup.
Interpreting Tables *How many genotypes are there for the smooth-pod phenotype?*

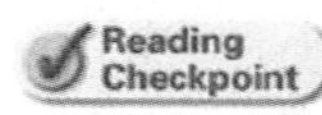

If a pea plant's genotype is *Ss*, what is its phenotype?

Codominance

For all of the traits that Mendel studied, one allele was dominant while the other was recessive. This is not always the case. For some alleles, an inheritance pattern called **codominance** exists. **In codominance, the alleles are neither dominant nor recessive. As a result, both alleles are expressed in the offspring.**

Look at Figure 10. Mendel's principle of dominant and recessive alleles does not explain why the heterozygous chickens have both black and white feathers. The alleles for feather color are codominant—neither dominant nor recessive. As you can see, neither allele is masked in the heterozygous chickens. Notice also that the codominant alleles are written as capital letters with superscripts—F^B for black feathers and F^W for white feathers. As the Punnett square shows, heterozygous chickens have the $F^B F^W$ allele combination.

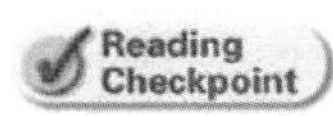

How are the symbols for codominant alleles written?

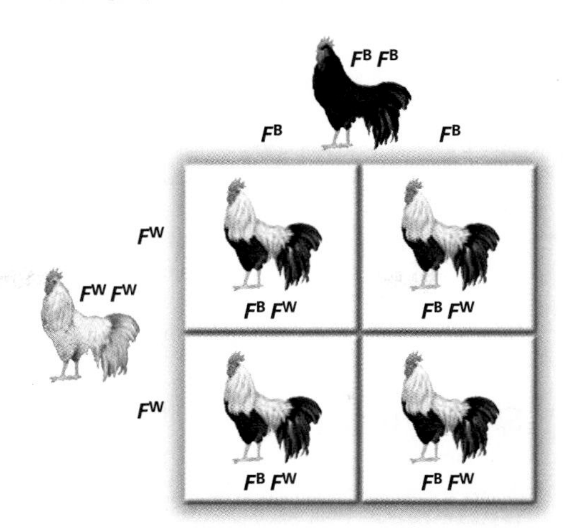

FIGURE 10
Codominance
The offspring of the cross in this Punnett square will have both black and white feathers.
Classifying *Will the offspring be heterozygous or homozygous? Explain your answer.*

Section 2 Assessment

Target Reading Skill Building Vocabulary Use your definitions to help you answer the questions.

Reviewing Key Concepts

1. a. Reviewing What is probability?
   b. Explaining If you know the parents' alleles for a trait, how can you use a Punnett square to predict the probable genotypes of the offspring?
   c. Predicting A pea plant with round seeds has the genotype *Rr*. You cross this plant with a wrinkled-seed plant, genotype *rr*. What is the probability that the offspring will have wrinkled seeds? (Use a Punnett square to help with the prediction.)
2. a. Defining Define *genotype* and *phenotype*.
   b. Relating Cause and Effect Explain how two organisms can have the same phenotype but different genotypes. Give an example.
   c. Applying Concepts A pea plant has a tall stem. What are its possible genotypes?
3. a. Explaining What is codominance? Give an example of codominant alleles and explain why they are codominant.
   b. Applying Concepts What is the phenotype of a chicken with the genotype $F^B F^W$?

Math Practice

4. Ratios A scientist crossed a tall pea plant with a short pea plant. Of the offspring, 13 were tall and 12 were short. Write the ratio of each phenotype to the total number of offspring. Express the ratios as fractions.
5. Percentage Use the fractions to calculate the percentage of the offspring that were tall and the percentage that were short.

Monitor Progress L2

Answers
Figure 9 Two
Figure 10 Heterozygous; they have alleles for white and black feathers.
Reading Checkpoint Smooth pods
Reading Checkpoint Capital letters with superscripts

Assess

Reviewing Key Concepts

1. a. A number that describes how likely it is that an event will occur **b.** A Punnett square shows all the possible combinations of alleles that can result from a genetic cross.
c. 50%; Punnett square should show two *Rr* and two *rr* possibilities.

2. a. Genotype—an organism's genetic makeup; phenotype—an organism's physical appearance **b.** A heterozygous organism will have the same phenotype as an organism that is homozygous for a dominant allele. For example, tall pea plants can be either heterozygous (*Tt*) or homozygous (*TT*).
c. *TT* or *Tt*

3. a. An inheritance pattern in which alleles for a trait are neither dominant nor recessive. For example, the alleles for black and white chicken feathers are codominant because both colors show **b.** Black and white feathers

Math Practice

4. $\frac{13}{25}$ and $\frac{12}{25}$
5. 52% and 48%

Reteach L1

Use the Punnett squares in this section to review the principles of probability.

All in One Teaching Resources L1

- Section Summary: *Probability and Heredity*
- Review and Reinforce: *Probability and Heredity*
- Enrich: *Probability and Heredity*

Lab zone Skills Lab

Make the Right Call! L2

Prepare for Inquiry

Key Concept
Punnett squares can predict the results of a genetic cross when the genotypes of both parents are known.

Skills Objectives
Students will be able to
- model the combination of alleles in a genetic cross
- predict the offspring of a genetic cross
- interpret data from models of genetic crosses

Class Time 40 minutes

All in One Teaching Resources
- Lab Worksheet: *Make the Right Call!*

Alternative Materials
Marbles of other colors may be substituted, but use two easily distinguishable colors. (Some students may be colorblind.) Other small colored objects that have a uniform shape and texture, such as buttons, can be used.

Guide Inquiry

Invitation
Discuss circumstances in which students make predictions in their lives. Then ask: **Why is it helpful to scientists to make accurate predictions in their experiments?** *(Accurate predictions make scientists more confident that they are asking the right questions and correctly understanding the phenomena that they are studying; they also help scientists to better plan their experiments.)*

Lab zone Skills Lab

Make the Right Call!

Problem
How can you predict the possible results of genetic crosses?

Skills Focus
making models, interpreting data

Materials
- 2 small paper bags
- marking pen
- 3 blue marbles
- 3 white marbles

Procedure
1. Label one bag "Bag 1, Female Parent." Label the other bag "Bag 2, Male Parent." Then read over Part 1, Part 2, and Part 3 of this lab. Write a prediction about the kinds of offspring you expect from each cross.

PART 1 Crossing Two Homozygous Parents

2. Copy the data table and label it *Data Table 1*. Then place two blue marbles in Bag 1. This pair of marbles represents the female parent's alleles. Use the letter *B* to represent the dominant allele for blue color.
3. Place two white marbles in Bag 2. Use the letter *b* to represent the recessive allele for white color.
4. For Trial 1, remove one marble from Bag 1 without looking in the bag. Record the result in your data table. Return the marble to the bag. Again, without looking in the bag, remove one marble from Bag 2. Record the result in your data table. Return the marble to the bag.
5. In the column labeled Offspring's Alleles, write *BB* if you removed two blue marbles, *bb* if you removed two white marbles, or *Bb* if you removed one blue marble and one white marble.
6. Repeat Steps 4 and 5 nine more times.

PART 2 Crossing Homozygous and Heterozygous Parents

7. Place two blue marbles in Bag 1. Place one white marble and one blue marble in Bag 2. Copy the data table again, and label it *Data Table 2*.
8. Repeat Steps 4 and 5 ten times.

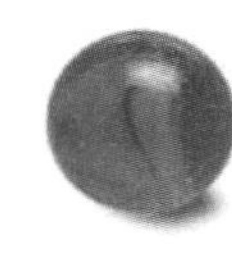

Data Table

Number ________

Trial	Allele From Bag 1 (Female Parent)	Allele From Bag 2 (Male Parent)	Offspring's Alleles
1			
2			
3			
4			
5			
6			

Introduce the Procedure
Have students read the entire procedure. Ask: **What do the marbles represent?** *(The alleles from each parent)* **Why should you not look inside the bag when you remove the marbles?** *(To make sure the combinations occur randomly)*

Expected Outcome
In the first cross (*BB* × *bb*), students observe that all offspring are *Bb*. In the second cross (*BB* × *Bb*), all offspring are blue, but some are homozygous (*BB*) and some are heterozygous (*Bb*). In the third cross (*Bb* × *Bb*), some offspring are blue and some are white. All white offspring are homozygous (*bb*). Blue offspring are either homozygous (*BB*) or heterozygous (*Bb*).

PART 3 Crossing Two Heterozygous Parents

9. Place one blue marble and one white marble in Bag 1. Place one blue marble and one white marble in Bag 2. Copy the data table again and label it *Data Table 3.*
10. Repeat Steps 4 and 5 ten times.

Analyze and Conclude

1. **Making Models** Make a Punnett square for each of the crosses you modeled in Part 1, Part 2, and Part 3.
2. **Interpreting Data** According to your results in Part 1, how many different kinds of offspring are possible when the homozygous parents (*BB* and *bb*) are crossed? Do the results you obtained using the marble model agree with the results shown by a Punnett square?
3. **Predicting** According to your results in Part 2, what percentage of offspring are likely to be homozygous when a homozygous parent (*BB*) and a heterozygous parent (*Bb*) are crossed? What percentage of offspring are likely to be heterozygous? Does the model agree with the results shown by a Punnett square?
4. **Making Models** According to your results in Part 3, what different kinds of offspring are possible when two heterozygous parents (*Bb* × *Bb*) are crossed? What percentage of each type of offspring are likely to be produced? Does the model agree with the results of a Punnett square?
5. **Inferring** For Part 3, if you did 100 trials instead of 10 trials, would your results be closer to the results shown in a Punnett square? Explain.
6. **Communicating** In a paragraph, explain how the marble model compares with a Punnett square. How are the two methods alike? How are they different?

More to Explore

In peas, the allele for yellow seeds (*Y*) is dominant over the allele for green seeds (*y*). What possible crosses do you think could produce a heterozygous plant with yellow seeds (*Yy*)? Use the marble model and Punnett squares to test your predictions.

Extend Inquiry

More to Explore Crosses that will produce a heterozygous plant (*Yy*) include *YY* × *yy*, *YY* × *Yy*, *Yy* × *Yy*, and *Yy* × *yy*.

Analyze and Conclude

1. Punnett square for Part 1:

	b	*b*
B	*Bb*	*Bb*
B	*Bb*	*Bb*

Punnett square for Part 2:

	B	*b*
B	*BB*	*Bb*
B	*BB*	*Bb*

Punnett square for Part 3:

	B	*b*
B	*BB*	*Bb*
b	*Bb*	*bb*

2. Only heterozygous blue offspring (*Bb*) are possible. The Punnett square shows the same results.

3. Student results may produce slightly different answers. As the number of trials increases, the results will more likely show that 50 percent of the offspring are likely to be homozygous (*BB*), while 50 percent are likely to be heterozygous (*Bb*). The Punnett square shows that 50 percent will be homozygous and 50 percent will be heterozygous.

4. Student results may vary due to chance, but all should observe that three different genotypes are possible: *BB, Bb,* and *bb*. From the Punnett square, students can predict that 25 percent are likely to be *BB*, 50 percent are likely to be *Bb*, and 25 percent are likely to be *bb*. The marble model will probably not totally agree with the Punnett square due to chance.

5. Probably; as the number of trials is increased, the results are more likely to match those predicted in a Punnett square because of chance.

6. Sample answer: The marble model and the Punnett square both show the genotypes of the parents and offspring, and demonstrate how the parent can donate one of two possible alleles to the offspring. The Punnett square gives all the possible genotypes of the offspring and their probabilities of occurring. The model gives the genotypes of the offspring based on chance, much like the actual combining of alleles in a real genetic cross.

The Cell and Inheritance

Objectives

After this lesson, students will be able to

C.3.3.1 Describe the role chromosomes play in inheritance.

C.3.3.2 Identify the events that occur during meiosis.

C.3.3.3 Explain the relationship between chromosomes and genes.

Target Reading Skill

Identifying Supporting Evidence

Explain that identifying supporting evidence helps students understand the relationship between the facts and the hypothesis.

Answers

One possible way to complete the graphic organizer:

Detail: Grasshoppers: 24 chromosomes in body cells, 12 in sex cells

Detail: Fertilized egg has 24 chromosomes.

Detail: Alleles exist in pairs in organisms.

All in One Teaching Resources

- Transparency C27

Preteach

Build Background Knowledge

L1

Relating Genetics and the Cell Cycle

Have students recall what they know about cells and cell structure. Challenge them to predict the location of Mendel's hereditary factors, or genes, within the cell. You might wish to record students' predictions on the board and have the class evaluate them as you study the section.

Section 3

The Cell and Inheritance

Reading Preview

Key Concepts

- What role do chromosomes play in inheritance?
- What events occur during meiosis?
- What is the relationship between chromosomes and genes?

Key Term

- meiosis

Target Reading Skill

Identifying Supporting Evidence As you read, identify the evidence that supports the hypothesis that chromosomes are important in inheritance. Write the evidence in a graphic organizer.

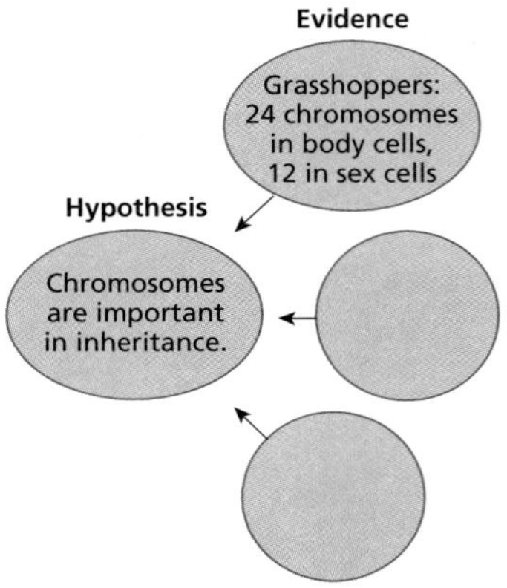

Evidence

Grasshoppers: 24 chromosomes in body cells, 12 in sex cells

Hypothesis

Chromosomes are important in inheritance.

Lab zone Discover Activity

Which Chromosome Is Which?

Mendel did not know about chromosomes or their role in genetics. Today we know that genes are located on chromosomes.

1. Label two craft sticks with the letter *A*. The craft sticks represent a pair of chromosomes in the female parent. Turn the sticks face down on a piece of paper.
2. Label two more craft sticks with the letter *a*. These represent a pair of chromosomes in the male parent. Turn the sticks face down on another piece of paper.
3. Turn over one craft stick "chromosome" from each piece of paper. Move both sticks to a third piece of paper. These represent a pair of chromosomes in the offspring. Note the allele combination that the offspring received.

Think It Over

Making Models Use this model to explain how chromosomes are involved in the inheritance of alleles.

Mendel's work showed that genes exist. But scientists in the early twentieth century did not know what structures in cells contained genes. The search for the answer to this puzzle is something like a mystery story. The story could be called "The Clue in the Grasshopper's Cells."

In 1903, Walter Sutton, an American geneticist, was studying the cells of grasshoppers. He wanted to understand how sex cells (sperm and egg) form. Sutton focused on the movement of chromosomes during the formation of sex cells. He hypothesized that chromosomes were the key to understanding how offspring have traits similar to those of their parents.

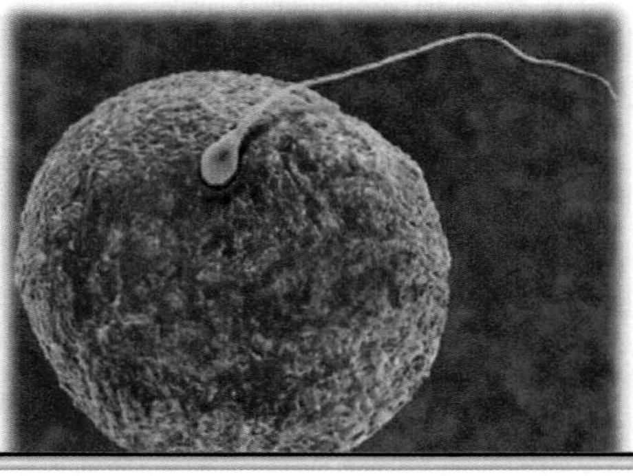

Egg ▶

◀ Sperm

Figure 11
Sex Cells
The large egg is a female sex cell, and the smaller sperm is a male sex cell.

Lab zone Discover Activity

Skills Focus Making models L2

Materials 4 craft sticks, 3 pieces of paper, marking pen

Time 10 minutes

Tips Receives only one allele from each parent.

Expected Outcome Students will realize that parents contribute only one of their two chromosomes to the offspring. The idea is to get students thinking about genes being carried on chromosomes and that the cell has a process to make sure only one allele of a gene is contributed to offspring.

Think It Over Genes are located on chromosomes, which must divide and separate so that the offspring get only one chromosome, or one allele, from each parent.

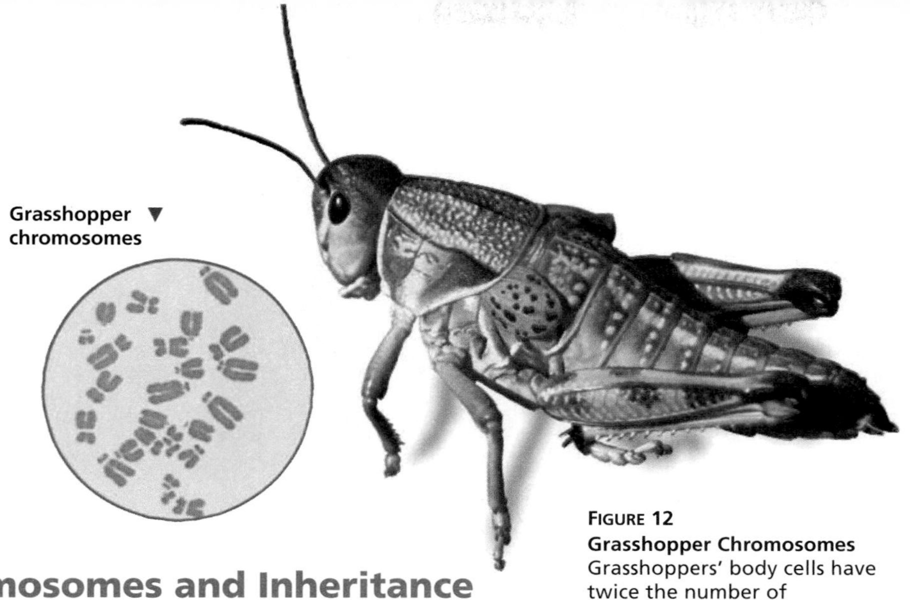

FIGURE 12
Grasshopper Chromosomes
Grasshoppers' body cells have twice the number of chromosomes as their sex cells.
Applying Concepts *What is the function of chromosomes?*

Chromosomes and Inheritance

Sutton needed evidence to support his hypothesis that chromosomes were important in the inheritance of traits. He found that evidence in grasshoppers' cells. The body cells of a grasshopper have 24 chromosomes. To his surprise, Sutton found that the grasshopper's sex cells have only 12 chromosomes. In other words, a grasshopper's sex cells have exactly half the number of chromosomes found in its body cells.

Chromosome Pairs Sutton observed what happened when a sperm cell and an egg cell joined during fertilization. The fertilized egg that formed had 24 chromosomes. As a result, the grasshopper offspring had exactly the same number of chromosomes in its cells as did each of its parents. The 24 chromosomes existed in 12 pairs. One chromosome in each pair came from the male parent, while the other chromosome came from the female parent.

Genes on Chromosomes Recall that alleles are different forms of a gene. Because of Mendel's work, Sutton knew that alleles exist in pairs in an organism. One allele in a pair comes from the organism's female parent and the other allele comes from the male parent. Sutton realized that paired alleles were carried on paired chromosomes. Sutton's idea came to be known as the chromosome theory of inheritance. **According to the chromosome theory of inheritance, genes are carried from parents to their offspring on chromosomes.**

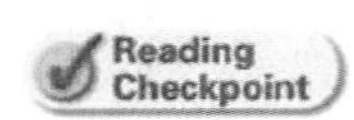
What is the relationship between alleles and chromosomes?

Instruct

Chromosomes and Inheritance

Teach Key Concepts L2

The Role of Chromosomes

Focus Review the definition and location of chromosomes.

Teach Ask: **What did Sutton observe about the relative numbers of chromosomes in the body cells and sex cells of grasshoppers?** *(The sex cells have half the number of chromosomes as body cells.)* **How many chromosomes does the fertilized egg receive from each parent?** *(The number that is present in each sex cell)* **How are genes passed from parent to offspring?** *(Sex cells contain half of each parent's chromosomes, which include the parent's genes. When the sex cells from each parent join during fertilization, the offspring receives a full set of genes.)* **What is the chromosomal theory of inheritance?** *(Genes are carried from parents to their offspring on chromosomes.)*

Apply Ask: **If human body cells each have 46 chromosomes, how many chromosomes do human sex cells have?** *(23)* **learning modality: logical/mathematical**

Independent Practice

All in One Teaching Resources L2

- Guided Reading and Study Worksheet: *The Cell and Inheritance*

Student Edition on Audio CD

Differentiated Instruction

Gifted and Talented L3
Modeling the Function of Meiosis
Provide various art materials to students, and challenge them to illustrate what might happen if sex cells did not have half the number of chromosomes in body cells. Have groups present their models to the class and explain why sex cells have half the chromosomes of body cells. **learning modality: visual**

Special Needs L1
Visualizing Chromosomes Show a picture of a cell and point out the chromosomes. Diagram two cells, each with one pair of chromosomes. Work backward to show how one chromosome came from the mother and one from the father. Point out the location of a gene. Show how it can have two alleles. **learning modality: visual**

Monitor Progress L2

Drawing Have students draw a diagram of a grasshopper body cell and sex cell and show the number of chromosomes in each of these cells.

Answers
Figure 12 Chromosomes carry genes from parents to offspring.

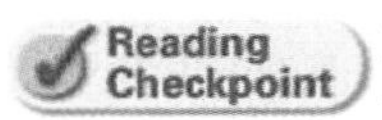
Paired alleles are carried on paired chromosomes.

Meiosis

For: Links on meiosis
Visit: www.SciLinks.org
Web Code: scn-0333

Download a worksheet to guide students' review of meiosis.

Help Students Read L2

Use Prior Knowledge Students absorb new material more quickly when they can relate it to previously learned concepts. Before they read about meiosis, have them write a paragraph explaining the steps in mitosis. As they read about meiosis, have them compare and contrast mitosis with meiosis, using what they have written.

Teach Key Concepts L2

Events in Meiosis

Focus Remind students that sex cells have half the number of chromosomes as body cells.

Teach Refer students to Figure 13. Point out that before meiosis occurs, every chromosome is copied, so the cell has four copies of each chromosome. Ask: **What happens during Meiosis I?** *(The chromosome pairs separate into two different cells.)* **What happens during Meiosis II?** *(The centromeres split and the chromosome copies separate.)* **How many sex cells are produced at the end of the meiosis?** *(Four)* **How do the sex cells differ from the parent cell?** *(The sex cells have half the number of chromosomes of the parent cell.)*

Apply Ask: **How is meiosis similar to mitosis?** *(Chromosomes are copied and line up to move to opposite sides of the cell. The cell divides.)* **Different?** *(In meiosis, the body cell divides twice, producing 4 sex cells that have half the number of chromosomes of the original body cell. Mitosis produces only 2 body cells, each with the same number of chromosomes as the parent cell.)* **learning modality: visual**

All in One Teaching Resources

- Transparency C28

FIGURE 13
Meiosis
During meiosis, a cell produces sex cells with half the number of chromosomes. **Interpreting Diagrams** *What happens before meiosis?*

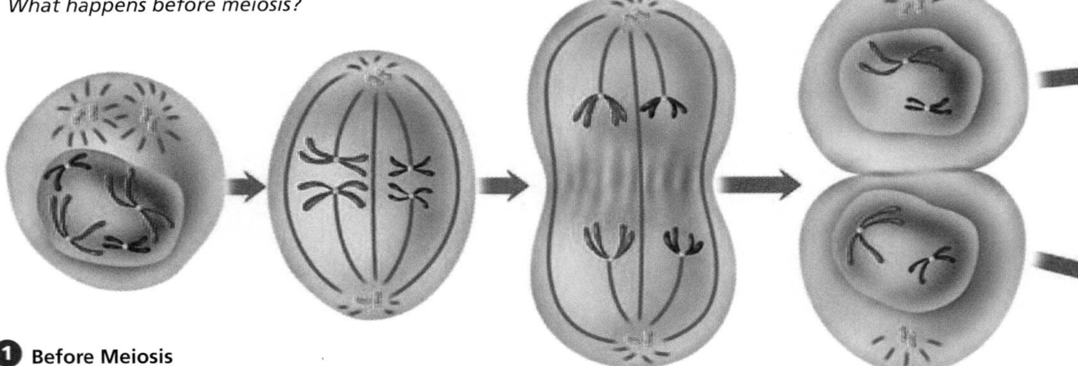

1 Before Meiosis
Before meiosis begins, every chromosome in the parent cell is copied. Centromeres hold the two chromatids together.

2 Meiosis I
A The chromosome pairs line up in the center of the cell.
B The pairs separate and move to opposite ends of the cell.
C Two cells form, each with half the number of chromosomes. Each chromosome still has two chromatids.

Meiosis

How do sex cells end up with half the number of chromosomes as body cells? To answer this question, you need to understand the events that occur during meiosis. **Meiosis** (my OH sis) is the process by which the number of chromosomes is reduced by half to form sex cells—sperm and eggs.

What Happens During Meiosis You can trace the events of meiosis in Figure 13. In this example, each parent cell has four chromosomes arranged in two pairs. **During meiosis, the chromosome pairs separate and are distributed to two different cells. The resulting sex cells have only half as many chromosomes as the other cells in the organism.** The sex cells end up with only two chromosomes each—half the number found in the parent cell. Each sex cell has one chromosome from each original pair.

When sex cells combine to form an organism, each sex cell contributes half the normal number of chromosomes. Thus, the offspring gets the normal number of chromosomes—half from each parent.

Go Online SCILINKS NSTA
For: Links on meiosis
Visit: www.SciLinks.org
Web Code: scn-0333

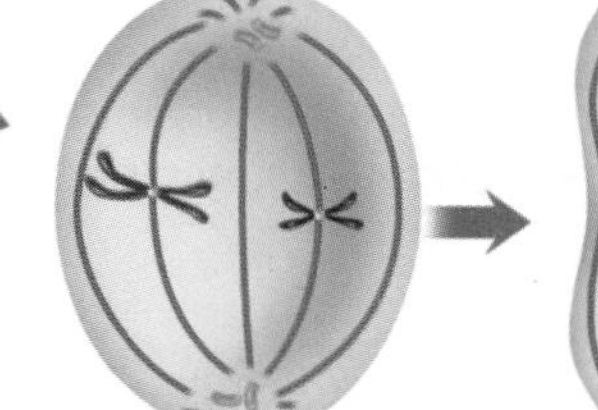

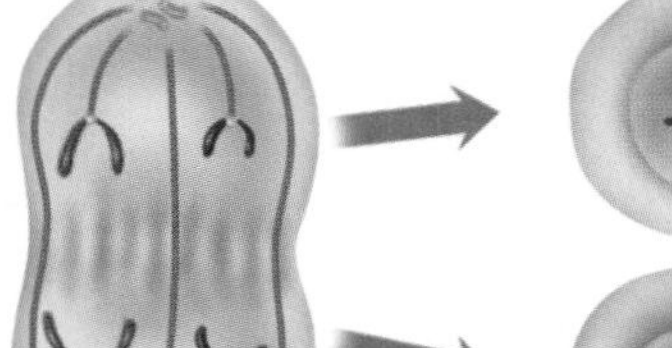

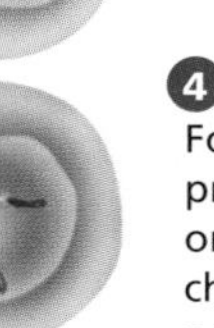

3 Meiosis II

A The chromosomes with their two chromatids move to the center of the cell.

B The centromeres split, and the chromatids separate. Single chromosomes move to opposite ends of the cell.

4 End of Meiosis
Four sex cells have been produced. Each cell has only half the number of chromosomes that the parent cell had at the beginning of meiosis. Each cell has only one chromosome from each original pair.

Meiosis and Punnett Squares A Punnett square is actually a way to show the events that occur at meiosis. When the chromosome pairs separate and go into two different sex cells, so do the alleles carried on each chromosome. One allele from each pair goes to each sex cell.

In Figure 14, you can see how the Punnett square accounts for the separation of alleles during meiosis. As shown across the top of the Punnett square, half of the sperm cells from the male parent will receive the chromosome with the *T* allele. The other half of the sperm cells will receive the chromosome with the *t* allele. In this example, the same is true for the egg cells from the female parent, as shown down the left side of the Punnett square. Depending on which sperm cell combines with which egg cell, one of the allele combinations shown in the boxes will result.

FIGURE 14
Meiosis Punnett Square
Both parents are heterozygous for the trait of stem height. The Punnett square shows the possible allele combinations after fertilization.

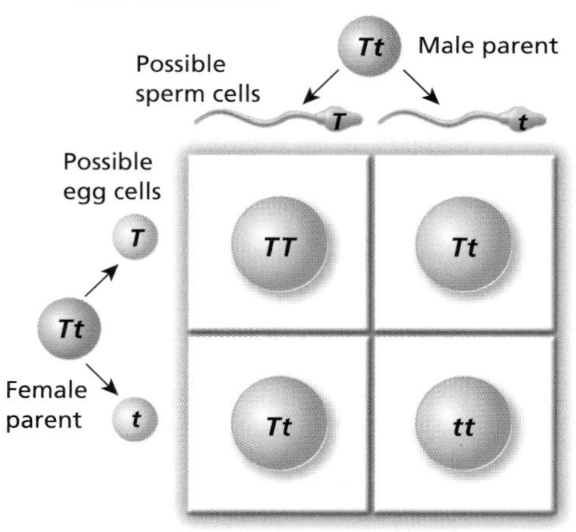

Lab zone Build Inquiry L1

Modeling Chromosomes During Meiosis

Materials 8 pipe cleaners (4 of one color and 4 of another), 4 beads

Time 15 minutes

Focus Review the steps in meiosis.

Teach Challenge students to model the steps in meiosis using the pipe cleaners to represent two chromosomes in a cell. Students use pipe cleaners of the same color to represent chromosome pairs, with different chromosome pairs having different colors. Monitor students to make sure they double each chromosome before meiosis begins by adding another pipe cleaner of the same color to each pipe cleaner chromosome. Students can use beads to hold the chromosome copies together or twist the pipe cleaners together at one point. Make sure students separate the chromosome pairs during Meiosis I and the chromosome copies during Meiosis II.

Apply Have students use pipe cleaners to model mitosis. Have them compare the number of total chromosomes that result in meiosis vs. mitosis. *(The total number of chromosomes that results is the same. However, they are distributed in the resulting cells in different ways. In meiosis, the result is 8 chromosomes distributed into 4 sex cells. In mitosis, the result is 8 chromosomes distributed into 2 body cells.)* **learning modality: kinesthetic**

Differentiated Instruction

English Learners/Beginning L1
Comprehension: Link to Visual
Pair beginners with more advanced English learners. Have the pairs of students go over each step in Figure 13, with the more advanced student helping the beginner understand what goes on in each step. The beginner can make sketches and take notes in his or her first language. **learning modality: visual**

English Learners/Intermediate L2
Comprehension: Link to Visual
Have students prepare two-column written explanations of each step in meiosis as shown in Figure 13. The first column should explain each step in the student's first language. The second column should have a corresponding explanation in English. The student can make a copy of this two-column explanation to share with a beginner. **learning modality: visual**

Monitor Progress L2

Writing Have students write an outline of meiosis in which each major step is a main heading in the outline. Students can save their outlines in their portfolios.

Portfolio

Answer
Figure 13 Every chromosome in the cell is copied.

A Lineup of Genes

Teach Key Concepts

L2

Chromosomes and Genes

Focus Refer students to Figure 15.

Teach Ask: **How are chromosomes and genes related?** *(Chromosomes are made up of many genes joined together.)*

Apply Have students show two ways to make a chromosome pair heterozygous for all genes. **learning modality: visual**

Monitor Progress

L2

Answer

Figure 15 Homozygous: C, e, F, G, I; Heterozygous: A, B, D, H

Assess

Reviewing Key Concepts

1. a. Body cells have twice the number of chromosomes (24) as sex cells (12). **b.** The fertilized egg gets 24 chromosomes. **c.** Just as the offspring get one allele from each parent for every gene, the offspring get half their chromosomes from one parent and half from the other parent.

2. a. The process by which the number of chromosomes is reduced by half to form sex cells **b.** Meiosis I: The duplicated chromosomes divide into two cells, each with half the number of chromosomes. Meiosis II: The two cells divide once more, producing sex cells that have half as many chromosomes as the body cells. **c.** In meiosis I, the members of each chromosome pair separate and end up in different cells.

3. a. They are joined together like beads on a string. **b.** They are lined up in the same order on both chromosomes.

Reteach

L1

Have students sketch the stages of meiosis on separate pieces of paper, then exchange with a partner. Each student should then put the sketches in order.

All in One Teaching Resources

- Section Summary: *The Cell and Inheritance*
- Review and Reinforce: *The Cell and Inheritance*
- Enrich: *The Cell and Inheritance*

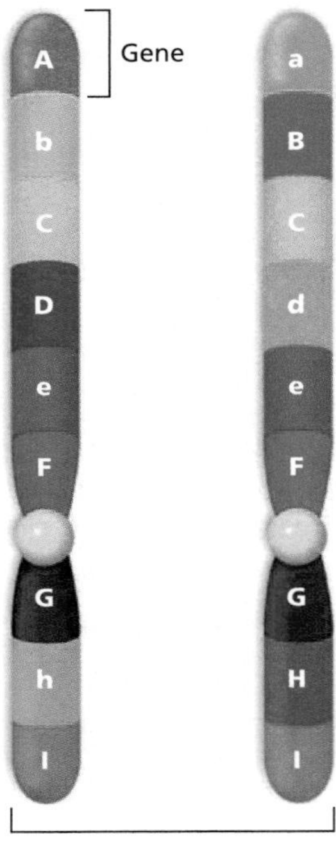

A Lineup of Genes

The body cells of humans contain 23 chromosome pairs, or 46 chromosomes. **Chromosomes are made up of many genes joined together like beads on a string.** Although you have only 23 pairs of chromosomes, your body cells each contain about 35,000 genes. Each gene controls a trait.

In Figure 15, one chromosome in the pair came from the female parent. The other chromosome came from the male parent. Notice that each chromosome in the pair has the same genes. The genes are lined up in the same order on both chromosomes. However, the alleles for some of the genes might be different. For example, the organism has the *A* allele on one chromosome and the *a* allele on the other. As you can see, this organism is heterozygous for some traits and homozygous for others.

FIGURE 15
Genes on Chromosomes
Genes are located on chromosomes. The chromosomes in a pair may have different alleles for some genes and the same alleles for others.
Classifying *For which genes is this organism homozygous? For which genes is it heterozygous?*

Section 3 Assessment

Target Reading Skill Identifying Supporting Evidence Refer to your graphic organizer about the chromosome theory of inheritance as you answer Question 1 below.

Reviewing Key Concepts

1. a. Comparing and Contrasting According to Sutton's observations, how does the number of chromosomes in a grasshopper's body cells compare to the number in its sex cells?
b. Describing Describe what happens to the number of chromosomes when two grasshopper sex cells join in fertilization.
c. Explaining How do Sutton's observations about chromosome number support the chromosome theory of inheritance?

2. a. Defining What is meiosis?
b. Interpreting Diagrams Briefly describe meiosis I and meiosis II. Refer to Figure 13.
c. Sequencing Use the events of meiosis to explain why a sex cell normally does not receive both chromosomes from a pair.

3. a. Describing How are genes arranged on a chromosome?
b. Comparing and Contrasting How does the order of genes in one member of a chromosome pair compare to the order of genes on the other chromosome?

Writing in Science

Newspaper Interview You are a newspaper reporter in the early 1900s. You want to interview Walter Sutton about his work with chromosomes. Write three questions you would like to ask Sutton. Then, for each question, write answers that Sutton might have given.

Lab zone Chapter Project

Keep Students on Track Students will determine the traits inherited from each parent for six offspring by using a coin toss. They will write a genotype for each trait on each parent's back. Then they will construct a paper pet for each offspring, showing the traits that each one has inherited.

Writing in Science

Writing Mode Questions and answers

Scoring Rubric

4 Includes complete description of Sutton's work and is written in the format of an interview with the scientist; questions require critical thinking
3 Includes all criteria, but questions are low-level comprehension type
2 Includes only two questions
1 Includes inaccurate information

Section 4 The DNA Connection

Reading Preview

Key Concepts

- What forms the genetic code?
- How does a cell produce proteins?
- How can mutations affect an organism?

Key Terms

- messenger RNA
- transfer RNA

Target Reading Skill

Sequencing A sequence is the order in which the steps in a process occur. As you read, make a flowchart that shows protein synthesis. Put the steps of the process in separate boxes in the flowchart in the order in which they occur.

Protein Synthesis

DNA provides code to form messenger RNA.
↓
Messenger RNA attaches to ribosome.
↓
[ ]

Lab zone Discover Activity

Can You Crack the Code?

1. Use the Morse code in the chart to decode the question in the message below. The letters are separated by slash marks.
   • – – / • • • • / • / • – • / • / • – / • – • / • / – – • / • / – • / • / • • • / • – • • / – – –/ – • – • / • – / – / • / – • • /
2. Write your answer to the question in Morse code.
3. Exchange your coded answer with a partner. Then decode your partner's answer.

A • –	N – •
B – • • •	O – – –
C – • – •	P • – – •
D – • •	Q – – • –
E •	R • – •
F • • – •	S • • •
G – – •	T –
H • • • •	U • • –
I • •	V • • • –
J • – – –	W • – –
K – • –	X – • • –
L • – • •	Y – • – –
M – –	Z – – • •

Think It Over

Forming Operational Definitions Based on your results from this activity, write a definition of the word *code*. Then compare your definition to one in a dictionary.

The young, white, ring-tailed lemur in the photograph below was born in a forest in southern Madagascar. White lemurs are extremely rare. Why was this lemur born with such an uncommon phenotype? To answer this question, you need to know how the genes on a chromosome control an organism's traits.

A white lemur and its mother ►

Section 4 The DNA Connection

Objectives

After this lesson, students will be able to

C.3.4.1 Explain what forms the genetic code.

C.3.4.2 Describe how a cell produces proteins.

C.3.4.3 Identify how mutations can affect an organism.

Target Reading Skill

Sequencing Explain that organizing information from beginning to end helps students understand a step-by-step process.

Answers

Possible way to complete the graphic organizer:

DNA provides code to form messenger RNA.
↓
Messenger RNA attaches to ribosome.
↓
Transfer RNA "reads" the messenger RNA.
↓
Amino acids are added to the growing protein.

All in One Teaching Resources

- Transparency C29

Preteach

Build Background Knowledge L1

Genes and Traits

Invite students to recall what they have learned about inheritance, DNA, and cell division up to this point. Then ask: **How do genes determine the traits of an organism?** *(Accept all answers without comment.)* Explain that students will learn more about this process in the section.

Lab zone Discover Activity

Skills Focus Forming operational definitions L2

Time 15 minutes

Tips Some students may require extra help in deciphering the code; you may want to pair students.

Expected Outcome The coded question is "Where are genes located?" The answer, "on chromosomes," is encoded here:

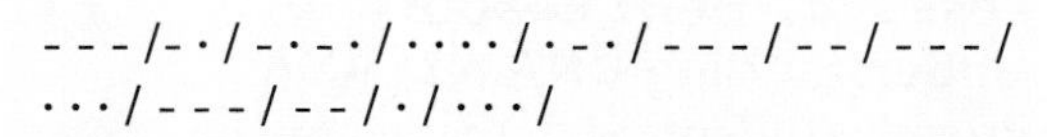

- - - /- · / - · - · / · · · · / · - - · / - - - / - - / - - - / · · · / - - - / - - / · / · · · /

Think It Over Students might define *code* as a set of symbols with specific meanings used to send messages. Some dictionaries define *code* as a system of symbols, letters, or words given arbitrary meanings, used for transmitting messages requiring secrecy or brevity.

Instruct

The Genetic Code

Help Students Read L1

Think Aloud Refer to the Content Refresher for guidelines on Think Aloud. Read the paragraphs on the genetic code aloud. As you read, pause and make a prediction, for example, you might predict that DNA provides the information to make proteins. Describe mental pictures of the order of the bases, and sketch them on the board. Ask students to stop you at any point at which they are confused so that the meaning can be clarified. Then have students read the next passage silently and apply the strategies you modeled. Ask students to share their strategies with the class.

Teach Key Concepts L2

How the Genetic Code Works

Focus Have students recall that chromosomes are made of genes.

Teach Ask: **What are chromosomes composed of?** *(DNA)* **What are genes?** *(Sections of a DNA molecule)* Refer students to Figure 16. Ask: **What forms the rungs of the DNA ladder?** *(The nitrogen bases adenine, thymine, guanine, and cytosine)* **Why is the sequence of bases important?** *(The sequence forms a code that tells the cell what protein to produce.)*

Apply Ask: **How are the nitrogen bases of DNA like the letters of the alphabet?** *(Like groups of letters that make up specific words, a group of three bases indicates a specific amino acid.)* **learning modality: logical/ mathematical**

Independent Practice

Teaching Resources

- Guided Reading and Study Worksheet: *The DNA Connection*

Student Edition on Audio CD

The Genetic Code

The main function of genes is to control the production of proteins in an organism's cells. Proteins help to determine the size, shape, color, and many other traits of an organism.

Genes and DNA Recall that chromosomes are composed mostly of DNA. In Figure 16, you can see the relationship between chromosomes and DNA. Notice that a DNA molecule is made up of four different nitrogen bases—adenine (A), thymine (T), guanine (G), and cytosine (C). These bases form the rungs of the DNA "ladder."

A gene is a section of a DNA molecule that contains the information to code for one specific protein. A gene is made up of a series of bases in a row. The bases in a gene are arranged in a specific order—for example, ATGACGTAC. A single gene on a chromosome may contain anywhere from several hundred to a million or more of these bases. Each gene is located at a specific place on a chromosome.

Order of the Bases A gene contains the code that determines the structure of a protein. **The order of the nitrogen bases along a gene forms a genetic code that specifies what type of protein will be produced.** Remember that proteins are long-chain molecules made of individual amino acids. In the genetic code, a group of three DNA bases codes for one specific amino acid. For example, the base sequence CGT (cytosine-guanine-thymine) always codes for the amino acid alanine. The order of the three-base code units determines the order in which amino acids are put together to form a protein.

FIGURE 16
The DNA Code
Chromosomes are made of DNA. Each chromosome contains thousands of genes. The sequence of bases in a gene forms a code that tells the cell what protein to produce. **Interpreting Diagrams** *Where in the cell are chromosomes located?*

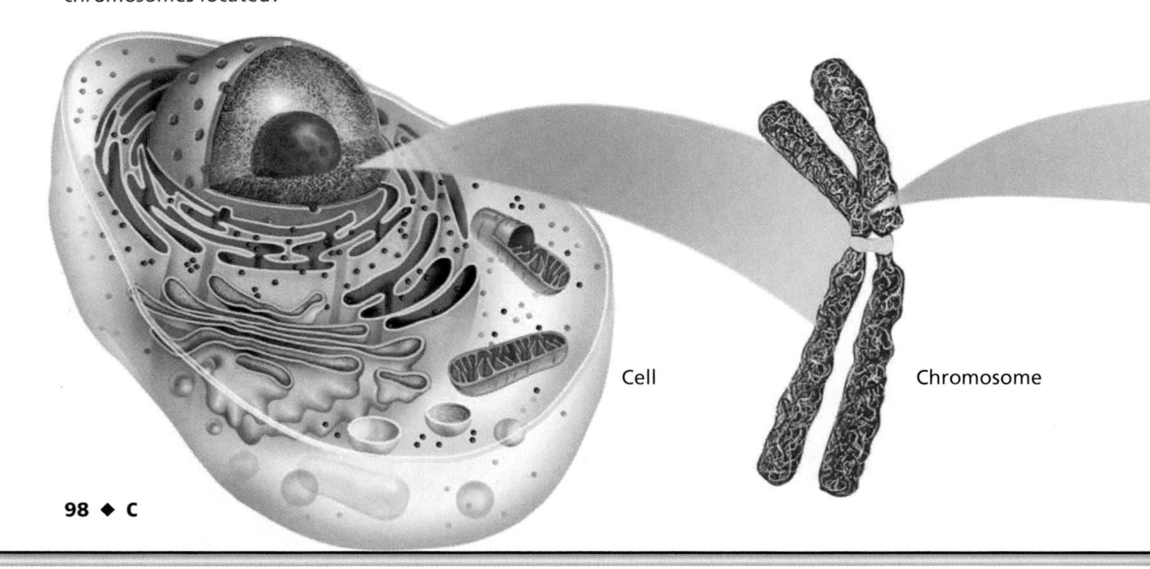

Differentiated Instruction

Less Proficient Readers L3
Understanding DNA and RNA
Provide students with the section on Student Edition on Audio CD and a copy of the passage The Genetic Code. Have them listen to this passage as they read along and highlight key phrases and sentences that explain the relationships among genes, chromosomes, and DNA. Then pair students with more proficient readers. Have them construct a concept map that includes and defines the terms *gene, chromosome, DNA, genetic code, nitrogen base,* and other words. **learning modality: verbal**

How Cells Make Proteins

The production of proteins is called protein synthesis. **During protein synthesis, the cell uses information from a gene on a chromosome to produce a specific protein.** Protein synthesis takes place on the ribosomes in the cytoplasm of a cell. As you know, the cytoplasm is outside the nucleus. The chromosomes, however, are found inside the nucleus. How, then, does the information needed to produce proteins get out of the nucleus and into the cytoplasm?

The Role of RNA Before protein synthesis can take place, a "messenger" must first carry the genetic code from the DNA inside the nucleus into the cytoplasm. This genetic messenger is called ribonucleic acid, or RNA.

Although RNA is similar to DNA, the two molecules differ in some important ways. Unlike DNA, which has two strands, RNA has only one strand. RNA also contains a different sugar molecule from the sugar found in DNA. Another difference between DNA and RNA is in their nitrogen bases. Like DNA, RNA contains adenine, guanine, and cytosine. However, instead of thymine, RNA contains uracil (YOOR uh sil).

Types of RNA There are several types of RNA involved in protein synthesis. **Messenger RNA** copies the coded message from the DNA in the nucleus, and carries the message to the ribosome in the cytoplasm. Another type of RNA, called **transfer RNA,** carries amino acids to the ribosome and adds them to the growing protein.

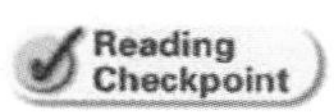

Reading Checkpoint How is RNA different from DNA?

Lab zone Skills Activity

Drawing Conclusions

The following is a sequence of nitrogen bases on one strand of a nucleic acid molecule.

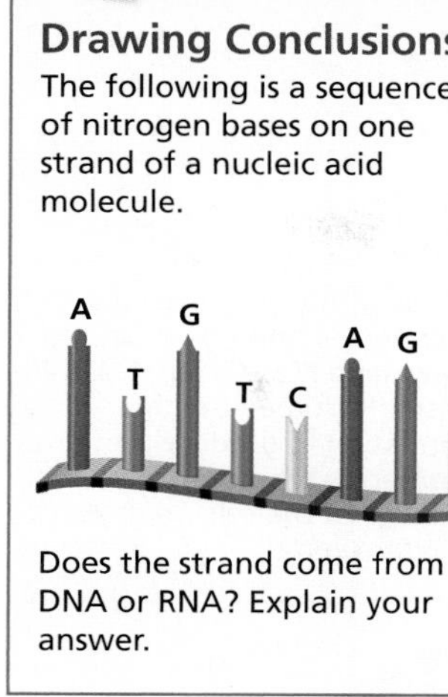

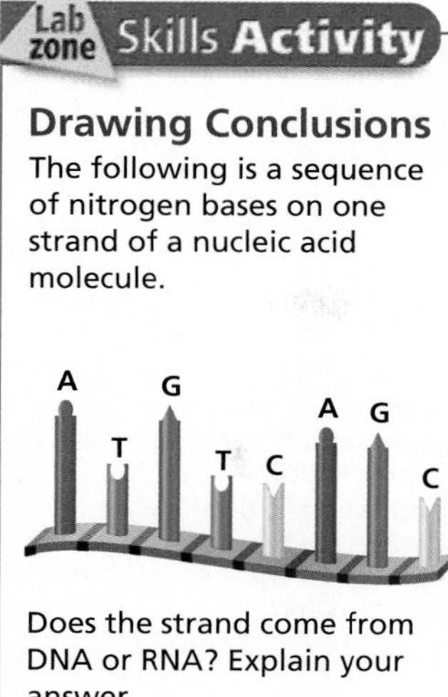

Does the strand come from DNA or RNA? Explain your answer.

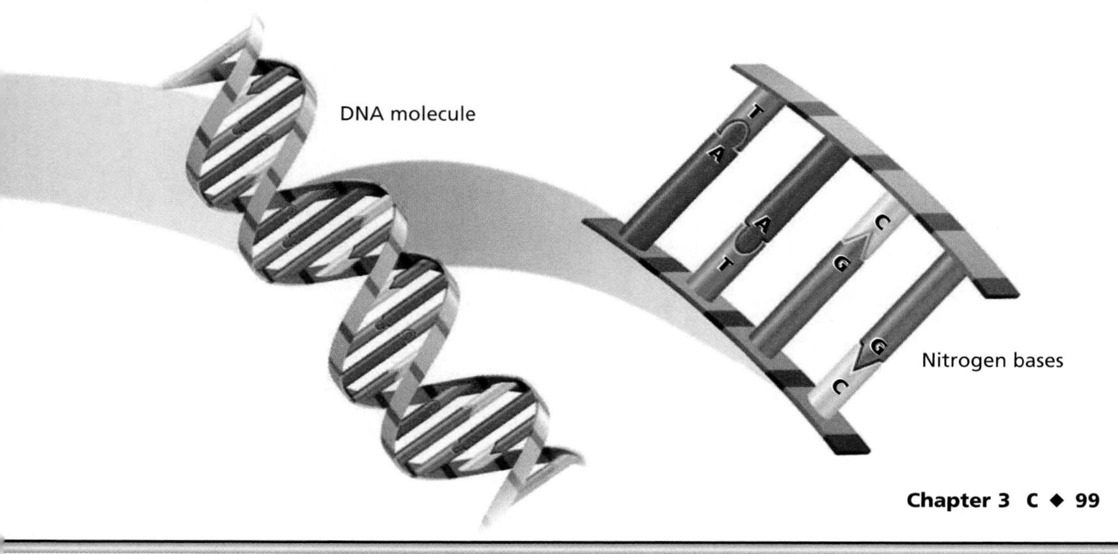

Lab zone Build Inquiry L1

Modeling the Genetic Code

Materials various craft materials, such as yarn, construction paper, tape, markers, pipe cleaners, and beads

Time 20 minutes

Focus Remind students that particular base sequences code for specific proteins.

Teach Challenge groups of students to make a model of DNA and invent a code in which base sequences stand for words. When the sequences are in order, the words make a sentence.

Apply Ask: **What would happen to your sentence if the order of the base sequences were changed?** *(The sentence might not make sense.)* **learning modality: kinesthetic**

How Cells Make Proteins

Teach Key Concepts L2

Understanding Protein Synthesis

Focus Ask: **What do genes code for?** *(The production of proteins)*

Teach Ask: **What happens during protein synthesis?** *(The cell uses information from a gene on a chromosome to produce a specific protein.)* **What is the role of messenger RNA?** *(To copy the coded message from the DNA in the nucleus and carry the message to the ribosome in the cytoplasm)* **Transfer RNA?** *(To carry amino acids to the ribosome and add them to the growing protein chain)*

Apply Ask students to infer why proteins are made in the cytoplasm instead of the nucleus. *(The cytoplasm has ribosomes, which are needed to carry out protein synthesis.)* **learning modality: verbal**

Lab zone Skills Activity

Skills Focus Drawing conclusions L2

Time 5 minutes

Tips You may wish to have students reread the passage The Role of RNA to help them answer the question.

Expected Outcome The strand comes from DNA because it contains thymine.

Extend Ask: **What base would the strand contain if it were RNA?** *(Uracil instead of thymine)* **What RNA bases would pair with this strand of DNA?** (A U G U C A G C) **learning modality: verbal**

Monitor Progress L2

Oral Presentation Call on students to describe the role and types of RNA.

Answers

Figure 16 In the nucleus

Reading Checkpoint RNA has only one strand; it has a different sugar molecule; instead of thymine, it contains uracil.

Use Visuals: Figure 17 L2

Visualizing Protein Synthesis

Focus Review the definitions of messenger RNA and transfer RNA.

Teach Direct students' attention to Step 1. Point out that DNA always stays inside the cell nucleus. Ask: **What is the first step in protein synthesis?** *(For the strands of the DNA molecule to separate)* **Why is this important?** *(The messenger RNA bases have to pair up with a single strand of DNA to form the messenger RNA strand.)* **What does the messenger RNA do in Step 2?** *(It leaves the nucleus, enters the cytoplasm, attaches to a ribosome, and provides the code for the protein molecule.)* **In Step 3, how is a protein chain formed?** *(Molecules of transfer RNA pick up the amino acids specified by each three-letter code. Each transfer RNA molecule puts the amino acid it is carrying in the correct order along the growing protein chain.)* Explain that in Step 4, more than one ribosome can attach to a single messenger RNA at one time.

Apply Ask: **Why is it important that protein synthesis be so carefully organized and carried out?** *(Proteins determine many traits of an organism and how that organism will function.)* **learning modality: visual**

All in One Teaching Resources

- Transparency C30

FIGURE 17
Protein Synthesis
To make proteins, messenger RNA copies information from DNA in the nucleus. Messenger RNA and transfer RNA then use this information to produce proteins. **Interpreting Diagrams** *In which organelle of the cell are proteins manufactured?*

Translating the Code The process of protein synthesis is shown in Figure 17. Look at the illustration as you read the following steps.

❶ The first step is for a DNA molecule to "unzip" between its base pairs. Then one of the strands of DNA directs the production of a strand of messenger RNA. To form the RNA strand, RNA bases pair up with the DNA bases. The process is similar to the process in which DNA replicates. Cytosine always pairs with guanine. However, uracil—not thymine— pairs with adenine.

❷ The messenger RNA then leaves the nucleus and enters the cytoplasm. In the cytoplasm, messenger RNA attaches to a ribosome. On the ribosome, the messenger RNA provides the code for the protein molecule that will form. During protein synthesis, the ribosome moves along the messenger RNA strand.

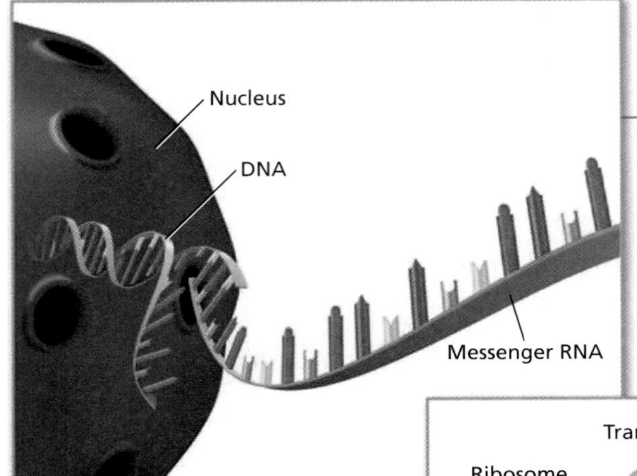

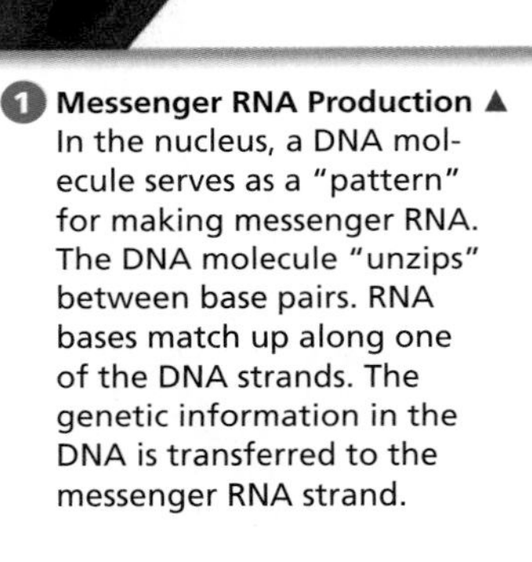

❶ **Messenger RNA Production ▲**
In the nucleus, a DNA molecule serves as a "pattern" for making messenger RNA. The DNA molecule "unzips" between base pairs. RNA bases match up along one of the DNA strands. The genetic information in the DNA is transferred to the messenger RNA strand.

❷ **Messenger RNA Attaches to a Ribosome ▼**
When the messenger RNA enters the cytoplasm, it attaches to a ribosome, where production of the protein chain begins. The ribosome moves along the messenger RNA strand.

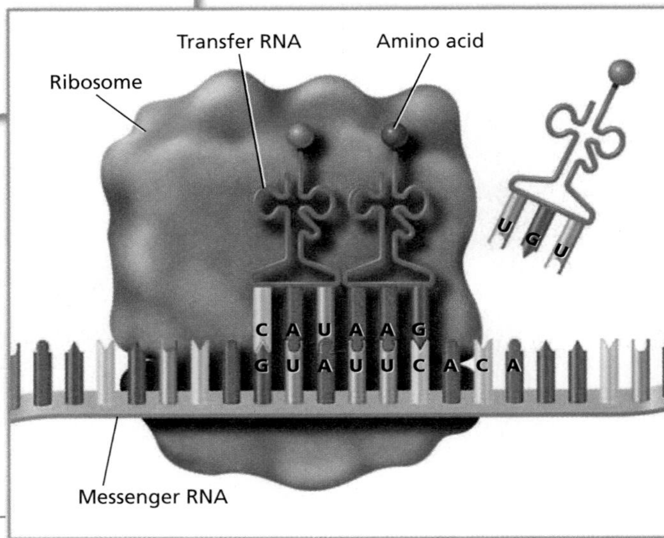

❸ Molecules of transfer RNA attach to the messenger RNA. The bases on the transfer RNA "read" the message by pairing up three-letter codes to bases on the messenger RNA. For example, you can see that a molecule of transfer RNA with the bases AAG pairs with the bases UUC on the messenger RNA. The molecules of transfer RNA carry specific amino acids. The amino acids link in a chain. The order of the amino acids in the chain is determined by the order of the three-letter codes on the messenger RNA.

❹ The protein molecule grows longer as each transfer RNA molecule puts the amino acid it is carrying along the growing protein chain. Once an amino acid is added to the protein chain, the transfer RNA is released into the cytoplasm and can pick up another amino acid. Each transfer RNA molecule always picks up the same kind of amino acid.

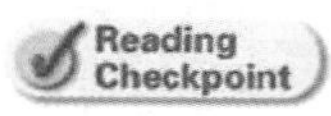

What is the function of transfer RNA?

For: Protein Synthesis activity
Visit: PHSchool.com
Web Code: cep-3034

❸ Transfer RNA Attaches to Messenger RNA ▼
Transfer RNA molecules carry specific amino acids to the ribosome. There they "read" the message in messenger RNA by matching up with three-letter codes of bases. The protein chain grows as each amino acid is attached.

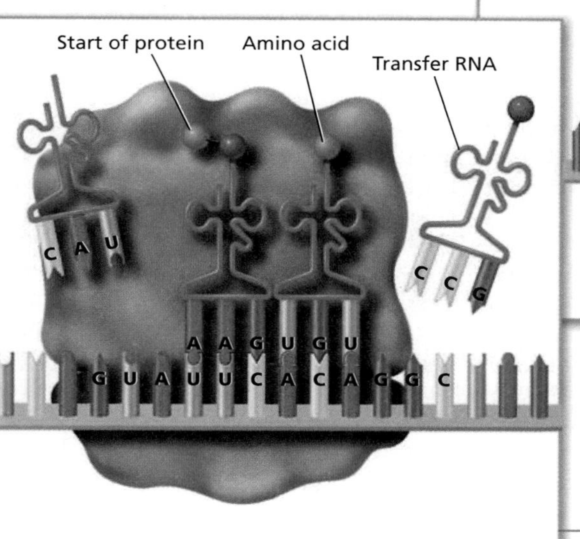

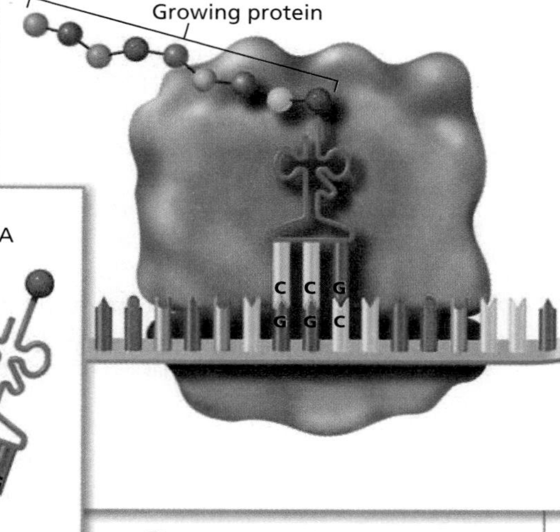

❹ Protein Production Continues ▲
The protein chain continues to grow until the ribosome reaches a three-letter code that acts as a stop sign. The ribosome then releases the completed protein.

For: Protein Synthesis activity
Visit: PHSchool.com
Web Code: cep-3034

Students can interact with the art of protein synthesis online.

L2

Modeling Protein Synthesis

Materials various craft materials

Time 20 minutes

Focus Summarize the steps in protein synthesis on the board.

Teach Challenge groups of students to make a "human" model of protein synthesis by having members assume the roles of DNA, messenger RNA, transfer RNA, and a ribosome. Students may use craft materials for props and to identify themselves. Ask groups to present their models to the class and explain what is happening in each step.

Apply Ask: **How are molecules of transfer RNA like workers in a factory?** *(Each type of transfer RNA has a different job in the making of proteins.)* **learning modality: kinesthetic**

Differentiated Instruction

Gifted and Talented L3
Researching the Causes of Cancer
Explain that cancer is a disease in which DNA is damaged, and body cells grow out of control. Some types of cancer are inherited, but most are thought to develop as a result of exposure to cancer-causing agents or random events in a cell. Ask interested students to research how these agents damage DNA: tobacco, ultraviolet light, and the hepatitis B virus. These agents cause the majority of lung, skin, and liver cancers, respectively. Have students report their results to the class and describe behaviors to reduce the risk of these cancers. **learning modality: verbal**

Monitor Progress L2

Writing Have students write instructions to a cell on how to make proteins. Instructions should include the roles of messenger RNA and transfer RNA, and the cell structures involved in protein synthesis. Students may place their instructions in their portfolio.

Answers
Figure 17 The ribosome
Reading Checkpoint To carry amino acids and add them to the growing protein chain

Mutations

Genetics: The Science of Heredity

Show the Video Field Trip to let students understand human genes and DNA.

Teach Key Concepts L2

How Mutations Affect an Organism

Focus Remind students that protein synthesis is a very precise process.

Teach Ask: **In what ways can a mistake be made in this process?** *(A single base may be substituted, added, or deleted during replication; chromosomes may not separate correctly during meiosis.)* **What are these mistakes called?** *(Mutations)* **How can mutations affect an organism?** *(They can be helpful or harmful depending on the environment.)*

Apply Have students make models of the mutations shown in the text and show why mutations in body cells do not affect offspring. **learning modality: kinesthetic**

All in One Teaching Resources

- Transparency C31

Address Misconceptions L1

Mutations Can Be Harmless or Helpful

Focus Some students may think that mutations can be only harmful.

Teach Ask a student to read the last paragraph under "Effects of Mutations" aloud. Explain what antibiotic resistance is. Ask: **How are the mutations that produce antibiotic resistance helpful to bacteria?** *(They enable bacteria to survive in the presence of antibiotics.)*

Apply Ask: **What kind of mutation might help an animal survive in a desert?** *(Possible answer: a mutation that reduced the animal's need for water.)* **learning modality: visual**

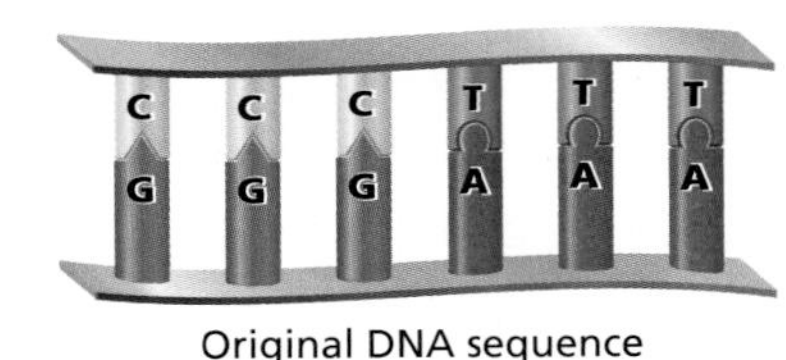

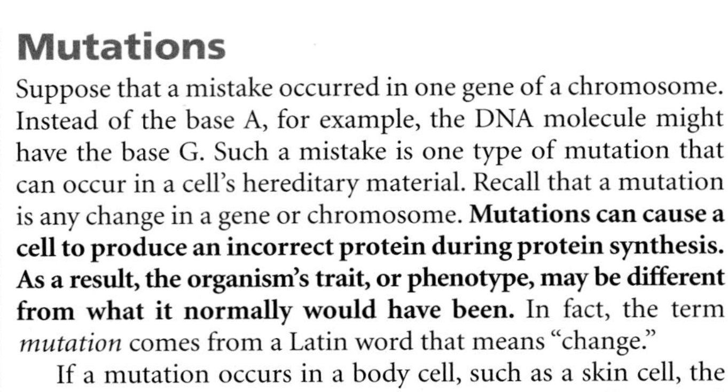

FIGURE 18
Mutations in Genes
The illustration shows three types of mutations that can occur in genes. **Comparing and Contrasting** *How are these mutations different from the mutations that occur when chromosomes do not separate during meiosis?*

Mutations

Suppose that a mistake occurred in one gene of a chromosome. Instead of the base A, for example, the DNA molecule might have the base G. Such a mistake is one type of mutation that can occur in a cell's hereditary material. Recall that a mutation is any change in a gene or chromosome. **Mutations can cause a cell to produce an incorrect protein during protein synthesis. As a result, the organism's trait, or phenotype, may be different from what it normally would have been.** In fact, the term *mutation* comes from a Latin word that means "change."

If a mutation occurs in a body cell, such as a skin cell, the mutation will not be passed on to the organism's offspring. If, however, a mutation occurs in a sex cell, the mutation can be passed on to an offspring and affect the offspring's phenotype.

Types of Mutations Some mutations are the result of small changes in an organism's hereditary material. For example, a single base may be substituted for another, or one or more bases may be removed from a section of DNA. This type of mutation can occur during the DNA replication process. Other mutations may occur when chromosomes don't separate correctly during meiosis. When this type of mutation occurs, a cell can end up with too many or too few chromosomes. The cell could also end up with extra segments of chromosomes.

Effects of Mutations Because mutations can introduce changes in an organism, they can be a source of genetic variety. Some mutations are harmful to an organism. A few mutations, however, are helpful, and others are neither harmful nor helpful. A mutation is harmful to an organism if it reduces the organism's chance for survival and reproduction.

Whether a mutation is harmful or not depends partly on the organism's environment. The mutation that led to the production of a white lemur would probably be harmful to an organism in the wild. The lemur's white color would make it more visible, and thus easier for predators to find. However, a white lemur in a zoo has the same chance for survival as a brown lemur. In a zoo, the mutation neither helps nor harms the lemur.

Helpful mutations, on the other hand, improve an organism's chances for survival and reproduction. Antibiotic resistance in bacteria is an example. Antibiotics are chemicals that kill bacteria. Gene mutations have enabled some kinds of bacteria to become resistant to certain antibiotics—that is, the antibiotics do not kill the bacteria that have the mutations. The mutations have improved the bacteria's ability to survive and reproduce.

Figure 19
Six-Toed Cat
Because of a mutation in one of its ancestors, this cat has six toes on each front paw.

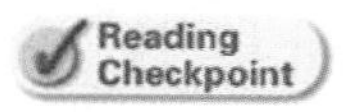

Reading Checkpoint What are two types of mutations?

Section 4 Assessment

Target Reading Skill Sequencing Refer to your flowchart as you answer Question 2.

Reviewing Key Concepts

1. a. Explaining What is the relationship between a gene, a DNA molecule, and a protein?
   b. Relating Cause and Effect How does a DNA molecule determine the structure of a specific protein?
   c. Inferring The DNA base sequence GGG codes for the amino acid proline. Could this same base sequence code for a different amino acid? Why or why not?
2. a. Listing List the sequence of events that happens during protein synthesis.
   b. Describing What is messenger RNA? Describe how it performs its function.
   c. Inferring Does transfer RNA perform its function in the nucleus or cytoplasm? Explain your answer.
3. a. Reviewing How does a mutation in a gene affect the order of DNA bases?
   b. Relating Cause and Effect How can a mutation in a gene cause a change in an organism's phenotype?

Writing in Science

Compare/Contrast Paragraph Write a paragraph comparing and contrasting gene mutations and chromosome mutations. In your paragraph, explain what the two types of mutations are, and how they are similar and different.

Monitor Progress L2

Answers

Figure 18 These mutations involve individual bases rather than entire chromosomes; the number of chromosomes in the cell does not change with this type of mutation.

Reading Checkpoint Mutations involving only a few bases; those that occur when chromosomes do not separate correctly

Assess

1. a. A gene is the part of a DNA molecule that codes for a certain protein. b. The sequence of bases on the DNA molecule codes for the sequence of bases on messenger RNA, which codes for the sequence of amino acids in a protein. c. No, each three-letter code specifies one type of amino acid.
2. a. Messenger RNA is produced using a strand of DNA as a pattern and moves into the cytoplasm where it attaches to a ribosome. There each three-letter code of bases in the messenger RNA is matched to the transfer RNA that carries the specified amino acid. The amino acids are attached in a correct sequence to form a protein molecule. b. It is RNA that copies the coded message from the DNA in the nucleus and carries the message to the ribosome in the cytoplasm. c. The cytoplasm; it carries amino acids to the ribosome and "reads" the messenger RNA.
3. a. A base may be substituted for another; one or more bases may be removed; bases may be added. b. The phenotype of the organism may be different as a result of the incorrect protein.

Reteach L1

Use the figures in this section to summarize the structure of DNA and how cells make proteins.

Performance Assessment L2

Writing Have students compare and contrast the way that bases pair in DNA replication and in translation, and why they are different.

All in One Teaching Resources

- Section Summary: *The DNA Connection*
- Review and Reinforce: *The DNA Connection*
- Enrich: *The DNA Connection*

Lab zone Chapter Project L3

Keep Students on Track Provide students with poster board to display their pet's family in a way that lets the viewers turn the pets over to read their genotypes. Have students construct a Punnett square for each trait. Check that they have correctly shown all the possible genotypes and phenotypes of the F_1 pets based on the genotypes of the parents.

Writing in Science

Writing Mode Compare/Contrast

Scoring Rubric

4 Includes complete description of both types of mutations, and compares and contrasts them; goes beyond requirements
3 Includes complete description but does not go beyond requirements
2 Includes only some of the criteria
1 Includes inaccurate description

Study Guide

- Complete student edition
- Section and chapter self-assessments
- Assessment reports for teachers

Help Students Read

Building Vocabulary

Word-Part Analysis Show students that the term *homozygous* is made up of the Greek words *homos,* meaning "same" and *zygos,* meaning "yoked" or "paired." Taken together, these words describe a cell formed from two gametes that have the same genetic makeup. In *heterozygous, heteros* is the Greek word meaning "other" or "different." This word describes a cell formed from two gametes that have a different genetic makeup.

Words in Context Select Key Terms from the chapter. Have students write a sentence for each term that places the term in a correct context. Provide them with one example before they begin: *Gene: A gene contains instructions for making proteins.*

Connecting Concepts

Concept Maps Help students develop one way to show how the information in this chapter is related. The inheritance of traits is determined by genes that are passed from parents to offspring in a predictable manner and that carry instructions for the synthesis of proteins. Have students brainstorm to identify the Key Concepts, Key Terms, details, and examples, and then write each one on a sticky note and attach it at random on chart paper or on the board.

Tell students that this concept map will be organized in hierarchical order and to begin at the top with the Key Concepts. Ask students these questions to guide them to categorize the information on the stickies: **What controls the inheritance of traits in organisms? How does probability help explain the results of a genetic cross? How does a cell produce proteins?**

Prompt students by using connecting words or phrases, such as "was revolutionized by," "which have the same," and "which show all the possible combinations of," to indicate the basis for the organization of the map. The phrases should form a sentence between or among a set of concepts.

Answer

Accept logical presentations by students.

All in One Teaching Resources

- Key Terms Review: *Genetics: The Science of Heredity*
- Connecting Concepts: *Genetics: The Science of Heredity*

Chapter 3 Study Guide

1 Mendel's Work

Key Concepts

- In all of Mendel's crosses, only one form of the trait appeared in the F_1 generation. However, in the F_2 generation, the "lost" form of the trait always reappeared in about one fourth of the plants.
- An organism's traits are controlled by the alleles it inherits from its parents. Some alleles are dominant, while other alleles are recessive.

Key Terms

heredity
trait
genetics
fertilization
purebred
gene
alleles
dominant allele
recessive allele
hybrid

2 Probability and Heredity

Key Concepts

- Probability is the likelihood that a particular event will occur.
- In a genetic cross, the allele that each parent will pass on to its offspring is based on probability.
- An organism's phenotype is its physical appearance, or visible traits. An organism's genotype is its genetic makeup, or allele combinations.
- In codominance, the alleles are neither dominant nor recessive. As a result, both alleles are expressed in the offspring.

Key Terms

probability
Punnett square
phenotype
genotype
homozygous
heterozygous
codominance

3 The Cell and Inheritance

Key Concepts

- According to the chromosome theory of inheritance, genes are carried from parents to their offspring on chromosomes.
- During meiosis, the chromosome pairs separate and are distributed to two different cells. The resulting sex cells have only half as many chromosomes as the other cells in the organism.
- Chromosomes are made up of many genes joined together like beads on a string.

Key Term

meiosis

4 The DNA Connection

Key Concepts

- The order of the nitrogen bases along a gene forms a genetic code that specifies what type of protein will be produced.
- During protein synthesis, the cell uses information from a gene on a chromosome to produce a specific protein.
- Mutations can cause a cell to produce an incorrect protein during protein synthesis. As a result, the organism's trait, or phenotype, may be different from what it normally would have been.

Key Terms

messenger RNA
transfer RNA

Review and Assessment

Go Online PHSchool.com
For: Self-Assessment
Visit: PHSchool.com
Web Code: cea-3030

Organizing Information

Concept Mapping Copy the concept map onto a separate sheet of paper. Then complete the concept map. (For more on Concept Mapping, see the Skills Handbook.)

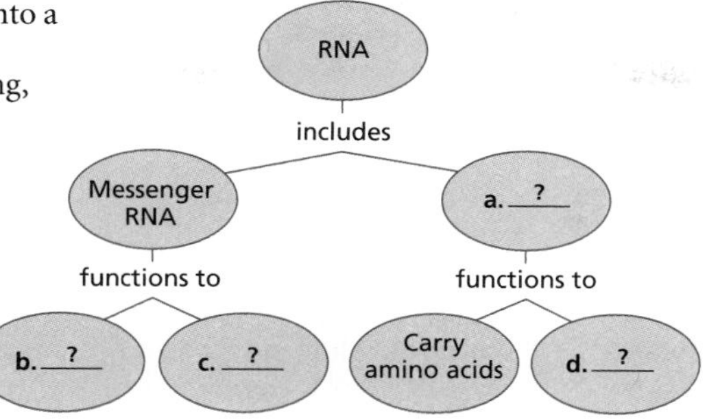

Reviewing Key Terms

Choose the letter of the best answer.

1. The different forms of a gene are called
   a. alleles. **b.** chromosomes.
   c. phenotypes. **d.** genotypes.
2. The likelihood that a particular event will occur is called
   a. chance.
   b. Punnett square.
   c. probability.
   d. recessive.
3. An organism with two identical alleles for a trait is
   a. heterozygous.
   b. homozygous.
   c. recessive.
   d. dominant.
4. If the body cells of an organism have 10 chromosomes, then the sex cells produced during meiosis would have
   a. 5 chromosomes.
   b. 10 chromosomes.
   c. 15 chromosomes.
   d. 20 chromosomes.
5. During protein synthesis, messenger RNA
   a. links one amino acid to another.
   b. releases the completed protein chain.
   c. provides a code from DNA in the nucleus.
   d. carries amino acids to the ribosome.

If the statement is true, write *true*. If it is false, change the underlined word or words to make the statement true.

6. The scientific study of heredity is called genetics.
7. An organism's physical appearance is its genotype.
8. In codominance, neither of the alleles is dominant or recessive.
9. Each transfer RNA molecule picks up one kind of protein.
10. Mutations in body cells are passed to offspring.

Writing in Science

Science Article You are a science reporter for a newspaper. Write an article about gene mutations. Explain what a mutation is and what determines whether it is helpful or harmful.

Genetics: The Science of Heredity
Video Preview
Video Field Trip
▶ Video Assessment

For: Self-Assessment
Visit: PHSchool.com
Web Code: cea-3030

Students can take a practice test online that is automatically scored.

All in One Teaching Resources

- Transparency C32
- Chapter Test
- Performance Assessment Teacher Notes
- Performance Assessment Student Worksheet
- Performance Assessment Scoring Rubric

***ExamView®* Computer Test Bank CD-ROM**

Review and Assessment

Organizing Information

a. Transfer RNA
b. Copy the coded message from the DNA
c. Carry the message to the ribosome in the cytoplasm
d. Add amino acids to the growing protein

Reviewing Key Terms

1. a **2.** c **3.** b **4.** a **5.** c
6. true
7. phenotype
8. true
9. amino acid
10. sex cells

Writing in Science

Writing Mode Description

Scoring Rubric

4 Includes definition of a mutation and what determines whether it is helpful or harmful; goes beyond requirements to explain details of the two types of mutations
3 Includes criteria but does not go beyond requirements to include the types of mutations
2 Includes only part of the criteria
1 Includes inaccurate information

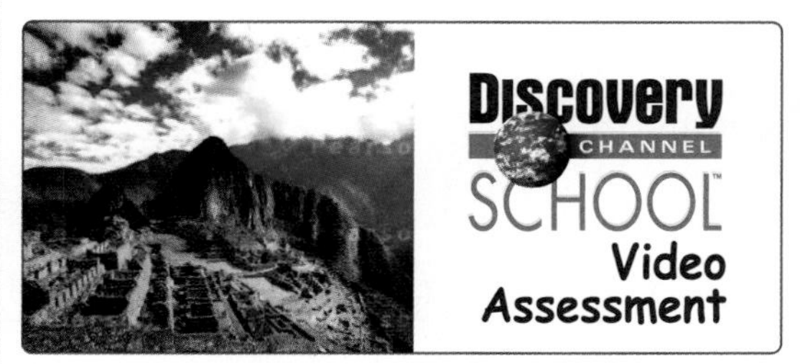

Genetics: The Science of Heredity

Show the Video Assessment to review chapter content and as a prompt for the writing assignment.

Checking Concepts

11. All the first generation offspring were tall.

12. There is a 1 in 2, or 50% chance, that the coin will land heads up on the sixth toss because each coin toss is an independent event. The result of one toss does not affect the following coin tosses.

13. There is a 50 percent (2 in 4) chance that an offspring will have a white coat *(bb)*. The Punnett square should look like the following:

	B	*b*
b	*Bb*	*bb*
b	*Bb*	*bb*

14. Transfer RNA carries the amino acid that corresponds to the code in the messenger RNA and adds it to the growing protein chain.

15. Mutations can cause a cell to produce an incorrect protein during protein synthesis by the substitution of a single base for another, or by adding or removing one or more bases from a section of DNA.

Review and Assessment

Checking Concepts

11. Describe what happened when Mendel crossed purebred tall pea plants with purebred short pea plants.

12. You toss a coin five times and it lands heads up each time. What is the probability that it will land heads up on the sixth toss? Explain your answer.

13. In guinea pigs, the allele for black fur (*B*) is dominant over the allele for white fur (*b*). In a cross between a heterozygous black guinea pig (*Bb*) and a homozygous white guinea pig (*bb*), what is the probability that an offspring will have white fur? Use a Punnett square to answer the question.

14. Describe the role of transfer RNA in protein synthesis.

15. How can mutations affect protein synthesis?

Thinking Critically

16. **Applying Concepts** In rabbits, the allele for a spotted coat is dominant over the allele for a solid-colored coat. A spotted rabbit was crossed with a solid-colored rabbit. The offspring all had spotted coats. What are the probable genotypes of the parents? Explain.

17. **Interpreting Diagrams** The diagram below shows a chromosome pair. For which genes is the organism heterozygous?

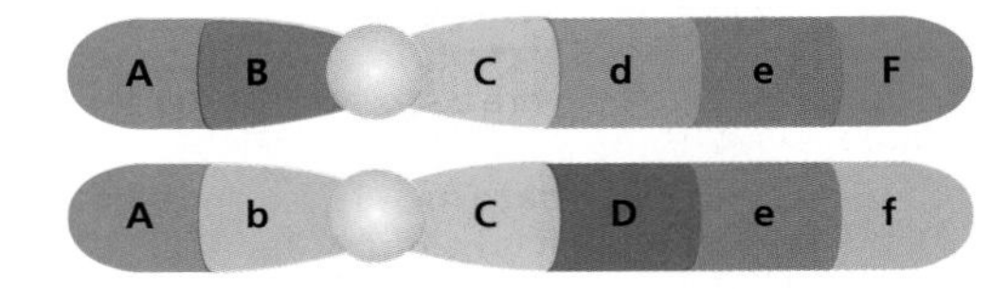

18. **Predicting** A new mutation in mice causes the coat to be twice as thick as normal. In what environments would this mutation be helpful? Why?

19. **Applying Concepts** If the body cells have 12 chromosomes, how many will the sex cells have?

20. **Relating Cause and Effect** Why are mutations that occur in an organism's body cells not passed on to its offspring?

Math Practice

21. **Percentage** A garden has 80 pea plants. Of the plants, 20 have short stems and 60 have tall stems. What percentage of the plants have short stems? What percentage have tall stems?

Applying Skills

Use the information in the table to answer Questions 22–24.

In peas, the allele for green pods (G) is dominant over the allele for yellow pods (g). The table shows the phenotypes of offspring produced from a cross of two plants with green pods.

Phenotype	Number of Offspring
Green pods	27
Yellow pods	9

22. **Calculating Percent** Calculate what percent of the offspring produce green pods. Calculate what percent have yellow pods.

23. **Inferring** What is the genotype of the offspring with yellow pods? What are the possible genotypes of the offspring with green pods?

24. **Drawing Conclusions** What are the genotypes of the parents? How do you know?

Lab zone Chapter Project

Performance Assessment Finalize your display of your pet's family. Be prepared to discuss the inheritance patterns in your pet's family. Examine your classmates' exhibits. See which offspring look most like, and least like, their parents. Can you find any offspring that "break the laws" of inheritance?

L3

Performance Assessment Make sure students understand that "breaking the laws" of inheritance refers to proposed inheritance patterns that violate the principles of heredity. This could happen, for example, when students propose that two homozygous recessive parents produce offspring with one or two dominant alleles.

Reflect and Record Encourage students to record how their paper pets helped them understand specific concepts and principles of genetics. For example, students could describe how the inheritance patterns of their paper pets demonstrated the inheritance of dominant and recessive alleles, or showed the relationship between genotype and phenotype.

Standardized Test Prep

Test-Taking Tip

Sequencing Events

A test question may ask you to arrange a series of events in order. You might be asked which event comes last, or which event comes before another event. Before you answer the question, think about the process the question asks about. Then think of the process's main events and try to put them in order.

For example, the question below asks about protein synthesis. Before looking at the answer choices, try to recall the correct sequence in which the events of protein synthesis occur. Then choose the answer that the question asks for.

Sample Question

Which of the following is the first event in the process of protein synthesis?

- **A** Messenger RNA enters the cytoplasm and attaches to a ribosome.
- **B** The coded message in DNA is copied when a molecule of messenger RNA is formed.
- **C** The protein chain grows until a stop code is reached.
- **D** Transfer RNA molecules carrying amino acids attach to messenger RNA.

Answer

The correct answer is **B.** For protein synthesis to begin, instructions must be carried from DNA in the nucleus to the cytoplasm. Messenger RNA performs that function.

Choose the letter of the best answer.

1. Which of the following is the first step in the formation of sex cells in an organism that has eight chromosomes?
   - **A** The two chromatids of each chromosome separate.
   - **B** Chromosome pairs line up next to each other in the center of the cell.
   - **C** The DNA in the eight chromosomes is copied.
   - **D** The chromatids move apart, producing cells with four chromosomes each.

The Punnett square below shows a cross between two pea plants, each with round seeds. Use the Punnett square to answer Questions 2–4.

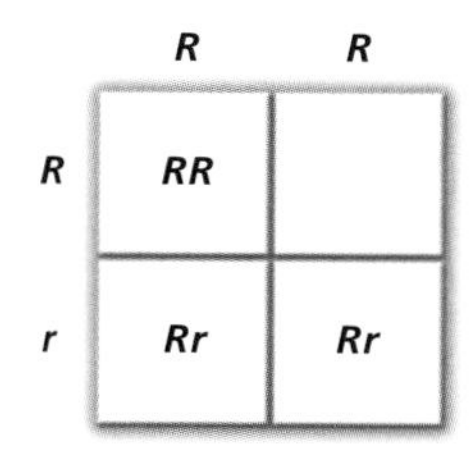

2. The missing genotype in the empty square is correctly written as
   - **F** Rr.
   - **G** rR.
   - **H** rr.
   - **J** RR.
3. Which statement is true about the cross shown in the Punnett square?
   - **A** Both parents are heterozygous for the trait.
   - **B** Both parents are homozygous for the trait.
   - **C** One parent is heterozygous and the other is homozygous for the trait.
   - **D** The trait is controlled by codominant alleles.
4. What percentage of the offspring of this cross will produce round seeds?
   - **F** 0%
   - **G** 25%
   - **H** 50%
   - **J** 100%
5. A section of DNA has the base sequence GCTTAA. The corresponding messenger RNA base sequence will be
   - **A** GCTTAA.
   - **B** CGAAUU.
   - **C** CGAATT.
   - **D** UUTTCG.

Constructed Response

6. Compare the processes and outcomes of mitosis and meiosis.

Standardized Test Prep

1. C **2.** J **3.** C **4.** J **5.** B

6. Sample answer: In mitosis, a cell divides to form two daughter cells that have sets of chromosomes that are complete and identical to each other and to the parent cell. Mitosis allows an organism's body to grow and replace cells. In meiosis, a cell divides twice to eventually produce cells with half the number of chromosomes as the parent cell. Meiosis is how sex cells are produced.

Thinking Critically

16. The solid-colored parent must be homozygous for the recessive allele (*ss*), and the spotted parent is probably homozygous for the dominant allele (*SS*). If the spotted parent were heterozygous (*Ss*), then 50% of the offspring would probably have been solid-colored.

17. B, D, F

18. A thicker coat is a helpful mutation in a very cold environment because it provides extra insulation to keep the mouse warm.

19. Six

20. Mutations in body cells do not affect sex cells. Only sex cells carry alleles to offspring.

Math Practice

21.25% have short stems, and 75% have tall stems.

Applying Skills

22. 75% green pods; 25% yellow pods

23. Yellow pods: *gg;* green pods: *GG* or *Gg*

24. Both parents are *Gg*. If both parents were *GG*, then none of the offspring would have yellow pods. If one parent were *GG* and the other were *Gg*, then again, none of the offspring would have yellow pods. Neither parent could be *gg*, because both parents have green pods, and *g* is a recessive allele for yellow pods.

Chapter at a Glance

PRENTICE HALL TeacherEXPRESS™ Plan • Teach • Assess

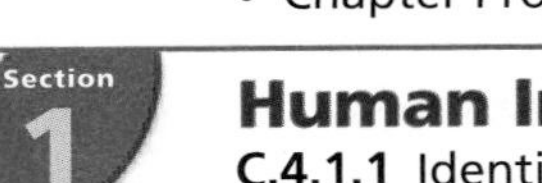

Teach Others About a Trait

Teaching Resources

- Chapter Project Teacher Notes, pp. 230–231
- Chapter Project Student Overview, pp. 232–233
- Chapter Project Student Worksheets, pp. 234–235
- Chapter Project Scoring Rubric, p. 236

Technology:

Video Preview

Local Standards

Human Inheritance

2–3 periods
1–1 1/2 blocks

C.4.1.1 Identify some patterns of inheritance in humans.
C.4.1.2 Describe the functions of the sex chromosomes.
C.4.1.3 Explain the relationship between genes and the environment.

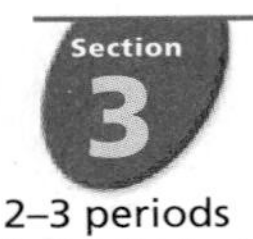

Human Genetic Disorders

2–3 periods
1–1 1/2 blocks

C.4.2.1 Identify two major causes of genetic disorders in humans.
C.4.2.2 Explain how geneticists trace the inheritance of traits.
C.4.2.3 Describe how genetic disorders are diagnosed and treated.

Section 3

Advances in Genetics

2–3 periods
1–1 1/2 blocks

C.4.3.1 Describe three ways of producing organisms with desired traits.
C.4.3.2 State the goal of the Human Genome Project.

Video Field Trip

Review and Assessment

All in One **Teaching Resources**

- Key Terms Review, p. 260
- Transparency C39
- Performance Assessment Teacher Notes, p. 270
- Performance Assessment Scoring Rubric , p. 271
- Performance Assessment Student Worksheet, p. 272
- Chapter Test, pp. 273–276

Go Online PHSchool.com

Video Assessment

Test Preparation

Test Preparation Blackline Masters

Chapter Activities Planner

For more activities

Student Edition	Inquiry	Time	Materials	Skills	Resources
Chapter Project, p. 109	Open-Ended	Ongoing (2 to 3 weeks)	All in One **Teaching Resources,** p. 230	Applying concepts, making models, communicating	**Lab zone Easy Planner** All in One **Teaching Resources,** Support pp. 230–231
Section 1					
Discover Activity, p. 110	Guided	15 minutes	Metric ruler, graph paper	Inferring	**Lab zone Easy Planner**
Try This Activity, p. 113	Guided	10 minutes	None	Designing experiments	**Lab zone Easy Planner**
Section 2					
Discover Activity, p. 117	Directed	10 minutes	None	Inferring	**Lab zone Easy Planner**
Skills Activity, p. 118	Guided	10 minutes	None	Predicting	**Lab zone Easy Planner**
Skills Lab, p. 122	Guided	40 minutes	12 index cards, scissors, marker	Interpreting data, predicting	**Lab zone Easy Planner** **Lab Activity Video** All in One **Teaching Resources,** Skills Lab: *Family Puzzle,* pp. 250–251
Section 3					
Discover Activity, p. 123	Guided	15 minutes	Plain white paper, ink pad, hand lens	Observing	**Lab zone Easy Planner**
Skills Activity, p. 127	Guided	15 minutes	Writing materials	Communicating	**Lab zone Easy Planner**
Skills Lab, p. 129	Guided	20 minutes	4–6 bar codes, hand lens	Drawing conclusions, inferring	**Lab zone Easy Planner** **Lab Activity Video** All in One **Teaching Resources,** Skills Lab: *Guilty or Innocent?,* pp. 258–259

Section 1 Human Inheritance

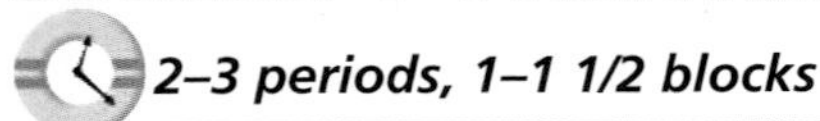
2–3 periods, 1–1 1/2 blocks

ABILITY LEVELS
- L1 Basic to Average
- L2 For All Students
- L3 Average to Advanced

Local Standards

Objectives

C.4.1.1 Identify some patterns of inheritance in humans.
C.4.1.2 Describe the functions of the sex chromosomes.
C.4.1.3 Explain the relationship between genes and the environment.

Key Terms

• multiple alleles • sex chromosomes • sex-linked gene • carrier

Preteach

Build Background Knowledge

Students share observations they have made about inherited traits.

How Tall Is Tall? 

Targeted Print and Technology Resources

All in One Teaching Resources

- L2 Reading Strategy Transparency C33: Identifying Main Ideas

 **PresentationExpress™ CD-ROM**

Instruct

Patterns of Human Inheritance Ask questions about the number of genes or alleles controlling traits to distinguish patterns of inheritance.

The Sex Chromosomes Use a Punnett square to explain the functions of sex chromosomes.

The Effect of Environment Use examples to explain how genes and the environment interact to determine the characteristics of an organism.

Targeted Print and Technology Resources

All in One Teaching Resources

- L2 Guided Reading, pp. 239–241
- L2 Transparency C34

www.SciLinks.org Web Code: scn-0341

Student Edition on Audio CD

Assess

Section Assessment Questions

Have students use their graphic organizers with main ideas and details to help them answer the questions.

Reteach

Use the figures in the section to review how sex is determined and how a sex-linked trait is inherited.

Targeted Print and Technology Resources

All in One Teaching Resources

- Section Summary, p. 238
- L1 Review and Reinforce, p. 242
- L3 Enrich, p. 243

Section 2 Human Genetic Disorders

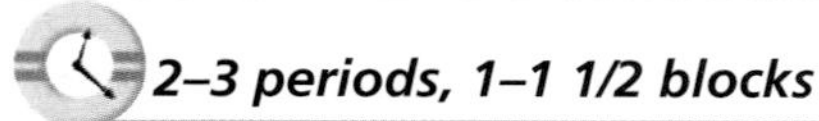
2–3 periods, 1–1 1/2 blocks

ABILITY LEVELS
- L1 Basic to Average
- L2 For All Students
- L3 Average to Advanced

Objectives

C.4.2.1 Identify two major causes of genetic disorders in humans.
C.4.2.2 Explain how geneticists trace the inheritance of traits.
C.4.2.3 Describe how genetic disorders are diagnosed and treated.

Local Standards

Key Terms

• genetic disorder • pedigree • karyotype

Preteach

Build Background Knowledge

Invite students to discuss the definition of a genetic disorder and to name examples.

How Many Chromosomes? 

Targeted Print and Technology Resources

All in One Teaching Resources

- L2 Reading Strategy Transparency C35: Comparing and Contrasting

PresentationExpress™ CD-ROM

Instruct

Causes of Genetic Disorders Discuss four genetic disorders in terms of their causes.

Pedigrees Use a pedigree to explain how inheritance is traced.

Managing Genetic Disorders Ask questions to help students consider how genetic disorders are diagnosed and treated.

Skills Lab *Family Puzzle* 

Targeted Print and Technology Resources

All in One Teaching Resources

- L2 Guided Reading, pp. 246–247
- L2 Transparency C36
- L2 Skills Lab: *Family Puzzle*, pp. 250–251

Lab Activity Video/DVD
Skills Lab: *Family Puzzle*

PHSchool.com Web Code: cep-3042

Student Edition on Audio CD

Assess

Section Assessment Questions

Have students use their graphic organizers comparing and contrasting genetic disorders to answer the questions.

Reteach

Use pedigrees to review how inheritance of traits can be traced in a family.

Targeted Print and Technology Resources

All in One Teaching Resources

- Section Summary, p. 245
- L1 Review and Reinforce, p. 248
- L3 Enrich, p. 249

Section 3 Advances in Genetics

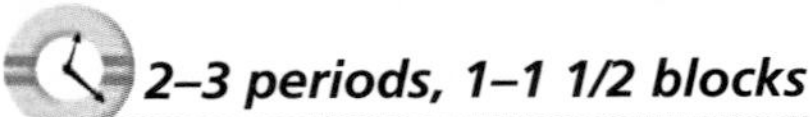
2–3 periods, 1–1 1/2 blocks

ABILITY LEVELS
- L1 Basic to Average
- L2 For All Students
- L3 Average to Advanced

Local Standards

Objectives

C.4.3.1 Describe three ways of producing organisms with desired traits.
C.4.3.2 State the goal of the Human Genome Project.

Key Terms

• selective breeding • inbreeding • hybridization • clone
• genetic engineering • gene therapy • genome

Preteach

Build Background Knowledge

Relate selective breeding to different breeds of dogs.

 *What Do Fingerprints Reveal?* 

Targeted Print and Technology Resources

 **Teaching Resources**

- L2 Reading Strategy Transparency C37: Asking Questions

 **PresentationExpress™ CD-ROM**

Instruct

Selective Breeding Use an example to define selective breeding, and discuss the different methods.

Cloning Explain how plants and animals can be cloned.

Genetic Engineering Use a diagram with ordered steps to describe genetic engineering.

Learning About Human Genetics Discuss the goal of the Human Genome Project.

 *Guilty or Innocent?* 

Targeted Print and Technology Resources

All in One Teaching Resources

- L2 Guided Reading, pp. 254–255
- L2 Transparency C38
- L2 Skills Lab: *Guilty or Innocent?,* pp. 258–259

Lab Activity Video/DVD
Skills Lab: *Guilty or Innocent?*

Video Field Trip

www.SciLinks.org Web Code: scn-0343

PHSchool.com Web Code: 3040

 **Student Edition on Audio CD**

Assess

Section Assessment Questions

Have students use their Asking Questions graphic organizers to help them answer the questions.

Reteach

Ask students to orally describe the different methods of producing organisms with desirable traits.

Targeted Print and Technology Resources

All in One Teaching Resources

- Section Summary, p. 253
- L1 Review and Reinforce, p. 256
- L3 Enrich, p. 257

Chapter 4 Content Refresher

For: Professional development support
Visit: www.SciLinks.org/PDLinks
Web Code: scf-0340

Professional Development

Section 1 Human Inheritance

Sex-Linked Inheritance Patterns Traits controlled by sex-linked recessive alleles often appear to skip generations in a pedigree. Such traits may pass from a man through his daughters, who do not have the trait but are carriers, to his grandsons. When a trait shows this inheritance pattern, it is likely to be controlled by a sex-linked recessive allele carried on the X chromosome.

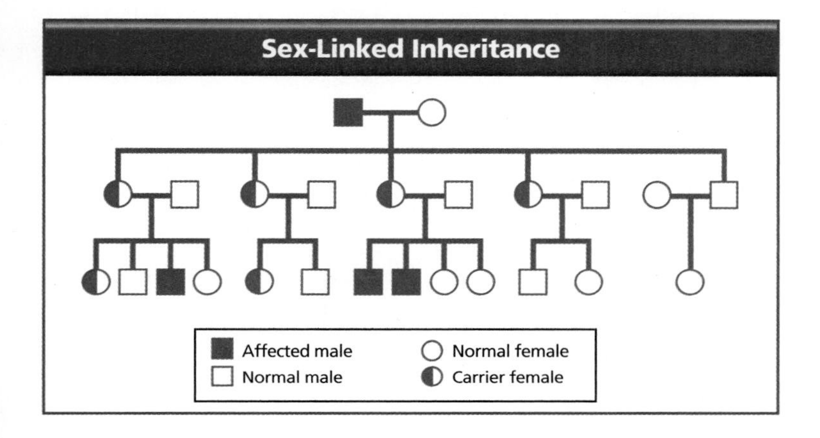

Section 2 Human Genetic Disorders

Too Many Chromosomes In addition to Down syndrome, a number of other syndromes are caused by extra chromosomes in a person's cells. Edwards syndrome is caused by an extra copy of chromosome 18. It occurs about once in every 8,000 live births. Symptoms include mental retardation and malformations of the head, heart, and kidneys. Death usually occurs in the first year. Patau syndrome is caused by an extra copy of chromosome 13. It occurs about once in every 20,000 live births. Symptoms include mental retardation and defects of the hands, heart, and genitals. Death typically occurs by age one. Klinefelter's syndrome is caused by an extra X chromosome in males. It occurs about once in every 500 live male births. Symptoms may include feminine features, sterility, and behavioral problems.

Address Misconceptions

Students may think that all genetic disorders will soon be cured with gene therapy. However, many genetic diseases cannot be cured in this way. For a strategy for overcoming this misconception, see **Address Misconceptions** in the section *Advances in Genetics.*

Section 3 Advances in Genetics

Gene Technology Two major problems must be solved in developing gene therapy for a particular genetic disorder. The first problem is finding the best way to correct the genetic defect that is causing the disorder. Options may include correcting a defective cell product, increasing the production of a cell product that is lacking, making diseased cells weaker, or blocking the operation of diseased cells. The other problem that must be solved is finding a way to carry the genetically engineered DNA to target cells. Viruses make excellent candidates for this role because of their ability to infect living cells. However, before a virus can be used safely, the viral DNA must be genetically engineered to make the virus harmless to the human patient.

Help Students Read

Directed Reading/Thinking Activity

Predict, Read, Confirm, Revise Predictions

Strategy Help students develop their own reading and thinking processes by setting a purpose for reading. Select a section of this chapter for students to read. Before modeling the strategy with students, divide the targeted section into approximately four equal portions. Present the steps as in the example below.

Example

1. **Preview** Tell students to survey the section by analyzing the titles, headings, visual elements, and boldfaced type. Have students also read the introductory and concluding paragraphs.
2. **Predict/Generate Questions** Ask students to predict and describe what they will learn, and to formulate their own questions that a teacher might ask. List students' questions on the board.
3. **Read/Evaluate and Refine Predictions** Have students read a portion of the section. Pause afterward for students to evaluate their predictions. Discuss any questions the text answered and prior misconceptions the text clarified. Ask students to formulate refined predictions and questions based on the new information.
4. Repeat the process for the remaining text portions.

- Complete student edition
- Video and audio
- Simulations and activities
- Section and chapter reviews

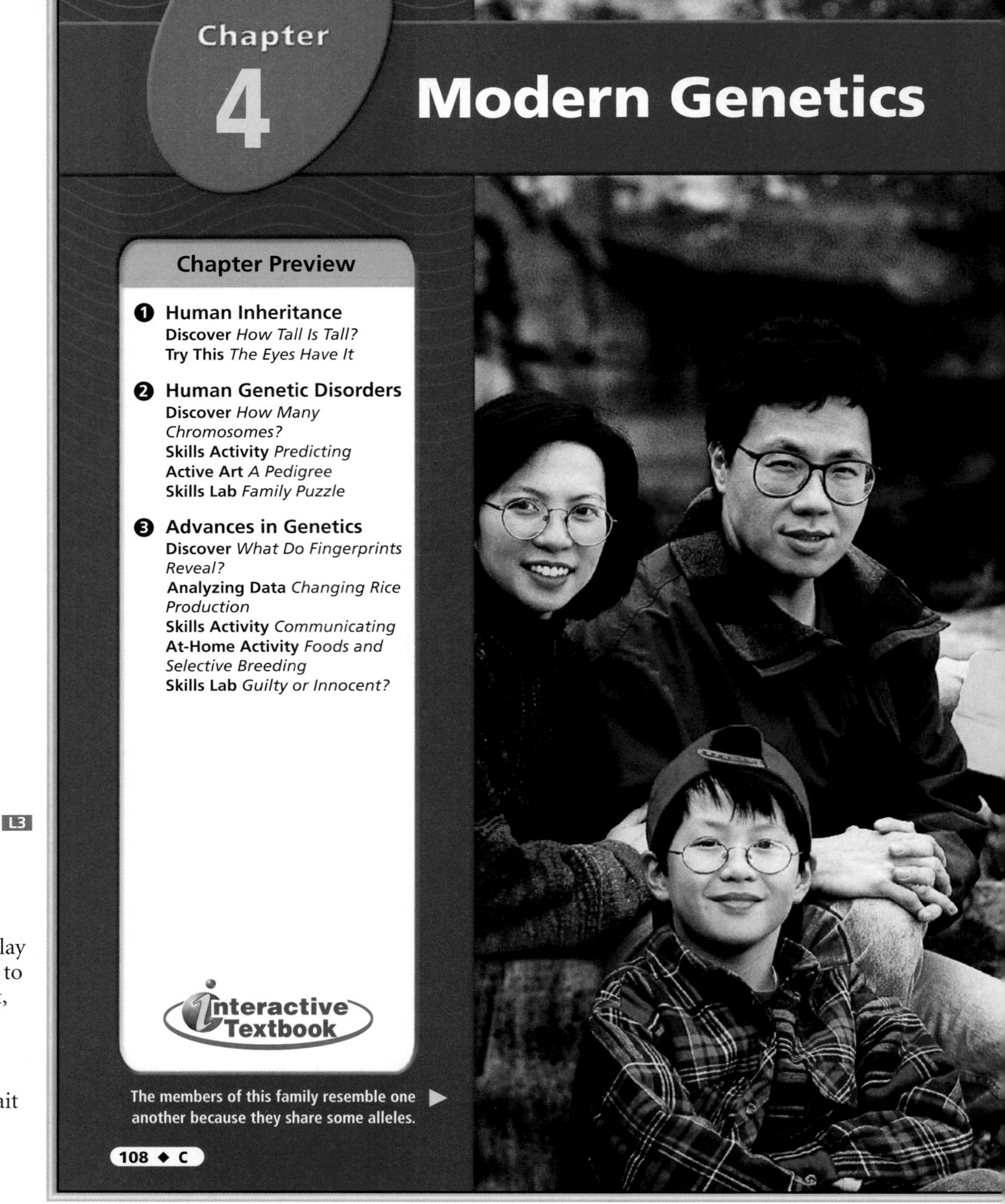

The members of this family resemble one another because they share some alleles.

L3

Objectives

This project will give students an opportunity to learn about a genetically inherited trait. Students will design a display that communicates their findings visually to young children. After this Chapter Project, students will be able to

- apply genetic concepts to describe inheritance patterns for a specific trait
- make a visual display showing how a trait is inherited and whom it can affect
- communicate information concerning inheritance of genes

Skills Focus

Applying concepts, making models, communicating

Project Time Line 2 to 3 weeks

All in One Teaching Resources

- Chapter Project Teacher Notes
- Chapter Project Overview
- Chapter Project Worksheet 1
- Chapter Project Worksheet 2
- Chapter Project Scoring Rubric

Developing a Plan

On the first day, allow class time for research and the exchange of ideas. On the second day, have students work on ideas for creating the displays. Request detailed sketches of plans during the next few days. After your approval, students will spend eight to ten days researching the traits and building their displays. Allow one or two class periods for students to present their displays to the class or to younger children.

Possible Materials

- Encourage students to use videos, computers, and art media.
- For posters, provide poster board, colored pens, construction paper, and an assortment of magazines and newspapers.

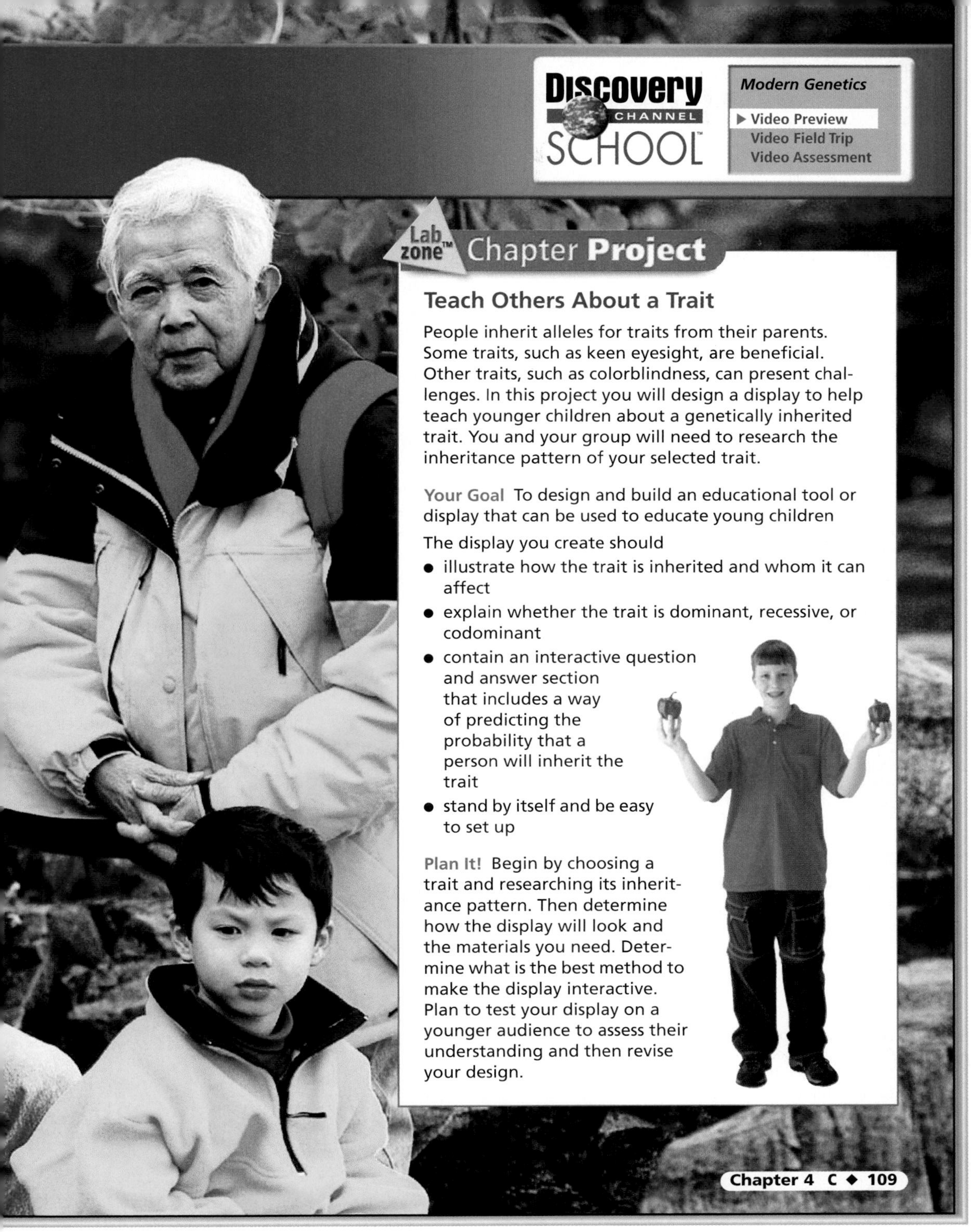

Discovery Channel School

Modern Genetics

▶ Video Preview
Video Field Trip
Video Assessment

Lab zone™ Chapter **Project**

Teach Others About a Trait

People inherit alleles for traits from their parents. Some traits, such as keen eyesight, are beneficial. Other traits, such as colorblindness, can present challenges. In this project you will design a display to help teach younger children about a genetically inherited trait. You and your group will need to research the inheritance pattern of your selected trait.

Your Goal To design and build an educational tool or display that can be used to educate young children

The display you create should
- illustrate how the trait is inherited and whom it can affect
- explain whether the trait is dominant, recessive, or codominant
- contain an interactive question and answer section that includes a way of predicting the probability that a person will inherit the trait
- stand by itself and be easy to set up

Plan It! Begin by choosing a trait and researching its inheritance pattern. Then determine how the display will look and the materials you need. Determine what is the best method to make the display interactive. Plan to test your display on a younger audience to assess their understanding and then revise your design.

Chapter 4 C ◆ 109

Modern Genetics

Show the Video Preview to introduce a topic related to the chapter.

Launching the Project

Call students' attention to the family photograph on these pages and ask: **What are some traits that the children in this family appear to share with their parents?** *(Students are likely to name obvious physical traits such as hair color or nose shape.)* Point out that in addition to traits such as these, children inherit thousands of other traits from their parents, including many traits that are not so apparent. Tell students that in this project, they will research how genetic traits pass from one generation to the next.

Performance Assessment

The Chapter Project Scoring Rubric will help you evaluate how well students complete the Chapter Project. You may want to share the scoring rubric with your students so they are clear about what will be expected of them. Students will be assessed on
- the thoroughness of their research on the genetically inherited trait
- the accuracy and creativity of their display
- the thoroughness and organization of their presentation of the display to a younger audience
- how well students work with others

Section 1 Human Inheritance

Objectives

After this lesson, students will be able to

C.4.1.1 Identify some patterns of inheritance in humans.

C.4.1.2 Describe the functions of the sex chromosomes.

C.4.1.3 Explain the relationship between genes and the environment.

Target Reading Skill

Identifying Main Ideas Explain that identifying main ideas and details helps students sort information into groups. Each group can have a main topic, subtopics, and details.

Answers

Possible answers:

Main Idea: Human traits are controlled by single genes with two alleles, single genes with multiple alleles, and multiple genes.

Details: Human traits controlled by single genes with two alleles have two distinctly different phenotypes; though a single gene can have multiple alleles, a person can carry only two of these alleles; multiple genes that control a trait act together to produce a single trait with a large number of phenotypes.

All in One Teaching Resources

- Transparency C33

Preteach

Build Background Knowledge L1

Recognizing Inherited Traits

Help students think of examples of inherited traits by asking: **What are some traits that children may share with one or both of their parents?** *(Students are likely to identify traits such as hair color, nose shape, or eye color.)*

Section 1 Human Inheritance

Reading Preview

Key Concepts

- What are some patterns of inheritance in humans?
- What are the functions of the sex chromosomes?
- What is the relationship between genes and the environment?

Key Terms

- multiple alleles
- sex chromosomes
- sex-linked gene
- carrier

Target Reading Skill

Identifying Main Ideas

As you read the Patterns of Human Inheritance section, write the main idea—the biggest or most important idea—in a graphic organizer like the one below. Then write three supporting details that further explain the main idea.

Main Idea

Human traits are controlled by single genes with two alleles, single genes with . . .

Detail | Detail | Detail

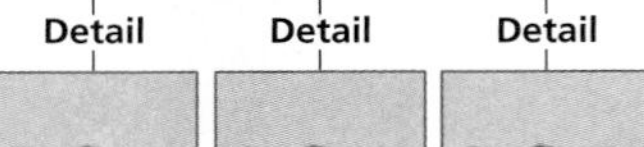

Lab zone Discover Activity

How Tall Is Tall?

1. Choose a partner. Measure each other's height to the nearest 5 centimeters. Record your measurements on the chalkboard.
2. Create a bar graph showing the number of students at each height. Plot the heights on the horizontal axis and the number of students on the vertical axis.

Think It Over

Inferring Do you think height in humans is controlled by a single gene, as it is in peas? Explain your answer.

The arrival of a baby is a happy event. Eagerly, the parents and grandparents gather around to admire the newborn baby. "Don't you think she looks like her father?" "Yes, but she has her mother's eyes."

When a baby is born, the parents, their families, and their friends try to determine whom the baby resembles. Chances are good that the baby will look a little bit like both parents. That is because both parents pass alleles for traits on to their offspring.

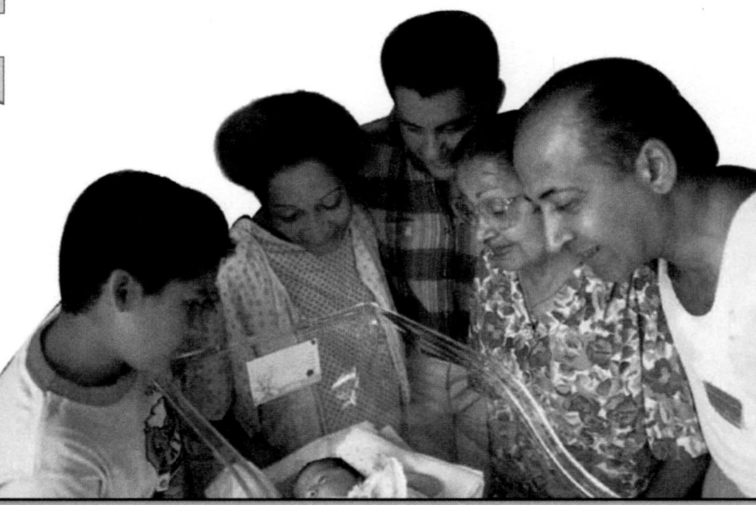

FIGURE 1
Family Resemblance
Because children inherit alleles for traits from their mother and father, children often look like their parents.

Lab zone Discover Activity

Skills Focus Inferring L1

Materials metric ruler, graph paper

Time 15 minutes

Tips If any students are in wheelchairs, you might want to have the class measure sitting height, which is the height from the base of the spine to the top of the head.

Expected Outcome The graph of students' heights is likely to include several bars, but not as many as there are students in the class.

Think It Over Students may infer that height in humans is controlled by more than one gene because the graph of students' heights has more bars than the two-bar graph Mendel would have drawn for the traits he studied.

Patterns of Human Inheritance

Take a few seconds to look at the other students in your classroom. Some people have curly hair; others have straight hair. Some people are tall, some are short, and many others are in between. You'll probably see eyes of many different colors, ranging from pale blue to dark brown. The different traits you see are determined by a variety of inheritance patterns. **Some human traits are controlled by single genes with two alleles, and others by single genes with multiple alleles. Still other traits are controlled by many genes that act together.**

Single Genes With Two Alleles A number of human traits are controlled by a single gene with one dominant allele and one recessive allele. These human traits have two distinctly different phenotypes, or physical appearances.

For example, a widow's peak is a hairline that comes to a point in the middle of the forehead. The allele for a widow's peak is dominant over the allele for a straight hairline. The Punnett square in Figure 2 illustrates a cross between two parents who are heterozygous for a widow's peak. Trace the possible combinations of alleles that a child may inherit. Notice that each child has a 3 in 4, or 75 percent, probability of having a widow's peak. There is only a 1 in 4, or 25 percent, probability that a child will have a straight hairline. When Mendel crossed peas that were heterozygous for a trait, he obtained similar percentages in the offspring.

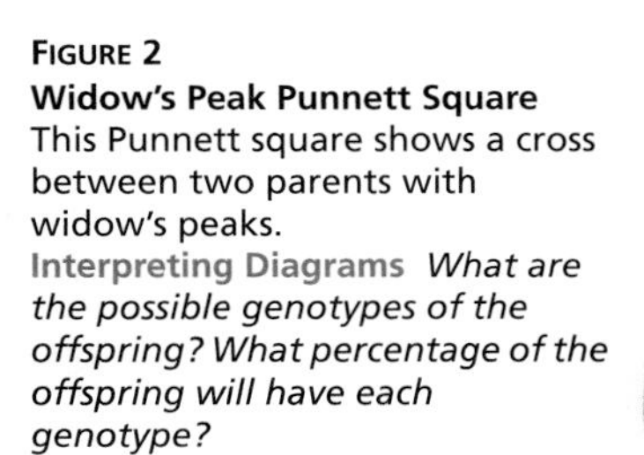

FIGURE 2
Widow's Peak Punnett Square
This Punnett square shows a cross between two parents with widow's peaks.
Interpreting Diagrams *What are the possible genotypes of the offspring? What percentage of the offspring will have each genotype?*

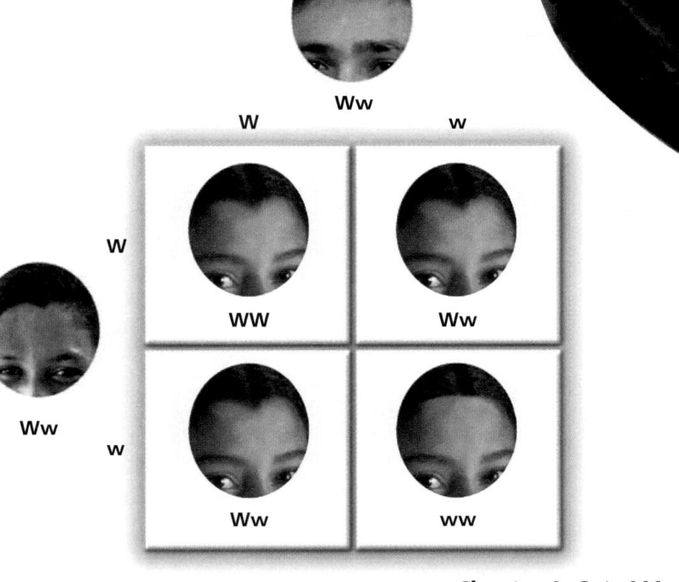

Instruct

Patterns of Human Inheritance

Teach Key Concepts L2

The Different Patterns of Inheritance

Focus Review the meanings of genotype and phenotype.

Teach Refer students to Figure 2. Ask: **What are the two alleles that parents could pass to their offspring?** *(Ww)* **How many genes control the inheritance of a widow's peak?** *(One)* **How many different alleles are involved?** *(Two)* Explain that one gene with two alleles is one pattern of inheritance. Another pattern is traits that are controlled by one gene with more than two alleles. Ask: **How many genes control the inheritance of blood type?** *(One)* **How many different alleles are involved?** *(Three)* **What is a third pattern of inheritance?** *(Traits controlled by many genes)* **How might you know that a trait is controlled by many genes?** *(It has a large number of phenotypes.)*

Apply Explain that human genes are inherited according to the same principles that Mendel discovered. Traits are determined by dominance or codominance regardless of the number of genes involved. **learning modality: verbal**

Independent Practice L2

All in One Teaching Resources

- Guided Reading and Study Worksheet: *Human Inheritance*

Student Edition on Audio CD

Differentiated Instruction

Less Proficient Readers L1

Making a Picture Dictionary Before students read this section, have them review the meanings of the terms *chromosome, gene, allele, trait, dominant, recessive, phenotype, genotype,* and *codominance.* Have students work in pairs to come up with simple definitions of each term using words they are familiar with. Then have them illustrate each term and use their terms and illustrations to create a picture dictionary. Encourage students to share their pictures with one another to reinforce their understanding. **learning modality: visual**

Monitor Progress L2

Drawing Have students draw a Punnett square that shows a cross between two heterozygotes for smile dimples (a trait controlled by a dominant allele).

Answer

Figure 2 *WW, Ww,* and *ww;* 25% will possibly have the *WW* genotype, 50% the *Ww* genotype, and 25% the *ww* genotype.

Help Students Read L2

Directed Reading/Thinking Activity (DRTA) Refer to the Content Refresher for guidelines on DRTA. Have students read the main headings and subheadings for the rest of this section. Then, have them make predictions about the main ideas that will be presented. For example, they may predict that some genes are found in males only or in females only. They may also form questions about the text, such as "How is colorblindness inherited?" Record all ideas on the board. After students have finished reading the section, have students confirm which of their predictions were correct, and provide answers to questions that were addressed in the passage.

Use Visuals: Figure 3 L2

Understanding Blood Types

Focus Remind students that some genes have more than two alleles.

Teach Make sure that students understand that the superscripts in Figure 3 are not exponents but labels that distinguish the two codominant alleles, I^A and I^B. Ask: **Which column in the table lists the genotypes? Which lists the phenotypes for blood types?** *(The right column lists the genotypes; the left column the phenotypes.)* **Which alleles are codominant?** *(*I^A *and* I^B*)* **What kind of allele is the *i*?** *(Recessive)*

Apply Ask: **Why are there more genotypes than phenotypes for blood types?** *(Two different genotypes—*I^AI^A *and* I^Ai*—result in the A phenotype, and two other genotypes—*I^BI^B *and* I^Bi*—result in the B phenotype.)* **learning modality: visual**

FIGURE 3
Inheritance of Blood Type
Blood type is determined by a single gene with three alleles. This chart shows which combinations of alleles result in each blood type.

Alleles of Blood Types

Blood Type	Combination of Alleles
A	I^AI^A or I^Ai
B	I^BI^B or I^Bi
AB	I^AI^B
O	ii

Single Genes With Multiple Alleles Some human traits are controlled by a single gene that has more than two alleles. Such a gene is said to have **multiple alleles**—three or more forms of a gene that code for a single trait. Even though a gene may have multiple alleles, a person can carry only two of those alleles. This is because chromosomes exist in pairs. Each chromosome in a pair carries only one allele for each gene.

Human blood type is controlled by a gene with multiple alleles. There are four main blood types—A, B, AB, and O. Three alleles control the inheritance of blood types. The allele for blood type A and the allele for blood type B are codominant. The allele for blood type A is written as I^A. The allele for blood type B is written I^B. The allele for blood type O—written *i*—is recessive. Recall that when two codominant alleles are inherited, neither allele is masked. A person who inherits an I^A allele from one parent and an I^B allele from the other parent will have type AB blood. Figure 3 shows the allele combinations that result in each blood type. Notice that only people who inherit two *i* alleles have type O blood.

Traits Controlled by Many Genes If you completed the Discover activity, you saw that height in humans has more than two distinct phenotypes. In fact, there is an enormous variety of phenotypes for height. Some human traits show a large number of phenotypes because the traits are controlled by many genes. The genes act together as a group to produce a single trait. At least four genes control height in humans, so there are many possible combinations of genes and alleles. Skin color is another human trait that is controlled by many genes.

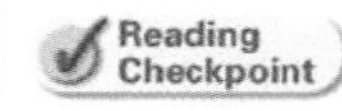

Why do some traits exhibit a large number of phenotypes?

FIGURE 4
Many Phenotypes
Skin color in humans is determined by three or more genes. Different combinations of alleles for each of the genes result in a wide range of possible skin colors.

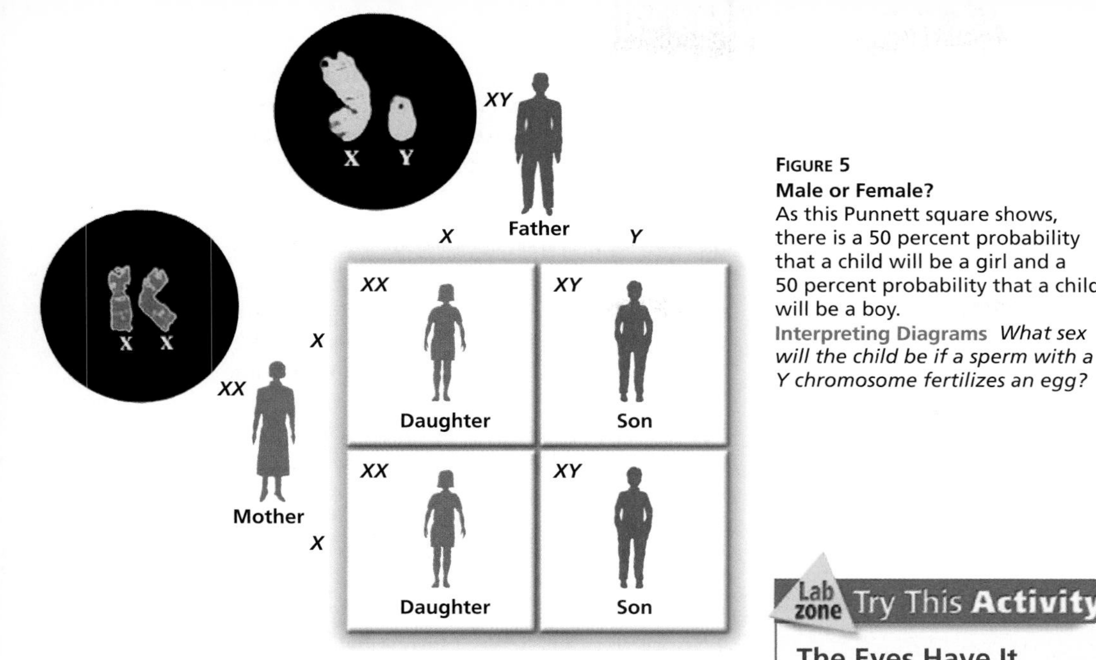

FIGURE 5
Male or Female?
As this Punnett square shows, there is a 50 percent probability that a child will be a girl and a 50 percent probability that a child will be a boy.
Interpreting Diagrams *What sex will the child be if a sperm with a Y chromosome fertilizes an egg?*

The Sex Chromosomes

The **sex chromosomes** are one of the 23 pairs of chromosomes in each body cell. **The sex chromosomes carry genes that determine whether a person is male or female. They also carry genes that determine other traits.**

Girl or Boy? The sex chromosomes are the only chromosome pair that do not always match. If you are a girl, your two sex chromosomes match. The two chromosomes are called X chromosomes. If you are a boy, your sex chromosomes do not match. One of them is an X chromosome, and the other is a Y chromosome. The Y chromosome is much smaller than the X chromosome.

Sex Chromosomes and Fertilization What happens to the sex chromosomes when egg and sperm cells form? Since both of a female's sex chromosomes are X chromosomes, all eggs carry one X chromosome. Males, however, have two different sex chromosomes. Therefore, half of a male's sperm cells carry an X chromosome, while half carry a Y chromosome.

When a sperm cell with an X chromosome fertilizes an egg, the egg has two X chromosomes. The fertilized egg will develop into a girl. When a sperm with a Y chromosome fertilizes an egg, the egg has one X chromosome and one Y chromosome. The fertilized egg will develop into a boy.

Lab zone Try This Activity

The Eyes Have It

One inherited trait is eye dominance—the tendency to use one eye more than the other. Here's how you can test yourself for this trait.

1. Hold your hand out in front of you at arm's length. Point your finger at an object across the room.
2. Close your right eye. With only your left eye open, observe how far your finger appears to move.
3. Repeat Step 2 with the right eye open. With which eye did your finger seem to remain closer to the object? That eye is dominant.

Designing Experiments
Is eye dominance related to hand dominance—whether a person is right-handed or left-handed? Design an experiment to find out. *Obtain your teacher's permission before carrying out your experiment.*

The Sex Chromosomes

Teach Key Concepts L2

Functions of Sex Chromosomes

Focus Refer students to Figure 5.

Teach Ask: **What determines whether a person is male or female?** *(Sex chromosomes)* **What combinations result in a male and in a female?** *(XY and XX)* Ask: **What other role do the sex chromosomes play?** *(They carry genes that determine other traits.)* **How is inheritance different between recessive genes on sex chromosomes and on other chromosomes?** *(It is rarer for a female to have the trait than a male.)*

Apply Ask: **If the man in Figure 5 had an allele *A* on his *X* chromosome, who would inherit it?** *(Only the daughters; the man's sons inherit only the* Y *chromosome from their father.)* **learning modality: logical/mathematical**

All in One Teaching Resources
- Transparency C34

L2

Applying Concepts of Inheritance

Materials colored pencils

Time 15 minutes

Focus Review the steps in meiosis.

Teach Challenge students to draw two simple diagrams of meiosis, contrasting the formation of sex cells in males and in females.

Apply Ask: **How do your diagrams show that the sperm determines the sex of a child?** *(Male sex cells contain an* X *or a* Y *chromosome, whereas female sex cells contain only an* X *chromosome.)* **learning modality: visual**

Lab zone Try This Activity

Skills Focus Designing experiments L2

Materials none

Time 10 minutes

Tips Make sure students focus on an object that is at least a few meters away from them.

Expected Outcome When students close one eye, their finger appears to be stationary; when they close the other eye, their finger appears to move. The right eye is dominant if the finger appears stationary when looking at it with the right eye, the left eye if looking at it with the left eye. One possible design for an experiment is to determine eye and hand dominance for a large sample of people, and look for patterns.

Monitor Progress L2

Writing Have students explain in their own words why about half of all babies born are boys and about half are girls. Students can place their paragraphs in their portfolios. Portfolio

Answers

Figure 5 Male

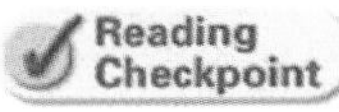

The traits are controlled by many genes.

Use Visuals: Figure 7 L2

Determining Colorblindness

Focus Remind students that for a recessive allele to show up in females, there must be one on each of the two X chromosomes that she inherits.

Teach Discuss the symbols used in the Punnett square. Then ask: **Why is the box for one son shaded?** *(He is colorblind.)* **Would you expect the son who is colorblind to have sons who are colorblind?** *(No; he can pass only the Y chromosome to his sons.)*

Apply Ask students to determine the alleles of both parents if there is a 50% chance that either a son or a daughter will be colorblind. *(The father would be colorblind and have alleles X^cY. The mother would be a carrier and have the alleles X^CX^c.)* **learning modality: visual**

L2

Modeling Sex-Linked Inheritance

Materials white, red, and green pipe cleaners

Time 15 minutes

Focus Remind students that all X-linked alleles are expressed in males, even if they are recessive, because males have just one X chromosome.

Teach Have students twist together two white pipe cleaners to represent a normal X chromosome, a red pipe cleaner and a green pipe cleaner to represent an X chromosome with the allele for red-green colorblindness, and a single white pipe cleaner to represent a Y chromosome. Encourage students to use their models to represent several different crosses and their expected outcomes.

Apply Have students use their models to answer these questions: **If the mother is colorblind and the father has normal vision, what is the probability that their sons will be colorblind?** *(100%)* **If the father is colorblind and the mother has normal vision, what is the probability that their daughters will be colorblind?** *(0%)* **learning modality: kinesthetic**

Sex-Linked Genes The genes for some human traits are carried on the sex chromosomes. Genes on the X and Y chromosomes are often called **sex-linked genes** because their alleles are passed from parent to child on a sex chromosome. Traits controlled by sex-linked genes are called sex-linked traits. One sex-linked trait is red-green colorblindness. A person with this trait cannot distinguish between red and green.

Recall that females have two X chromosomes, whereas males have one X chromosome and one Y chromosome. Unlike most chromosome pairs, the X and Y chromosomes have different genes. Most of the genes on the X chromosome are not on the Y chromosome. Therefore, an allele on an X chromosome may have no corresponding allele on a Y chromosome.

Like other genes, sex-linked genes can have dominant and recessive alleles. In females, a dominant allele on one X chromosome will mask a recessive allele on the other X chromosome. But in males, there is usually no matching allele on the Y chromosome to mask the allele on the X chromosome. As a result, any allele on the X chromosome—even a recessive allele—will produce the trait in a male who inherits it. Because males have only one X chromosome, males are more likely than females to have a sex-linked trait that is controlled by a recessive allele.

FIGURE 6
Colorblindness
The lower photo shows how a red barn and green fields look to a person with red-green colorblindness.

Normal vision ▼

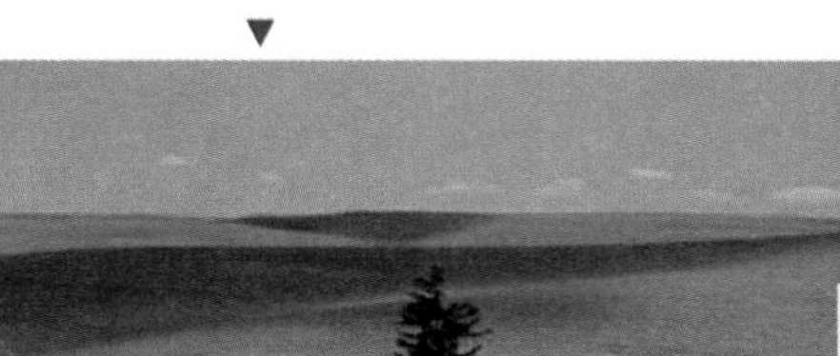

Red-green colorblind vision ▼

114 ◆ C

Inheritance of Colorblindness Colorblindness is a trait controlled by a recessive allele on the X chromosome. Many more males than females have red-green colorblindness. You can understand why this is the case by examining the Punnett square in Figure 7. Both parents in this example have normal color vision. Notice, however, that the mother is a carrier of colorblindness. A **carrier** is a person who has one recessive allele for a trait and one dominant allele. A carrier of a trait controlled by a recessive allele does not have the trait. However, the carrier can pass the recessive allele on to his or her offspring. In the case of sex-linked traits, only females can be carriers.

As you can see in Figure 7, there is a 25 percent probability that this couple will have a colorblind child. Notice that none of the couple's daughters will be colorblind. On the other hand, the sons have a 50 percent probability of being colorblind. For a female to be colorblind, she must inherit two recessive alleles for colorblindness, one from each parent. A male needs to inherit only one recessive allele. This is because there is no gene for color vision on the Y chromosome. Thus, there is no allele that could mask the recessive allele on the X chromosome.

Reading Checkpoint **What is the sex of a person who is a carrier for colorblindness?**

For: Links on genetics
Visit: www.SciLinks.org
Web Code: scn-0341

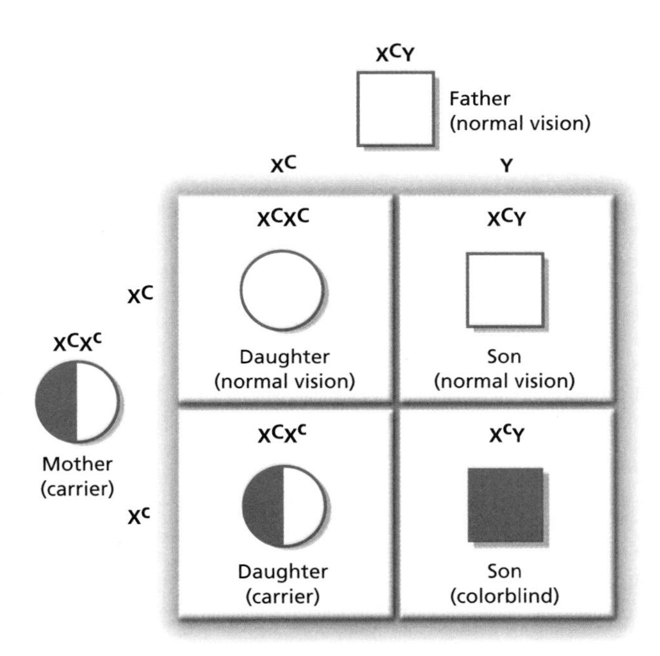

FIGURE 7
Colorblindness Punnett Square
Red-green colorblindness is a sex-linked trait. A girl who receives only one recessive allele (written X^c) for red-green colorblindness will not have the trait. However, a boy who receives one recessive allele will be colorblind.
Applying Concepts *What allele combination would a daughter need to inherit to be colorblind?*

For: Links on genetics
Visit: www.SciLinks.org
Web Code: scn-0341

Download a worksheet to guide students' review of genetics.

The Effect of Environment

Teach Key Concepts L2

Genes and the Environment

Focus Provide this example for students: Tell them to imagine two plants. One receives more sunlight than the other and grows taller and fuller. Ask: **If the two plants have the same genes, what is the difference in how they grow?** *(They are exposed to different environments.)*

Teach Ask: **What does this example demonstrate about the relationship between genes and environment?** *(Genes and the environment interact to determine characteristics.)* **What are some human traits that are influenced by the environment?** *(Height and skills such as playing a musical instrument)*

Apply Ask students how their speech represents the interaction of genetics and environment. *(The way their voice sounds is a combination of the structure of their vocal cords and mouth, which is genetic, and the way their family speaks [slowly or quickly, soft or loud], which is environmental. Language, accent, and dialect are determined by environment.)* **learning modality: logical/mathematical**

Monitor Progress L2

Skills Check Have students solve the following problem: **Mary and her mother are both colorblind. Is Mary's father colorblind, too? How do you know?** *(Because Mary is colorblind, she must have inherited an X^c allele from each parent. Therefore, Mary's father's genotype must be X^cY, so he is colorblind, too.)*

Answers

Figure 7 X^cX^c

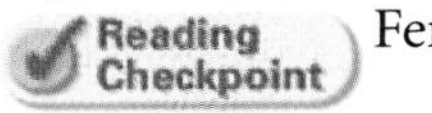
Female

Differentiated Instruction

Gifted and Talented L3
Inferring Inheritance Patterns
Challenge students to infer how the inheritance of a sex-linked trait controlled by a dominant allele would differ from the inheritance of a sex-linked trait controlled by a recessive allele. *(A sex-linked trait controlled by a recessive allele is more common in males because males need to inherit just one recessive allele to have the trait. A trait controlled by a dominant allele would be equally common in males and females because females, like males, would need to inherit only one dominant allele to have the trait.)* Have students make a Punnett Square to show how a sex-linked dominant allele would be passed to offspring. **learning modality: logical/mathematical**

Monitor Progress L2

Answer

Reading Checkpoint A poor diet could prevent a person from growing as tall as possible, as genetically determined.

Assess

Reviewing Key Concepts

1. a. Single genes with two alleles: widow's peak; single genes with multiple alleles: blood type; and multiple genes: skin color **b.** Four: A, B, AB, and O; the alleles for blood types A and B are codominant, and the allele for blood type O is recessive. Type A blood results from two *A* alleles or one *A* and one *i*; type B blood results from two *B* alleles or one *B* and one *i*; type AB blood results from one *A* allele and one *B* allele; and type O results from two *i* alleles. **c.** No; blood type AB has the genotype I^AI^B, while blood type O has the genotype *ii*. Each of his parents passed on an *i* allele, so neither could have blood type AB.

2. a. To carry genes that determine whether a person is male or female, and to carry other traits **b.** The *Y* chromosome is much smaller than the *X* chromosome. Females have two *X* chromosomes, and males have an *X* and a *Y* chromosome. **c.** Red-green colorblindness is determined by a recessive allele on the *X* chromosome. The condition is more common among males because males need to inherit only one recessive allele to express the trait, while females need two.

3. a. No; genes and the environment interact to determine many of a person's characteristics. **b.** Athletic build and coordination may be inherited abilities that work together with environmental factors of practice, instruction, and exercises that strengthen muscles.

Reteach L1

Use Figures 5 and 7 to review how sex is determined and how a sex-linked trait is inherited.

All in One Teaching Resources

- Section Summary: *Human Inheritance*
- Review and Reinforce: *Human Inheritance*
- Enrich: *Human Inheritance*

FIGURE 8
Heredity and Environment
When a person plays a violin, genetically determined traits such as muscle coordination interact with environmental factors such as time spent in practice.

The Effect of Environment

In humans and other organisms, the effects of genes are often influenced by the environment—an organism's surroundings. **Many of a person's characteristics are determined by an interaction between genes and the environment.**

You have learned that several genes work together to help determine human height. However, people's heights are also influenced by their environments. People's diets can affect their height. A diet lacking in protein, certain minerals, or certain vitamins can prevent a person from growing as tall as might be possible.

Environmental factors can also affect human skills, such as playing a musical instrument. For example, physical traits such as muscle coordination and a good sense of hearing will help a musician play well. But the musician also needs instruction on how to play the instrument. Musical instruction is an environmental factor.

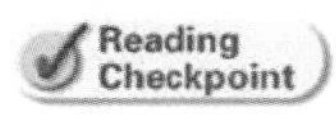

How can environmental factors affect a person's height?

Section 1 Assessment

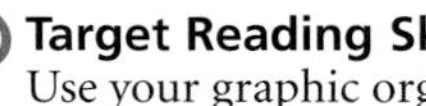

Target Reading Skill Identifying Main Ideas Use your graphic organizer to help you answer Question 1 below.

Reviewing Key Concepts

1. a. Identifying Identify three patterns of inheritance in humans. Give an example of a trait that follows each pattern.
   b. Summarizing How many human blood types are there? Summarize how blood type is inherited.
   c. Drawing Conclusions Aaron has blood type O. Can either of his parents have blood type AB? Explain your answer.
2. a. Reviewing What are the functions of the sex chromosomes?
   b. Comparing and Contrasting Contrast the sex chromosomes found in human females and human males.
   c. Relating Cause and Effect Explain how red-green colorblindness is inherited. Why is the condition more common in males than in females?
3. a. Reviewing Are a person's characteristics determined only by genes? Explain.
   b. Applying Concepts Explain what factors might work together to enable a great soccer player to kick a ball a long distance.

Writing in Science

Heredity and Environment Think of an ability you admire, such as painting, dancing, snowboarding, or playing games skillfully. Write a paragraph explaining how genes and the environment might work together to enable a person to develop this ability.

Lab zone Chapter Project

Keep Students on Track Check that students have sketched a plan for displaying their information and that the plan is realistic. Advise students to keep a running list of materials or equipment they will need. Remind them that displays should include an interactive portion that helps the viewer predict the probability that a person will inherit the trait.

Writing in Science

Writing Mode Explanation

Scoring Rubric

4 Includes complete explanation and goes beyond requirements, for example, by including many environmental factors
3 Includes all criteria but does not go beyond requirements
2 Only brief explanation
1 Incomplete or inaccurate explanation

Section 2

Human Genetic Disorders

Reading Preview

Key Concepts

- What are two major causes of genetic disorders in humans?
- How do geneticists trace the inheritance of traits?
- How are genetic disorders diagnosed and treated?

Key Terms

- genetic disorder • pedigree
- karyotype

Target Reading Skill

Comparing and Contrasting
As you read, compare and contrast the types of genetic disorders by completing a table like the one below.

Disorder	Description	Cause
Cystic fibrosis	Abnormally thick mucus	Loss of three DNA bases

Lab zone Discover Activity

How Many Chromosomes?

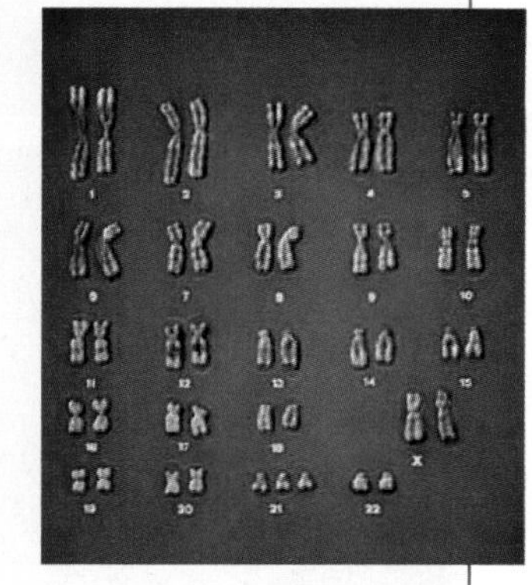

The photo at right shows the chromosomes from a cell of a person with Down syndrome, a genetic disorder. The chromosomes have been sorted into pairs.

1. Count the number of chromosomes in the photo.
2. How does the number of chromosomes compare to the usual number of chromosomes in human cells?

Think It Over
Inferring How do you think a cell could have ended up with this number of chromosomes? (*Hint:* Think about the events that occur during meiosis.)

The air inside the stadium was hot and still. The crowd cheered loudly as the runners approached the starting blocks. At the crack of the starter's gun, the runners leaped into motion and sprinted down the track. Seconds later, the race was over. The runners, bursting with pride, hugged each other and their coaches. These athletes were running in the Special Olympics, a competition for people with disabilities. Many of the athletes who compete in the Special Olympics have disabilities that result from genetic disorders.

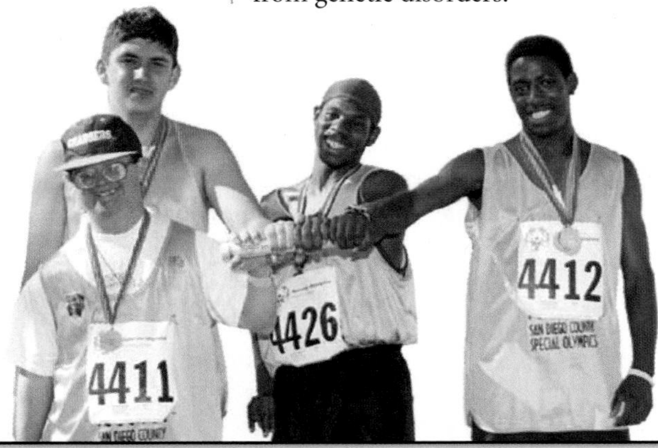

◀ Runners in the Special Olympics

Lab zone Discover Activity

Skills Focus Inferring L1

Materials none

Time 10 minutes

Tips Provide any students who have vision impairments with a hand lens for examining the photo.

Expected Outcome Students will count 47 chromosomes in the photo, or one more than the 46 chromosomes normally found in human cells, because there is an extra copy of chromosome 21.

Think It Over Students may correctly say that the extra chromosome is due to failure of the chromosomes to separate during meiosis.

Section 2

Human Genetic Disorders

Objectives

After this lesson, students will be able to

C.4.2.1 Identify two major causes of genetic disorders in humans.

C.4.2.2 Explain how geneticists trace the inheritance of traits.

C.4.2.3 Describe how genetic disorders are diagnosed and treated.

Target Reading Skill

Comparing and Contrasting Explain that comparing and contrasting information shows how ideas, facts, and events are similar and different. The results of the comparison can have importance.

Answers
Possible answers:
Disorder: Cystic fibrosis; *Description:* Body produces abnormally thick mucus; *Cause:* Recessive allele due to removal of three DNA bases
Disorder: Sickle-cell disease; *Description:* Red blood cells are sickle-shaped and have reduced ability to hold oxygen; *Cause:* Codominant allele
Disorder: Hemophilia; *Description:* Blood clots slowly or not at all; *Cause:* Recessive allele on X chromosome
Disorder: Down syndrome; *Description:* Mental retardation and heart defects; *Cause:* An extra copy of chromosome 21

All in One Teaching Resources

- Transparency C35

Preteach

Build Background Knowledge L1

Discussing Genetic Disorders
Ask: **What do you think a genetic disorder is?** *(An abnormal condition that is inherited)* **What are some genetic disorders you have heard about?** *(Accept all student responses without comment at this time.)*

Instruct

Help Students Read **L1**

KWL Have students make a chart with columns titled *What I Know, What I Want to Know,* and *What I Learned.* In the first column, they write what they know about the four disorders in the text. They fill out the second column with what they want to know. After reading the text, they complete the third column.

Causes of Genetic Disorders

Teach Key Concepts **L2**

Common Genetic Disorders

Focus Review with students the different ways that mutations can occur.

Teach Explain that the four diseases discussed result from a mutation in the DNA or a gene, or a change in the structure or number of chromosomes. Ask: **What causes cystic fibrosis?** *(A mutation in which three bases are removed from a DNA molecule)* **What causes sickle-cell disease?** *(A mutation that affects the protein hemoglobin)* **What causes hemophilia?** *(A recessive allele on the X chromosome)* **Why is it more common in males?** *(The allele that causes it is on the X chromosome.)* **What causes Down syndrome?** *(A person's cells have an extra copy of chromosome 21.)*

Apply How could a genetic disorder like cystic fibrosis be cured? *(By changing or replacing the gene that causes the disease)* **learning modality: verbal**

Independent Practice **L2**

All in One Teaching Resources

- Guided Reading and Study Worksheet: *Human Genetic Disorders*

Student Edition on Audio CD

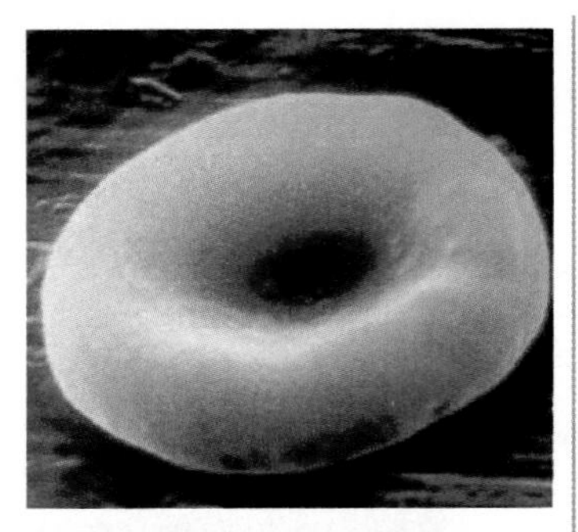

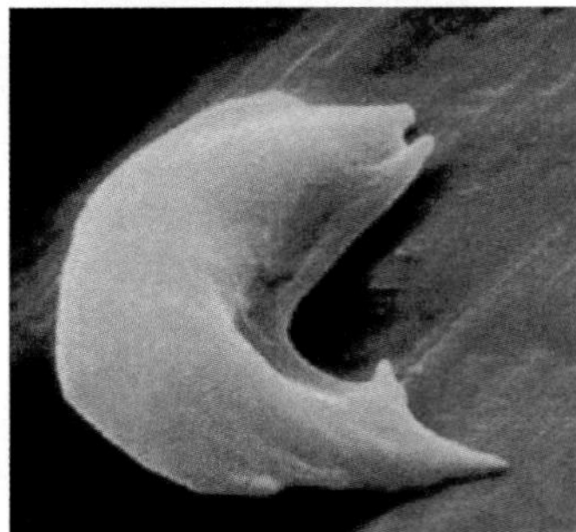

Figure 9
Sickle-Cell Disease
Normally, red blood cells are shaped like round disks (top). In a person with sickle-cell disease, red blood cells can become sickle-shaped (bottom).

Causes of Genetic Disorders

A **genetic disorder** is an abnormal condition that a person inherits through genes or chromosomes. **Some genetic disorders are caused by mutations in the DNA of genes. Other disorders are caused by changes in the overall structure or number of chromosomes.** In this section, you will learn about some common genetic disorders.

Cystic Fibrosis Cystic fibrosis is a genetic disorder in which the body produces abnormally thick mucus in the lungs and intestines. The thick mucus fills the lungs, making it hard for the affected person to breathe. Cystic fibrosis is caused by a recessive allele on one chromosome. The recessive allele is the result of a mutation in which three bases are removed from a DNA molecule.

Sickle-Cell Disease Sickle-cell disease affects hemoglobin, a protein in red blood cells that carries oxygen. When oxygen concentrations are low, the red blood cells of people with the disease have an unusual sickle shape. Sickle-shaped red blood cells clog blood vessels and cannot carry as much oxygen as normal cells. The allele for the sickle-cell trait is codominant with the normal allele. A person with two sickle-cell alleles will have the disease. A person with one sickle-cell allele will produce both normal hemoglobin and abnormal hemoglobin. This person usually will not have symptoms of the disease.

Hemophilia Hemophilia is a genetic disorder in which a person's blood clots very slowly or not at all. People with the disorder do not produce one of the proteins needed for normal blood clotting. The danger of internal bleeding from small bumps and bruises is very high. Hemophilia is caused by a recessive allele on the X chromosome. Because hemophilia is a sex-linked disorder, it occurs more frequently in males than in females.

Down Syndrome In Down syndrome, a person's cells have an extra copy of chromosome 21. In other words, instead of a pair of chromosomes, a person with Down syndrome has three of that chromosome. Down syndrome most often occurs when chromosomes fail to separate properly during meiosis. People with Down syndrome have some degree of mental retardation. Heart defects are also common, but can be treated.

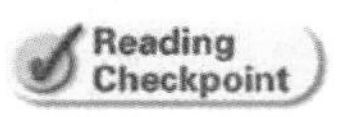

Reading Checkpoint **How is the DNA in the sickle-cell allele different from the normal allele?**

Lab zone Skills Activity

Predicting

A man has sickle-cell disease. His wife does not have the disease, but is heterozygous for the sickle-cell trait. Predict the probability that their child will have sickle-cell disease. (*Hint:* Construct a Punnett square.)

Lab zone Skills Activity

Skills Focus Predicting **L2**

Materials none

Time 10 minutes

Expected Outcome The probability that their child will have sickle-cell disease is 50%.

Extend Ask: **If the couple has a son who does not have symptoms of sickle-cell disease, could he still have abnormal hemoglobin?** *(Yes; he is heterozygous for the sickle-cell trait. A person with only one sickle-cell allele will produce both normal and abnormal hemoglobin but will not have symptoms of the disease.)* **learning modality: logical/mathematical**

Pedigrees

Imagine that you are a geneticist who is interested in tracing the occurrence of a genetic disorder through several generations of a family. What would you do? **One important tool that geneticists use to trace the inheritance of traits in humans is a pedigree.** A **pedigree** is a chart or "family tree" that tracks which members of a family have a particular trait.

The trait in a pedigree can be an ordinary trait, such as a widow's peak, or a genetic disorder, such as cystic fibrosis. Figure 10 shows a pedigree for albinism, a condition in which a person's skin, hair, and eyes lack normal coloring.

For: Pedigree activity
Visit: PHSchool.com
Web Code: cep-3042

FIGURE 10
A Pedigree
The father in the photograph has albinism. The pedigree shows the inheritance of the allele for albinism in three generations of a family. Interpreting Diagrams *Where is an albino male shown in the pedigree?*

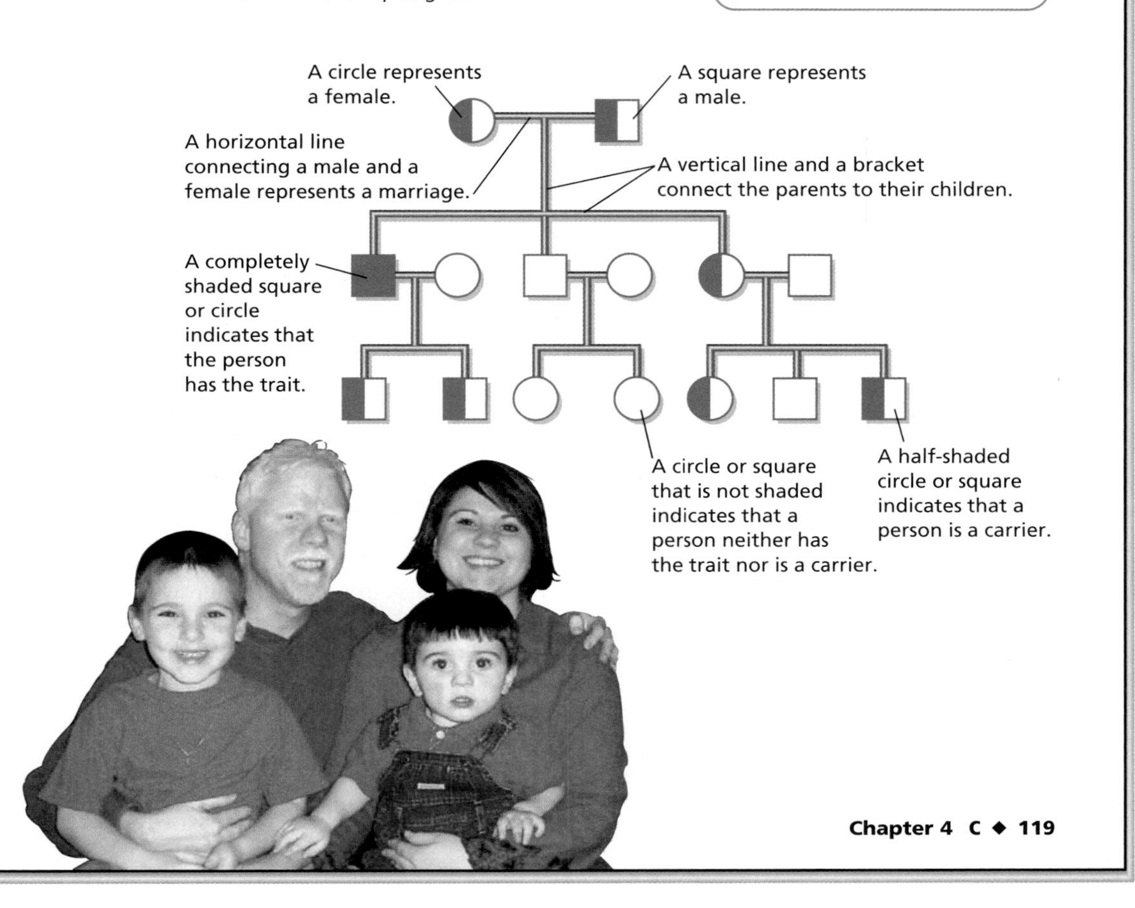

Pedigrees

For: Pedigree activity
Visit: PHSchool.com
Web Code: cep-3042

Students can interact with the art of a pedigree online.

Teach Key Concepts L2

How Inheritance Is Traced

Focus Refer students to Figure 10.

Teach Have volunteers read the captions in the figure, then identify the genotypes and phenotypes for each individual.

Apply Have students make a Punnett square to show all possible genotypes of the children of the couple in the first generation of the pedigree. **learning modality: visual**

All in One Teaching Resources

- Transparency C36

L2

Interpreting a Pedigree

Materials poster board, marker

Time 15 minutes

Focus Review the meaning of codominance.

Teach Have students construct a two-generation pedigree for sickle-cell disease, starting with *Ss* × *Ss*.

Apply Have students explain why the phenotype for having one sickle-cell allele is different from the phenotype for having one allele for cystic fibrosis. **learning modality: visual**

Differentiated Instruction

English Learners/Beginning L1
Comprehension: Link to Visual Draw a pedigree showing the trait of widow's peak, and explain each line, square, and circle as you draw it. Write the symbols for the genotypes beside each figure, and draw faces that show the trait in the circles and squares. Then have students draw their own pedigree for another trait and explain it to you. **learning modality: visual**

English Learners/Intermediate L2
Comprehension: Link to Visual Have students do the Beginning activity, then write sentences in their own words explaining how to interpret the pedigree. **learning modality: visual**

Monitor Progress L2

Skills Check Have students draw a pedigree that shows the inheritance of cystic fibrosis in a family. Students can place these pedigrees in their portfolio.

Answers

Figure 10 The male in the second generation on the far left

Reading Checkpoint It codes for a hemoglobin of a different shape from the normal allele.

Managing Genetic Disorders

Teach Key Concepts

L2

Diagnosing and Treating Genetic Disorders

Focus Tell students that genetic testing is now available for hundreds of disorders.

Teach Ask: **What is a karyotype?** *(A karyotype is a picture of all of the chromosomes in a cell, arranged in pairs.)* **What type of genetic disorders can be determined by looking at a karyotype?** *(Disorders resulting from a change in the number or structure of chromosomes)* **How do counselors help people who have a family history of a genetic disorder?** *(They help couples understand their chances of passing the genes or traits on to offspring.)* **How do people who have genetic disorders deal with them?** *(There are treatments for some disorders, and education and training helps many people live active, productive lives.)*

Apply Have students imagine they are genetic counselors who must determine the chance of a couple having a child with cystic fibrosis, when both husband and wife are carriers. *(Students draw a Punnett square for two heterozygotes. The Punnett square should show that 25% of the couple's children would be likely to inherit two recessive alleles.)* Ask: **If the couple has two children without cystic fibrosis, what is the chance that their third child will have it? Their fourth child?** *(Each child has a 25% chance of having cystic fibrosis.)* **learning modality: logical/mathematical**

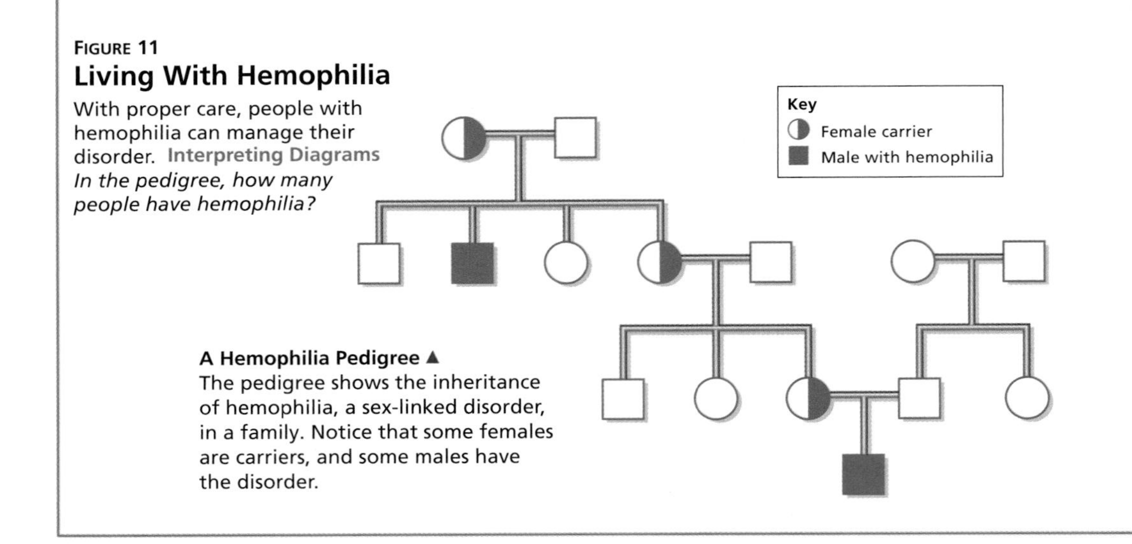

FIGURE 11
Living With Hemophilia
With proper care, people with hemophilia can manage their disorder. **Interpreting Diagrams** *In the pedigree, how many people have hemophilia?*

A Hemophilia Pedigree ▲
The pedigree shows the inheritance of hemophilia, a sex-linked disorder, in a family. Notice that some females are carriers, and some males have the disorder.

Managing Genetic Disorders

Years ago, doctors had only Punnett squares and pedigrees to help them predict whether a child might have a genetic disorder. **Today, doctors use tools such as karyotypes to help diagnose genetic disorders. People with genetic disorders are helped through medical care, education, job training, and other methods.**

Karyotypes To detect chromosomal disorders such as Down syndrome, a doctor examines the chromosomes from a person's cells. The doctor uses a karyotype to examine the chromosomes. A **karyotype** (KA ree uh typ) is a picture of all the chromosomes in a cell. The chromosomes in a karyotype are arranged in pairs. A karyotype can reveal whether a person has the correct number of chromosomes in his or her cells. If you did the Discover activity, you saw a karyotype from a girl with Down syndrome.

Genetic Counseling A couple that has a family history of a genetic disorder may turn to a genetic counselor for advice. Genetic counselors help couples understand their chances of having a child with a particular genetic disorder. Genetic counselors use tools such as karyotypes, pedigree charts, and Punnett squares to help them in their work.

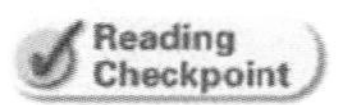

What do genetic counselors do?

120 ◆ C

Differentiated Instruction

Special Needs L1

Illustrating the Cause of Down's Syndrome Help students use colored pipe cleaners and the diagrams from a previous section to illustrate the chromosomes as the cell goes through Meiosis I and Meiosis II. Point out that the chromosome pairs can fail to separate correctly in either stage. Students end up with four sets of pipe cleaners to represent the possible individuals formed when sex cells unite. Two individuals should be normal, one should contain only one chromosome of a certain color, and one should contain three chromosomes of that color. **learning modality: visual**

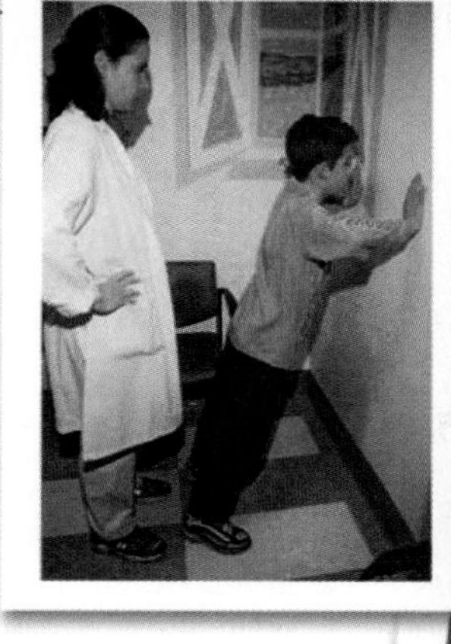

Physical Therapy ▶ Trained medical workers help hemophilia patients cope with their disorder. Here, a boy receives physical therapy.

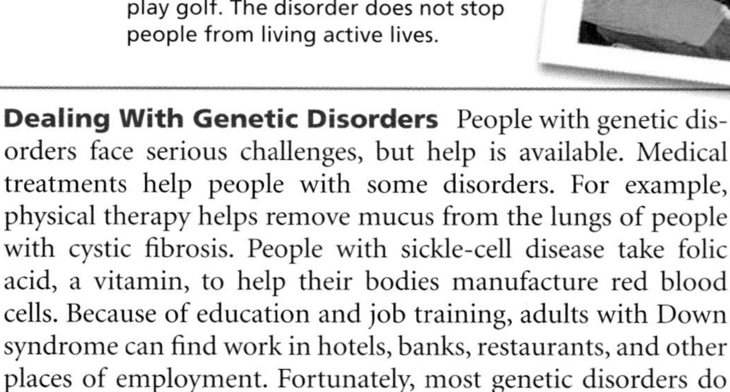

Sports ▶ A boy with hemophilia learns how to play golf. The disorder does not stop people from living active lives.

Dealing With Genetic Disorders People with genetic disorders face serious challenges, but help is available. Medical treatments help people with some disorders. For example, physical therapy helps remove mucus from the lungs of people with cystic fibrosis. People with sickle-cell disease take folic acid, a vitamin, to help their bodies manufacture red blood cells. Because of education and job training, adults with Down syndrome can find work in hotels, banks, restaurants, and other places of employment. Fortunately, most genetic disorders do not prevent people from living active, productive lives.

Section 2 Assessment

Target Reading Skill

Comparing and Contrasting Use the information in your table to help you answer Question 1 below.

Reviewing Key Concepts

1. a. **Identifying** Identify the two major causes of genetic disorders in humans.
   b. **Explaining** Which of those two major causes is responsible for Down syndrome?
   c. **Describing** How are the cells of a person with Down syndrome different from those of a person without the disorder?
2. a. **Defining** What is a pedigree?
   b. **Inferring** Why are pedigrees helpful in understanding genetic disorders?
   c. **Applying Concepts** Sam has hemophilia. Sam's brother, mother, and father do not have hemophilia. Draw a pedigree showing who has the disorder and who is a carrier.
3. a. **Reviewing** What is a karyotype?
   b. **Inferring** Would a karyotype reveal the presence of sickle-cell disease? Why or why not?

Writing in Science

Creating a Web Site Create an imaginary Web site to inform the public about genetic disorders. Write a description of one disorder for the Web site.

Lab zone Chapter Project

Keep Students on Track Check that students have begun constructing their displays and that they correctly identify the way their trait is inherited. Suggest that students begin to prepare a rough draft of a written description of their presentation. Help students determine the best way to organize the information for their own understanding.

Writing in Science

Writing Mode Explanation

Scoring Rubric

4 Includes complete description of a genetic disorder and goes beyond requirements, for example, providing information on diagnosis and treatment
3 Includes required criteria but does not go beyond requirements
2 Includes only brief description
1 Includes inaccurate or incomplete description

Monitor Progress L2

Answers

Figure 11 Two

Reading Checkpoint They help couples understand their chances of having a child with a particular genetic disorder.

Assess

Reviewing Key Concepts

1. a. Mutations in DNA or changes in the overall structure or number of chromosomes **b.** A change in the overall number of chromosomes **c.** Each of the cells of a person with Down syndrome has three copies of chromosome 21; normal cells have two copies of chromosome 21.
2. a. A chart that tracks which members of a family have a particular trait **b.** A pedigree allows scientists and genetic counselors to infer how a genetic disorder is passed from one generation to the next. **c.** The square for Sam should be completely shaded, indicating that he has the disease. Sam's mother's circle should be half-shaded, indicating that she is a carrier. The squares for Sam's father and brother should be blank.
3. a. A picture of all the chromosomes in a cell, arranged in pairs **b.** No; sickle-cell disease is not related to the number of chromosomes in a cell.

Reteach L1

Use the pedigrees in Figures 10 and 11 to review how inheritance of traits can be traced in a family. Have students identify characteristics of a pedigree for a recessive trait, a pedigree for a dominant trait, and a pedigree for a sex-linked trait.

All in One Teaching Resources

- Section Summary: *Human Genetic Disorders*
- Review and Reinforce: *Human Genetic Disorders*
- Enrich: *Human Genetic Disorders*

Family Puzzle

L2

Prepare for Inquiry

Skills Objectives
Students will be able to
- interpret data on phenotypes to construct a family pedigree
- predict the probability of having cystic fibrosis based on the pedigree

Class Time 40 minutes

All in One Teaching Resources
- Lab Worksheet: *Family Puzzle*

Guide Inquiry

Invitation
Draw a pedigree on the board showing a wife with a genetic disorder and a healthy husband who have an affected daughter and a healthy son. Ask: **Can you tell if the trait is controlled by a dominant or recessive allele?** *(No)* Extend the pedigree back one generation by adding two healthy parents for the wife. Then ask the same question. *(Recessive; otherwise, at least one of the wife's parents would also have the trait.)* Point out that the more generations a pedigree has, the more obvious the pattern of inheritance.

Introduce the Procedure
Check that students know how to construct pedigrees. Have students review the part of the chapter that discusses how to interpret pedigrees.

Troubleshooting the Experiment
- Check that students have drawn and labeled the pedigree correctly.
- Tell students they will need to draw Punnett squares to answer Question 2.

Analyze and Conclude
1. Joshua's parents are both heterozygous (*Nn*); the genotypes of Bella's parents cannot be determined for certain, but at least one must be heterozygous, and the other could be either heterozygous or homozygous for the normal allele (*NN*).
2. Because both parents are heterozygous (*Nn*), there is a 25 percent chance of each child inheriting two *n* alleles and having cystic fibrosis.
3. Genetic counselors cannot usually draw firm conclusions about a hereditary condition with information about just one or two generations; more than one inheritance pattern may explain the facts when the information is limited. For example, both sex-linked traits and recessive traits can skip generations.

Extend Inquiry

More to Explore The traits affect males and females about equally. If cystic fibrosis in the case study were sex-linked, Ian would have inherited the disorder from his mother, not from both parents, as appears to have been the case. Also, Joshua's sister probably would not have the disease.

Family Puzzle

Problem

A husband and wife want to understand the probability that their children might inherit cystic fibrosis. How can you use the information in the box labeled Case Study to predict the probability?

Skills Focus

interpreting data, predicting

Materials

- 12 index cards • scissors • marker

Procedure

1. Read the Case Study. In your notebook, draw a pedigree that shows all the family members. Use circles to represent the females, and squares to represent the males. Shade in the circles or squares representing the individuals who have cystic fibrosis.
2. You know that cystic fibrosis is controlled by a recessive allele. To help you figure out Joshua and Bella's family pattern, create a set of cards to represent the alleles. Cut each of six index cards into four smaller cards. On 12 of the small cards, write *N* to represent the dominant normal allele. On the other 12 small cards, write *n* for the recessive allele.
3. Begin by using the cards to represent Ian's alleles. Since he has cystic fibrosis, what alleles must he have? Write in this genotype next to the pedigree symbol for Ian.
4. Joshua's sister, Sara, also has cystic fibrosis. What alleles does she have? Write in this genotype next to the pedigree symbol that represents Sara.
5. Now use the cards to figure out what genotypes Joshua and Bella must have. Write their genotypes next to their symbols in the pedigree.
6. Work with the cards to figure out the genotypes of all other family members. Fill in each person's genotype next to his or her symbol in the pedigree. If more than one genotype is possible, write in both genotypes.

Case Study: Joshua and Bella
- Joshua and Bella have a son named Ian. Ian has been diagnosed with cystic fibrosis.
- Joshua and Bella are both healthy.
- Bella's parents are both healthy.
- Joshua's parents are both healthy.
- Joshua's sister, Sara, has cystic fibrosis.

Analyze and Conclude

1. **Interpreting Data** What were the possible genotypes of Joshua's parents? What were the genotypes of Bella's parents?
2. **Predicting** Joshua also has a brother. What is the probability that he has cystic fibrosis? Explain.
3. **Communicating** Imagine that you are a genetic counselor. A couple asks why you need information about many generations of their families to draw conclusions about a hereditary condition. Write an explanation you can give to them.

More to Explore

Review the pedigree that you just studied. What data suggest that the traits are not sex-linked? Explain.

Section 3

Tech & Design

Advances in Genetics

Reading Preview

Key Concepts

- What are three ways of producing organisms with desired traits?
- What is the goal of the Human Genome Project?

Key Terms

- selective breeding
- inbreeding
- hybridization
- clone
- genetic engineering
- gene therapy
- genome

Target Reading Skill

Asking Questions Before you read, preview the red headings. In a graphic organizer like the one below, ask a question for each heading. As you read, write answers to your questions.

Advances in Genetics

Question	Answer
What is selective breeding?	Selective breeding is . . .

Lab zone Discover Activity

What Do Fingerprints Reveal?

1. Label a sheet of paper with your name. Then roll one of your fingers from side to side on an ink pad. Make a fingerprint by carefully rolling your inked finger on the paper.
2. Divide into groups. Each group should choose one member to use the same finger to make a second fingerprint on a sheet of paper. Leave the paper unlabeled.
3. Exchange your group's fingerprints with those from another group. Compare each labeled fingerprint with the fingerprint on the unlabeled paper. Decide whose fingerprint it is.
4. Wash your hands after completing this activity.

Think It Over

Observing Why are fingerprints used to identify people?

Would you like to have your picture taken with a 9,000-year-old family member? Adrian Targett, a history teacher in the village of Cheddar in England, has actually done that. All that's left of his ancient relative, known as "Cheddar Man," is a skeleton. The skeleton was discovered in a cave near the village. DNA analysis indicates that Targett and Cheddar Man are relatives.

Like your fingerprints, your DNA is different from everyone else's. Because of advances in genetics, DNA evidence can show many things, such as family relationships.

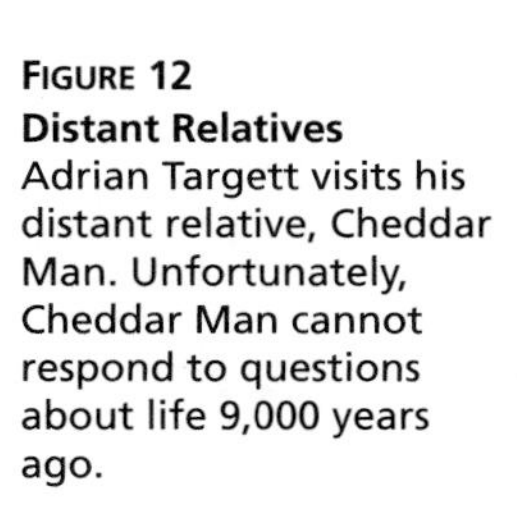

FIGURE 12
Distant Relatives
Adrian Targett visits his distant relative, Cheddar Man. Unfortunately, Cheddar Man cannot respond to questions about life 9,000 years ago.

Lab zone Discover Activity

Skills Focus Observing L1

Materials plain white paper, ink pad, hand lens

Time 15 minutes

Tips Help students recognize similarities and differences among the fingerprints by pointing out examples of whirls, loops, and other standard features of fingerprints.

Expected Outcome By comparing a group's unlabeled fingerprints with its labeled fingerprints, students identify who made the unlabeled print.

Think It Over Each person's fingerprints are unique.

Section 3

Advances in Genetics

Objectives

After this lesson, students will be able to

C.4.3.1 Describe three ways of producing organisms with desired traits.

C.4.3.2 State the goal of the Human Genome Project.

Target Reading Skill

Asking Questions Explain that changing a heading into a question helps students anticipate the ideas, facts, and events they are about to read.

Answers

Possible questions and answers include: **What is selective breeding?** *(Selective breeding is the process of selecting organisms with desired traits to be parents of the next generation.)* **Why are organisms cloned?** *(To produce offspring with desired traits)* **What is genetic engineering?** *(A process in which genes from one organism are transferred into the DNA of another organism)* **What advance has helped us learn about human genetics?** *(The Human Genome Project)*

All in One Teaching Resources

- Transparency C37

Preteach

Build Background Knowledge L1

Selective Breeding

Ask: **What are some breeds of dogs that have very different characteristics?** *(Possible answers: Dachshund, Chihuahua, and Great Dane)* Explain that the different breeds were produced by mating animals that have certain traits. In this section, students will learn about selective breeding and other ways of producing organisms with desirable traits.

Instruct

Selective Breeding

Teach Key Concepts L2

Producing Selected Traits

Focus Tell students that dog breeders use selective breeding to produce purebred dogs that are good hunters or retrievers, for example.

Teach Ask: **Based on this example, what is selective breeding?** *(A technique to produce offspring with desirable traits)* **What are inbreeding and hybridization?** *(Inbreeding is crossing two individuals that have similar characteristics. Hybridization is crossing two genetically different individuals.)*

Apply Have students imagine they have a purebred tall pea plant with yellow pods and a purebred short pea plant with green pods. Ask: **What technique would produce a tall pea plant with yellow pods?** *(Inbreeding)* **learning modality: logical/mathematical**

Independent Practice L2

All in One Teaching Resources

- Guided Reading and Study Worksheet: *Advances in Genetics*

Student Edition on Audio CD

L1

Applying Concepts of Hybridization

Materials seed catalogs

Time 10 minutes

Focus Review hybridization.

Teach Have students use the catalogs to list the characteristics of two different hybrid varieties of a certain plant.

Apply Ask students to infer how selective breeding of food plants has benefited people. *(It has increased the amount of food available so people can be better fed or more people can be fed.)* **learning modality: verbal**

Selective Breeding

Genetic techniques have enabled people to produce organisms with desirable traits. **Selective breeding, cloning, and genetic engineering are three methods for developing organisms with desirable traits.**

The process of selecting organisms with desired traits to be parents of the next generation is called **selective breeding**. Thousands of years ago, in what is now Mexico, the food that we call corn was developed in this way. Every year, farmers saved seeds from the healthiest plants that produced the best food. In the spring, they planted those seeds. By repeating this process over and over, farmers developed plants that produced better corn. People have used selective breeding with many different plants and animals. Two selective breeding techniques are inbreeding and hybridization.

Inbreeding The technique of **inbreeding** involves crossing two individuals that have similar characteristics. For example, suppose a male and a female turkey are both plump and grow quickly. Their offspring will probably also have those desirable qualities. Inbred organisms have alleles that are very similar to those of their parents.

Inbred organisms are genetically very similar. Therefore, inbreeding increases the probability that organisms may inherit alleles that lead to genetic disorders. For example, inherited hip problems are common in many breeds of dogs.

Hybridization In **hybridization** (hy brid ih ZAY shun), breeders cross two genetically different individuals. The hybrid organism that results is bred to have the best traits from both parents. For example, a farmer might cross corn that produces many kernels with corn that is resistant to disease. The result might be a hybrid corn plant with both of the desired traits.

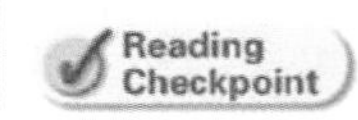

What is the goal of hybridization?

FIGURE 13
Inbreeding
Turkeys such as the one with white feathers were developed by inbreeding. Breeders started with wild turkeys.

Wild turkey

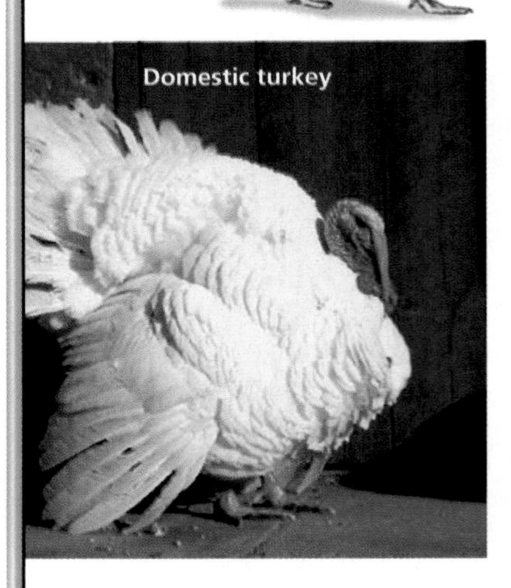

FIGURE 14
Hybridization
McIntosh and Red Delicious apples were crossed to produce Empire apples. **Applying Concepts** *What desirable traits might breeders have been trying to produce?*

McIntosh

×
Red Delicious

=
Empire

Math Analyzing Data

Changing Rice Production

The graph shows how worldwide rice production changed between 1965 and 2000. New, hybrid varieties of rice plants are one factor that has affected the amount of rice produced.

1. **Reading Graphs** According to the graph, how did rice production change between 1965 and 2000?
2. **Reading Graphs** How many metric tons of rice per hectare were produced in 1965? How many were produced in 2000?
3. **Calculating** Calculate the approximate difference between rice production in 1965 and 2000.
4. **Developing Hypotheses** What factors besides new varieties of plants might help account for the difference in rice production between 1965 and 2000?

Worldwide Rice Production

Rice Production (metric tons per hectare): 0, 1, 2, 3, 4

Year: 1970, 1980, 1990, 2000

Cloning

For some organisms, a technique called cloning can be used to produce offspring with desired traits. A **clone** is an organism that has exactly the same genes as the organism from which it was produced. It isn't hard to clone some kinds of plants, such as an African violet. Just cut a stem from one plant, and put the stem in soil. Water it, and soon you will have a whole new plant. The new plant is genetically identical to the plant from which the stem was cut.

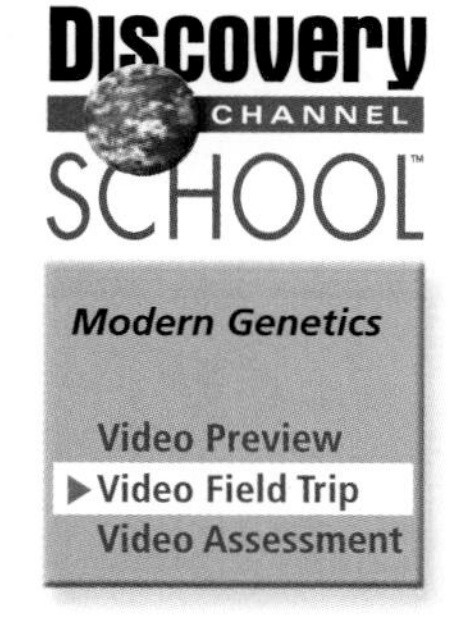

Researchers have also cloned animals such as sheep and pigs. The methods for cloning these animals are complex. They involve taking the nucleus of an animal's body cell and using that nucleus to produce a new animal.

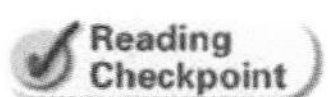

How can a clone of a plant be produced?

FIGURE 15
Cloned Goats
These goats were produced by cloning.

Modern Genetics

Show the Video Field Trip to let students learn more about cloning.

Math Analyzing Data

Math Skill Making and interpreting graphs

Focus Explain that line graphs are often used to analyze a trend over time.

Teach Ask students what the x and the y axes represent. *(x: Year; y: Rice production in metric tons per hectare)*

Answers

1. Rice production increased (doubled).
2. 2 in 1965; 4 in 2000
3. 2 metric tons/hectare
4. Possible answer: genetic advances, fertilizers, improved harvesting methods

Cloning

Teach Key Concepts L2

Cloning in Plants and Animals

Focus Tell students that the first clone of an adult mammal was a sheep named Dolly.

Teach Ask: **How is a plant cloned?** *(Cut a stem from one plant and grow it.)* **An animal?** *(Use the nucleus of a body cell to produce a new animal.)*

Apply Ask: **Why are identical twins not clones by the text definition?** *(They are not genetically identical to their parents.)* **learning modality: logical/mathematical**

Differentiated Instruction

English Learners/Beginning L1
Comprehension: Modified Cloze
Give students a list of simple sentences that describe the methods for producing organisms with desirable traits, but leave some key words blank. For example, "Different breeds of dogs are produced by _____." Provide students with a list of correct answers, and have them fill in each blank. Model how to do the first one. **learning modality: verbal**

English Learners/Intermediate L2
Comprehension: Modified Cloze Give students the cloze sentences described for the Beginning activity, but fill in incorrect answers and have students correct them. **learning modality: verbal**

Monitor Progress L2

Skills Check Have students compare inbreeding and hybridization.

Answers

Figure 14 Possible answer: Taste, shelf life, resistance to insects

Reading Checkpoint To produce an organism with the best traits from both parents

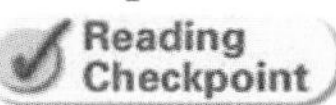

Grow a cutting of the original plant.

Genetic Engineering

Help Students Read

L2

Monitoring Your Understanding Before students read *Genetic Engineering*, ask them to stop and monitor their understanding after each paragraph. Explain that if they have not fully understood it, they can apply one of the reading techniques that has worked for them in the past, such as outlining, summarizing, or identifying main ideas.

Teach Key Concepts

L2

Selecting an Organism's Traits

Focus Have students look at Figure 16. Give them time to read the captions.

Teach Explain that in genetic engineering, specific genes are transferred into the DNA of another organism. Refer students to Figure 16, and have students trace the steps in creating bacteria that produce insulin. Ask questions such as **What is a plasmid?** *(A small ring of DNA in a bacterial cell)* **Why are the bacteria in step 5 able to produce insulin?** *(They contain copies of the human insulin gene.)*

Apply Challenge students to think of advantages that genetic engineering has over selective breeding. *(Producing the desired traits may be more difficult with breeding; genetic engineering can target the specific genes coding for a trait.)* **learning modality: logical/mathematical**

All in One Teaching Resources

- Transparency C38

For: Links on genetic engineering
Visit: www.SciLinks.org
Web Code: scn-0343

Download a worksheet to guide students' review of genetic engineering.

Genetic Engineering

Geneticists have developed another powerful technique for producing organisms with desired traits. In this process, called **genetic engineering**, genes from one organism are transferred into the DNA of another organism. Genetic engineering can produce medicines and improve food crops.

Genetic Engineering in Bacteria One type of genetically engineered bacteria produces a protein called insulin. Injections of insulin are needed by many people with diabetes. Recall that bacteria have a single DNA molecule in the cytoplasm. Some bacterial cells also contain small circular pieces of DNA called plasmids. In Figure 16, you can see how scientists insert the DNA for a human gene into the plasmid of a bacterium.

FIGURE 16
Genetic Engineering
Scientists use genetic engineering to create bacterial cells that produce important human proteins such as insulin.
Interpreting Diagrams *How does a human insulin gene become part of a plasmid?*

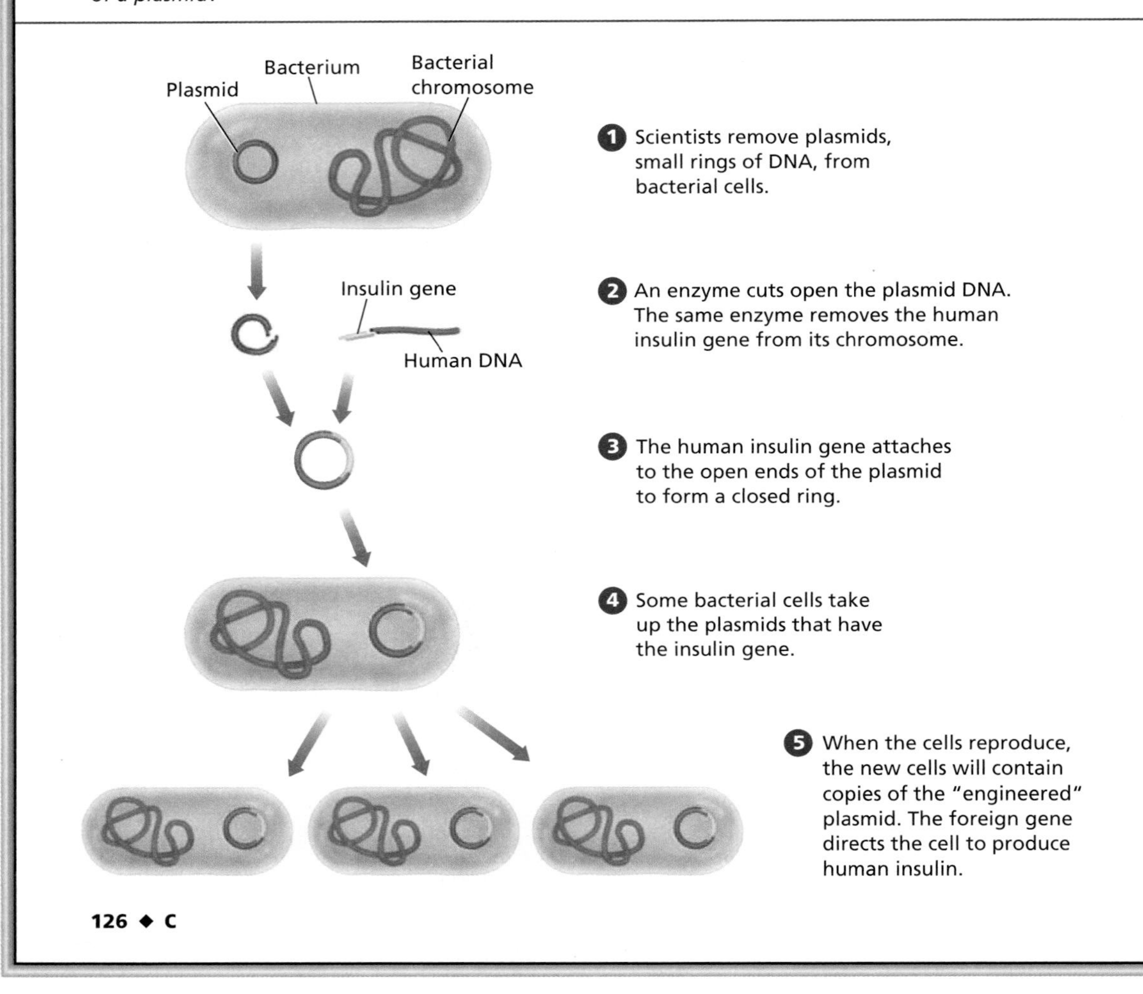

Differentiated Instruction

Less Proficient Readers L1

Drawing Diagrams Have students draw simple diagrams that illustrate selective breeding, cloning, and genetic engineering on three separate index cards. Ask them to label the diagrams in their own words. Then have students use their diagrams to make a chart that compares and contrasts the methods. **learning modality: verbal**

Gifted and Talented L3

Researching the Human Genome Project Have students search for more information about the Human Genome Project via Web sites sponsored by the U.S. Department of Energy and the National Institutes of Health, the two government agencies that coordinate the project, and report their findings to the class. **learning modality: verbal**

FIGURE 17
Genetically Engineered Fish
The bright red zebra danios are the result of genetic engineering.

Once the gene is inserted into the plasmid, the bacterial cell and all its offspring will contain this human gene. As a result, the bacteria produce the protein that the human gene codes for—in this case, insulin. Because bacteria reproduce quickly, large amounts of insulin can be produced in a short time.

Genetic Engineering in Other Organisms Scientists can also use genetic engineering techniques to insert genes into animals. For example, human genes can be inserted into the cells of cows. The cows then produce the human protein for which the gene codes in their milk. Scientists have used this technique to produce the blood clotting protein needed by people with hemophilia.

Genes have also been inserted into the cells of plants, such as tomatoes and rice. Some of the genes enable the plants to survive in cold temperatures or in poor soil. Other genetically engineered crops can resist insect pests.

Gene Therapy Someday it may be possible to use genetic engineering to correct some genetic disorders in humans. This process, called **gene therapy**, will involve inserting copies of a gene directly into a person's cells. For example, doctors may be able to treat hemophilia by replacing the defective allele on the X chromosome. The person's blood would then clot normally.

Concerns About Genetic Engineering Some people are concerned about the long-term effects of genetic engineering. For example, some people think that genetically engineered crops may not be entirely safe. People fear that these crops may harm the environment or cause health problems in humans. To address such concerns, scientists are trying to learn more about the effects of genetic engineering.

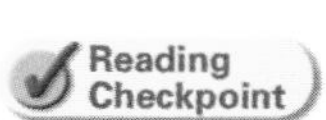
Reading Checkpoint **How do genetic engineering techniques enable scientists to produce clotting proteins?**

For: Links on genetic engineering
Visit: www.SciLinks.org
Web Code: scn-0343

Lab zone Skills Activity

Communicating

Suppose you work for a drug company that uses genetically engineered bacteria to produce insulin. Write an advertisement for the drug that includes a simplified explanation of how the drug is produced.

L2

Modeling Gene Splicing

Materials two pieces of yarn of different colors, blunt scissors, tape, art materials

Time 10 minutes

Focus Remind students that DNA is found in the cytoplasm of bacterial cells.

Teach Challenge students to create a model of DNA with yarn and then to use the model to demonstrate the steps in genetic engineering as illustrated in Figure 16. They might make and cut out large, simple shapes to represent a human cell and a bacterial cell, and arrange the DNA within the "cells" as part of the model.

Apply Remind students that enzymes act on specific sites. Ask: **Do the restriction enzymes have to be the same for both the plasmid and the human gene?** *(Yes; the DNA ends must match for them to join.)* **learning modality: kinesthetic**

Address Misconceptions

L1

The Future of Gene Therapy

Focus Students may think that all genetic disorders will soon be cured with gene therapy.

Teach Point out that gene therapy is unlikely to be used extensively in the near future because the techniques are new and still being tested.

Apply Ask: **Why is a disease such as hemophilia a good candidate for gene therapy?** *(It is caused by a defect in a single gene.)* **learning modality: logical/mathematical**

Lab zone Skills Activity

Skills Focus Communicating L3

Materials writing materials

Time 15 minutes

Expected Outcome Students will write an advertisement explaining how insulin is produced through genetically engineered bacteria. Scientists insert the human gene for insulin into the plasmid of a bacterium, and the bacterium and all of its offspring will produce the protein.

Extend Ask: **Why do the bacteria have to be genetically engineered in order to produce insulin?** *(The bacteria do not naturally produce insulin. The gene must be inserted into their DNA in order for them to make the human protein.)* **learning modality: verbal**

Monitor Progress

L2

Oral Presentation Call on students to describe ways that genetic engineering is being used.

Answers

Figure 16 The human gene is removed from a chromosome and attaches to the open ends of a cut plasmid in a bacterial cell to form a closed ring.

Reading Checkpoint Human genes are inserted into the cells of cows so that the cows produce milk that contains blood clotting proteins.

Learning About Human Genetics

Teach Key Concepts L2

Goal of the Human Genome Project

Focus Remind students that genetic engineering depends on identifying what specific genes code for.

Teach Ask: **What is the goal of the Human Genome Project?** *(To identify the DNA sequence of every human gene)*

Apply Tell students that more than 1,400 disease genes have been identified through this project. **learning modality: verbal**

Monitor Progress L2

Answer

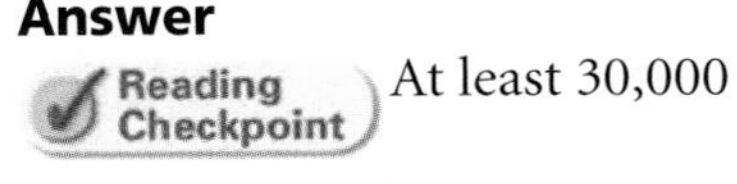
At least 30,000

Assess

Reviewing Key Concepts

1. a. Selective breeding, cloning, and genetic engineering **b.** Selective breeding—crossing two individuals to obtain particular characteristics; cloning—producing an organism with the same genes as another organism; genetic engineering—transferring genes from one organism into the DNA of another
c. Cloning; many houseplants can be cloned by cutting the stem from one plant and putting the stem in soil.
2. a. All the DNA in one cell of an organism **b.** A research study with the goal of identifying the DNA sequence of every gene in the human genome. **c.** Scientists may eventually be able to insert copies of the normal gene into the genes of people with a genetic disorder.

Reteach L1

Call on students to explain the different methods of producing organisms with desirable traits.

All in One Teaching Resources

- Section Summary: *Advances in Genetics*
- Review and Reinforce: *Advances in Genetics*
- Enrich: *Advances in Genetics*

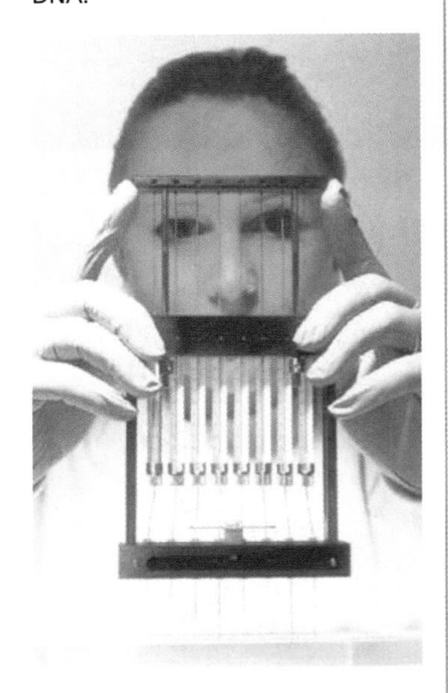

FIGURE 18
The Human Genome Project
Scientists on the Human Genome Project continue to study human DNA.

Learning About Human Genetics

Recent advances have enabled scientists to learn a great deal about human genetics. The Human Genome Project and DNA fingerprinting are two applications of this new knowledge.

The Human Genome Project Imagine trying to crack a code that is 6 billion letters long. That's exactly what scientists working on the Human Genome Project have been doing. A **genome** is all the DNA in one cell of an organism. **The main goal of the Human Genome Project has been to identify the DNA sequence of every gene in the human genome.** The Human Genome Project has completed a "first draft" of the human genome. The scientists have learned that the DNA of humans has at least 30,000 genes. The average gene has about 3,000 bases. Scientists will some day know the DNA sequence of every human gene.

DNA Fingerprinting DNA technology used in the Human Genome Project can also identify people and show whether people are related. DNA from a person's cells is broken down into small pieces, or fragments. Selected fragments are used to produce a pattern called a DNA fingerprint. Except for identical twins, no two people have exactly the same DNA fingerprint. You will learn more about DNA fingerprinting in Technology and Society.

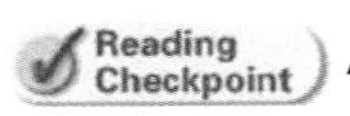
About how many genes are in the human genome?

Section 3 Assessment

Target Reading Skill Asking Questions Work with a partner to check your answers in your graphic organizer.

Reviewing Key Concepts

1. a. Listing List three methods that scientists can use to develop organisms with desirable traits.
   b. Describing Briefly describe each method.
   c. Applying Concepts Lupita has a houseplant. Which method would be the best way of producing a similar plant for a friend? Explain your answer.
2. a. Defining What is a genome?
   b. Explaining What is the Human Genome Project?
   c. Relating Cause and Effect How might knowledge gained from the Human Genome Project be used in gene therapy?

Lab zone At-Home Activity

Food and Selective Breeding Go to a grocery store with a parent or other family member. Discuss how fruits and vegetables have been produced by selective breeding. Choose a fruit or vegetable, and identify the traits that make it valuable.

Lab zone At-Home Activity

Food and Selective Breeding L1
Vegetables and fruits that students might focus on because of their variety are squash and pears. Suggest that students ask the store's produce manager what traits each variety is known for.

Lab zone Chapter Project

Keep Students on Track Check that students are completing their displays. Have them write out their presentations using correct terms they have learned in the chapter. Advise students to practice their presentations. Remind them to check their final written descriptions against their displays to make sure that they match and both are correct.

Lab zone **Skills Lab**

Guilty or Innocent?

Problem

A crime scene may contain hair, skin, or blood from a criminal. These materials all contain DNA that can be used to make a DNA fingerprint. A DNA fingerprint, which consists of a series of bands, is something like a bar code. How can a DNA fingerprint identify individuals?

Skills Focus

drawing conclusions, inferring

Materials

- 4–6 bar codes
- hand lens

Procedure

1. Look at the photograph of DNA band patterns shown at right. Each person's DNA produces a unique pattern of these bands.
2. Now look at the Universal Product Code, also called a bar code, shown below the DNA bands. A bar code can be used as a model of a DNA band pattern. Compare the bar code with the DNA bands to see what they have in common. Record your observations.
3. Suppose that a burglary has taken place, and you're the detective leading the investigation. Your teacher will give you a bar code that represents DNA from blood found at the crime scene. You arrange to have DNA samples taken from several suspects. Write a sentence describing what you will look for as you try to match each suspect's DNA to the DNA sample from the crime scene.
4. You will now be given bar codes representing DNA samples taken from the suspects. Compare those bar codes with the bar code that represents DNA from the crime scene.
5. Use your comparisons to determine whether any of the suspects was present at the crime scene.

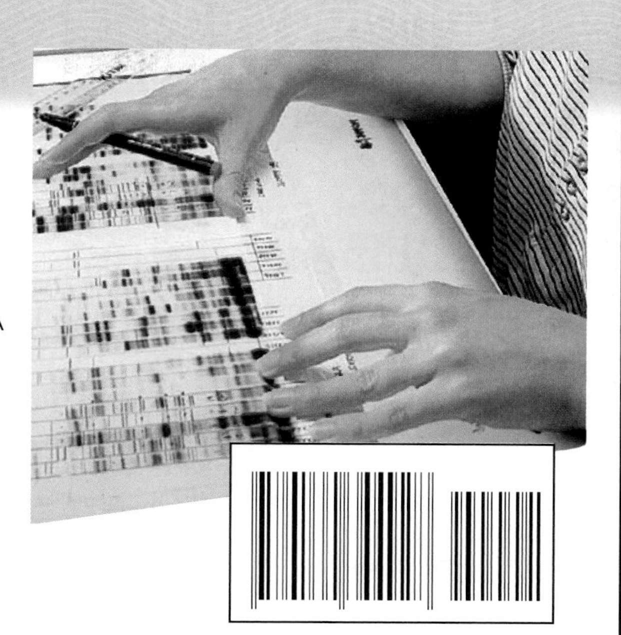

Analyze and Conclude

1. **Drawing Conclusions** Based on your findings, were any of the suspects present at the crime scene? Support your conclusion with specific evidence.
2. **Inferring** Why do people's DNA patterns differ so greatly?
3. **Drawing Conclusions** How would your conclusions be affected if you learned that the suspect whose DNA matched the evidence had an identical twin?
4. **Communicating** Suppose you are a defense lawyer. DNA evidence indicates that the bloodstain at the scene of a crime belongs to your client. Do you think this DNA evidence should be enough to convict your client? Write a speech you might give to the jury in defense of your client.

More to Explore

Do you think the DNA fingerprints of a parent and a child would show any similarities? Explain your thinking.

Guilty or Innocent? L2

Prepare for Inquiry

Key Concept

A person's DNA forms a unique pattern of bands that can be used to identify the person.

Skills Objectives

Students will be able to

- draw conclusions about which suspect was present at the crime scene based on the comparisons
- infer why people's DNA patterns differ so greatly

Class Time 20 minutes

All in One Teaching Resources

- Lab Worksheet: *Guilty or Innocent?*

Advance Planning

Remove bar codes from commercial products and cut the numbers from them. Each student's set of bar codes should contain one that is identical to the bar code from the crime scene. You could mount the bar codes on heavy paper and laminate them so they can be reused.

Alternative Materials

If you can obtain actual DNA fingerprints, the lab will be more realistic. Provide a hand lens for any student who has vision impairments.

Guide Inquiry

Troubleshooting the Experiment

Advise students to examine the patterns of bands very carefully because the differences may be minor and easily overlooked.

Expected Outcome

One of the suspect DNA samples is identical to the DNA sample from the crime scene.

Analyze and Conclude

1. Yes—the suspect whose DNA sample matches the DNA sample from the crime scene
2. No two people, except for identical twins, have the same sequence of bases in their DNA.
3. It would be impossible to conclude which twin was at the crime scene.
4. Students may say no because DNA evidence identifies only who was at the crime scene and not who committed the crime. Students also may say that errors can be made in analyzing the DNA evidence.

Extend Inquiry

More to Explore The DNA fingerprints should look more similar than the DNA fingerprints of unrelated people because parents and children share many genes.

Technology and Society

DNA Fingerprinting

Key Concept
DNA fingerprinting is used in many situations. Students research and analyze the use of this technology.

Build Background Knowledge
Ask: **What is the function of genes in a cell?** *(A gene contains the code that determines the structure of a protein.)* **What determines what type of protein will be produced?** *(The order of the nitrogen bases along a gene)* Have a student volunteer read the first paragraph, and then review the steps in producing a DNA fingerprint. Explain that only a portion of the DNA is identified, not the entire genome. The chance that two individuals will have a matching DNA portion varies from one in 800,000 to one in one billion.

Introduce the Debate
Have a student volunteer read the paragraphs *Analyzing DNA* and *Limitations of DNA Fingerprinting*. Explain that in the U.S., a national database of DNA fingerprints is maintained only of adult convicted criminals. Some people have advocated for the DNA fingerprints of all citizens to be maintained. Critics point out that the greater the number of people in the database, the greater the chance of similar profiles. They cite privacy issues and the variability of the quality of DNA fingerprinting from lab to lab. Proponents argue that DNA fingerprints are simply a means of identification, like birth certificates and dental records. Laws are already in place to protect against using genetic information to discriminate against people. A national database would make it easier to fight crime and terrorism.

Technology and Society • Tech & Design •

DNA Fingerprinting

What do you have that no one else has? Unless you are an identical twin, your DNA is unique. Because one person's DNA is like no one else's, it can be used to produce genetic "fingerprints." These fingerprints can tie a person to the scene of a crime. They can prevent the wrong person from going to jail. They can also be used to identify skeletal remains. Today, soldiers and sailors give blood and saliva samples so their DNA fingerprints can be saved. Like the identification tags that soldiers wear, DNA records can be used to identify the bodies of unknown soldiers or civilians.

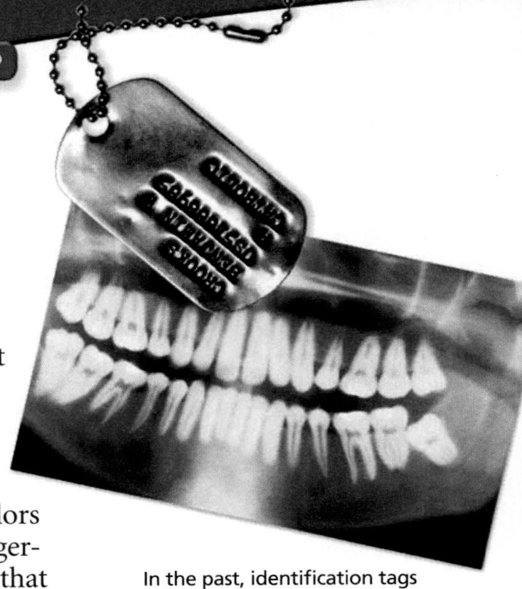

In the past, identification tags and dental records were the main methods for identifying skeletal remains.

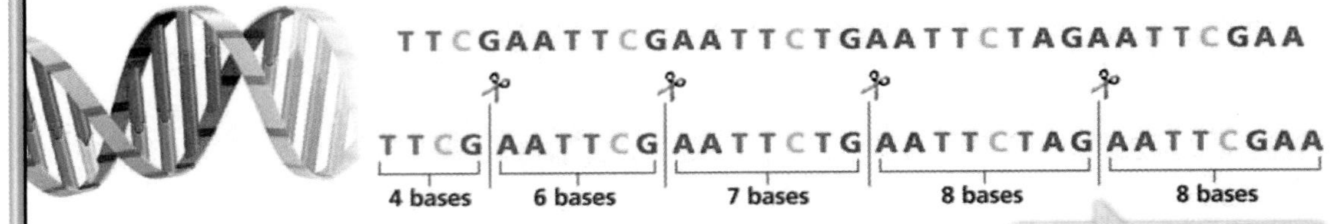

This enzyme cuts the DNA every time it encounters the DNA sequence GAATTC.

1 After a sample of DNA is extracted from the body, an enzyme cuts the DNA strand into several smaller pieces.

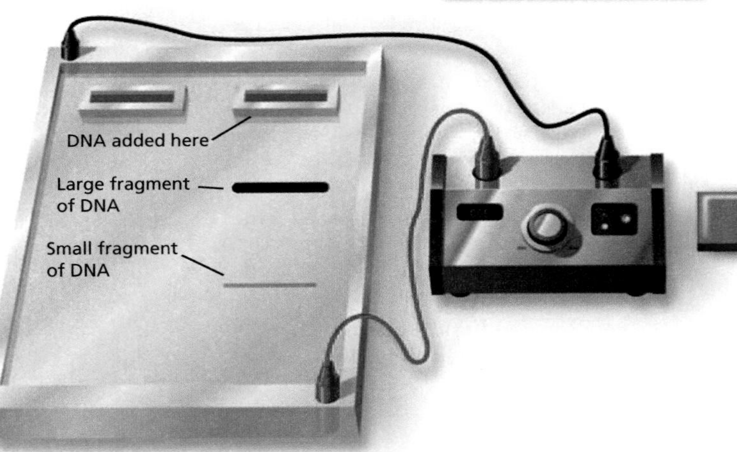

2 The cut-up DNA fragments are loaded into a gel that uses electric current to separate fragments. Larger fragments of DNA move through the gel more slowly than the smaller fragments.

Background

History of Science
DNA fingerprinting was invented in 1984 by Professor Sir Alec Jeffreys at the University of Leicester in the United Kingdom. It was first used in an immigration dispute to prove that a boy returning to the UK from Ghana really was the son of legal immigrants. In 1987 in Leicester, the first criminal case involving DNA evidence resulted in the conviction of the true murderer and exoneration of an innocent person. One very interesting use of the technique confirmed that a skeleton was the remains of an Auschwitz camp doctor, Josef Mengele, who escaped to South America in 1979. DNA from the skeleton was compared with DNA from Mengele's wife and son, who were still alive in Germany.

Analyzing DNA

In one method of DNA analysis, DNA from saliva, blood, bones, teeth, or other fluids or tissues is taken from cells. Special enzymes are added to cut the DNA into small pieces. Selected pieces are put into a machine that runs an electric current through the DNA and sorts the pieces by size. The DNA then gets stained and photographed. When developed, a unique banded pattern, similar to a product bar code, is revealed. The pattern can be compared to other samples of DNA to determine a match.

Limitations of DNA Fingerprinting

Like all technology, DNA fingerprinting has its limitations. DNA is very fragile and the films produced can be difficult to read if the DNA samples are old. In rare instances, DNA from the people testing the samples can become mixed in with the test samples and produce inaccurate results. DNA testing is also time consuming and expensive.

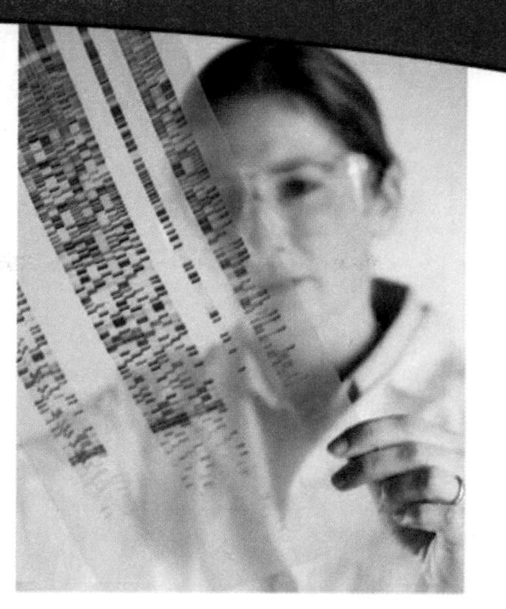

▲ Scientist reading a DNA fingerprint

❸ Once the DNA fragments have separated, the gel is stained. The unique banded pattern is a DNA fingerprint.

Weigh the Impact

1. Identify the Need
Make a list of at least five situations in which DNA fingerprinting could be useful.

2. Research
Research the situations you listed in Question 1 to find out if DNA analysis is or can be used in each.

3. Write
Choose one application of DNA analysis and write one or two paragraphs to explain when the application can be used.

For: More on DNA fingerprinting
Visit: PHSchool.com
Web Code: ceh-3040

Facilitate the Discussion

- Have students participate in a mock hearing to decide whether a national DNA fingerprinting database should be established. This would require every citizen to have DNA samples taken and stored. Students can role-play medical insurance companies, people with genetic disorders, judges who try criminal cases, victims of crimes in which the criminal was never identified, and citizens on both sides of the issue.
- After the hearing, ask students to try to reach a compromise on the fairest way to use DNA fingerprinting.

Weigh the Impact

1. Students may provide a situation using an example from the feature. Other situations include finding out whether people are related and diagnosing a genetic disorder.
2. Require students to access at least three sources for their answers.
3. Paragraphs should include specific situations in which DNA fingerprinting is being used and the limitations of using DNA fingerprinting for that application.

For: More on DNA fingerprinting
Visit: PHSchool.com
Web Code: ceh-3040

Students can research this issue online.

Extend

Encourage students to investigate the laws in your state regarding the admissibility of DNA evidence in a court of law. Students may also want to find out more about the outcomes in which DNA was used in real-life situations.

Study Guide

- Complete student edition
- Section and chapter self-assessments
- Assessment reports for teachers

Help Students Read

Building Vocabulary

Word Analysis Have students look up the meaning of the word *engineering. (The application of scientific and mathematical principles to design ways of solving practical problems)* Then have students use this information to write a definition for *genetic engineering. (The application of genetic principles to design processes for inserting the DNA for certain traits in an organism)*

Words in Context Select key terms from the chapter. Have students write a sentence for each term that uses the term in a correct context. Provide them with one example before they begin: *Carrier: Because the boy had hemophilia and neither of his parents showed symptoms of the disease, his mother must have been a carrier.*

Connecting Concepts

Concept Maps Help students develop a concept map to show how the information in this chapter is related. Have students brainstorm to identify the key concepts, key terms, details, and examples, then write each one on a sticky note. They will use these sticky notes to construct the concept map.

Tell students that this concept map will be organized in hierarchical order and to begin at the top with the key concepts. Ask students these questions to guide them to categorize the information on the stickies: **In what ways are human traits controlled by genes? What are two causes of genetic disorders? What are some examples disorders that can be inherited? How can scientists develop organisms with desirable traits?**

Chapter 4 Study Guide

1 Human Inheritance

Key Concepts

- Some human traits are controlled by single genes with two alleles, and others by single genes with multiple alleles. Still other traits are controlled by many genes that act together.
- The sex chromosomes carry genes that determine whether a person is male or female. They also carry genes that determine other traits.
- Many of a person's characteristics are determined by an interaction between genes and the environment.

Key Terms

multiple alleles
sex chromosomes
sex-linked gene
carrier

2 Human Genetic Disorders

Key Concepts

- Some genetic disorders are caused by mutations in the DNA of genes. Other disorders are caused by changes in the overall structure or number of chromosomes.
- One important tool that geneticists use to trace the inheritance of traits in humans is a pedigree.
- Today doctors use tools such as karyotypes to help detect genetic disorders. People with genetic disorders are helped through medical care, education, job training, and other methods.

Key Terms

genetic disorder
pedigree
karyotype

3 Advances in Genetics

Key Concepts

- Selective breeding, cloning, and genetic engineering are three methods for developing organisms with desirable traits.
- The main goal of the Human Genome Project has been to identify the DNA sequence of every gene in the human genome.

Key Terms

selective breeding
inbreeding
hybridization
clone
genetic engineering
gene therapy
genome

Prompt students by using connecting words or phrases, such as "involves the study of," "which can be caused by," and "which includes diseases such as," to indicate the basis for the organization of the map. The phrases should form a sentence between or among a set of concepts.

Answer

Accept logical presentations by students.

All in One Teaching Resources

- Key Terms Review: *Modern Genetics*
- Connecting Concepts: *Modern Genetics*

Review and Assessment

Go Online PHSchool.com
For: Self-Assessment
Visit: PHSchool.com
Web Code: cea-3040

Organizing Information

Concept Mapping Copy the concept map about human traits onto a separate sheet of paper. Then complete it and add a title. (For more on Concept Mapping, see the Skills Handbook.)

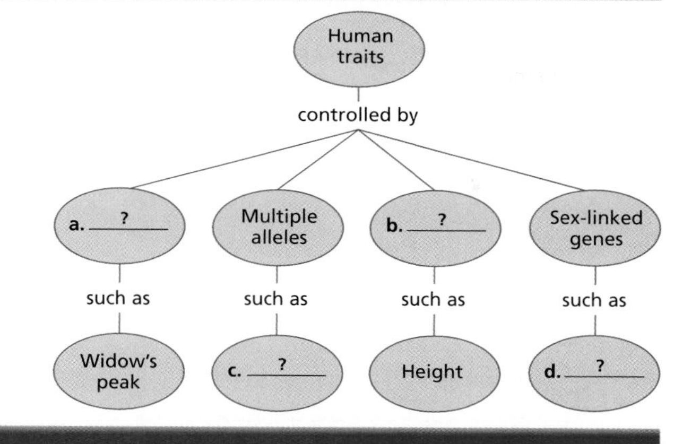

Reviewing Key Terms

Choose the letter of the best answer.

1. A human trait that is controlled by a single gene with multiple alleles is
   a. dimples. **b.** blood type.
   c. height. **d.** skin color.
2. A sex-linked disorder is
   a. cystic fibrosis.
   b. sickle-cell disease.
   c. hemophilia.
   d. Down syndrome.
3. Which of the following would most likely be used to diagnose Down syndrome?
   a. a karyotype
   b. a pedigree
   c. a blood-clotting test
   d. a Punnett square
4. Inserting a human gene into a bacterial plasmid is an example of
   a. inbreeding.
   b. selective breeding.
   c. DNA fingerprinting.
   d. genetic engineering.
5. An organism that has the same genes as the organism from which it was produced is called a
   a. clone. **b.** hybrid.
   c. genome. **d.** pedigree.

If the statement is true, write *true*. If it is false, change the underlined word or words to make the statement true.

6. A widow's peak is a human trait that is controlled by a single gene.
7. A male inherits two X chromosomes.
8. A karyotype tracks which members of a family have a trait.
9. Hybridization is the crossing of two genetically similar organisms.
10. A genome is all the DNA in one cell of an organism.

Writing in Science

Fact Sheet You are a scientist in a cloning lab. Write a fact sheet that explains what the process of cloning involves. Describe at least one example.

Modern Genetics
Video Preview
Video Field Trip
▶ Video Assessment

Review and Assessment

Organizing Information

a. Single genes with two alleles
b. Many genes
c. Blood type (or skin color)
d. Colorblindness (or Hemophilia) *Sample title:* The Inheritance of Human Traits

Reviewing Key Terms

1. b **2.** c **3.** a **4.** d **5.** a
6. true
7. female
8. pedigree
9. Inbreeding
10. true

Writing in Science

Writing Mode Explanation
Scoring Rubric
4 Includes description of the cloning process and goes beyond requirements in some way, for example, describes more than one example
3 Includes criteria but does not go beyond requirements
2 Includes only brief description
1 Includes incomplete or inaccurate information

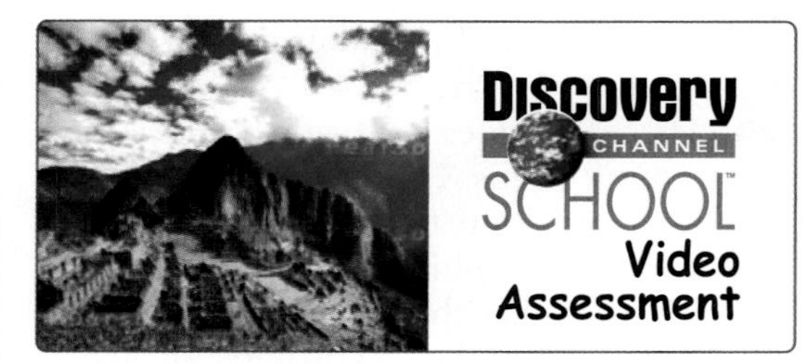

Modern Genetics

Show the Video Assessment to review chapter content and as a prompt for the writing assignment.

Go Online PHSchool.com
For: Self-Assessment
Visit: PHSchool.com
Web Code: cea-3040

Students can take a practice test online that is automatically scored.

All in One Teaching Resources
- Transparency C39
- Chapter Test
- Performance Assessment Teacher Notes
- Performance Assessment Student Worksheet
- Performance Assessment Scoring Rubric

***ExamView®* Computer Test Bank CD-ROM**

Checking Concepts

11. Skin color in humans is controlled by many genes.

12. Males need to inherit just one allele to have the trait, whereas females need to inherit two alleles.

13. Sickle-cell disease is a genetic disorder in which red blood cells contain an abnormal form of hemoglobin. People who have the disease inherit a copy of a recessive allele from each parent.

14. A pedigree is a chart that tracks which members of a family have a particular trait. Geneticists use pedigrees to trace the inheritance of traits.

15. Sample answer: Physical therapy can help remove mucus from the lungs of people with cystic fibrosis. People with sickle-cell disease can take folic acid to help their bodies manufacture red blood cells.

16. The horse breeder would mate only horses that have golden coats. The breeder would always select offspring with golden coats to be parents of the next generation.

17. Doctors would replace the defective allele on the X chromosome with a copy of a normal allele.

18. The Human Genome Project is a research study with the goal of identifying the DNA sequence of every gene in the human genome.

Thinking Critically

19. The mother has normal color vision but is a carrier of the colorblindness allele. Her genotype is X^CX^c. The father is colorblind. His genotype is X^cY.

20. The father does not have the allele for hemophilia on his X chromosome, so he does not contribute the trait. If the mother is a carrier of hemophilia, one of her X chromosomes has the allele for normal clotting and the other X chromosome has the allele for hemophilia. The son has a 50 percent chance of inheriting an X chromosome that carries the allele for hemophilia and therefore of having hemophilia. Note: The question asks about sons only, so there are two possible genotypes, not four.

21. Emily has cystic fibrosis. The mother, the father, and Sarah are carriers.

Review and Assessment

Checking Concepts

11. Explain why there are a wide variety of phenotypes for skin color in humans.
12. Traits controlled by recessive alleles on the X chromosome are more common in males than in females. Explain why.
13. What is sickle-cell disease? How is this disorder inherited?
14. What is a pedigree? How do geneticists use pedigrees?
15. Describe two ways in which people with genetic disorders can be helped.
16. Explain how a horse breeder might use selective breeding to produce horses that have golden coats.
17. Describe how gene therapy might be used in the future to treat a person with hemophilia.
18. What is the Human Genome Project?

Thinking Critically

19. **Problem Solving** A woman with normal color vision has a colorblind daughter. What are the genotypes and phenotypes of both parents?
20. **Calculating** If a mother is a carrier of hemophilia and the father does not have hemophilia, what is the probability that their son will have the trait? Explain your answer.
21. **Interpreting Diagrams** The allele for cystic fibrosis is recessive. Identify which members of the family in the pedigree have cystic fibrosis and which are carriers.

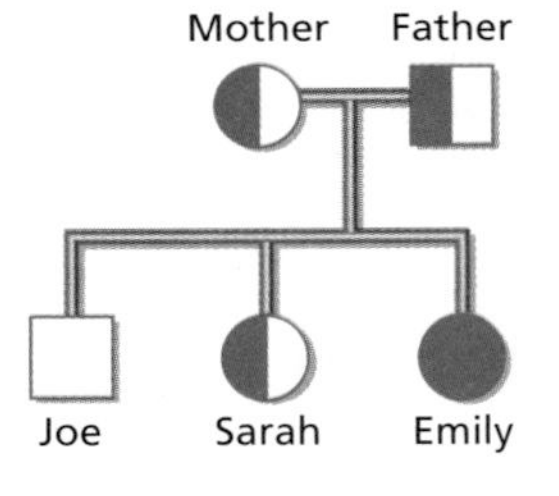

Applying Skills

Use the Punnett square to answer Questions 22–24.

The Punnett square below shows how muscular dystrophy, a sex-linked recessive disorder, is inherited.

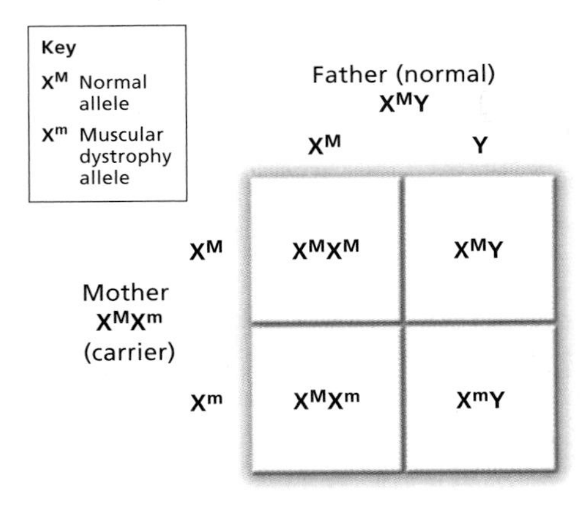

22. **Interpreting Data** What is the probability that a daughter of these parents will have muscular dystrophy? Explain your answer.
23. **Interpreting Data** What is the probability that a son of these parents will have muscular dystrophy? Explain your answer.
24. **Inferring** Is it possible for a woman to have muscular dystrophy? Why or why not?

Lab zone Chapter Project

Performance Assessment Present your display board to your class. Highlight important facts about the genetic trait you selected. Discuss the innovative designs you incorporated into the display board. In your presentation, highlight the interactive part of your project.

Lab zone Chapter Project

L3

Performance Assessment Encourage students to provide constructive feedback to help each other improve their presentations and displays. If possible, arrange for students to present their displays to a younger audience. The display should include an interactive portion that shows the probability of inheriting the trait. Encourage the young children to ask questions about each display as it is presented.

Reflect and Record After all presentations, have students evaluate their own displays in light of their classmates' displays. Students can identify what was most effective in conveying the material and make suggestions they think would have made their display better.

Standardized Test Prep

Test-Taking Tip

Interpreting Diagrams

If you are asked to interpret a pedigree diagram, first determine the trait that the pedigree shows. For example, the pedigree for Questions 3–4 shows the inheritance of sickle-cell disease. Remember that a circle represents a female and a square represents a male. Also look for a key that explains what the symbols in this particular pedigree show.

Use the pedigree for Questions 3–4 to answer the sample question below.

Sample Question

Which of the following is true for the first generation shown in the pedigree?

A Both the man and the woman have sickle-cell disease.
B Both the man and the woman are carriers of sickle-cell disease.
C Only the woman is a carrier of sickle-cell disease.
D Only the man is a carrier of sickle-cell disease.

Answer

The correct answer is **C**. Since the circle is half shaded, the woman is a carrier.

Choose the letter of the best answer.

1. A woman is heterozygous for the trait of hemophilia. Her husband does not have hemophilia. What is the probability that their son will have hemophilia?
A 0%
B 25%
C 50%
D 100%

2. Down syndrome is an example of a genetic disorder in which
F one DNA base has been added.
G one DNA base has been deleted.
H one chromosome is substituted for another.
J an extra chromosome is added to a pair.

Use the pedigree to answer Questions 3–4.

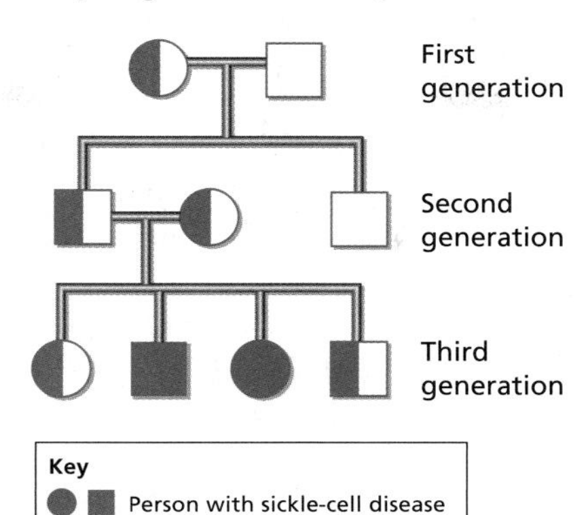

3. How many people in the second generation have sickle-cell disease?
A none **B** one person
C two people **D** three people

4. Which statement is true about the third generation in the pedigree?
F No one has sickle-cell disease.
G Everyone has sickle-cell disease.
H Everyone has at least one allele for sickle-cell disease.
J No one has any alleles for sickle-cell disease.

5. To produce a human protein through genetic engineering, scientists use
A a bacterial gene inserted into a human chromosome.
B a human gene inserted into a plasmid.
C a bacterial gene inserted into a plasmid.
D a human gene inserted into a human chromosome.

Constructed Response

6. Explain why, for each pregnancy, human parents have a 50 percent probability of having a boy and a 50 percent probability of having a girl. Your answer should include the terms *X chromosome* and *Y chromosome.*

Applying Skills

22. The probability is 0%; the father cannot contribute a recessive allele for muscular dystrophy, so it is not possible for a daughter to receive two X chromosomes with the recessive allele.
23. The probability is 50%; the mother is a carrier of muscular dystrophy, so one of her X chromosomes has the allele for normal health and the other X chromosome has the allele for muscular dystrophy. A son has a 50% chance of inheriting an X chromosome that carries the allele for muscular dystrophy and therefore of having muscular dystrophy.
24. It is possible for a woman to have muscular dystrophy if her father has it and her mother is a carrier. It is a recessive disorder, so she would have to inherit the allele for muscular dystrophy on the X chromosomes of both her parents.

Standardized Test Prep

1. C **2.** J **3.** A **4.** H **5.** B
6. The mother always contributes an X chromosome to the baby's genome. The father has an X chromosome and a Y chromosome, so the child has a 50% chance of receiving a Y chromosome and therefore a 50% chance of being a boy.

Chapter at a Glance

Life's Long Calendar

Technology | **Local Standards**

All in One Teaching Resources
- Chapter Project Teacher Notes, pp. 286–287
- Chapter Project Student Overview, pp. 288–289
- Chapter Project Student Worksheets, pp. 290–291
- Chapter Project Scoring Rubric, p. 292

Video Preview

Darwin's Theory

2–3 periods
1–1 1/2 blocks

C.5.1.1 Describe important observations Darwin made on his voyage.
C.5.1.2 State the hypothesis Darwin made to explain differences between similar species.
C.5.1.3 Explain how natural selection leads to evolution.

Video Field Trip

Evidence of Evolution

2–3 periods
1–1 1/2 blocks

C.5.2.1 State evidence that supports the theory of evolution.
C.5.2.2 Explain how scientists infer evolutionary relationships among organisms.
C.5.2.3 Describe how new species form.

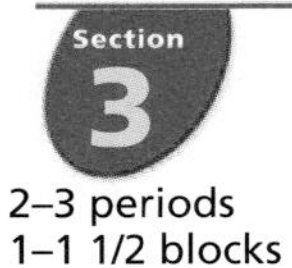

The Fossil Record

2–3 periods
1–1 1/2 blocks

C.5.3.1 Describe how most fossils form.
C.5.3.2 Explain how scientists can determine a fossil's age.
C.5.3.3 State what the Geologic Time Scale is.
C.5.3.4 Identify some unanswered questions about evolution.

Review and Assessment

All in One Teaching Resources
- Key Terms Review, p. 318
- Transparency C46
- Performance Assessment Teacher Notes, p. 325
- Performance Assessment Scoring Rubric p. 326
- Performance Assessment Student Worksheet, p. 327
- Chapter Test, pp. 328–331

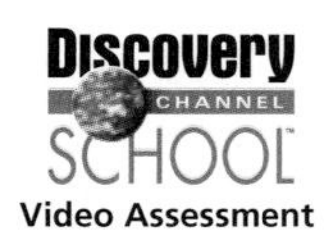

Video Assessment

Test Preparation

Test Preparation Blackline Masters

Chapter Activities Planner

For more activities

Student Edition	Inquiry	Time	Materials	Skills	Resources
Chapter Project, p. 137	Open-Ended	Ongoing (2 to 3 weeks)	**All in One Teaching Resources,** p. 286	Calculating, making models, communicating	**Lab zone Easy Planner** **All in One Teaching Resources,** Support pp. 286–287
Section 1					
Discover Activity, p. 138	Guided	15 minutes	Metric ruler, 10 sunflower seeds, hand lens	Classifying	**Lab zone Easy Planner**
Try This Activity, p. 141	Guided	10 minutes	Bird seed, paper plate, 20 raisins, tweezers, hair clips, hairpins, clothes pins, stopwatch, paper cup	Inferring	**Lab zone Easy Planner**
Skills Activity, p. 143	Guided	10 minutes	15 black buttons, 15 white buttons, large sheet of plain white paper, stopwatch	Making models	**Lab zone Easy Planner**
Skills Lab, pp. 146–147	Guided	40 minutes	Scissors, marking pen, construction paper, 2 colors	Predicting, making models	**Lab zone Easy Planner** **Lab Activity Video** **All in One Teaching Resources,** Skills Lab: *Nature at Work,* pp. 300–302
Section 2					
Discover Activity, p. 148	Open-Ended	10 minutes	6 to 8 pens	Classifying	**Lab zone Easy Planner**
Skills Activity, p. 150	Guided	5 minutes	None	Drawing conclusions	**Lab zone Easy Planner**
Skills Lab, p. 154	Guided	30 minutes	None	Interpreting data, drawing conclusions	**Lab zone Easy Planner** **Lab Activity Video** **All in One Teaching Resources,** Skills Lab: *Telltale Molecules,* pp. 309–310
Section 3					
Discover Activity, p. 155	Open-Ended	5 minutes	None	Inferring	**Lab zone Easy Planner**
Try This Activity, p. 156	Guided	10 minutes	Fresh fruit, two plastic containers, water	Inferring	**Lab zone Easy Planner**

Section 1 Darwin's Theory

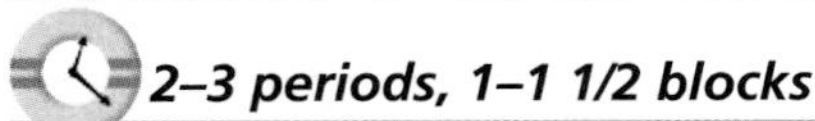
2–3 periods, 1–1 1/2 blocks

ABILITY LEVELS
- L1 Basic to Average
- L2 For All Students
- L3 Average to Advanced

Objectives

C.5.1.1 Describe important observations Darwin made on his voyage.

C.5.1.2 State the hypothesis Darwin made to explain differences between similar species.

C.5.1.3 Explain how natural selection leads to evolution.

Key Terms

• species • fossil • adaptation • evolution • scientific theory
• natural selection • variation

Local Standards

Preteach

Build Background Knowledge

Students share knowledge they have about Charles Darwin.

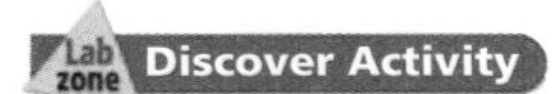 *How Do Living Things Vary?* 

Targeted Print and Technology Resources

All in One Teaching Resources
- L2 Reading Strategy Transparency C40: Relating Cause and Effect

PresentationExpress™ CD-ROM

Instruct

Darwin's Observations Discuss observations Darwin made on his voyage and why they were significant.

Galápagos Organisms Examine the conclusions Darwin drew from his observations of the organisms on the Galápagos Islands.

Evolution State Darwin's theory of evolution and how he arrived at it.

Natural Selection Explain how natural selection relates to evolution, and apply to an example.

Lab zone Skills Lab *Nature at Work* L2

Targeted Print and Technology Resources

All in One Teaching Resources
- L2 Guided Reading, pp. 295–297
- L2 Skills Lab: *Nature at Work*, pp. 300–302

Lab Activity Video/DVD
Skills Lab: *Nature at Work*

www.SciLinks.org Web Code: scn-0351

Student Edition on Audio CD

Assess

Section Assessment Questions

Have students use their graphic organizers with the causes of natural selection to help them answer the questions.

Reteach

Examine figures to review how variation in a species relates to natural selection.

Targeted Print and Technology Resources

All in One Teaching Resources
- Section Summary, p. 294
- L1 Review and Reinforce, p. 298
- L3 Enrich, p. 299

Section 2 Evidence of Evolution

 *2–3 periods, 1–1 1/2 blocks*

ABILITY LEVELS
L1 Basic to Average
L2 For All Students
L3 Average to Advanced

Objectives

C.5.2.1 State evidence that supports the theory of evolution.
C.5.2.2 Explain how scientists infer evolutionary relationships among organisms.
C.5.2.3 Describe how new species form.

Key Terms

• homologous structures • branching tree

Local Standards

Preteach

Build Background Knowledge

Invite students to classify familiar animals.

How Can You Classify Species? 

Targeted Print and Technology Resources

L2 Reading Strategy Transparency C41: Identifying Supporting Evidence

 **PresentationExpress™ CD-ROM**

Instruct

Interpreting the Evidence Analyze how fossils, early development, and body structures support the theory of evolution.

Inferring Species Relationships Examine how scientists infer evolutionary relationships among species from evidence.

How Do New Species Form? Describe how separation of organisms leads to the formation of a new species, and apply to an example.

Telltale Molecules 

Targeted Print and Technology Resources

All in One Teaching Resources

L2 Guided Reading, pp. 305–306
L2 Transparency C42
L2 Skills Lab: *Telltale Molecules,* pp. 309–310

Lab Activity Video/DVD
Skills Lab: *Telltale Molecules*

www.SciLinks.org Web Code: scn-0352

 **Student Edition on Audio CD**

Assess

Section Assessment Questions

Have students use their graphic organizers with evidence supporting the theory of evolution to answer the questions.

Reteach

Use figures in this section to discuss how evidence for evolution can be used to show how species are related.

Targeted Print and Technology Resources

All in One Teaching Resources

• Section Summary, p. 304
L1 Review and Reinforce, p. 307
L3 Enrich, p. 308

Section 3 The Fossil Record

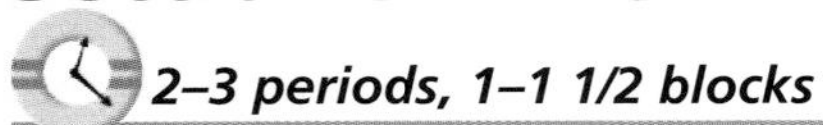

2–3 periods, 1–1 1/2 blocks

ABILITY LEVELS
- L1 Basic to Average
- L2 For All Students
- L3 Average to Advanced

Local Standards

Objectives

C.5.3.1 Describe how most fossils form.
C.5.3.2 Explain how scientists can determine a fossil's age.
C.5.3.3 State what the Geologic Time Scale is.
C.5.3.4 Identify some unanswered questions about evolution.

Key Terms

• petrified fossil • mold • cast • relative dating • radioactive dating
• radioactive element • half-life • fossil record • extinct • gradualism
• punctuated equilibria

Preteach

Build Background Knowledge

Ask students to discuss how scientists can know some much about dinosaurs.

Discover Activity *What Can You Learn From Fossils?* L1

Targeted Print and Technology Resources

All in One Teaching Resources
- L2 Reading Strategy: Building Vocabulary

PresentationExpress™ CD-ROM

Instruct

How Do Fossils Form? Explain how most fossils form, and distinguish the types of fossils.

Determining a Fossil's Age Compare and contrast relative dating and radioactive dating.

What Do Fossils Reveal? Explain the Geologic Time Scale, and apply to an example.

Unanswered Questions Ask questions to help students examine unknowns about mass extinctions and the rate of evolution.

Targeted Print and Technology Resources

All in One Teaching Resources
- L2 Guided Reading, pp. 313–315
- L2 Transparencies C43, C44, C45

PHSchool.com Web Code: cep-3053

Student Edition on Audio CD

Assess

Section Assessment Questions

Have students use their definitions to help them answer the questions.

Reteach

Use the visuals to summarize how fossils are formed and what they tell us about life on Earth.

Targeted Print and Technology Resources

All in One Teaching Resources
- Section Summary, p. 312
- L1 Review and Reinforce, p. 316
- L3 Enrich, p. 317

Chapter 5 Content Refresher

Section 1 Darwin's Theory

Lamarck's Theory of Evolution Darwin was not the first person to propose a theory of evolution. In the early 1800s, a well-known French naturalist named Jean-Baptiste Lamarck also developed a theory of evolution. Lamarck thought that changes in an organism during its lifetime could be passed on to its offspring. For example, Lamarck thought that giraffes could stretch their necks to feed on the leaves of tall trees. These giraffes would have offspring with longer necks. This idea is often called "the inheritance of acquired characteristics," and it is now known to be incorrect. Changes in an organism cannot be passed on to its offspring unless they are controlled by genes.

Section 2 Evidence of Evolution

Vestigial Organs Vestigial organs are one type of homologous structure. A vestigial organ is a structure that has little or no apparent function in the organism that possesses it, even though corresponding structures are fully functional in other organisms. For example, certain snake species have vestiges of leg bones. Since snakes crawl rather than walk, the leg bones have no function. The snakes with vestigial leg bones probably descended from a vertebrate ancestor that used legs to move.

Section 3 The Fossil Record

Index Fossils and Relative Dating

An index fossil is the fossil of an extinct species, such as trilobites and ammonites, that existed for a relatively short period but over a large area. Scientists use index fossils as a way of estimating the ages of other fossils. For example, if a fossil of an unknown age is found near a trilobite in the same rock layer, such as in Layer A in the illustration, scientists assume that the fossil is approximately the same age as the trilobite.

Address Misconceptions

Many students think that most species that have existed on Earth have left fossil remains. However, only a fraction of one percent is likely to have been preserved as fossils. For a strategy for overcoming this misconception, see **Address Misconceptions** in the section *The Fossil Record.*

Scientists also use index fossils to match up rock layers that may be at a distance from one another or have become separated. For example, in the illustration, the left and right sides of Layers A, B, and C are separated by a valley. The presence of trilobites in Layer A on both sides of the valley indicate that those layers are the same age; likewise, the ammonites in Layer C indicate that these layers match on both sides of the valley.

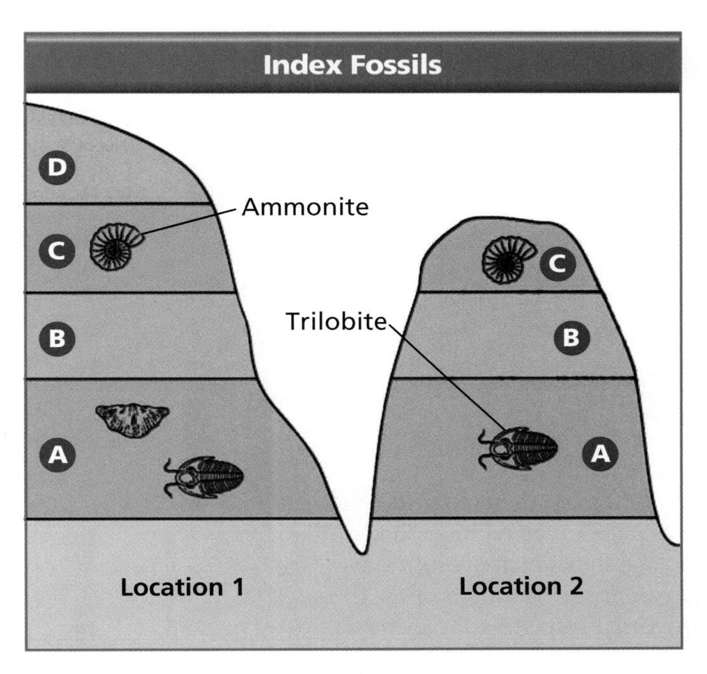

Help Students Read

Outlining

Understanding Text Structure

Strategy Outlining using headings as major divisions is a good strategy to apply to an entire section, if it is not excessively long. Outlining is best applied to sections in which the headings are parallel, and in which there are main headings and subheadings.

Example

1. Before students read, have them preview a section's title and headings. Make a skeleton outline for the section.

2. Have students copy the skeleton outline and fill in details under each main heading and subheading as they read.

Interactive Textbook

- Complete student edition
- Video and audio
- Simulations and activities
- Section and chapter reviews

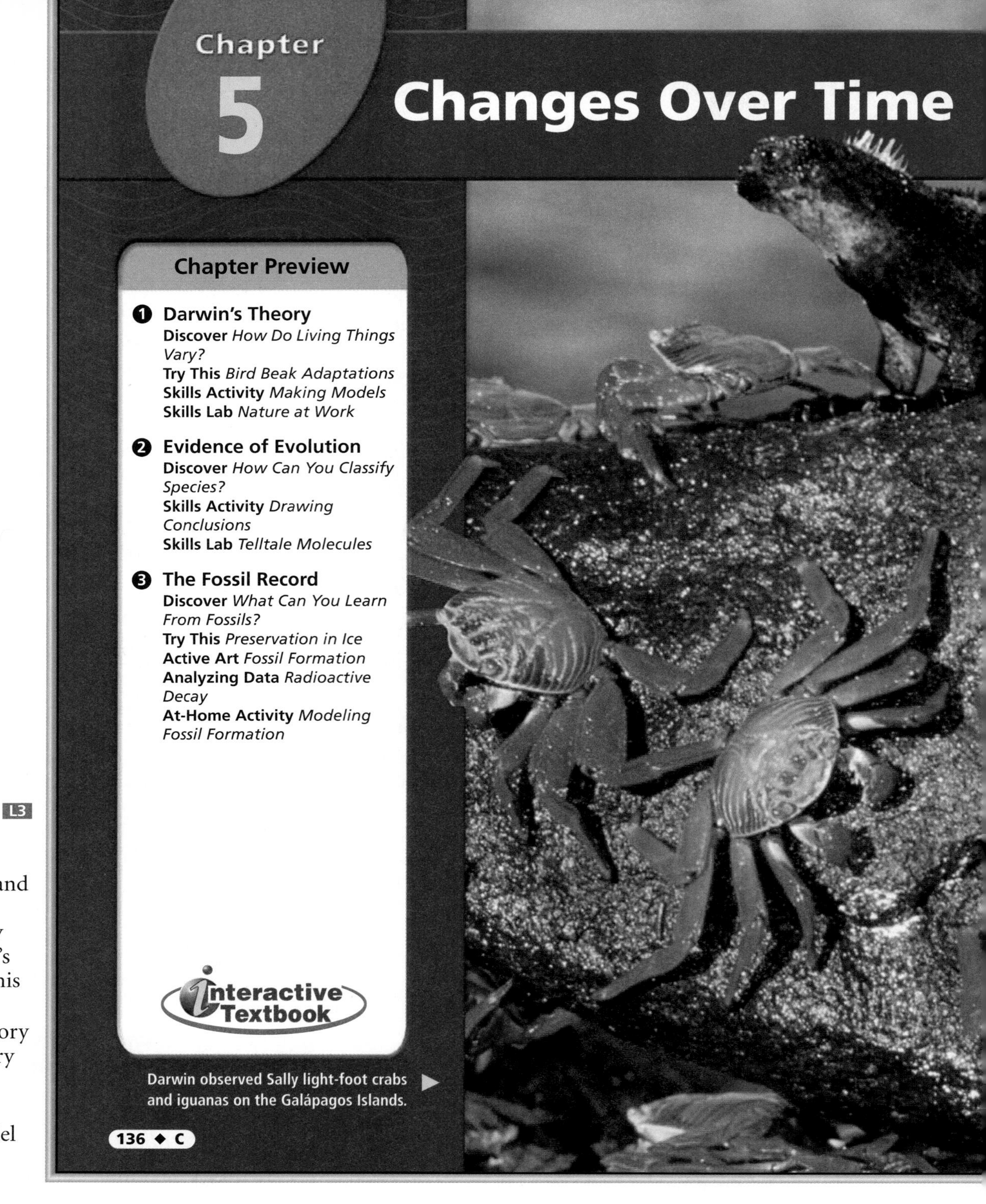

Chapter 5

Changes Over Time

Chapter Preview

Interactive Textbook

Darwin observed Sally light-foot crabs and iguanas on the Galápagos Islands.

136 ◆ C

L3

Objectives

This project will help students to understand the large time spans involved in geologic time and to place significant evolutionary events within an accurate model of Earth's history: a timeline drawn to scale. After this Chapter Project, students will be able to

- make scale models representing the history of life on Earth, with major evolutionary events included
- calculate the scale of a model
- communicate the features of their model to the class

Skills Focus

Calculating, making models, communicating

Project Time Line 2 to 3 weeks

All in One Teaching Resources

- Chapter Project Teacher Notes
- Chapter Project Overview
- Chapter Project Worksheet 1
- Chapter Project Worksheet 2
- Chapter Project Scoring Rubric

Developing a Plan

On the first day, have students review the project rules and procedures. Invite questions and comments. Then divide the class into groups of three or four students each, and let the groups meet to discuss the types of timelines they could make.

Possible Materials

- Students will need calculators, meter sticks, and metric tape to construct all models that use units of length to represent millions of years.
- Provide a variety of source materials for students to research additional evolutionary events to include in their timelines.
- Other materials will vary depending on the formats that students choose.

Lab zone™ Chapter **Project**

Life's Long Calendar

Earth's history goes back billions of years. This chapter project will help you understand this huge time span. In this project, you'll find a way to convert enormous time periods into a more familiar scale.

Your Goal To use a familiar measurement scale to create two timelines for Earth's history

To complete the project you must

- represent Earth's history using a familiar scale, such as months on a calendar or yards on a football field
- use your chosen scale twice, once to plot out 5 billion years of history, and once to focus on the past 600 million years
- include markers on both scales to show important events in the history of life

Plan It! Preview Figure 16 in this chapter to see what events occurred during the two time periods. In a small group, discuss some familiar scales you might use for your timelines. You could select a time interval such as a year or a day. Alternatively, you could choose a distance interval such as the length of your schoolyard or the walls in your classroom. Decide on the kind of timelines you will make. Then plan and construct your timelines.

Chapter 5 C ◆ 137

Changes Over Time

Show the Video Preview to introduce the Galápagos Islands.

Launching the Project

Draw a long line across the board, and label the left end *Beginning of Earth* and the right end *Present*. Have students preview Figure 16. Ask: **How long ago did Earth begin?** *(about 4.6 billion years ago)* Write *4,600,000,000* on the board. **When did the first animals appear on Earth?** *(about 600 million years ago)* Write *600,000,000* below the first number with place values aligned. Ask: **Where should I mark the line to show when the first animals appeared?** *(Close to the "Present" end)* Point out that if students made only one timeline to scale, all the events that happened from the beginning of the Paleozoic Era to the present would be crowded into a very small section. Explain that to solve this problem, they will make two timelines in this project.

Performance Assessment

The Chapter Project Scoring Rubric will help you evaluate how well students complete the Chapter Project. You may want to share the scoring rubric with your students so they are clear about what will be expected of them. Students will be assessed on

- their accuracy in calculating the scales for the two models
- their ability to construct two scale models of Earth's history with important evolutionary events accurately marked
- their effectiveness in communicating the model-making process and results to others
- their participation in their groups

Section 1 Darwin's Theory

Objectives

After this lesson, students will be able to

C.5.1.1 Describe important observations Darwin made on his voyage.

C.5.1.2 State the hypothesis Darwin made to explain differences between similar species.

C.5.1.3 Explain how natural selection leads to evolution.

Target Reading Skill

Relating Cause and Effect Explain that cause is the reason for what happens. The effect is what happens because of the cause. Relating cause and effect helps students relate the reason for what happens to what happens as a result.

Answer

Possible answers:

Causes

Overproduction: More offspring are produced than can survive.

Variations: Members of the same species differ.

Competition: Offspring compete for survival.

Selection: Some variations make individuals better fit for survival.

Environmental Change: Changes in environment can affect an individual's survival.

Genes: Genes that help determine survival are passed from parent to offspring.

All in One Teaching Resources

- Transparency C40

Preteach

Build Background Knowledge L1

Discussing Darwin

Many students will have read articles or seen television specials about Darwin or the Galápagos Islands. Ask: **Who was Charles Darwin?** *(A scientist who came up with the idea of evolution by natural selection)* **What interested Darwin about the Galápagos Islands?** *(They have a lot of unusual organisms, such as giant lizards and tortoises.)*

Section 1 Darwin's Theory

Reading Preview

Key Concepts

- What important observations did Darwin make on his voyage?
- What hypothesis did Darwin make to explain the differences between similar species?
- How does natural selection lead to evolution?

Key Terms

- species
- fossil
- adaptation
- evolution
- scientific theory
- natural selection
- variation

Target Reading Skill

Relating Cause and Effect In a graphic organizer, identify factors that cause natural selection.

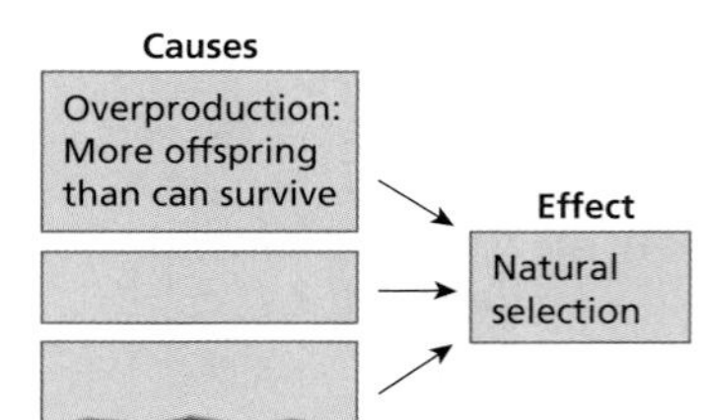

Lab zone Discover Activity

How Do Living Things Vary?

1. Use a ruler to measure the length and width of 10 sunflower seeds. Record each measurement.
2. Now use a hand lens to carefully examine each seed. Record each seed's shape, color, and number of stripes.

Think It Over

Classifying In what ways are the seeds in your sample different from one another? In what ways are they similar? How could you group the seeds based on their similarities and differences?

In December 1831, the British ship HMS *Beagle* set sail from England on a five-year trip around the world. On board was a 22-year-old named Charles Darwin. Darwin eventually became the ship's naturalist—a person who studies the natural world. His job was to learn as much as he could about the living things he saw on the voyage. Darwin observed plants and animals he had never seen before. He wondered why they were so different from those in England. Darwin's observations led him to develop one of the most important scientific theories of all time: the theory of evolution by natural selection.

FIGURE 1
The Voyage of the *Beagle*
Charles Darwin sailed on the *Beagle* to the Galápagos Islands. He saw many unusual organisms on the islands, such as giant tortoises and the blue-footed booby.
Interpreting Maps *After leaving South America, where did the* Beagle *go?*

Replica of the *Beagle* ▶

Lab zone Discover Activity

Skills Focus Classifying L1

Materials metric ruler, 10 sunflower seeds, hand lens

Time 15 minutes

Tips Tell students that differences among seeds in their sample may be slight and hard to detect. Advise them to examine the seeds carefully.

Expected Outcome Students will observe that the seeds in their sample differ in such traits as size, shape, color, or number of stripes.

Think It Over The seeds in each sample may differ in some traits and be similar in others. Depending on the makeup of their sample, students may group seeds that are similar in size, shape, color, number of stripes, or other traits.

Darwin's Observations

As you can see in Figure 1, the *Beagle* made many stops along the coast of South America. From there, the ship traveled to the Galápagos Islands. Darwin observed living things as he traveled. He thought about relationships among those organisms. **Darwin's important observations included the diversity of living things, the remains of ancient organisms, and the characteristics of organisms on the Galápagos Islands.**

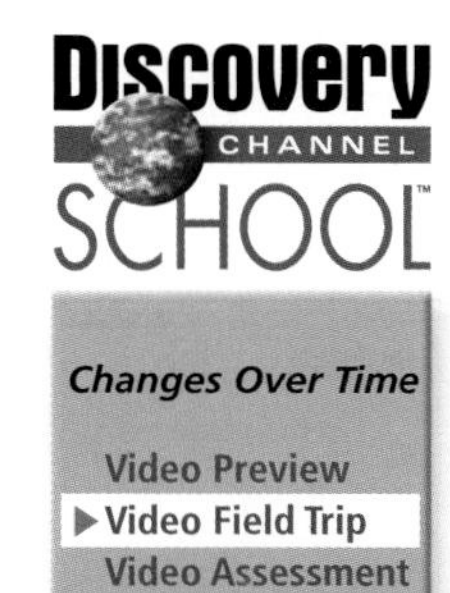

Diversity Darwin was amazed by the tremendous diversity of living things that he saw. In Brazil, he saw insects that looked like flowers and ants that marched across the forest floor like huge armies. In Argentina, he saw sloths, animals that moved very slowly and spent much of their time hanging in trees.

Today scientists know that organisms are even more diverse than Darwin could ever have imagined. Scientists have identified more than 1.7 million species of organisms on Earth. A **species** is a group of similar organisms that can mate with each other and produce fertile offspring.

Fossils Darwin saw the fossil bones of animals that had died long ago. A **fossil** is the preserved remains or traces of an organism that lived in the past. Darwin was puzzled by some of the fossils he observed. For example, he saw fossil bones that resembled the bones of living sloths. The fossil bones were much larger than those of the sloths that were alive in Darwin's time. He wondered what had happened to the giant creatures from the past.

Reading Checkpoint What is a fossil?

▲ Giant tortoise

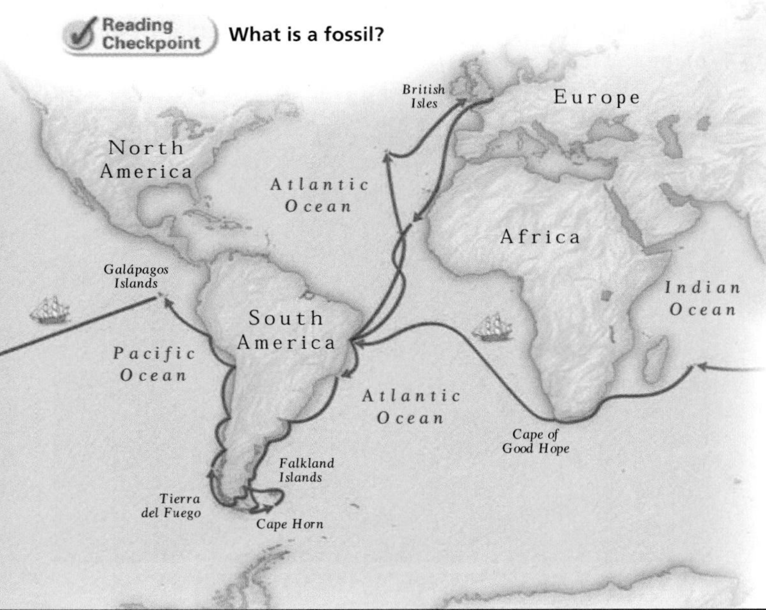

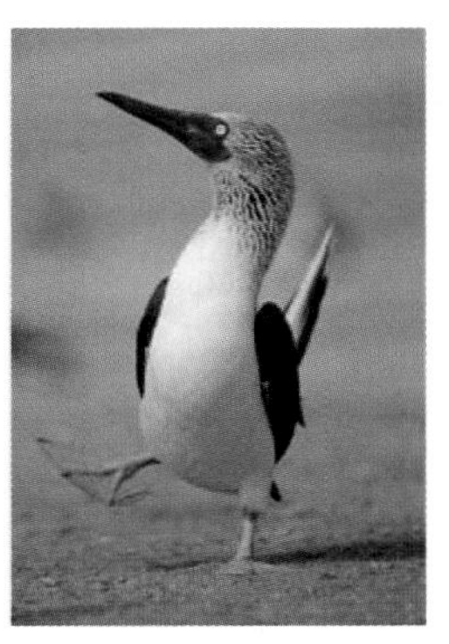
▲ Blue-footed booby

Instruct

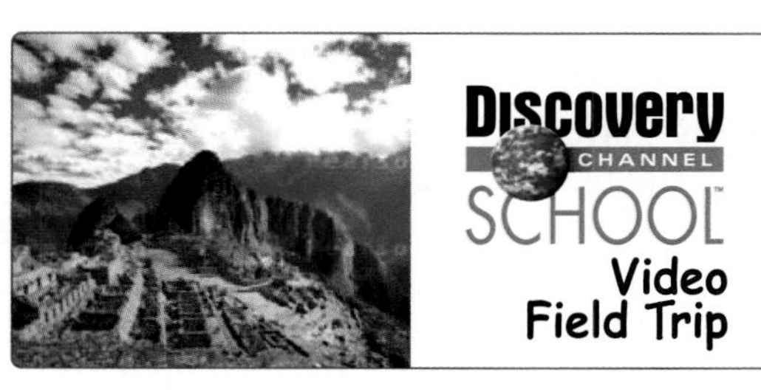

Changes Over Time
Show the Video Field Trip to let students preview Darwin's ideas.

Darwin's Observations

Teach Key Concepts L2

Darwin's Voyage

Focus Remind students that the variety of living things on Earth is called biological diversity.

Teach Ask: **What observations did Darwin make?** *(He noted the diversity of living things, the remains of ancient organisms, and the characteristics of organisms on the Galápagos Islands.)* **What struck him about these observations?** *(He was amazed by the tremendous diversity he saw, and he wondered what had happened to the animals that left fossil bones.)*

Apply Explain that in Darwin's day, most people believed that all living things were created at the same time and that they never changed. Darwin's observations led him to wonder about these ideas. **learning modality: verbal**

Independent Practice L2

All in One Teaching Resources

- Guided Reading and Study Worksheet: *Darwin's Theory*

Student Edition on Audio CD

Differentiated Instruction

Special Needs L1

Working With a Partner Partner students who have difficulty reading and processing information with more able students. As students read each section, have them rewrite in their own words each of the boldfaced statements and the statements defining key terms. Then have them write questions about each of the statements they have written. After students have finished reading the section, have them exchange their questions with other pairs of students, and answer one another's questions. **learning modality: verbal**

Monitor Progress L2

Writing Have students describe in their own words the insights that Darwin gained from his voyage.

Answers

Figure 1 The Galápagos Islands

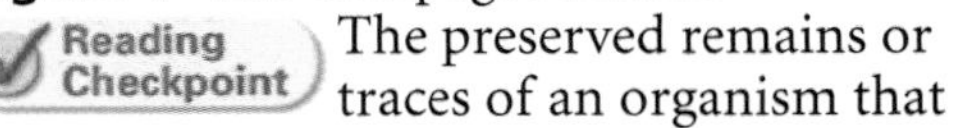
Reading Checkpoint The preserved remains or traces of an organism that lived in the past

Galápagos Organisms

Teach Key Concepts

L2

Comparing Organisms

Focus Have students look back at Figure 1 and note that the Galápagos Islands were isolated from the mainland.

Teach Point out that islands make good places for studying how organisms change over time. Ask: **What kinds of comparisons did Darwin make on his voyage?** *(He compared Galápagos organisms to South American organisms, and he compared organisms among the islands.)* **What did Darwin conclude from these observations?** *(He hypothesized that the animals on the islands came from the mainland but had changed over time.)* **What did Darwin notice about slight differences between species?** *(The differences made it possible for the organisms to survive and reproduce in their particular environment.)*

Apply Have students examine Figure 2. Point out that variations in a trait such as color may make organisms better suited for their environment. Ask: **What difference in the environment do you think might make the color of each species an adaptation?** *(Students may say the colors in the environment: the green iguana's color helps it blend in with its leafy environment, and the marine iguana's color helps it blend in with its rocky environment.)* **learning modality: logical/mathematical**

Galápagos Organisms

In 1835, the *Beagle* reached the Galápagos Islands. Darwin observed many unusual life forms on these small islands, such as giant tortoises, or land turtles. Some of these tortoises could look him in the eye! After returning to England, Darwin thought about the organisms he had seen. He compared Galápagos organisms to organisms that lived elsewhere. He also compared organisms on different islands in the Galápagos group. He was surprised by some of the similarities and differences he saw.

Comparisons to South American Organisms Darwin found many similarities between Galápagos organisms and those in South America. Many of the birds on the islands, including hawks, mockingbirds, and finches, resembled those on the mainland. Many of the plants were similar to plants Darwin had collected on the mainland.

However, there were important differences between the organisms on the islands and those on the mainland. The iguanas on the Galápagos Islands had large claws that allowed them to grip slippery rocks, where they fed on seaweed. The iguanas on the mainland had smaller claws. Smaller claws allowed the mainland iguanas to climb trees, where they ate leaves. You can see these differences in Figure 2.

From his observations, Darwin hypothesized that a small number of different plant and animal species had come to the Galápagos Islands from the mainland. They might have been blown out to sea during a storm or set adrift on a fallen log. Once the plants and animals reached the islands, they reproduced. Eventually, their offspring became different from their mainland relatives.

FIGURE 2
Comparing Iguanas
Iguanas on mainland South America (above) have smaller claws than iguanas on the Galápagos Islands. **Comparing and Contrasting** *In what other ways are the iguanas different?*

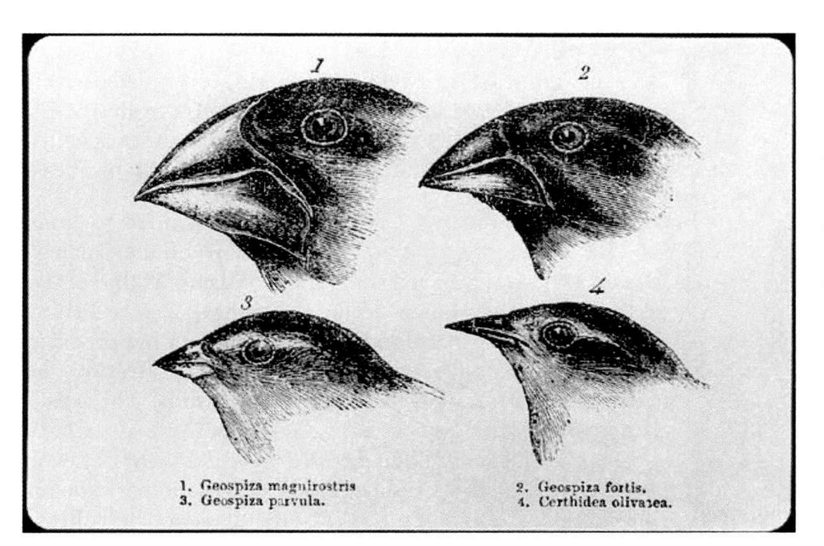

FIGURE 3
Galápagos Finches
Darwin made these drawings of four species of Galápagos finches. The structure of each bird's beak is an adaptation related to the type of food the bird eats. **Comparing and Contrasting** *Identify some specific differences in these finches' beaks.*

Comparisons Among the Islands As he traveled from one Galápagos island to the next, Darwin also noticed many differences among organisms. For example, the tortoises on one island had dome-shaped shells. Those on another island had saddle-shaped shells. A government official in the islands told Darwin that he could tell which island a tortoise came from just by looking at its shell.

Adaptations Like the tortoises, the finches on the Galápagos were noticeably different from one island to the next. The most obvious differences were the varied sizes and shapes of the birds' beaks, as shown in Figure 3. An examination of the different finches showed that each species was well suited to the life it led. Finches that ate insects had narrow, needle-like beaks. Finches that ate seeds had strong, wide beaks.

Beak shape is an example of an **adaptation,** a trait that helps an organism survive and reproduce. The finches' beak structures help in obtaining food. Other adaptations help organisms avoid being eaten. For example, some plants, such as milkweed, are poisonous or have a bad taste. A variety of adaptations aid in reproduction. The bright colors of some flowers attract insects. When an insect lands on a flower, the insect may pick up pollen grains, which produce sperm. The insect then may carry the pollen grains to another flower, enabling fertilization to take place.

Reading Checkpoint **How did the beaks of Galápagos finches differ from one island to another?**

Lab zone Try This Activity

Bird Beak Adaptations

Use this activity to explore adaptations in birds.

1. Scatter a small amount of bird seed on a paper plate. Scatter 20 raisins on the plate to represent insects.
2. Obtain a variety of objects such as tweezers, hair clips, and clothespins. Pick one object to use as a "beak."
3. See how many seeds you can pick up and drop into a cup in 10 seconds.
4. Now see how many "insects" you can pick up and drop into a cup in 10 seconds.
5. Use a different "beak" and repeat Steps 3 and 4.

Inferring What type of beak worked well for seeds? For insects? How are different-shaped beaks useful for eating different foods?

Lab zone Try This Activity

Skills Focus Inferring L2

Materials bird seed, paper plate, 20 raisins, tweezers, hair clips, hairpins, clothes pins, stopwatch, paper cup

Time 10 minutes

Tips Have students work in pairs so one student picks up objects while the other watches the clock.

Expected Outcome Some objects are better for picking up seeds and others for raisins. Likewise, some beaks are better for seeds and others for insects.

Extend Ask: **Which species in Figure 3 appear to be adapted to a diet of seeds, and which to a diet of insects?** *(Seeds: 1, 2, and possibly 3; insects: 4)* **learning modality: kinesthetic**

L2

Interpreting Scientific Drawings

Materials drawings of related bird species from a field identification guide

Time 10 minutes

Focus Point out that much of Darwin's time during the voyage of the *Beagle* was spent observing and comparing different organisms.

Teach Provide students with drawings from a field guide that show several related species of birds, such as several species of ducks, warblers, herons, or woodpeckers. Have students examine the drawings carefully and make lists of all the similarities and differences they observe among the species pictured. Then, have pairs of students compare lists. Emphasize that being a good observer requires care and skill.

Apply Ask: **What are some other ways these birds might be similar or different that you cannot observe visually?** *(Possible ways include their songs and the texture of their feathers.)* **learning modality: visual**

Monitor Progress

Oral Presentation Call on students to name examples of the diversity that Darwin observed.

Answers

Figure 2 One iguana is green and lives in a tree and the other iguana is gray and lives on rocks.

Figure 3 The beaks differ in their degree of pointedness and their size. Species 1 and 2 have wider beaks than species 3 and 4. Species 3 has a short beak, and species 4 has a long, narrow beak.

Reading Checkpoint They differed in size and shape. Some were narrow and needle-like, while others were strong and wide.

Evolution

Teach Key Concepts L2

Development of the Theory of Evolution

Focus Review with students that Darwin observed adaptations that helped organisms survive and reproduce in different environments.

Teach Ask: **What did Darwin believe led to the different adaptations in species on the Galápagos Islands?** *(He reasoned that the organisms that arrived on the islands faced conditions that were different from those on the mainland. Over many generations, the species became better adapted to the new conditions.)* **What did Darwin's ideas come to be known as?** *(The theory of evolution)* **What is evolution?** *(Evolution is the gradual change in a species over time.)*

Apply Ask: **How is the way that traits are inherited related to the theory of evolution?** *(If traits were not inherited, evolution would not occur; evolution depends upon passing traits to offspring with the result that the species gradually changes over many generations.)* **learning modality: logical/ mathematical**

Help Students Read L2

Compare and Contrast Have students read the passages on Evolution and Natural Selection. Then have students describe the similarities and differences between selective breeding and natural selection.

▲ Seattle Slew, great-grandfather of Funny Cide

Distorted Humor, ▲ father of Funny Cide

Funny Cide ►

Evolution

After he returned to England, Darwin continued to think about what he had seen during his voyage on the *Beagle*. Darwin spent the next 20 years consulting with other scientists, gathering more information, and thinking through his ideas.

Darwin's Reasoning Darwin especially wanted to understand the different adaptations of organisms on the Galápagos Islands. **Darwin reasoned that plants or animals that arrived on the Galápagos Islands faced conditions that were different from those on the mainland. Perhaps, Darwin hypothesized, the species gradually changed over many generations and became better adapted to the new conditions.** The gradual change in a species over time is called **evolution**.

Darwin's ideas are often referred to as the theory of evolution. A **scientific theory** is a well-tested concept that explains a wide range of observations. From the evidence he collected, Darwin concluded that organisms on the Galápagos Islands had changed over time. However, Darwin did not know how the changes had happened.

Selective Breeding Darwin studied other examples of changes in living things to help him understand how evolution might occur. One example that Darwin studied was the offspring of animals produced by selective breeding. English farmers in Darwin's time used selective breeding to produce sheep with fine wool. Darwin himself had bred pigeons with large, fan-shaped tails. By repeatedly allowing only those pigeons with many tail feathers to mate, breeders had produced pigeons with two or three times the usual number of tail feathers. Darwin thought that a process similar to selective breeding might happen in nature. But he wondered what process selected certain traits.

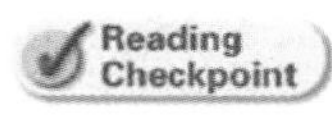

What is a scientific theory?

FIGURE 4
Selective Breeding
Race horses are selectively bred to obtain the trait of speed. Funny Cide's father, Distorted Humor, and great-grandfather, Seattle Slew, were known for their speed.

Differentiated Instruction

Less Proficient Readers L1

Relating Selective Breeding to Natural Selection Have students relate these topics by making a compare/contrast table with the following heads, then write in the details for selective breeding and natural selection. **1) Advantage of Traits Selected** *(Benefit humans; benefit the organism)*; **2) Examples of Traits Selected** *(Fine wool in sheep; ability to escape predators)*; **3) How Traits Are Selected** *(Humans select the organisms to reproduce; environmental conditions favor the reproduction of organisms with certain traits)*. Ask: **Why can the term *artificial selection* be used to mean selective breeding?** *(Artificial human choices, not natural events, control the process.)* **learning modality: logical/ mathematical**

FIGURE 5
Overproduction and Variation
Like actual sea turtles, the turtles in this illustration produce many more offspring than will survive. Some turtles are better adapted than others to survive in their environment.
Relating Cause and Effect *What adaptations might help young sea turtles survive?*

Natural Selection

In 1858, Darwin and another British biologist, Alfred Russel Wallace, each proposed an explanation for how evolution could occur in nature. The next year, Darwin described this mechanism in a book entitled *The Origin of Species.* In his book, Darwin proposed that evolution occurs by means of natural selection. **Natural selection** is the process by which individuals that are better adapted to their environment are more likely to survive and reproduce than other members of the same species. Darwin identified factors that affect the process of natural selection: overproduction, competition, and variations. Figure 5 and Figure 6 show how natural selection might happen in a group of turtles.

Overproduction Darwin knew that most species produce far more offspring than can possibly survive. In many species, so many offspring are produced that there are not enough resources—food, water, and living space—for all of them. Many female insects, for example, lay thousands of eggs. If all newly hatched insects survived, they would soon crowd out all other plants and animals. Darwin knew that this doesn't happen. Why not?

Variations As you learned in your study of genetics, members of a species differ from one another in many of their traits. Any difference between individuals of the same species is called a **variation.** For example, certain insects may be able to eat foods that other insects of their species avoid. The color of a few insects may be different from that of most other insects in their species.

Lab zone Skills Activity

Making Models

Scatter 15 black buttons and 15 white buttons on a sheet of white paper. Have a partner time you to see how many buttons you can pick up in 10 seconds. Pick up the buttons one at a time. Did you collect more buttons of one color than the other? Why? How can a variation such as color affect the process of natural selection?

Natural Selection

Teach Key Concepts L2

Natural Selection Can Lead to Evolution

Focus Remind students that Darwin thought that a kind of selective breeding process occurred naturally.

Teach Ask: **What did Darwin call this idea?** *(Natural selection)* **Explain his proposal that natural selection leads to evolution.** *(Helpful variations gradually accumulate in a species over many generations, while unfavorable ones disappear.)*

Apply Ask: **How might natural selection have led from shorter-necked giraffes to long-necked ones?** *(Mutations produced some giraffes with slightly longer necks. Those giraffes could reach plants that other giraffes could not reach and had a better chance of surviving and passing on their genes. Over many generations, longer necks evolved.)* **learning modality: logical/mathematical**

Lab zone Build Inquiry L2

Observing Favorable Traits

Materials nature magazines or biology textbooks

Time 15 minutes

Focus Ask students to brainstorm types of adaptations.

Teach Have students identify and record adaptations that allow plants and animals to better survive in their environment.

Apply Ask students to describe some characteristics that are adaptations in some environments but harmful in others. *(Example: white fur)* **learning modality: visual**

Lab zone Skills Activity

Skills Focus Making models L1

Materials 15 black buttons, 15 white buttons, plain white paper, stopwatch

Time 10 minutes

Tips All the buttons should be identical except for color.

Expected Outcome Students are likely to pick up more black buttons. A variation such as color can affect natural selection by making an organism more or less likely to be seen by a predator.

Extend Ask: **What other variations might affect whether an organism is captured by a predator?** *(Sample: intelligence and acuteness of senses.)* **learning modality: kinesthetic**

Monitor Progress 

Writing Have students summarize the factors in natural selection.

Answers

Figure 5 Sample answer: Hard shells, ability to swim quickly, and keen eyesight

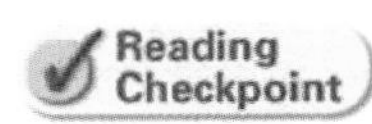
A well-tested concept that explains a wide range of observations

Use Visuals: Figures 5 and 6 L2

Factors of Natural Selection

Focus Have students review the factors of natural selection.

Teach Ask: **What factors of natural selection are demonstrated in Figures 5 and 6?** *(Overproduction—there are more turtles than will survive; variation—the turtles have different swimming abilities; and competition—the turtles are competing to escape from a predator; selection—some turtles are better able to survive in their environment; survival and reproduction—only some turtles reproduce.)*

Apply Ask: **What is the outcome of this selection process?** *(The turtle that is not eaten survives and passes its traits on to the next generation.)* **learning modality: visual**

L3

Designing an Experiment

Materials markers and poster board

Time 20 minutes

Focus Remind students that only traits that are controlled by genes can result in evolution.

Teach Divide the class into groups, and challenge students in each group to brainstorm an experiment to demonstrate that traits acquired during an organism's lifetime are not passed on to the next generation. Have each group draw diagrams that show how the group would test the hypothesis and illustrate the steps of the experiment. *(One way is to change experimental organisms in some way, for example, by dyeing the hair of lab rats, and then observing whether the changed trait appears in their offspring.)* Have each group elect a spokesperson to present its poster and describe its experimental plan to the rest of the class. Urge the class to give the group feedback on its ideas.

Apply Ask: **Why don't acquired traits result in evolution?** *(Because only genes, not acquired characteristics, are passed from parents to their offspring)* **learning modality: logical/mathematical**

Competition
Turtles compete with one another. A faster turtle may escape from a predator.

Selection
Variations such as speed make some turtles better able to survive in their environment.

FIGURE 6
Competition and Selection
Variations among turtles make some of them better able to survive. Turtles that survive to become adults will be able to reproduce.
Applying Concepts *What are some variations that sea turtles might exhibit?*

Competition Since food and other resources are limited, the members of a species must compete with each other to survive. Competition does not always involve direct physical fights between members of a species. Instead, competition is usually indirect. For example, many insects do not find enough to eat. Others are caught by predators. Only a few insects will survive.

Selection Darwin observed that some variations make individuals better adapted to their environment. Those individuals are more likely to survive and reproduce. Their offspring may inherit the helpful characteristic. The offspring, in turn, will be more likely to survive and reproduce, and thus pass on the characteristic to their offspring. After many generations, more members of the species will have the helpful characteristic.

In effect, the environment has "selected" organisms with helpful traits to become parents of the next generation. **Darwin proposed that, over a long time, natural selection can lead to change. Helpful variations may gradually accumulate in a species, while unfavorable ones may disappear.**

Environmental Change A change in the environment can affect an organism's ability to survive. The environmental change can therefore lead to selection. For example, monkey flowers are a type of plant. Most monkey flowers cannot grow in soil that has a high concentration of copper. However, because of genetic variation, some varieties of monkey flower now grow near copper mines, in spite of the copper in the soil.

Here is how natural selection might have resulted in monkey flowers that can grow in copper-contaminated soil. When the soil around a mine first became contaminated, a small number of monkey-flower plants may have been able to survive in the high level of copper. These plants grew and reproduced. After many generations, most of the seeds that sprouted in the soil produced monkey flowers that could withstand the copper.

For: Links on Charles Darwin
Visit: www.SciLinks.org
Web Code: scn-0351

Survival and Reproduction Only a few turtles survive long enough to reproduce. The offspring may inherit the favorable traits of the parents.

Genes and Natural Selection Without variations, all the members of a species would have the same traits. Natural selection would not occur because all individuals would have an equal chance of surviving and reproducing. But where do variations come from? How are they passed on from parents to offspring?

Darwin could not explain what caused variations or how they were passed on. As scientists later learned, variations can result from mutation and the shuffling of alleles during meiosis. Genes are passed from parents to their offspring. Because of this, only traits that are inherited, or controlled by genes, can be acted upon by natural selection.

Section 1 Assessment

Target Reading Skill
Relating Cause and Effect Work with a partner to check the information in your graphic organizer.

Reviewing Key Concepts

1. a. **Listing** List three general kinds of observations that Darwin made during the voyage of the *Beagle*.
   b. **Comparing and Contrasting** Contrast Galápagos iguanas to South American iguanas.
   c. **Applying Concepts** What is an adaptation? Explain how the claws of the Galápagos and South American iguanas are adaptations.
2. a. **Reviewing** How did Darwin explain why Galápagos species had different adaptations than similar South American species?
   b. **Developing Hypotheses** How does selective breeding support Darwin's hypothesis?
3. a. **Defining** What is variation? What is natural selection?
   b. **Relating Cause and Effect** How do variation and natural selection work together to help cause evolution?
   c. **Applying Concepts** Suppose the climate in an area becomes much drier than it was before. What kinds of variations in the area's plants might be acted on by natural selection?

Writing in Science

Interview You are a nineteenth-century reporter interviewing Charles Darwin about his theory of evolution. Write three questions you would ask him. Then write answers that Darwin might have given.

Lab zone Chapter Project

Keep Students on Track Review students' plans to make sure they have chosen workable models. In preparation, you might have students make a scale model of their own life history to date. When students are comfortable with the process, let each group start its first timeline.

Writing in Science

Writing Mode Interview

Scoring Rubric

4 Includes criteria and goes beyond requirements, for example, writing questions from the point of view of most people in Darwin's day
3 Includes criteria but does not go beyond requirements
2 Includes only brief information
1 Includes inaccurate or incomplete information

For: Links on Charles Darwin
Visit: www.SciLinks.org
Web Code: scn-0351

Download a worksheet to guide students' review of Darwin's work.

Monitor Progress L2

Answer
Figure 6 Sample answer: Size, color, ability to swim fast

Assess

Reviewing Key Concepts

1. a. The diversity of living things, fossils, and the characteristics of organisms on the Galápagos Islands **b.** The Galápagos iguanas had large claws that allowed them to grip slippery rocks. The South American iguanas had smaller claws that were used for climbing trees. **c.** A trait that helps an organism survive and reproduce; Galápagos iguanas have claws that enable them to cling to rocks to eat seaweed. South American iguanas have claws that enable them to cling to trees to eat leaves.
2. a. He hypothesized that species changed over many generations and became better adapted to their new conditions. **b.** Like natural selection, selective breeding changes a species' traits over many generations.
3. a. Variation: any difference between individuals of the same species; natural selection: the process by which individuals that are better adapted to their environment are more likely to survive and reproduce than other members of the same species
b. With variation, members of a species will have different traits. In the process of natural selection, helpful variations gradually accumulate in a species while unfavorable ones disappear. **c.** Sample answer: Plants that could store water more easily, for example, plants with thicker leaves, would survive and produce more plants like themselves.

Reteach L1

Use the figures to review how variation in a species relates to natural selection.

All in One Teaching Resources

- Section Summary: *Darwin's Theory*
- Review and Reinforce: *Darwin's Theory*
- Enrich: *Darwin's Theory*

Nature at Work

L2

Prepare for Inquiry

Key Concept
Natural selection can lead to changes in a species' traits over time.

Skills Objectives
Students will be able to
- predict how changing environmental conditions will affect natural selection in the model
- make a dynamic model of natural selection in mice

Class Time 40 minutes

All in One Teaching Resources
- Lab Worksheet: *Nature at Work*

Advance Planning 
Prepare enough mouse and event cards so each group of students has a complete set.

Guide Inquiry

Invitation
Tell students that they will simulate natural selection in mice of two different colors. Ask: **How do you think variation of color in a species might affect natural selection?** *(Some colors might make individuals better able to hide from predators, making them more likely to survive and reproduce. Other colors might make it more difficult for individuals to hide from predators, making them less likely to survive and reproduce.)*

Nature at Work

Problem
How do species change over time?

Skills Focus
predicting, making models

Materials
- scissors
- marking pen
- construction paper, 2 colors

Procedure 

1. Work on this lab with two other students. One student should choose construction paper of one color and make the team's 50 "mouse" cards, as described in Table 1. The second student should choose a different color construction paper and make the team's 25 "event" cards, as described in Table 2. The third student should copy the data table and record all the data.

PART 1 A White Sand Environment

2. Mix up the mouse cards.
3. Begin by using the cards to model what might happen to a group of mice in an environment of white sand dunes. Choose two mouse cards. Allele pairs *WW* and *Ww* produce a white mouse. Allele pair *ww* produces a brown mouse. Record the color of the mouse with a tally mark in the data table.
4. Choose an event card. An "S" card means the mouse survives. A "D" or a "P" card means the mouse dies. A "C" card means the mouse dies if its color contrasts with the white sand dunes. (Only brown mice will die when a "C" card is drawn.) Record each death with a tally mark in the data table.
5. If the mouse lives, put the two mouse cards in a "live mice" pile. If the mouse dies, put the cards in a "dead mice" pile. Put the event card at the bottom of its pack.
6. Repeat Steps 3 through 5 with the remaining mouse cards to study the first generation of mice. Record your results.
7. Leave the dead mice cards untouched. Mix up the cards from the live mice pile. Mix up the events cards.
8. Repeat Steps 3 through 7 for the second generation. Then repeat Steps 3 through 6 for the third generation.

PART 2 A Forest Floor Environment

9. How would the data differ if the mice in this model lived on a dark brown forest floor? Record your prediction in your notebook.
10. Make a new copy of the data table. Then use the cards to test your prediction. Remember that a "C" card now means that any mouse with white fur will die.

Data Table

Type of Environment:

Generation	Population		Deaths	
	White Mice	Brown Mice	White Mice	Brown Mice
1				
2				
3				

Introduce the Procedure
Ask: **Why do the mouse cards represent alleles rather than phenotypes?** *(Alleles are passed on to the next generation, not phenotypes)* Point out that choosing alleles to make up the next generation is a realistic way to model reproduction and the inheritance of traits; choosing phenotypes is not.

Troubleshooting the Experiment
Check that students are assigning the right phenotype to each genotype. Remind them that the *W* allele for white fur is dominant to the *w* allele for brown fur.

Table 1: Mouse Cards		
Number	**Label**	**Meaning**
25	*W*	Dominant allele for white fur
25	*w*	Recessive allele for brown fur

Table 2: Event Cards		
Number	**Label**	**Meaning**
5	S	Mouse survives.
1	D	Disease kills mouse.
1	P	Predator kills mice of all colors.
18	C	Predator kills mice that contrast with the environment.

Analyze and Conclude

1. **Calculating** In Part 1, how many white mice were there in each generation? How many brown mice? In each generation, which color mouse had the higher death rate? (*Hint:* To calculate the death rate for white mice, divide the number of white mice that died by the total number of white mice, then multiply by 100%.)
2. **Predicting** If the events in Part 1 occurred in nature, how would the group of mice change over time?
3. **Observing** How did the results in Part 2 differ from those in Part 1?
4. **Making Models** How would it affect your model if you increased the number of "C" cards? What would happen if you decreased the number of "C" cards?
5. **Communicating** Imagine that you are trying to explain the point of this lab to Charles Darwin. Write an explanation that you could give to him. To prepare to write, answer the following questions: What are some ways in which this investigation models natural selection? What are some ways in which natural selection differs from this model?

Design an Experiment

Choose a different species with a trait that interests you. Make a set of cards similar to these cards to investigate how natural selection might bring about the evolution of that species. *Obtain your teacher's permission before carrying out your investigation.*

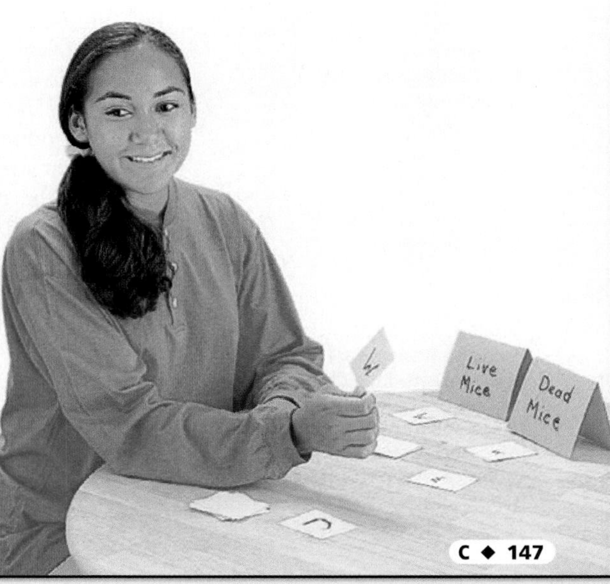

Sample Data Table

Type of Environment: White Sand				
Gener–ation	**White Mice**	**Brown Mice**	**Deaths of White Mice**	**Deaths of Brown Mice**
1	18	7	2	5
2	16	2	2	1
3	14	1	1	1

Expected Outcome

The number of mice declines with each generation, with the number of brown mice declining faster than the number of white mice in Part 1, and the number of white mice declining faster than the number of brown mice in Part 2.

Analyze and Conclude

1. Answers will depend on the genotypes of the mice in each generation and the order in which the mouse and event cards are drawn. For the sample data, there were 18 white mice in the first generation, of which 2 died, yielding a death rate of 11% for the white mice. There were also 7 brown mice in the first generation, of which 5 died, yielding a death rate of 71% for the brown mice.

2. The population of mice would contain more and more mice with white fur.

3. In Part 2, the population contains more brown mice each generation because white mice are selected against, whereas in Part 1, the population contains more white mice each generation because the brown mice are selected against.

4. If you increased the number of "C" cards, natural selection against mice that contrast with the environment would be stronger and contrasting-color mice would decrease in number more quickly. If you decreased the number of "C" cards, natural selection against mice that contrast with the environment would be weaker and contrasting-color mice would decrease in number more slowly.

5. This investigation models natural selection in that an organism's chances of surviving and reproducing depend both on the organism's inherited traits and on the environment in which the organism lives. Natural selection differs from the model in that other environmental factors besides predators and disease, and other traits besides fur color, are likely to influence an organism's chances of surviving and reproducing.

Extend Inquiry

Design an Experiment Urge students to select a trait that is controlled by a recessive allele so they can see how dominance affects the rate at which natural selection changes the genetic makeup of the population. The trait they choose to model may be real or hypothetical.

Section 2

Evidence of Evolution

Objectives

After this lesson, students will be able to

C.5.2.1 State evidence that supports the theory of evolution.

C.5.2.2 Explain how scientists infer evolutionary relationships among organisms.

C.5.2.3 Describe how new species form.

Target Reading Skill

Identifying Supporting Evidence

Explain that identifying supporting evidence helps students understand the relationship between the facts and the hypothesis.

Answers

Possible answers: Theory—Evolution; Evidence—Fossils show that organisms that lived in the past were very different from organisms alive today; patterns of early development show that some different organisms look similar during their early stages; similar body structures in different species show that the organisms shared a common ancestor.

All in One Teaching Resources

- Transparency C41

Preteach

Build Background Knowledge L1

Comparing Species of Animals

On the board write the following list: horse, rabbit, zebra, squirrel, donkey, deer, chipmunk, and mouse. Then ask: **Which animals would you group together based on their similarities?** *(Students are likely to place the horse, zebra, donkey, and deer in one group and the rabbit, squirrel, chipmunk, and mouse in another.)* Tell students that in this section, they will see how scientists use similarities among living species to infer how the species evolved.

Section 2

Evidence of Evolution

Reading Preview

Key Concepts

- What evidence supports the theory of evolution?
- How do scientists infer evolutionary relationships among organisms?
- How do new species form?

Key Terms

- homologous structures
- branching tree

Target Reading Skill

Identifying Supporting Evidence Evidence consists of facts that can be confirmed by testing or observation. As you read, identify the evidence that supports the theory of evolution. Write the evidence in a graphic organizer like the one below.

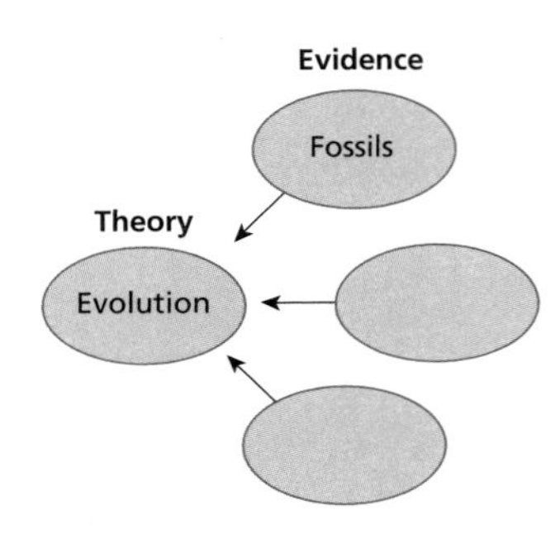

Lab zone Discover Activity

How Can You Classify Species?

1. Collect six to eight different pens. Each pen will represent a different species of similar organisms.
2. Choose a trait that varies among your pen species, such as size or ink color. Using this trait, try to divide the pen species into two groups.
3. Now choose another trait. Divide each group into two smaller groups.

Think It Over

Classifying Which of the pen species share the most characteristics? What might the similarities suggest about how the pen species evolved?

Does natural selection occur today? Evidence indicates that the answer is yes. Consider, for example, what happens when chemicals called pesticides are used to kill harmful insects such as the cockroaches below. When a pesticide is first used in a building, it kills almost all the insects. But a few insects have traits that protect them from the pesticide. These insects survive.

The surviving insects reproduce. Some of their offspring inherit the pesticide protection. The surviving offspring, in turn, reproduce. Every time the pesticide is used, the only insects that survive are those that are resistant to the harmful effects of the pesticide. After many years, most of the cockroaches in the building are resistant to the pesticide. Therefore, the pesticide is no longer effective in controlling the insects. The development of pesticide resistance is one type of evidence that supports Darwin's theory of evolution.

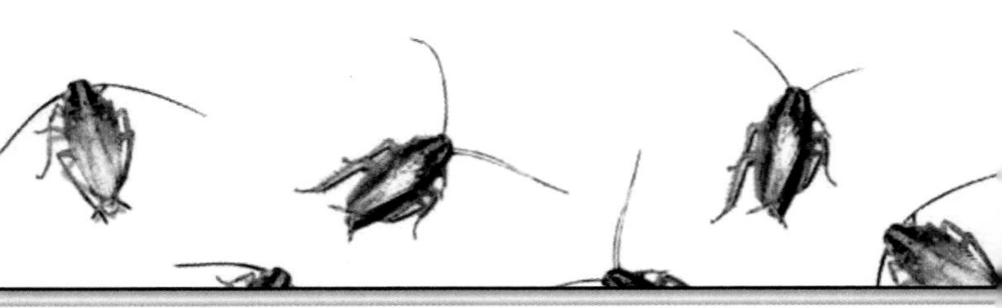

FIGURE 7
Pesticide Resistance
Many insects, including cockroaches such as these, are no longer killed by some pesticides. Increased pesticide resistance is evidence that natural selection is happening.

148 ◆ C

Lab zone Discover Activity

Skills Focus Classifying L1

Materials 6 to 8 pens

Time 10 minutes

Tips Have extra pens to guarantee enough for each student. Include pens that are somewhat different from one other.

Expected Outcome How students classify their pens will depend on their particular sample of pens and the traits they choose for classification.

Think It Over Students may say that the pen species that are most similar evolved from a common ancestor.

Interpreting the Evidence

Since Darwin's time, scientists have found a great deal of evidence that supports the theory of evolution. **Fossils, patterns of early development, and similar body structures all provide evidence that organisms have changed over time.**

Fossils By examining fossils, scientists can infer the structures of ancient organisms. Fossils show that, in many cases, organisms that lived in the past were very different than organisms alive today. You will learn more about the importance of fossils in the next section.

Similarities in Early Development Scientists also make inferences about evolutionary relationships by comparing the early development of different organisms. Suppose you were asked to compare an adult fish, salamander, chicken, and opossum. You would probably say they look quite different from each other. However, during early development, these four organisms are similar, as you can see in Figure 8. For example, during the early stages of development all four organisms have a tail and a row of tiny slits along their throats. These similarities suggest that these vertebrate species are related and share a common ancestor.

For: Links on evolution
Visit: www.SciLinks.org
Web Code: scn-0352

FIGURE 8
Similarities in Development
These animals look similar during their early development.
Comparing and Contrasting *What are some similarities you observe? What are some differences?*

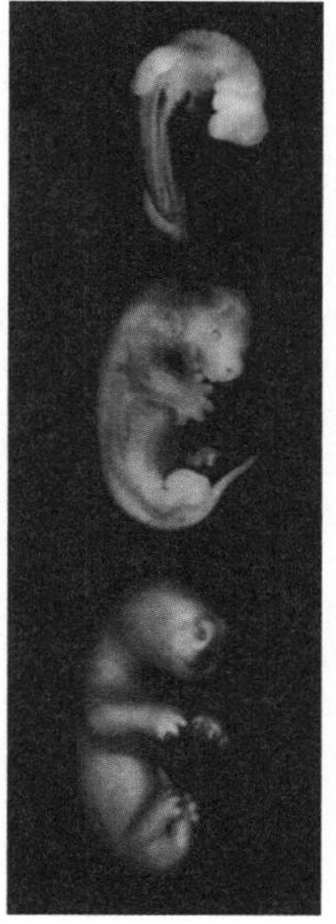

Opossum

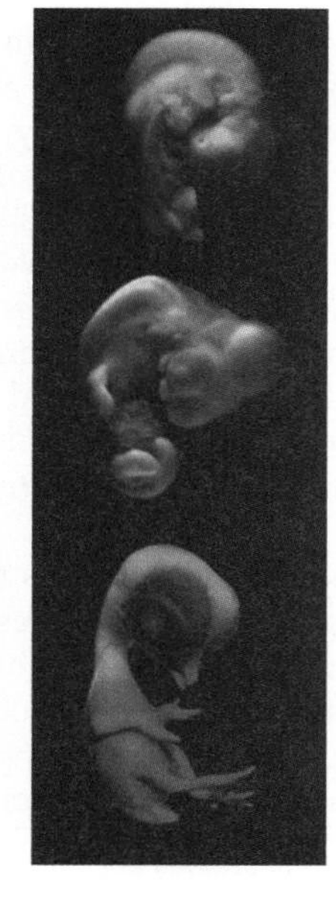

Chicken

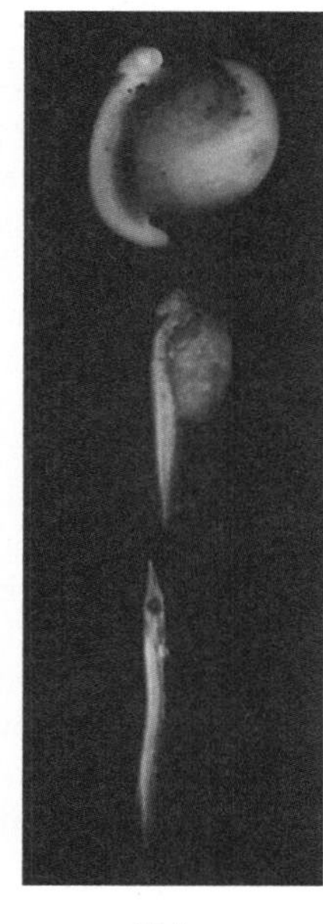

Fish

Salamander

Go Online SCILINKS NSTA

For: Links on evolution
Visit: www.SciLinks.org
Web Code: scn-0352

Download a worksheet to guide students' review of evolution.

Instruct

Interpreting the Evidence

Teach Key Concepts L2

Evidence in Support of Evolution

Focus Read the boldfaced sentence aloud.

Teach Ask: **How do fossils support the theory of evolution?** *(They show that organisms changed over time.)* **What can you learn from studying embryos about how species are related?** *(During the early stages of development, embryos of related species might share common characteristics.)* **What can body structures tell you about how species might be related?** *(Organisms with homologous structures might have evolved from a common ancestor.)*

Apply Have students examine the homologous structures in Figure 9. Ask them to infer why the structures evolved differently. *(Each limb is an adaptation that helps the organism survive in a different environment.)* **learning modality: visual**

Independent Practice L2

All in One Teaching Resources

- Guided Reading and Study Worksheet: *Evidence of Evolution*

Student Edition on Audio CD

Differentiated Instruction

English Learners/Beginning L1
Comprehension: Key Concepts
Rewrite the boldfaced statement in Interpreting the Evidence into three sentences and the boldfaced sentence in Inferring Species Relationships into five sentences. Pair students with students who are proficient in English. After students read the sections, have them use the captions, visuals, and text to identify a real-life example of each piece of evidence supporting evolution and species relationships. **learning modality: visual**

English Learners/Intermediate L2
Comprehension: Key Concepts Have students do the Beginning activity, then write in their own words how each example relates to the evidence. **learning modality: verbal**

Monitor Progress L2

Oral Presentation Call on students to describe similarities in living species that indicate evolutionary relationships.

Answer

Figure 8 Possible answers: similarities include large heads, curved backs, tails. Differences: in the later stages, some have developed limbs, while others have not. Heads have acquired distinctive shapes.

Help Students Read L2

Visualizing Have students read the section on similarities in body structure and homologous structures. Then have students close their eyes and imagine what the bones of the forelimb of a common ancestor of the bird, dolphin, and dog shown in Figure 9 might look like. Have them speculate what that ancestor used its forelimb for. Then have them compare and contrast how each animal shown uses its forelimb.

L2

Observing Similar Species

Materials illustrations of vertebrate skeletons from zoology and anatomy textbooks and encyclopedias

Time 15 minutes

Focus Use a taxonomic chart to point out that all vertebrates are classified together, in a subphylum of the phylum Chordata.

Teach Ask students to use the resources to identify similar, important features of the body plan and internal functions of vertebrates. Make sure they examine images of a variety of vertebrates—fish, amphibians, reptiles, birds, and mammals. Challenge them to write a brief paragraph that compares the skeletal structures and explains how such similarities are used to infer evolutionary relationships.

Apply Ask: **What evidence suggests that all of these animals share a common ancestor?** *(Sample answer: all the animals have a backbone, skull, and ribcage. Many have four limbs.)* **learning modality: visual**

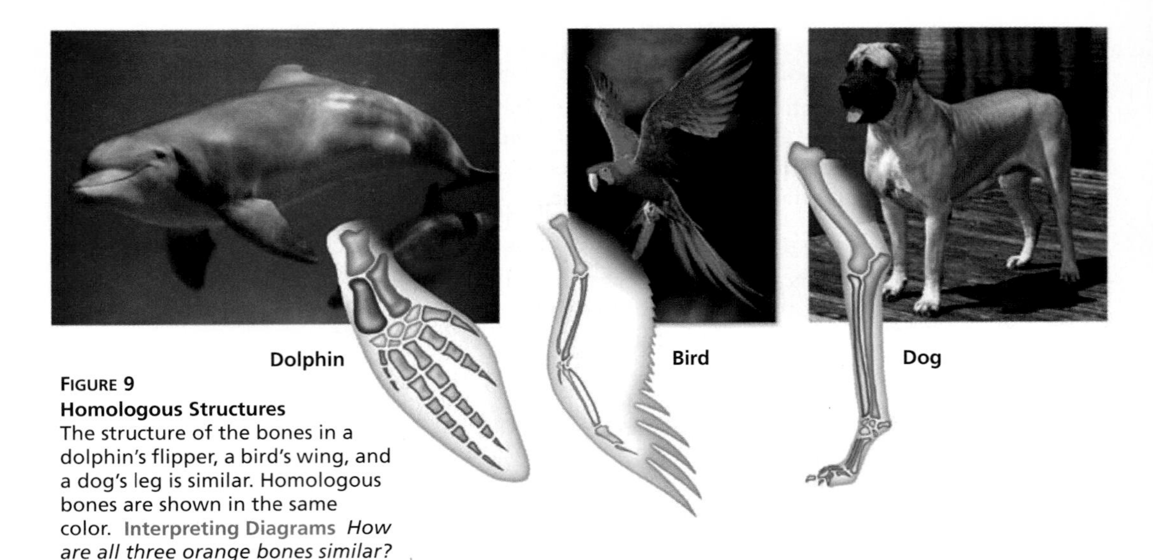

FIGURE 9
Homologous Structures
The structure of the bones in a dolphin's flipper, a bird's wing, and a dog's leg is similar. Homologous bones are shown in the same color. **Interpreting Diagrams** *How are all three orange bones similar?*

Similarities in Body Structure Long ago, scientists began to compare the body structures of living species to look for clues about evolution. In fact, this is how Darwin came to understand that evolution had occurred on the Galápagos Islands. An organism's body structure is its basic body plan, such as how its bones are arranged. Fishes, amphibians, reptiles, birds, and mammals, for example, all have a similar body structure—an internal skeleton with a backbone. This is why scientists classify all five groups of animals together as vertebrates. All of these groups probably inherited a similar structure from an early vertebrate ancestor that they shared.

Look closely at the structure of the bones in the bird's wing, dolphin's flipper, and dog's leg that are shown in Figure 9. Notice that the bones in the forelimbs of these three animals are arranged in a similar way. These similarities provide evidence that these three organisms all evolved from a common ancestor. Similar structures that related species have inherited from a common ancestor are known as **homologous structures** (hoh MAHL uh gus).

Sometimes scientists find fossils that support the evidence provided by homologous structures. For example, scientists have recently found fossils of ancient whalelike creatures. The fossils show that the ancestors of today's whales had legs and walked on land. This evidence supports other evidence that whales and humans share a common ancestor.

Lab zone Skills Activity

Drawing Conclusions

Look at the drawing below of the bones in a crocodile's leg. Compare this drawing to Figure 9. Do you think that crocodiles share a common ancestor with birds, dolphins, and dogs? Support your answer with evidence.

Crocodile

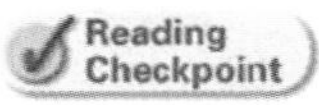

In what way are the body structures of fishes, amphibians, reptiles, and mammals similar?

Lab zone Skills Activity

Skills Focus Drawing conclusions L2

Materials none

Time 5 minutes

Tips If students have difficulty identifying similarities, advise them to focus on the number and arrangement of bones.

Expected Outcome Students are likely to say that crocodiles share a common ancestor with birds, dolphins, and dogs because of the similar structure of the bones in their legs.

Extend Ask: **What other animals do you think would have forelimbs similar in structure to those of crocodiles, birds, dolphins, and dogs?** *(Possible answers include other reptiles, birds, or mammals.)* **learning modality: logical/mathematical**

Inferring Species Relationships

Fossils, early development patterns, and body structure provide evidence that evolution has occurred. Scientists have also used these kinds of evidence to infer how organisms are related to one another. Not too long ago, fossils, embryos, and body structures were the only tools that scientists had to determine how species were related. Today, scientists can also compare the DNA and protein sequences of different species. **Scientists have combined the evidence from DNA, protein structure, fossils, early development, and body structure to determine the evolutionary relationships among species.**

Similarities in DNA Why do some species have similar body structures and development patterns? Scientists infer that the species inherited many of the same genes from a common ancestor. Recently, scientists have begun to compare the genes of different species to determine how closely related the species are.

Recall that genes are made of DNA. By comparing the sequence of nitrogen bases in the DNA of different species, scientists can infer how closely related the two species are. The more similar the DNA sequences, the more closely related the species are. For example, DNA analysis has shown that elephants and tiny elephant shrews, shown in Figure 10, are closely related.

The DNA bases along a gene specify what type of protein will be produced. Therefore, scientists can also compare the order of amino acids in a protein to see how closely related two species are.

Combining Evidence In most cases, evidence from DNA and protein structure has confirmed conclusions based on fossils, embryos, and body structure. For example, recent DNA comparisons show that dogs are more similar to wolves than they are to coyotes. Scientists had already reached this conclusion based on similarities in the structure and development of these three species.

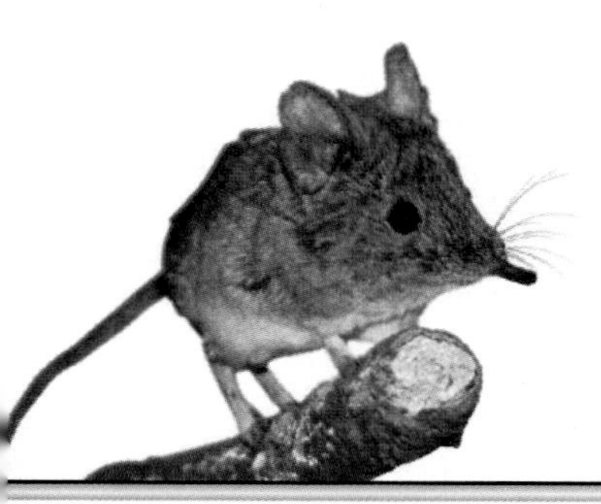

FIGURE 10
DNA and Relationships
Because of its appearance, the tiny elephant shrew was thought to be closely related to mice and other rodents. However, DNA comparisons have shown that the elephant shrew is actually more closely related to elephants.

Differentiated Instruction

Special Needs L1
Understanding Branching Trees Help students construct their family tree with three generations. If they are unable to do this, use your own family or create a fictitious one. Explain that the family tree and the branching tree show relationships among descendants of a common ancestor. Point out that species with a recent common ancestor are like siblings in a family, and species with a remote common ancestor are like distant cousins. **learning modality: visual**

Inferring Species Relationships

Teach Key Concepts L2

Evidence for Species Relationships

Focus Review the evidence for evolution.

Teach Point out that evidence from DNA has helped scientists determine evolutionary relationships among species. Ask: **What does DNA tell you about how similar two species are?** *(The more similar their DNA sequences, the more closely related they are.)* Explain that the more closely related the DNA of two species, the more recently they shared a common ancestor. Scientists use all of this information to construct branching trees. Ask: **What is a branching tree?** *(A diagram that shows how scientists think different groups of organism are related)*

Apply Provide the following scenario: Tell students to imagine three hypothetical species—A, B, and C. A and C are more similar in body structure than A and B or B and C. A and B are more similar in their early development than A and C or B and C. The DNA base sequences of A and B are more similar than the DNA base sequences of A and C or B and C. Challenge students to explain the evolutionary relationships among the three species. *(A and B are more closely related to each other than either species is related to C because of the similarities in their early development and DNA.)* Have students draw a branching tree to illustrate these relationships. **learning modality: logical/mathematical**

All in One Teaching Resources
- Transparency C42

Monitor Progress L2

Drawing Have students draw a branching tree that shows how dogs, wolves, and coyotes are related. Students can place their drawings in their portfolios.

Portfolio

Answers

Figure 9 They are all in the same position relative to the other limb bones; they are all relatively short and thick compared to the other limb bones.

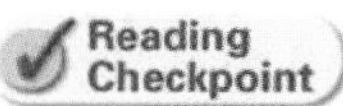
They all have an internal skeleton with a backbone.

How Do New Species Form?

Teach Key Concepts

Formation of Species

Focus Remind students that a species is a group of similar organisms that can mate with each other and produce fertile offspring.

Teach Ask: **How can separation of organisms within the same species lead to the formation of a new species?** *(The environments for each group may be different. Each group might then evolve with different traits.)* Emphasize that genetic variations that occur in one group and spread through the population could be different from variations in the other group.

Apply Tell students to suppose that the Grand Canyon were suddenly filled in. Ask: **Would the Abert's squirrel and the Kaibab squirrel continue to evolve differently?** *(Possibly not; they are still the same species and might start interbreeding.)* Ask students to predict what would happen to the genotypes and phenotypes of the two types of squirrels. *(They would gradually become more similar.)* **learning modality: logical/mathematical**

L2

Large Scale Isolation

Materials map of Pangaea

Time 10 minutes

Focus Tell students that Pangaea was a landmass in which all the continents were once connected.

Teach Display a map of Pangaea. Point out that Australia broke away from Pangaea 250 million years ago, while other continents were still joined as recently as 50 million years ago.

Apply Ask: **How might the breaking away of Australia have led to the formation of new species?** *(Marsupial species such as kangaroos, koala, and wombats might have formed when a group of individuals remained isolated from the rest of Pangaean mammals long enough to evolve different traits.)* **learning modality: visual**

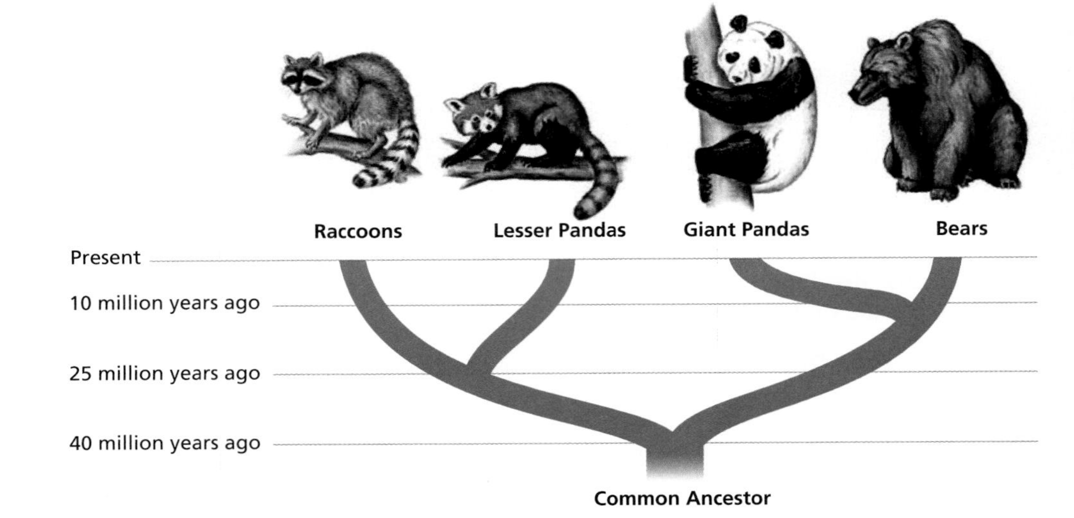

FIGURE 11
A Branching Tree
This branching tree shows how scientists now think that raccoons, lesser pandas, giant pandas, and bears are related.
Interpreting Diagrams *Are giant pandas more closely related to lesser pandas or to bears?*

Sometimes, however, scientists have changed their hypotheses about species relationships. For example, lesser pandas were once thought to be closely related to giant pandas. Recently, however, DNA analysis and other methods have shown that giant pandas and lesser pandas are not closely related. Instead, giant pandas are more closely related to bears, while lesser pandas are more closely related to raccoons.

Branching Trees Scientists use the combined evidence of species relationships to draw branching trees. A **branching tree** is a diagram that shows how scientists think different groups of organisms are related. Figure 11 shows how raccoons, lesser pandas, giant pandas, and bears may be related.

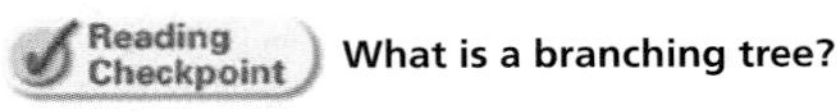

Reading Checkpoint **What is a branching tree?**

How Do New Species Form?

Natural selection explains how variations can lead to changes in a species. But how could an entirely new species form? **A new species can form when a group of individuals remains isolated from the rest of its species long enough to evolve different traits.** Isolation, or complete separation, occurs when some members of a species become cut off from the rest of the species. Group members may be separated by such things as a river, a volcano, or a mountain range.

Abert's squirrel and the Kaibab squirrel both live in forests in the Southwest. As you can see in Figure 12, the populations of the two kinds of squirrel are separated by the Grand Canyon. The Kaibab and Abert's squirrels belong to the same species, but they have slightly different characteristics. For example, the Kaibab squirrel has a black belly, while Abert's squirrel has a white belly. It is possible that one day Abert's squirrel and the Kaibab squirrel will become so different from each other that they will be separate species.

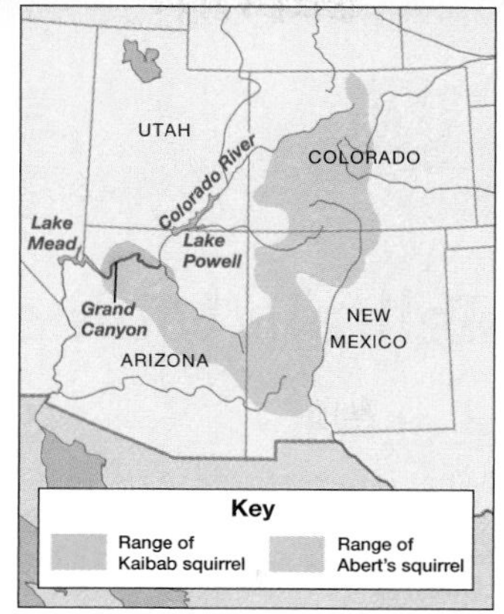

FIGURE 12
Kaibab and Abert's Squirrels
These two kinds of squirrels have been isolated from one another for a long time. Eventually, this isolation may result in two different species.

Section 2 Assessment

Target Reading Skill
Identifying Supporting Evidence Refer to your graphic organizer about the theory of evolution as you answer Question 1 below.

Reviewing Key Concepts

1. a. **Listing** List three kinds of evidence that support the theory of evolution.
   b. **Comparing and Contrasting** What major difference have scientists discovered between today's whales and the fossils of whales' ancient ancestors?
   c. **Drawing Conclusions** How does this difference show that whales and animals with four legs are probably descended from a common ancestor?
2. a. **Identifying** When scientists try to determine how closely related species are, what evidence do they examine?
   b. **Inferring** Of the kinds of evidence you listed above, which are probably the most reliable? Explain your answer.
   c. **Applying Concepts** Insects and birds both have wings. What kinds of evidence might show whether or not insects and birds are closely related? Explain your answer.
3. a. **Reviewing** How can isolation lead to the formation of new species?
   b. **Predicting** A species of snake lives in a forest. A new road separates one group of the snakes from another. Is it likely that these two groups of snakes will become separate species? Why or why not?

Writing in Science

Explaining a Branching Tree Suppose the branching tree in Figure 11 is part of a museum exhibit. Write an explanation of the branching tree for museum visitors. Describe the relationships shown on the tree and identify evidence supporting the relationships.

Monitor Progress L2

Answers
Figure 11 Bears

Reading Checkpoint A diagram that shows how scientists think different groups of organisms are related

Assess

Reviewing Key Concepts

1. a. Any three: Fossils, similarities in early development, similarities in body structure, DNA, and protein structure **b.** Whales' ancient ancestors had legs and walked on land, while modern whales do not. **c.** The four legs of ancient whales are homologous structures of the legs of modern land animals.
2. a. Evidence from DNA, protein structure, fossils, early development, and body structure **b.** DNA and protein structure are probably most reliable because they show specific distinct patterns that can be easily compared. **c.** DNA, protein structure, and early development would probably show that insects and birds are not closely related.
3. a. When a group of individuals remains isolated from the rest of its species long enough to evolve different traits, a new species can form. **b.** It is not likely because a road is not wide enough to prevent the snakes from crossing the road and mating with one another.

Reteach L1

Use the figures in this section to discuss how similarities in early development, body structure, and DNA sequences can be used to map out how species are related to one another.

Performance Assessment L2

Writing Have students explain how species can change using the Galápagos finches as an example.

All in One Teaching Resources
- Section Summary: *Evidence of Evolution*
- Review and Reinforce: *Evidence of Evolution*
- Enrich: *Evidence of Evolution*

Writing in Science

Writing Mode Explanation
Scoring Rubric
4 Includes all criteria and goes beyond requirements, for example, writing simply for a general audience
3 Includes all criteria, but does not consider the background of the audience
2 Includes only brief description
1 Includes inaccurate or incomplete information

Telltale Molecules L2

Prepare for Inquiry

Key Concept

The more similar the amino acid sequence in proteins of different species, the more closely the species are related.

Skills Objectives

Students will be able to
- interpret data on amino acid sequences in proteins
- draw conclusions about how the species are related

Class Time 30 minutes

All in One Teaching Resources
- Lab Worksheet: *Telltale Molecules*

Guide Inquiry

Invitation

Ask: **What is a genetic code?** *(The order of the nitrogen bases along a gene)* **How do cells use a genetic code to make proteins?** *(The nitrogen bases code for the production of specific amino acids, which are the building blocks of proteins.)* **What are genes made of?** *(DNA)*

Introduce the Procedure

Have students read the entire lab, and then ask: **What is the objective of this lab activity?** *(To use the amino acid sequence of a protein to determine the evolutionary relationship among several animals)* **What do the letters in the table represent?** *(Each letter represents a different amino acid.)* Suggest that students create a table to record the number of differences between the horse and each of the other animals.

Expected Outcome

Students infer which species are most closely related and which are least closely related to the horse.

Lab zone Skills Lab

Telltale Molecules

Problem

What information can protein structure reveal about evolutionary relationships among organisms?

Skills Focus

interpreting data, drawing conclusions

Procedure

1. Examine the table below. It shows the sequence of amino acids in one region of a protein, cytochrome c, for six different animals.
2. Predict which of the five other animals is most closely related to the horse. Which animal do you think is most distantly related?
3. Compare the amino acid sequence of the horse to that of the donkey. How many amino acids differ between the two species? Record that number in your notebook.
4. Compare the amino acid sequences of each of the other animals to that of the horse. Record the number of differences in your notebook.

Analyze and Conclude

1. **Interpreting Data** Which animal's amino acid sequence was most similar to that of the horse? What similarities and difference(s) did you observe?
2. **Drawing Conclusions** Based on these data, which species is most closely related to the horse? Which is most distantly related?
3. **Interpreting Data** For the entire protein, the horse's amino acid sequence differs from the other animals' as follows: donkey, 1 difference; rabbit, 6; snake, 22; turtle, 11; and whale, 5. How do the relationships indicated by the entire protein compare with those for the region you examined?
4. **Communicating** Write a paragraph explaining why data about amino acid sequences can provide information about evolutionary relationships among organisms.

More to Explore

Use the amino acid data to construct a branching tree that includes horses, donkeys, and snakes. The tree should show one way that the three species could have evolved from a common ancestor.

Section of Cytochrome c Protein in Animals

Animal	Amino Acid Position														
	39	40	41	42	43	44	45	46	47	48	49	50	51	52	53
Horse	A	B	C	D	E	F	G	H	I	J	K	L	M	N	O
Donkey	A	B	C	D	E	F	G	H	Z	J	K	L	M	N	O
Rabbit	A	B	C	D	E	Y	G	H	Z	J	K	L	M	N	O
Snake	A	B	C	D	E	Y	G	H	Z	J	K	W	M	N	O
Turtle	A	B	C	D	E	V	G	H	Z	J	K	U	M	N	O
Whale	A	B	C	D	E	Y	G	H	Z	J	K	L	M	N	O

Analyze and Conclude

1. The donkey's; it was similar in all amino acid positions except position 47.
2. The donkey is most closely related; the turtle and snake are least closely related.
3. They are very similar.
4. As two or more species evolve from a common ancestor, their DNA may undergo different mutations, causing changes in the amino acids making up common proteins. The fewer differences in the amino acids, the more closely the given species are related.

Extend Inquiry

More to Explore The branching trees should show that the horse and donkey have the most recent common ancestor and that the horse and snake have the most distant common ancestor.

Section 3

Integrating Earth Science

The Fossil Record

Reading Preview

Key Concepts

- How do most fossils form?
- How can scientists determine a fossil's age?
- What is the Geologic Time Scale?
- What are some unanswered questions about evolution?

Key Terms

- petrified fossil
- mold
- cast
- relative dating
- radioactive dating
- radioactive element
- half-life
- fossil record
- extinct
- gradualism
- punctuated equilibria

Target Reading Skill

Building Vocabulary After you read the section, write a definition of each Key Term in your own words.

Lab zone Discover Activity

What Can You Learn From Fossils?

1. Look at the fossil in the photograph. Describe the fossil's characteristics in as much detail as you can.
2. From your description in Step 1, try to figure out how the organism lived. How did it move? Where did it live?

Think It Over
Inferring What type of present-day organism do you think is related to the fossil? Why?

The fossil dinosaur below has been nicknamed "Sue." If fossils could talk, Sue might say something like this: "I don't mind that museum visitors call me 'Sue,' but I do get annoyed when they refer to me as 'that old fossil.' I'm a 67-million-year old *Tyrannosaurus rex*, and I should get some respect. I was fearsome. My skull is one and a half meters long, and my longest tooth is more than 30 centimeters. Ah, the stories I could tell! But I'll have to let my bones speak for themselves. Scientists can learn a lot from studying fossils like me."

Of course, fossils can't really talk or think. But fossils such as Sue reveal life's history.

FIGURE 13 Dinosaur Fossil
The dinosaur nicknamed "Sue" was discovered in 1990 in South Dakota. Sue is now in the Field Museum in Chicago.

C ◆ 155

Section 3

The Fossil Record

Objectives

After this lesson, students will be able to

C.5.3.1 Describe how most fossils form.
C.5.3.2 Explain how scientists can determine a fossil's age.
C.5.3.3 State what the Geologic Time Scale is.
C.5.3.4 Identify some unanswered questions about evolution.

Target Reading Skill

Building Vocabulary Explain that knowing the definitions of Key Terms helps students understand what they read.

Answers
Have students write what they know about each Key Term before reading the definitions in the section. Explain that connecting what they already know about Key Terms helps them to remember the terms. As they read each passage that contains Key Terms, remind them to write the definitions in their own words.

Preteach

Build Background Knowledge

Evidence of Dinosaurs L1
Most students are likely to know a lot about dinosaurs. Ask: **How do we know so much about dinosaurs if none of them is alive now?** *(From their remains, which have been preserved as fossils)* Tell students they will learn how fossils are formed and how they are used to understand evolution.

Lab zone Discover Activity

Skills Focus Inferring L1

Time 5 minutes

Tips Provide a hand lens for students who need or want it. After the activity, inform students that the fossil pictured is a trilobite, an ocean-bottom-dwelling animal that existed about 540 to 250 million years ago.

Expected Outcome Students are likely to describe the overall shape and obvious physical features of the fossil, including what appear to be a shell and numerous legs.

Think It Over Students may say the fossil is related to present-day insects or crabs because it resembles them in its physical features.

Instruct

How Do Fossils Form?

Teach Key Concepts L2

Fossil Formation

Focus Remind students that fossils are the remains of organisms or physical evidence of their existence, such as tracks.

Teach Ask: **How do most fossils form?** *(When organisms die and become buried in sediments)* **What must happen for a petrified fossil to form?** *(The organism's remains must become buried in sediment and then be replaced by minerals.)* **How can you tell a mold from a cast?** *(The mold is a hollow shape, while the cast is a solid form that looks like the organism that formed the mold.)*

Apply Ask: **Why do preserved remains often provide more information about an animal than a petrified fossil?** *(Preserved remains can include soft and hard body parts, while a petrified fossil shows the structure of only the hard parts.)* **learning modality: logical/mathematical**

All in One Teaching Resources

- Transparency C43

Help Students Read L2

Outlining Refer to the Content Refresher for guidelines on Outlining. Have students create an outline of this section as they read.

Independent Practice

All in One Teaching Resources

- Guided Reading and Study Worksheet: *The Fossil Record*

Student Edition on Audio CD

FIGURE 14
Fossil Formation
Most fossils, such as the fossil crocodile shown here, form in sedimentary rock. Relating Cause and Effect *In the process of fossil formation, what materials replace the crocodile's remains?*

How Do Fossils Form?

The formation of any fossil is a rare event. Usually only the hard parts of the organism, such as the bones or shells of animals, form fossils. **Most fossils form when organisms that die become buried in sediments.** Sediments are particles of soil and rock. When a river flows into a lake or ocean, the sediments that the river carries settle to the bottom. Layers of sediments may cover the dead organisms. Over millions of years, the layers may harden to become sedimentary rock. Figure 14 shows how a fossil can form.

Petrified Fossils Some remains that become buried in sediments are actually changed to rock. Minerals dissolved in the water soak into the buried remains. Gradually, the minerals replace the remains, changing them into rock. Fossils that form in this way are called **petrified fossils.**

Molds and Casts Sometimes shells or other hard parts buried by sediments gradually dissolve. An empty space remains in the place that the hard part once occupied. A hollow space in sediment in the shape of an organism or part of an organism is called a **mold.** A mold may become filled with hardened minerals, forming a cast. A **cast** is a copy of the shape of the organism that made the mold.

Preserved Remains Organisms can also be preserved in substances other than sediments. For example, entire organisms, such as huge elephant-like mammoths that lived thousands of years ago, have been preserved in ice.

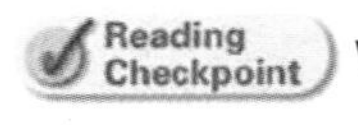

Reading Checkpoint **What is the difference between a mold and a cast?**

Lab zone Try This Activity

Preservation in Ice

1. Place fresh fruit, such as apple slices, strawberries, and blueberries, in an open plastic container.
2. Completely cover the fruit with water. Put the container in a freezer.
3. Place the same type and amount of fresh fruit in another open container. Leave it somewhere where no one will disturb it.
4. After three days, observe the contents of both containers.

Inferring Use your observations to explain why fossils preserved in ice can include soft, fleshy body parts.

Lab zone Try This Activity

Skills Focus Inferring L1

Materials fresh fruit, two plastic containers, water

Time 10 minutes

Tips Make sure students find a place to put the container of fruit that is left out so it will not be disturbed. Warn students not to eat the fruit that has been left out.

Expected Outcome The frozen fruit is well preserved, whereas the fruit that was left out is starting to spoil. Freezing prevents the soft parts from drying out and/or rotting.

Extend Ask: **How do you think a mammoth or other animal might get preserved in this way?** *(Accept any reasonable response, such as an avalanche burying the animal or the animal falling into a crevice in a glacier.)* **learning modality: visual**

For: Fossil Formation activity
Visit: PHSchool.com
Web Code: cep-3053

Determining a Fossil's Age

To understand how living things have changed through time, scientists need to be able to determine the ages of fossils. They can then determine the order in which past events occurred. This information can be used to reconstruct the history of life on Earth.

For example, suppose a scientist is studying two fossils of ancient snails, Snail A and Snail B. The fossils are similar, but they are different enough that they are not the same species. Perhaps, the scientist hypothesizes, Snail A's species changed over time and eventually gave rise to Snail B's species. To help determine whether this hypothesis could be valid, the scientist must first learn which fossil—A or B—is older. **Scientists can determine a fossil's age in two ways: relative dating and radioactive dating.**

Relative Dating Scientists use **relative dating** to determine which of two fossils is older. To understand how relative dating works, imagine that a river has cut down through layers of sedimentary rock to form a canyon. If you look at the canyon walls, you can see the layers of sedimentary rock piled up one on top of another. The layers near the top of the canyon were formed most recently. These layers are the youngest rock layers. The lower down the canyon wall you go, the older the layers are. Therefore, fossils found in layers near the top of the canyon are younger than fossils found near the bottom of the canyon.

Relative dating can only be used when the rock layers have been preserved in their original sequence. Relative dating can help scientists determine whether one fossil is older than another. However, relative dating does not tell scientists the fossil's actual age.

Go Online active art

For: Fossil Formation activity
Visit: PHSchool.com
Web Code: cep-3053

Students explore how fossils are formed.

Lab zone Teacher **Demo**

Modeling Fossil Formation L1

Materials clear plastic container, sand, soil, shells, other small objects

Time 10 minutes

Focus Review how most fossils form.

Teach Layer sand and soil in the container. Scatter shells and other objects throughout the layers.

Apply Ask: **How would real animal remains become buried in this way?** *(By wind or water dropping sand and soil on them)* **learning modality: visual**

Determining a Fossil's Age

Teach Key Concepts L2

Relative vs. Radioactive Dating

Focus Point out that the age of fossils is very important in determining how organisms have changed over time.

Teach Ask: **What is relative dating?** *(A technique used to determine which of two fossils is older by comparing the sequence of rock layers)* **What method is used to determine the actual age of a fossil?** *(Radioactive dating)*

Apply Ask: **What geologic events might disturb the original sequence of rock layers?** *(Erosion; movement along a fault)* **learning modality: logical/mathematical**

Differentiated Instruction

Special Needs L1

Modeling Molds and Casts Instruct students to lay a flat piece of clay on a baking sheet and make an impression in the clay with a small object such as a shell. Then have students pour a small amount of prepared gelatin into the depression and put the baking sheet in a refrigerator overnight. The next day, advise students to gently dislodge the hardened gelatin from the clay. The gelatin should have the same shape as the object that made the depression in the clay. Ask: **Which part of your model represents a mold?** *(The depression in the clay)* **A cast?** *(The gelatin shape)* **learning modality: kinesthetic**

Monitor Progress L2

Skills Check Have students sequence how most fossils form.

Answers

Figure 14 Sediments, which may harden into rock

Reading Checkpoint A mold is a hollow space in sediment in the shape of an organism. A cast is a copy of the shape of an organism that made the mold.

Math Analyzing Data

Math Skill Making and interpreting graphs

Focus Point out that a line graph is often used to show change in quantities over time.

Teach Tell students that the two lines are representing the same sample: One slope is negative and one slope is positive to indicate that one type of element is changing into another.

Answers

1. The red line represents the amount of potassium-40. The blue line represents the amount of argon-40.
2. Potassium-40*:* 1 gram; argon-40*:* 0 grams
3. About 1.3 billion years
4. 0.5 gram (50%) of each; the half-life of potassium-40 is 1.3 billion years, which means that half will break down into argon-40 every 1.3 billion years

What Do Fossils Reveal?

Teach Key Concepts

L2

Understanding Geologic Time

Focus Explain that because the Earth is billions of years old, years or centuries are not helpful for thinking about Earth's long history.

Teach Use Figure 16 to help explain that Earth's history is called the Geologic Time Scale. Ask: **What is this time scale based on?** *(The ages of many different fossils and rocks and when new groups of organisms evolved)* **What are the units of the Geologic Time Scale?** *(Eras and periods)*

Apply Ask students to calculate what percentage of Earth's history is Precambrian Time. *(About 87%—4 billion years ÷ 4.6 billion years)* Refer students to Figure 15. Ask: **At what position on the clock face would Precambrian Time end?** *(About 10:30 P.M.—12 hours × 87%)*
learning modality: logical/mathematical

Math Analyzing Data

Radioactive Decay

The half-life of potassium-40, a radioactive element, is 1.3 billion years. This means that half of the potassium-40 in a sample will break down into argon-40 every 1.3 billion years. The graph shows the breakdown of a 1-gram sample of potassium-40 into argon-40 over billions of years.

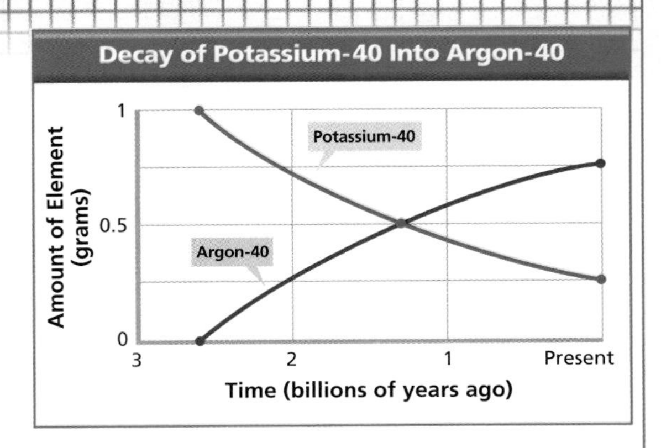

1. **Reading Graphs** What does the red line represent? What does the blue line represent?
2. **Reading Graphs** At 2.6 billion years ago, how much of the sample consisted of potassium 40? How much of the sample consisted of argon-40?
3. **Reading Graphs** At what point in time do the two graph lines cross?
4. **Interpreting Data** At the point where the graph lines cross, how much of the sample consisted of potassium-40? How much consisted of argon-40? Explain why this is the case.

Radioactive Dating A technique called **radioactive dating** allows scientists to determine the actual age of fossils. The rocks that fossils are found near contain **radioactive elements,** which are unstable elements that decay, or break down, into different elements. The **half-life** of a radioactive element is the time it takes for half of the atoms in a sample to decay. The graph in Analyzing Data shows how a sample of potassium-40, a radioactive element, breaks down into argon-40 over time.

Scientists can compare the amount of a radioactive element in a sample to the amount of the element into which it breaks down. This information can be used to calculate the age of the rock, and thus the age of the fossil.

What is a half-life?

What Do Fossils Reveal?

Like pieces in a jigsaw puzzle, fossils can help scientists piece together information about Earth's past. From the fossil record, scientists have learned information about the history of life on Earth. The millions of fossils that scientists have collected are called the **fossil record.**

Extinct Organisms Almost all of the species preserved as fossils are now extinct. A species is **extinct** if no members of that species are still alive. Most of what scientists know about extinct species is based on the fossil record.

The Geologic Time Scale The fossil record provides clues about how and when new groups of organisms evolved. Using radioactive dating, scientists have calculated the ages of many different fossils and rocks. From this information, scientists have created a "calendar" of Earth's history that spans more than 4.6 billion years. Scientists have divided this large time span into smaller units called eras and periods. **This calendar of Earth's history is sometimes called the Geologic Time Scale.**

The largest span of time in the Geologic Time Scale is Precambrian Time, also called the Precambrian (pree KAM bree un). It covers the first 4 billion years of Earth's history. Scientists know very little about the Precambrian because there are few fossils from these ancient times. After the Precambrian, the Geologic Time Scale is divided into three major blocks of time, or eras. Each era is further divided into shorter periods. In Figure 16 on the next two pages, you can see the events that occurred during each time period.

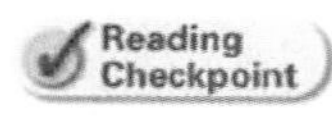
What is the largest span in the Geologic Time Scale?

FIGURE 15
Earth's History as a Clock
Fossils found in rock layers tell the history of life on Earth. The history of life can be compared to 12 hours on a clock.
Interpreting Diagrams *At what time on a 12-hour time scale did plants appear on land?*

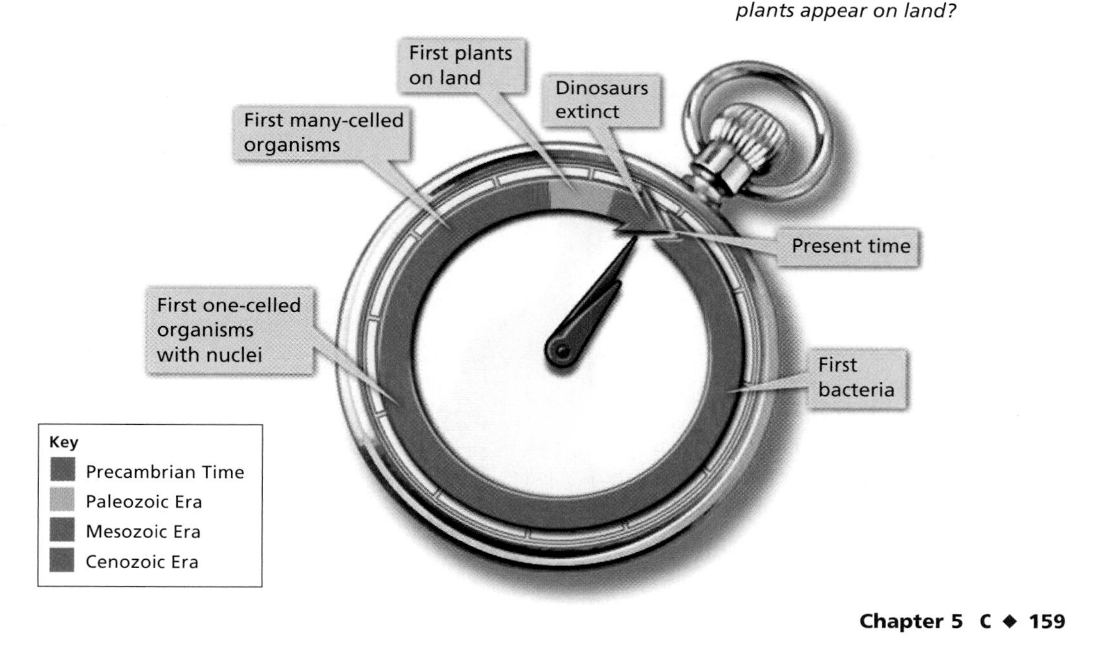

L3

Modeling the Geologic Time Scale

Materials map of your local area, bulletin board, pushpins, small strips of paper

Time 20 minutes

Focus Refer students to Figure 16. Point out that the length of periods varies because the Geologic Time Scale is divided based on major events in the history of life, not a set number of years.

Teach Have students use Figure 16 to determine how long ago each period and era in the history of Earth occurred. Then have them calculate the distance in kilometers that is proportionate to each length of time. For example, the Cambrian Period began 544 million years ago, so it could be represented by 5.44 km on the map. Hang the map on a bulletin board. Place pushpins labeled with strips of paper on the map to represent each time period. Have the starting point be the school. Explain that as you move away from the school, you are going back in time. For example, the beginning of the Cambrian Period will be located 5.44 km from the school. The beginning of Precambrian Time will not likely fit on the map. Have students use the map's scale to determine where in the room or building its label would go.

Apply Ask students to think of other ways to graphically represent the Geologic Time Scale. **learning modality: kinesthetic**

Differentiated Instruction

English Learners/Beginning L1
Vocabulary: Science Glossary Explain that the word "relative" as in *relative dating* is used as a means of comparison. Point out the rock layers in Figure 14 and use the term to describe each one. Discuss the meanings of the other Key Terms in this section. Have students write the definitions in their science glossaries in English and in their native languages. Encourage them to illustrate the terms. **learning modality: verbal**

English Learners/Intermediate L2
Vocabulary: Science Glossary Ask students to write sentences in their own words using each key term. **learning modality: visual**

Monitor Progress L2

Skills Check Have students create a table that compares and contrasts relative and radioactive dating. Students can save their tables in their portfolios.

Answers

Figure 15 about 11:00

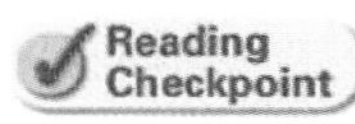
The time it takes for half the atoms of a sample of a radioactive element to decay, or break down

Reading Checkpoint Precambrian Time

Use Visuals: Figure 16 L2

Exploring Life's History

Focus Remind students that geologic eras are based on major events.

Teach Point out that this timeline is different from other timelines because the numbers from left to right are decreasing rather than increasing. Ask student volunteers to read the captions at the bottom. Inform students that the earliest life forms on Earth were confined to the water. Ask questions about the timeline such as: **When did the first land plants and animals appear on Earth?** *(During the Silurian Period, about 430 million years ago)* **Which evolved first, reptiles or amphibians?** *(Amphibians)* **When did the first dinosaurs and mammals evolve?** *(In the Triassic Period, about 220 million years ago)*

Apply Ask: **What evolutionary development made it possible for animals to move from the oceans to land?** *(Plant life developed on land.)* **learning modality: visual**

All in One Teaching Resources

- Transparencies C44, C45

Address Misconceptions L2

Fossils Are Rare

Focus Many students think that most species that have existed on Earth have left fossil remains.

Teach Explain that of the millions of extinct species, only a fraction of one percent is likely to have been preserved as fossils. During much of Earth's history, organisms were one-celled or invertebrates.

Apply Ask: **Why have many more fossils of organisms that lived after Precambrian Time been discovered?** *(After Precambrian Time, organisms with hard body parts started appearing. They were more likely to form fossils. Also, organisms in general became more abundant.)* **learning modality: logical/mathematical**

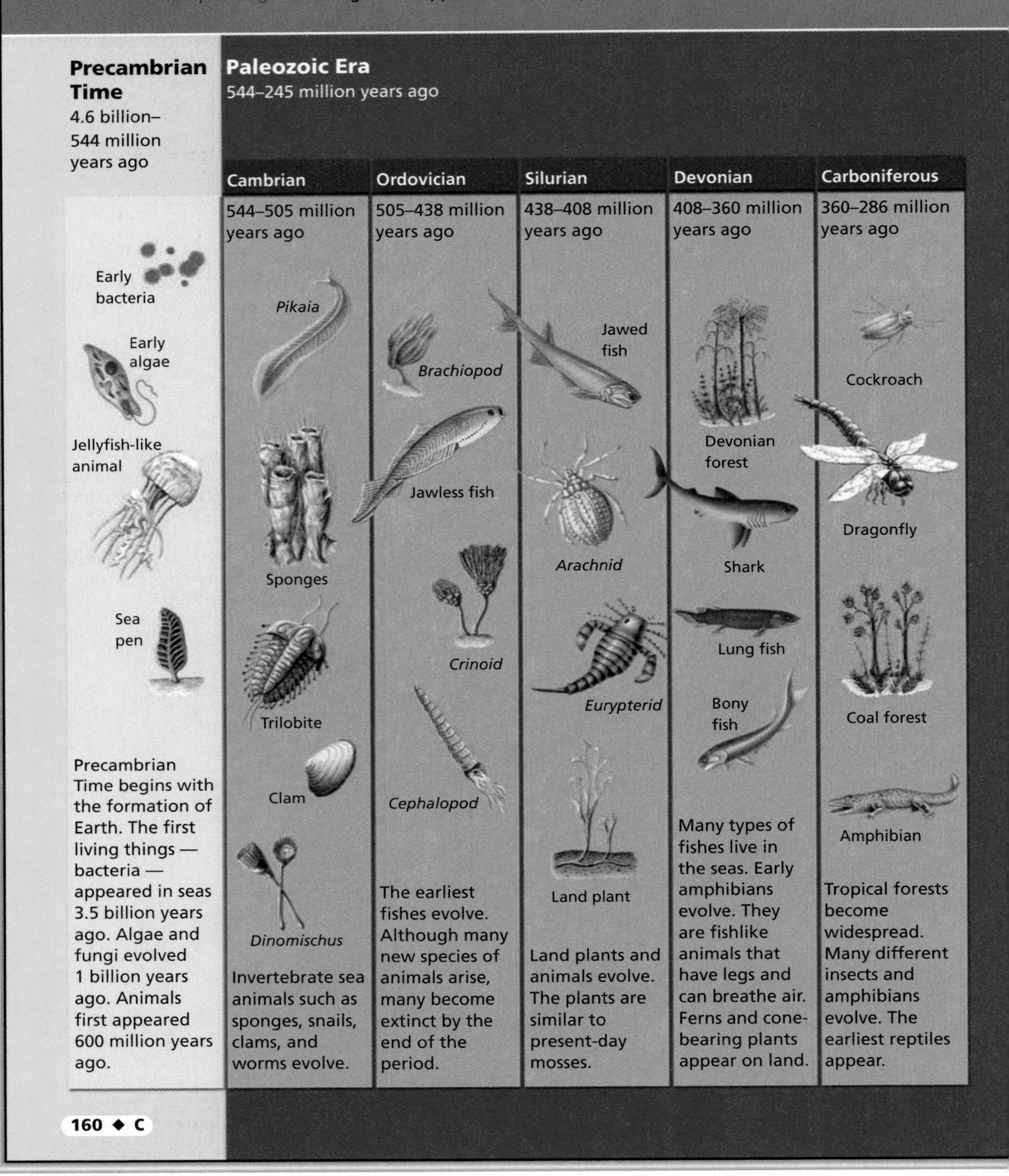

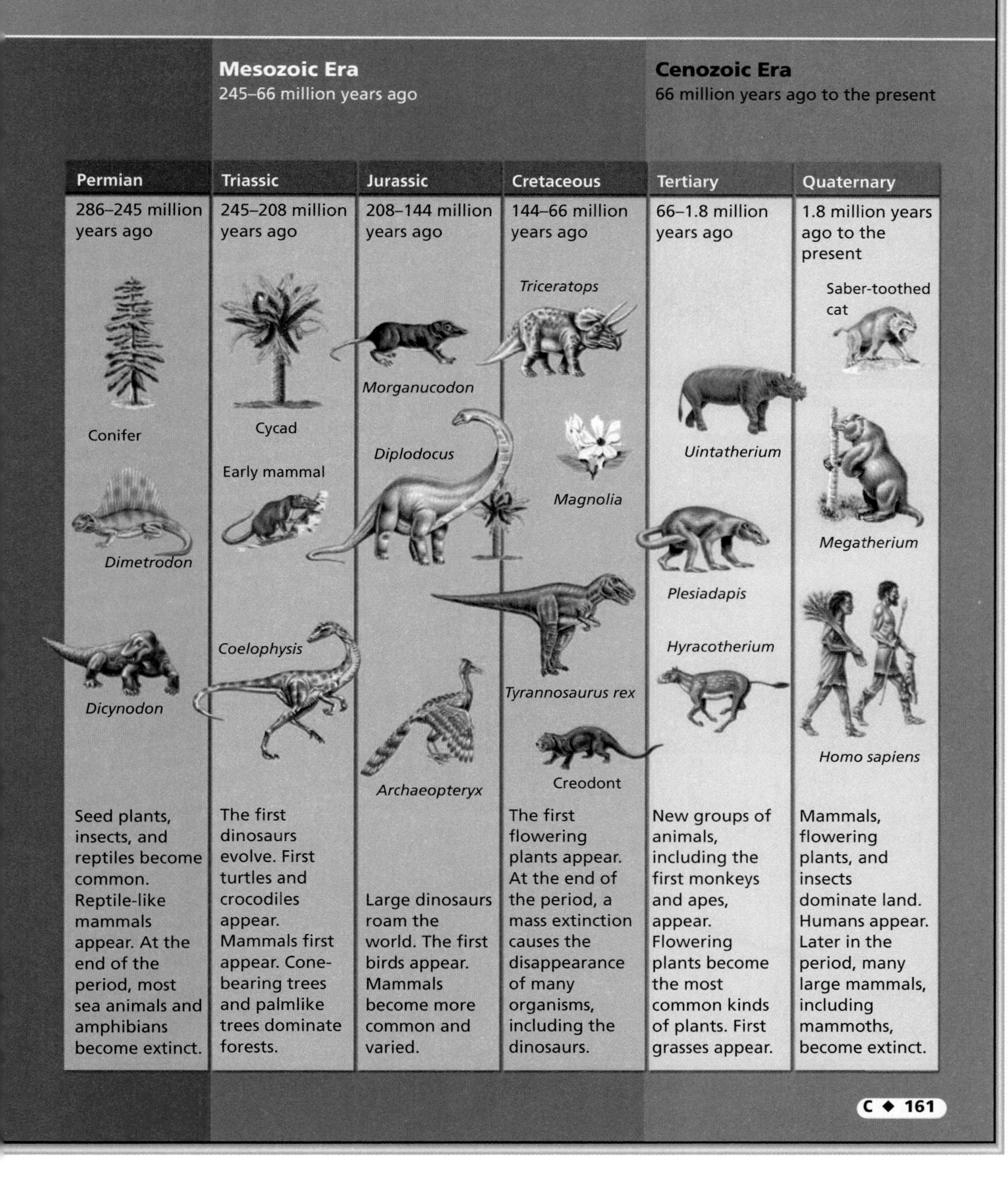

Lab zone Build Inquiry L2

Applying Concepts of Geologic Time

Materials poster board, dice, index cards, markers, small toys or other items for game tokens

Time 30 minutes

Focus Divide the class into groups, and challenge each group to create a board game called *A Trip Through Geologic Time* to reinforce their knowledge of Earth's life history.

Teach The game board should start in Precambrian Time and continue to the present. To advance around the game board (and through time), players are required to answer questions, perhaps written on chance cards, about each period. Escaping from carnivorous dinosaurs, skirting around treacherous tar pits, or avoiding similar relevant obstacles in particular time periods might be included on the game board to add excitement to the game and require students to apply more of the information from Figure 16. After groups have played their own games, urge them to exchange and play one another's games.

Apply Ask: **Is the timeline in your board game to scale?** *(It is not likely because the major events in life's history would be too crowded or the game board would be too large.)* Ask students to explain how they dealt with scale. **learning modality: kinesthetic**

Differentiated Instruction

Gifted and Talented L3

Communicating Ask students to imagine they have traveled to an earlier period in Earth's history. Have them write an eyewitness report, modeled on a television or newspaper story. Encourage them to use additional references for more information, such as descriptions of climate. Ask volunteers to present their reports, and challenge other students to identify the time periods described. **learning modality: verbal**

Less Proficient Readers L1

Creating Study Aids Pair students with more proficient readers. Have them make flash cards with the periods, events, and organisms of the Geologic Time Scale, and use them to quiz each other. **learning modality: verbal**

Monitor Progress L2

Oral Presentation Call on students to describe an event in the evolution of plants or animals, based on the information in Figure 16.

Answer

Figure 16 Fishes appeared in the Ordovician Period, before amphibians, which appeared in the Devonian Period.

Unanswered Questions

Teach Key Concepts

L2

Gaps in the Fossil Record

Focus Tell students that the end of the Paleozoic Era and the Mesozoic Era were marked by major extinctions.

Teach Ask: **What is a mass extinction?** *(A mass extinction occurs when many types of organisms become extinct at the same time.)* **What question do scientists have about mass extinctions?** *(What caused them?)* **How could an asteroid hitting Earth cause a mass extinction?** *(The impact could throw up huge clouds of dust which would block sunlight, making the climate cooler and killing plants. With fewer plants, many animals would starve.)* **What other event do scientists think could cause a mass extinction?** *(Volcanic eruptions)* **What is another unanswered question about evolution?** *(At what rate does evolution occur?)* **Which theories explain how rapidly species change?** *(Gradualism, which is the theory that proposes that evolution occurs slowly but steadily, and punctuated equilibria, which is the theory that evolution occurs quickly during relatively short periods.)*

Apply Explain that an intermediate life form is an organism that is a link between a more modern organism and its ancestor. Ask: **Why are fossils of intermediate life forms likely to be rare if the theory of punctuated equilibria explains how evolution occurs?** *(The theory proposes that new species evolve rapidly over a short period of time, so the chances of fossils of intermediate species forming are reduced.)* **learning modality: logical/mathematical**

FIGURE 17
Mass Extinctions
An asteroid may have caused the mass extinction that occurred about 65 million years ago.
Relating Cause and Effect *How could an asteroid have caused climate change?*

▲ An asteroid zooms toward Earth.

The asteroid ▲ hits Earth, sending up clouds of dust.

Many plants and animals die from ▼ the effects of the collision.

Unanswered Questions

The fossil record has provided scientists with a lot of important information about past life on Earth. The fossil record, however, is incomplete, because most organisms died without leaving fossils behind. These gaps in the fossil record leave many questions unanswered. **Two unanswered questions about evolution involve the causes of mass extinctions and the rate at which evolution occurs.**

Mass Extinctions When many types of organisms become extinct at the same time, a mass extinction has occurred. Several mass extinctions have taken place during the history of life. One mass extinction, for example, occurred at the end of the Cretaceous Period, about 65 million years ago. During the Cretaceous mass extinction, many kinds of plants and animals, including the dinosaurs, disappeared forever.

Scientists are not sure what causes mass extinctions, but they hypothesize that major climate changes may be responsible. For example, a climate change may have caused the mass extinction at the end of the Cretaceous Period. An asteroid, which is a rocky mass from space, may have hit Earth, throwing huge clouds of dust and other materials into the air. The dust clouds would have blocked sunlight, making the climate cooler, and killing plants. If there were fewer plants, many animals would have starved. Some scientists, however, think volcanic eruptions, not an asteroid, caused the climate change.

Gradualism Scientists also are not sure how rapidly species change. One theory, called **gradualism,** proposes that evolution occurs slowly but steadily. According to this theory, tiny changes in a species gradually add up to major changes over very long periods of time. This is how Darwin thought evolution occurred.

If the theory of gradualism is correct, the fossil record should include intermediate forms between a fossil organism and its descendants. However, there are often long periods of time in which fossils show little or no change. Then, quite suddenly, fossils appear that are distinctly different. One possible explanation for the lack of intermediate forms is that the fossil record is incomplete. Scientists may eventually find more fossils to fill the gaps.

Punctuated Equilibria A theory that accounts for the gaps in the fossil record is called **punctuated equilibria.** According to this theory, species evolve quickly during relatively short periods. These periods of rapid change are separated by long periods of little or no change. Today most scientists think that evolution can occur gradually at some times and more rapidly at others.

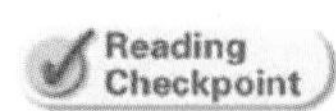
What theory proposes that evolution occurs slowly but steadily?

FIGURE 18
Trilobite
Trilobites were once common in Earth's oceans, but they were destroyed in a mass extinction.

Section 3 Assessment

Target Reading Skill Building Vocabulary Use your definitions to help you answer the questions below.

Reviewing Key Concepts

1. a. Reviewing What are sediments? How are they involved in the formation of fossils?
   b. Classifying Identify the types of fossils.
   c. Comparing and Contrasting Which of the major types of fossils do not form in sediments? Describe how this type can form.
2. a. Identifying What are the two methods of determining a fossil's age?
   b. Describing Describe each method.
   c. Applying Concepts Some fossil organisms are frozen rather than preserved in sediment. Which method of dating would you use with frozen fossils? Why?
3. a. Defining What is the Geologic Time Scale? Into what smaller units is it divided?
   b. Interpreting Diagrams Look at Figure 16. Did the organisms during Precambrian Time have hard body parts?
   c. Relating Cause and Effect Give one reason why there are few Precambrian fossils.
4. a. Reviewing What are two unanswered questions about evolution?
   b. Comparing and Contrasting How are the theories of gradualism and punctuated equilibria different? How are they similar?

Lab zone At-Home Activity

Modeling Fossil Formation With an adult family member, spread some mud in a shallow pan. Use your fingertips to make "footprints" across the mud. Let the mud dry and harden. Explain how this is similar to fossil formation.

Monitor Progress L2

Answers

Figure 17 An asteroid hitting Earth would have thrown huge clouds of dust and other materials into the air. The dust clouds would have blocked sunlight, making the climate cooler.

Reading Checkpoint Gradualism

Assess

Reviewing Key Concepts

1. a. Sediments are particles of soil and rock; fossils form when organisms that die become buried in sediments. **b.** Petrified fossils, molds and casts, and preserved remains **c.** Preserved remains; the entire organism is preserved in a substance other than sediment.

2. a. Relative dating and radioactive dating **b.** Relative dating involves using position to compare the ages of rock layers and, therefore, the ages of the fossils in the layers. Radioactive dating involves comparing the amount of a radioactive element in a sample to the amount of the element into which it breaks down. **c.** Radioactive dating, because ice does not settle into distinct layers

3. a. The calendar of Earth's history; eras and periods **b.** No, they had only soft body parts. **c.** Sample answer: Few Precambrian organisms had the hard parts of organisms, such as the bones or shells of animals, that usually form fossils. (Students may also say that there were relatively few Precambrian organisms.)

4. a. What caused mass extinctions? At what rate does evolution occur? **b.** Different: Gradualism states that evolution occurs slowly and steadily, whereas punctuated equilibria states that evolution occurs rapidly during short periods separated by long periods of no change. Similar: Both theories propose that organisms evolve; both attempt to explain the fossil record.

Reteach L1

Use the visuals in this section to summarize how fossils are formed and to review what they tell us about the history of life on Earth.

All in One Teaching Resources

- Section Summary: *The Fossil Record*
- Review and Reinforce: *The Fossil Record*
- Enrich: *The Fossil Record*

Lab zone At-Home Activity

Modeling Fossil Formation L1

Advise students to use mud that contains a lot of clay and enough water to make it the consistency of yogurt or pudding.

Lab zone Chapter Project

Keep Students on Track Review each group's first timeline, and offer comments before the group starts its second timeline. Confirm that students understand that because the second timeline is an enlargement of one section of the first timeline, its scale will be different. Provide source materials for students to use.

Study Guide

- Complete student edition
- Section and chapter self-assessments
- Assessment reports for teachers

Help Students Read

Building Vocabulary

Word-Part Analysis Help students to learn the names of the eras in the Geologic Time Scale by explaining the word roots. The combining form *-zoic* comes from the Greek word for "life," *paleo-* from the Greek word for "ancient," *meso-* from the Greek word for "middle," and *ceno-* from the Greek word for "recent." After students have learned the meanings of the combining forms, check their understanding by asking: **What do the terms *Paleozoic, Mesozoic,* and *Cenozoic* mean?** *(Ancient life, middle life, and recent life)*

Plural Forms Students may think that the term *species* is plural and that the singular form is *specie*. Explain that the term *species* is both singular and plural. Then have them use the word in a sentence to illustrate this fact. For example, they might say, "All humans belong to one species, but humans and chimpanzees belong to two different species."

Connecting Concepts

Concept Maps Help students develop a concept map to show how the information in this chapter is related. The theory of evolution explains how organisms have changed through time and is supported by evidence from fossils, early development of animals, physiological structures, and DNA sequences. Have students brainstorm to identify the Key Concepts, Key Terms, details, and examples, then write each one on a sticky note and attach it at random on chart paper or on the board. They will use these notes to construct the concept map.

Chapter 5 Study Guide

1 Darwin's Theory

Key Concepts

- Darwin's important observations included the diversity of living things, the remains of ancient organisms, and the characteristics of organisms on the Galápagos Islands.
- Darwin reasoned that plants or animals that arrived on the Galápagos Islands faced conditions that were different from those on the mainland. Perhaps, Darwin hypothesized, the species gradually changed over many generations and became better adapted to the new conditions.
- Darwin proposed that, over a long period of time, natural selection can lead to change. Helpful variations may gradually accumulate in a species, while unfavorable ones may disappear.

Key Terms

species
fossil
adaptation
evolution
scientific theory
natural selection
variation

2 Evidence of Evolution

Key Concepts

- Fossils, patterns of early development, and similar body structures all provide evidence that organisms have changed over time.
- Scientists have combined the evidence from DNA, protein structure, fossils, early development, and body structure to determine the evolutionary relationships among species.
- A new species can form when a group of individuals remains separated from the rest of its species long enough to evolve different traits.

Key Terms

homologous structures
branching tree

3 The Fossil Record

Key Concepts

- Most fossils form when organisms that die become buried in sediments.
- Scientists can determine a fossil's age in two ways: relative dating and radioactive dating.
- The calendar of Earth's history is sometimes called the Geologic Time Scale.
- Two unanswered questions about evolution involve mass extinctions and the rate at which evolution occurs.

Key Terms

petrified fossil
mold
cast
relative dating
radioactive dating
radioactive element
half-life
fossil record
extinct
gradualism
punctuated equilibria

Tell students that this concept map will be organized in hierarchical order and to begin at the top with the Key Concepts. Ask students these questions to guide them to categorize the information on the stickies: **What factors affect natural selection? What kinds of evidence support the theory of evolution? How do scientists summarize the history of life on Earth?**

Prompt students by using connecting words or phrases, such as "is supported by," "is affected by," and "can be broken into," to indicate the basis for the organization of the map. The phrases should form a sentence between or among a set of concepts.

Answer

Accept logical presentations by students.

All in One Teaching Resources

- Key Terms Review: *Changes Over Time*
- Connecting Concepts: *Changes Over Time*

Review and Assessment

Go Online PHSchool.com
For: Self-Assessment
Visit: PHSchool.com
Web Code: cea-3050

Organizing Information

Sequencing Copy the flowchart about fossil formation onto a separate sheet of paper. Complete the flowchart by writing a sentence describing each stage in the process of fossil formation. Then add a title. (For more on Sequencing, see the Skills Handbook.)

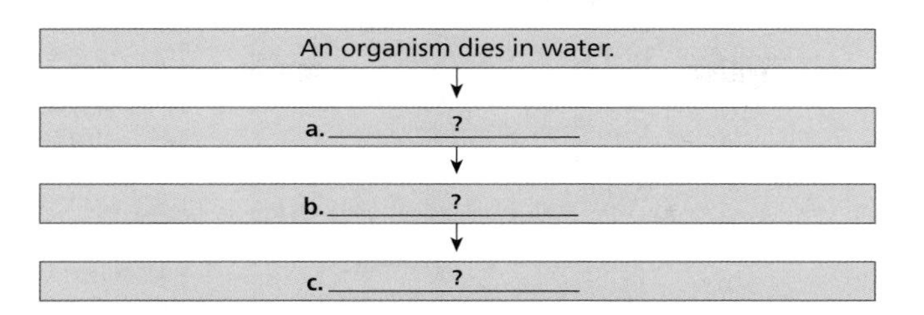

Reviewing Key Terms

Choose the letter of the best answer.

1. Changes in a species over long periods of time are called
   a. half-life.
   b. evolution.
   c. homologous structures.
   d. developmental stages.
2. A trait that helps an organism survive and reproduce is called a(n)
   a. variation.
   b. adaptation.
   c. species.
   d. selection.
3. Similar structures that related species have inherited from a common ancestor are called
   a. adaptations.
   b. punctuated equilibria.
   c. ancestral structures.
   d. homologous structures.
4. Fossils formed when an organism dissolves and leaves an empty space in a rock are called
   a. casts.
   b. mold.
   c. preserved remains.
   d. petrified fossils.
5. The rate of decay of a radioactive element is measured by its
   a. year.
   b. era.
   c. period.
   d. half-life.

If the statement is true, write *true*. If it is false, change the underlined word or words to make the statement true.

6. Darwin's idea about how evolution occurs is called natural selection.
7. Most members of a species show differences, or variations.
8. A diagram that shows how organisms might be related is called gradualism.
9. The technique of relative dating can be used to determine the actual age of a fossil.
10. According to the theory of punctuated equilibria, evolution occurs slowly but steadily.

Writing in Science

Notebook Entry Imagine that you are a biologist exploring the Galápagos Islands. Write a notebook entry on one of the unusual species you have found on the islands. Include a description of how it is adapted to its environment.

Changes Over Time
Video Preview
Video Field Trip
▶ Video Assessment

Go Online PHSchool.com
For: Self-Assessment
Visit: PHSchool.com
Web Code: cea-3050

Students can take a practice test online that is automatically scored.

All in One Teaching Resources
- Transparency C46
- Chapter Test
- Performance Assessment Teacher Notes
- Performance Assessment Student Worksheet
- Performance Assessment Scoring Rubric

***ExamView®* Computer Test Bank CD-ROM**

Review and Assessment

Organizing Information

Sample answer:
a. The organism is buried under sediment.
b. Over millions of years, the sediments harden and become rock, and the hard parts of the organism are replaced by minerals.
c. The fossil becomes exposed on the surface of a rock.
Sample title: Fossil Formation

Reviewing Key Terms

1. b **2.** b **3.** d **4.** b **5.** d
6. true
7. true
8. a branching tree
9. radioactive dating
10. gradualism

Writing in Science

Writing Mode Description

Scoring Rubric
4 Includes complete description of an unusual species on the Galápagos written in the format of a notebook entry; goes beyond requirements, for example, providing extensive detail
3 Includes all criteria but does not go beyond requirements
2 Includes only brief description
1 Includes incomplete and inaccurate description

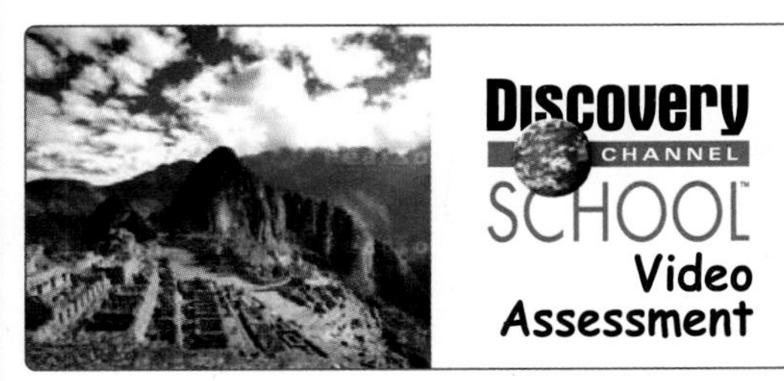

Changes Over Time

Show the Video Assessment to review chapter content and as a prompt for the writing assignment.

Checking Concepts

11. The overproduction of offspring leads to competition in which only the better adapted organisms survive and reproduce.

12. Examples will vary. Possible answer: A large number of turtles are born every year but only a few will be able to swim fast enough to escape predators. Because being able to swim faster makes the turtles more likely to survive and reproduce, natural selection leads to an increase through time in the fast-swimming trait.

13. A new species can form when a group of individuals remains geographically isolated from the rest of its species long enough to reproduce separately and evolve different traits. Geographic isolation can be caused by the formation of features such as rivers and mountain ranges.

14. They could look for similarities in the DNA or protein structures of the organisms.

15. Related species inherit the same basic developmental plan from their common ancestor.

16. When a species is extinct, none of its members are alive. Scientists obtain information about extinct species from fossils.

17. A mass extinction occurs when many types of organisms become extinct at the same time. Mass extinctions may be caused by major climate changes due to events such as an asteroid hitting Earth.

Review and Assessment

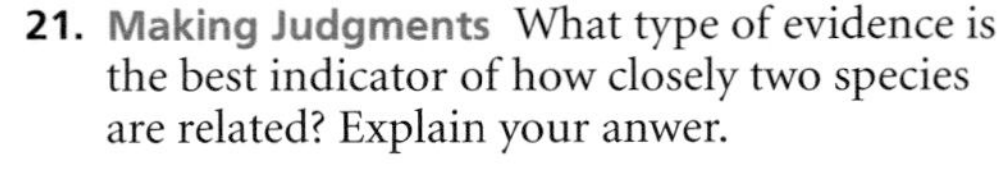

Checking Concepts

11. What role does the overproduction of organisms play in natural selection?

12. Use an example to explain how natural selection can lead to evolution.

13. Explain how geographic isolation can result in the formation of a new species.

14. On the basis of similar body structures, scientists hypothesize that two species are closely related. What other evidence would the scientists look for to support their hypothesis?

15. Explain why similarities in the early development of different species suggest that the species are related.

16. What is meant by *extinct?* How do scientists obtain information about extinct species?

17. What are mass extinctions? What may cause mass extinction?

Thinking Critically

18. **Relating Cause and Effect** Why did Darwin's visit to the Galápagos Islands have such an important influence on his development of the theory of evolution?

19. **Applying Concepts** Some insects look just like sticks. How could this be an advantage to the insects? How could this trait have evolved through natural selection?

20. **Predicting** Which of the organisms shown below is least likely to become a fossil? Explain your answer.

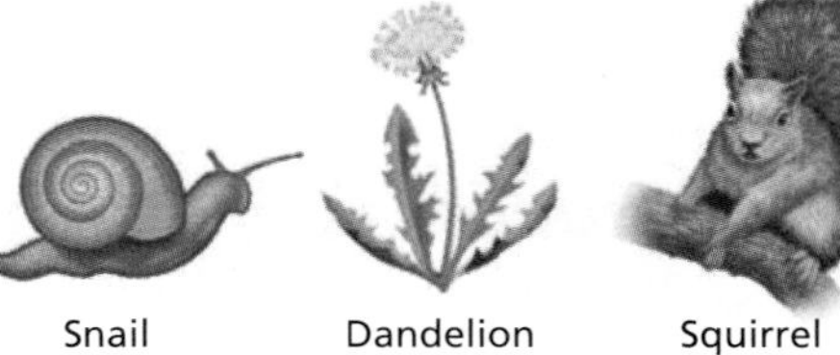

Snail Dandelion Squirrel

21. **Making Judgments** What type of evidence is the best indicator of how closely two species are related? Explain your anwer.

22. **Comparing and Contrasting** How are selective breeding and natural selection similar? How are they different?

Applying Skills

Use the data in the table below to answer Questions 23–25.

Radioactive carbon-14 decays to nitrogen with a half-life of 5,730 years. The table contains information about the amounts of carbon-14 and nitrogen in three fossils. The table also gives information about the position of each fossil in rock layers.

Fossil	Amount of Carbon-14 in Fossil	Amount of Nitrogen in Fossil	Position of Fossil in Rock Layers
A	1 gram	7 grams	Bottom layer
B	4 grams	4 grams	Top layer
C	2 grams	6 grams	Middle layer

23. **Inferring** Use the positions of the fossils in the rock layers to put the fossils in their probable order from the youngest to the oldest.

24. **Calculating** Calculate the age of each fossil using the data about carbon-14 and nitrogen.

25. **Drawing Conclusions** Do your answers to Questions 23 and 24 agree or disagree with each other? Explain.

Lab zone Chapter Project

Performance Assessment Complete both your timelines. Display your completed timelines for the class. Be prepared to explain why you chose the scale that you did. Also, describe how your timelines are related to each other.

Lab zone Chapter Project

L3

Performance Assessment Give each group an opportunity to show its two timelines to the rest of the class, describe how the models were made, and explain how the second timeline relates to the first timeline. Ask each group to point out any evolutionary events that were not included in the textbook's timeline. Encourage the rest of the class to ask questions.

Reflect and Record Ask students to describe how the timelines helped them to understand the long periods involved in the evolution of life. Students will probably realize that making a second timeline for the past 600 million years allowed them to see the time spans and placements of evolutionary events much more clearly. Let students share their ideas in a class discussion.

Standardized Test Prep

Test-Taking Tip

Anticipating the Answer

You can sometimes figure out an answer before you look at the answer choices. After you think of your own answer, compare it with the answer choices. Select the answer that most closely matches your own answer. This strategy can be especially useful for questions that test vocabulary. Try to answer the question below before you look at the answer choices.

Sample Question

A well-tested concept that explains a wide range of observations is known as a(n)

A hypothesis.
B controlled experiment.
C scientific theory.
D inference.

Answer

Choice **C** is correct, because the definition of *scientific theory* is "a well-tested concept that explains a wide range of observations." Even though the other answer choices are all scientific processes, none is the correct answer.

Choose the letter of the best answer.

1. The process by which individuals that are better adapted to their environment are more likely to survive and reproduce than other members of the same species is called

A natural selection.
B evolution.
C competition.
D overproduction.

2. Which of the following is the best example of an adaptation that helps an organism survive in its environment?

F green coloring in a lizard living on gray rocks
G a thick coat of fur on an animal that lives in the desert
H extensive root system in a desert plant
J thin, delicate leaves on a plant in a cold climate

3. Which of the following is the weakest evidence supporting a close evolutionary relationship between two animals?

A The bones of a bird's wings are similar to the bones of a dog's legs.
B Human embryos look like turtle embryos in their early development.
C Lesser pandas look like bears.
D The amino acid sequence in mouse hemoglobin is similar to the amino acid sequence in chimpanzee hemoglobin.

Use the diagram below and your knowledge of science to answer Questions 4–5.

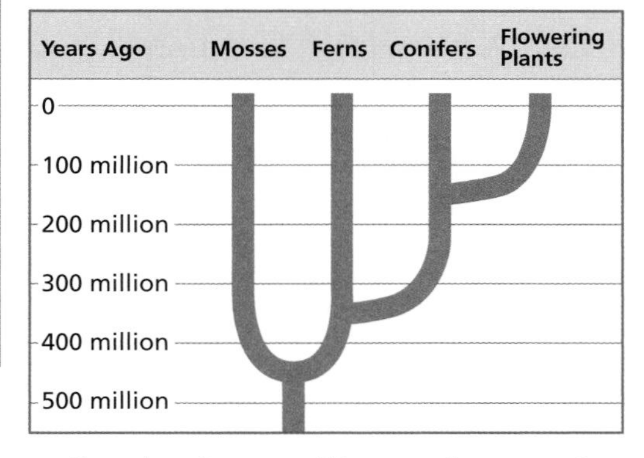

4. About how long ago did mosses first appear?

F 100 million years ago
G 150 million years ago
H 350 million years ago
J 450 million years ago

5. Which group of plants would have DNA that is most similar to the DNA of flowering plants?

A mosses
B ferns
C conifers
D They would all be equally alike.

Constructed Response

6. Relative dating and radioactive dating are two methods for determining the age of a fossil. Compare and contrast these two methods.

Thinking Critically

18. The islands were characterized by a great diversity of environments containing generally similar species that exhibited different adaptations suited to each particular environment. This had the effect of leading Darwin to develop his theory.

19. Insects that look like sticks are camouflaged among twigs and may be overlooked by predators. If the trait increases the insect's chances of surviving and reproducing, then insects with the trait would become more common than insects without it.

20. The dandelion is least likely to become a fossil because it does not have hard parts, such as bones, teeth, or a shell.

21. DNA similarities and similarities in amino acid sequence in protein; DNA and proteins have highly specific structures.

22. Both involve passing on desired traits to the next generation of organisms. In selective breeding, humans choose the traits and which organisms to cross or mate. In natural selection, the process occurs through competition and survival of the fittest.

Applying Skills

23. Based on the positions of the fossils in rock layers, B is the youngest, C is intermediate in age, and A is the oldest.

24. Based on the carbon-14 and nitrogen data, A is 17,190 years old, B is 5,730 years old, and C is 11,460 years old.

25. The answers agree because C is 5,730 years older than B, and A is 5,730 older than C. This places the fossils in the same order age-wise as relative dating.

Standardized Test Prep

1. A **2.** H **3.** C **4.** J **5.** C

6. Relative dating involves looking at the rock layers that the fossils are in to see which layer was deposited first, while radioactive dating involves comparing the amount of a radioactive element in a sample to the amount of the element into which it breaks down. Both methods are used to determine the ages of rocks, but relative dating only tells which of two or more rocks is older or younger, while radioactive dating gives the actual age of the rock.

Interdisciplinary Exploration

Dogs—Loyal Companions

This interdisciplinary feature presents the central theme of domestic dogs by connecting four different disciplines: science, social studies, language arts, and mathematics. The four explorations are designed to capture students' interest and help them see how the content they are studying in science relates to other school subjects and real-world events. Share with others for a team-teaching experience.

All in One Teaching Resources

- Interdisciplinary Exploration: *Science*
- Interdisciplinary Exploration: *Social Studies*
- Interdisciplinary Exploration: *Language Arts*
- Interdisciplinary Exploration: *Mathematics*

Build Background Knowledge

Dogs as Companions

Ask: **What are some different types of dogs?** *(German shepherd, Labrador retriever, poodle, rottweiler, sheep dog.)* **For what reasons do people have dogs?** *(As pets, as guard dogs, as hunting dogs, as police dogs, to herd sheep, to pull sleds, to be companions for people who are visually impaired or hearing impaired)*

Introduce the Exploration

Have students think about the early mutualistic relationship between humans and wolves over 10,000 years ago. Ask: **How would the wolves benefit from being near humans?** *(They may be able to find food more easily by eating scraps and garbage)* **How would humans benefit from having wolves nearby?** *(The wolves may bark as a warning when strangers were near, the wolves helped keep the living area clean by eating scraps and garbage.)*

Interdisciplinary Exploration

Egyptian Art More than 3,000 years ago, an artist drew three dogs chasing a hyena.

Dogs— Loyal Companions

What's your image of a dog?

- **A powerful Great Dane?**
- **A tiny, lively Chihuahua?**
- **A protective German shepherd guide dog?**
- **A friendly, lovable mutt?**

Most dogs are descendants of the gray wolf, which was originally found throughout Europe, Asia, and North America. Dogs were the first animals to be domesticated, or tamed. As far back as 9,000 years ago, farmers who raised sheep, cattle, and goats tamed dogs to herd and guard the livestock.

After taming dogs, people began to breed them for traits that people valued. Early herding dogs helped shepherds. Speedy hunting dogs learned to chase deer and other game. Strong, sturdy working dogs pulled sleds and even rescued people. Small, quick terriers hunted animals, such as rats. "Toy" dogs were companions to people of wealth and leisure. More recently, sporting dogs were trained to flush out and retrieve birds. Still others were bred to be guard dogs. But perhaps the real reasons people bred dogs were for loyalty and companionship.

Girl with dalmatian

168 ◆ C

From Wolf to Purebred

About 10,000 years ago, some wolves may have been attracted to human settlements. They may have found it easier to feed on food scraps than to hunt for themselves. Gradually the wolves came to depend on people for food. The wolves, in turn, kept the campsites clean and safe. They ate the garbage and barked to warn of approaching strangers. These wolves were the ancestors of the dogs you know today.

Over time, dogs became more and more a part of human society. People began to breed dogs for the traits needed for tasks such as herding sheep and hunting. Large, aggressive dogs, for example, were bred to be herding dogs, while fast dogs with a keen sense of smell were bred to be hunting dogs. Today, there are hundreds of breeds. They range from the tiny Chihuahua to the massive Saint Bernard, one of which can weigh as much as 50 Chihuahuas.

Today, people breed dogs mostly for their appearance and personality. Physical features such as long ears or a narrow snout are valued in particular breeds of dogs. To create "pure" breeds of dogs, breeders use a method known as inbreeding. Inbreeding involves mating dogs that are genetically very similar. Inbreeding is the surest way to produce dogs with a uniform physical appearance.

One undesirable result of inbreeding is an increase in genetic disorders. Experts estimate that 25 percent of all purebred dogs have a genetic disorder. Dalmatians, for example, often inherit deafness. German shepherds may develop severe hip problems. Mixed-breed dogs, in contrast, are less likely to inherit genetic disorders.

Fur Color in Retrievers
In Labrador retrievers, the allele for dark-colored fur is dominant over the allele for yellow fur.

Science Activity

Most traits that dogs are bred for are controlled by more than one gene. A few traits, however, show simpler inheritance patterns. For example, in Labrador retrievers, a single gene with one dominant and one recessive allele determines whether the dog's fur will be dark or yellow. The allele for dark fur (D) is dominant over the allele for yellow fur (d).

- Construct a Punnett square for a cross between two Labrador retrievers that are both heterozygous for dark fur (Dd).
- Suppose there were eight puppies in the litter. Predict how many would have dark fur and how many would have yellow fur.
- Construct a second Punnett square for a cross between a Labrador retriever with yellow fur (dd) and one with dark fur (Dd). In a litter with six puppies, predict how many would have dark fur and how many would have yellow fur.

Background

Facts and Figures *Canis familiaris* is the scientific name for the domestic dog. The dog is believed to be the first animal to be domesticated. The domestic dog is a descendent of the wolf, *Canis rufus.* After thousands of years of selective breeding there are more than 300 breeds of dogs. The American Kennel Club (AKC) recognizes 150 breeds of dogs and divides them into seven categories: terrier, working, sporting, hound, herding, toy, and nonsporting. Working dogs include Doberman pinschers, rottweilers, Great Danes, and Alaskan malamutes. Sporting dogs include Labrador retrievers, weimaraners, and Irish setters. Herding dogs include sheep dogs, German shepherds, and Welsh corgis.

Explore Science Concepts

Review Help students recall that traits are passed from parent to offspring through genetic material. By breeding two dogs that both have a desired trait, the chances of their offspring having the desired trait increases.

Discuss Ask: **For what reasons do people breed dogs?** *(So that they have traits that allow them to hunt, herd, guard, or run better; also for appearance and personality)* **What traits would you want a hunting dog to have?** *(Possible answers: to be able to run quickly, to have a good sense of smell, to be able to retrieve, to be able to swim well)* **What traits would you want a herding dog to have?** *(To be aggressive and be able to herd, to have a lot of energy, to be able to be outside in extreme weather)* **What is inbreeding?** *(Inbreeding involves mating dogs that are genetically similar to each other.)* **What is a disadvantage of inbreeding?** *(It increases the chances of genetic disorders in the offspring.)*

Science Activity

Focus Students should recall that they are being given the genotypes of the dogs to use in the Punnett squares. Each genotype will be expressed as a phenotype, in this case either dark or yellow fur.

Teach Remind students how to construct a Punnett square. Students should make the Punnett square, then examine the genotypes to determine what percentage of offspring will have each phenotype.

Expected Outcome In the cross between the dogs that are both heterozygous for dark fur, 75 percent of the offspring will probably have dark fur and 25 percent will have yellow fur. Out of eight puppies, six will probably have dark fur and two will have yellow fur. In the cross between the yellow-fur dog and the heterozygous dark-fur dog, 50 percent of the offspring will probably have dark fur and 50 percent will probably have yellow fur. Out of six puppies, three will probably have dark fur and three will probably have yellow fur.

Social Studies

Explore Social Studies Concepts

Use Maps Provide students with copies of world maps on 11 x 17 sheets of paper. The maps can be pre-labeled or students can label them as an extra challenge. Have students use encyclopedias, library resources, and the Internet to research the geographic origin of different dog breeds. Students can label their maps with the dog breeds and the corresponding area or country from which they originate. *(Sample answers: Alaskan malamute—northwestern Alaska; Basenji—Africa; Belgian sheepdog—Belgium; Chihuahua—Mexico; Collie—Scotland; Mastiff—England; Pomeranian—Germany; Portuguese water dog—Portugal; Samoyed—Siberia)*

Teach Key Concepts

Review Some dogs have characteristics that make them better adapted to living in a cold climate. Some dogs have characteristics that make them well adapted for certain activities, such as hunting.

Discuss Ask: **How is the Lhasa Apso well adapted for cold conditions?** *(The breed has a long, thick coat that protects it from cold air.)* **How are the basset hound and the dachshund well adapted for hunting?** *(The basset hound has short legs and a compact body that help it run through underbrush. The dachshund has short legs and a long body that can fit into the burrows of animals such as badgers and rats.)*

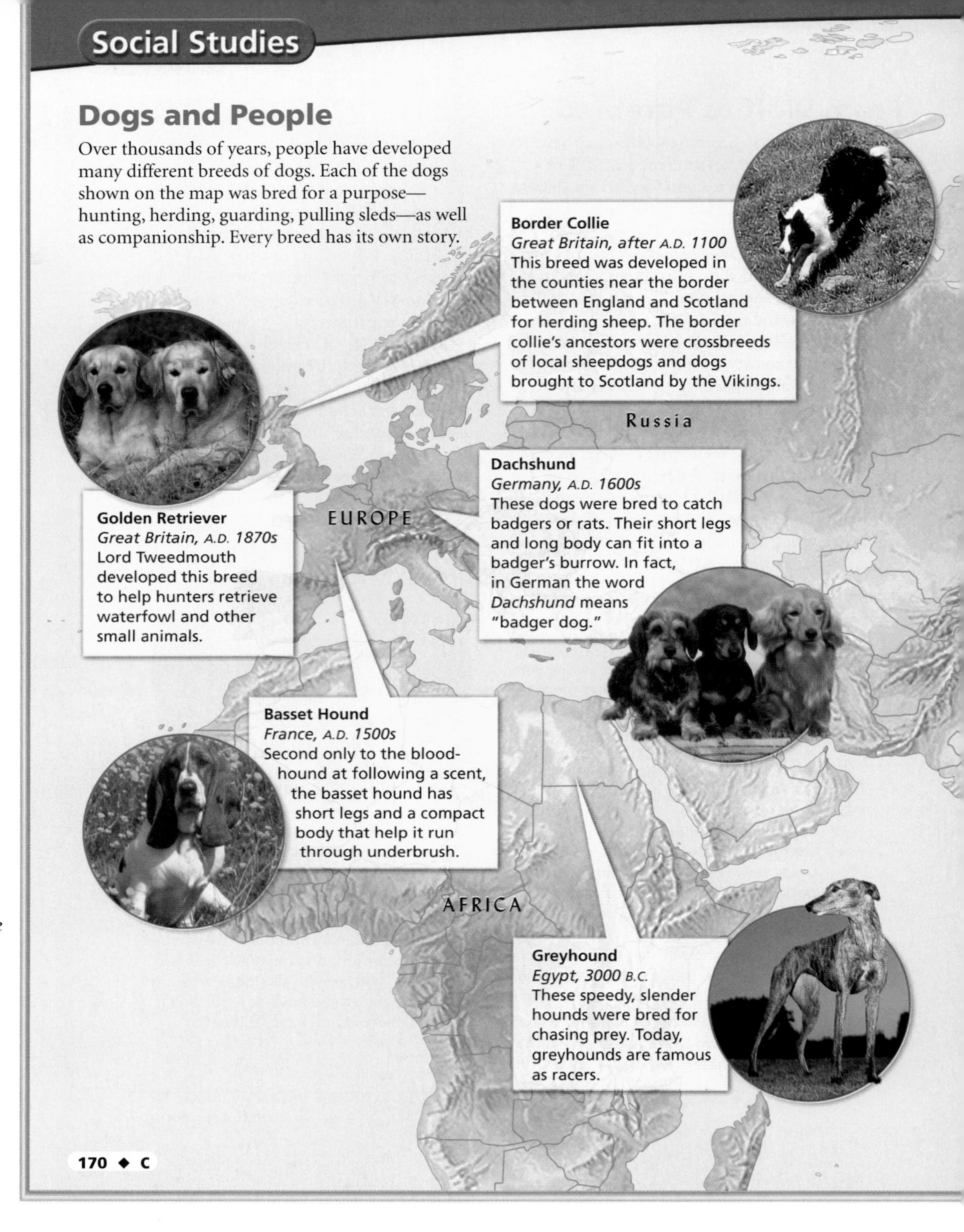

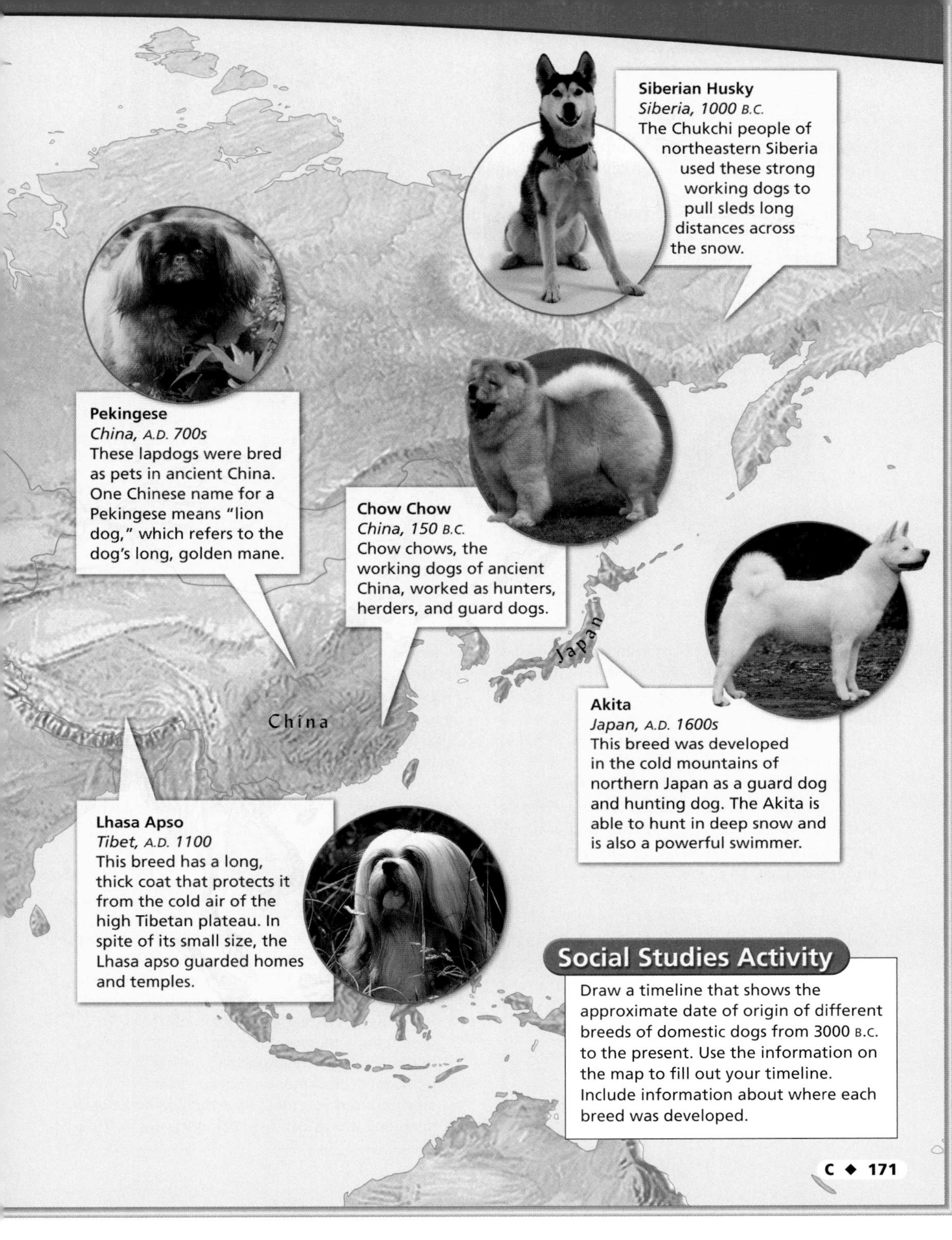

Class Activity Have students think about the impact that dogs have on our society in the United States. Have students look through the phone directory, research on the Internet, magazines, and newspapers, and think about television and radio to find examples of how much dogs are a part of people's lives. Encourage students to look for services and products such as doggie day care, dog groomers, dog sitters, dog walkers, dog food, dog snacks, dog beds, and dog seat belts. Students can make a collage out of advertisements they find in magazines and include drawings of their own to represent other services and products they discovered.

Guest Speaker Arrange for the trainer of a working dog, such as a companion animal or a police dog, to speak to the class. Encourage students to write down questions for the speaker before the presentation. Questions about how the dog is trained and a typical day "at work" are important.

Social Studies Activity

Focus Students should reorganize the material presented on the pages into a timeline.

Teach Have students read the pages carefully to determine at which date their timelines should begin. Remind students that the timeline will be similar to a number line with negative numbers. The date 3500 B.C. will be on the far left with dates progressing towards zero. The A.D. dates should increase after zero.

Expected Outcome The dates and breeds should be organized as follows: 3000 B.C. —Greyhound; 1000 B.C. —Siberian husky; 150 B.C. —Chow Chow; A.D. 700 —Pekingese; A.D. 1100 —Lhasa Apso; after A.D. 1100 —border collie; A.D. 1500s —basset hound; A.D. 1600s —Akita; A.D. 1600s —dachshund; A.D. 1870s —golden retriever.

Background

Facts and Figures Dogs are trained to help people in many different ways. Dogs can be trained to be guide dogs for people that are visually impaired. They can be companion animals for hearing-impaired people or people who are physically challenged. Dogs are used by the police to search for both perpetrators and victims of crimes. Police dogs can be trained to respond to the smell of drugs or money and used in airports or at border patrols. Some dogs are trained as rescue dogs to search for disaster victims such as after an earthquake or an avalanche. Some dogs work pulling sleds or herding sheep or cattle. Dogs are also used as part of therapy for autistic children or people confined to a hospital or nursing home.

Language Arts

Explore Language Arts Concepts

Discuss James Herriot's writing was descriptive. He uses adjectives, adverbs, and descriptive phrases to bring the reader to a faraway scene. Ask: **How do you think his wife feels in the first paragraph of the story?** *(She is excited, possibly frustrated and worried about losing the dog. She is frustrated and in a rush because her husband has been gone so long.)* **How do you know this?** *(Herriot uses the adverb "agitatedly" to describe his wife's tone of voice. She scolds him by saying, "What a long time you've been out there," and he uses an exclamation point at the end of her statement.)* **What words and phrases does he use to describe the puppy?** *(tiny, brindle, twisting, writhing, tail wagging furiously, pink tongue)* **Would you infer that the puppy's mother and grandmother had a lot of energy or that they were lethargic dogs? Why?** *(They had lots of energy. The dogs "darted out and stood up at our legs, tails lashing, mouths panting in delight.")*

Oral Presentation Bring in several of James Herriot's books. Have students take turns reading aloud from the books to the class. Ask: **How does Herriot's writing transport the reader to the scene? How does reading his stories make you feel?**

Language Arts Activity

Focus Have students identify an event they would like to write about. Have them take a few minutes to quietly recall the event and their feelings surrounding it.

Teach Encourage students to use vivid adjectives to describe the event and their feelings.

Scoring Rubric

4 Includes detailed description of event, including their emotions at the time, how they made a decision; correctly punctuated dialog and well-constructed paragraphs

3 Includes all criteria but details are somewhat sketchy; writing style is good

2 Includes some criteria; writing style is minimally acceptable

1 Includes few details; poorly written

Picking a Puppy

People look for different traits in the dogs they choose. Here is how one expert selected his dog based on good breeding and personality.

James Herriot, a country veterinarian in Yorkshire, England, had owned several dogs during his lifetime. But he had always wanted a Border terrier. These small, sturdy dogs are descendants of working terrier breeds that lived on the border of England and Scotland. For centuries they were used to hunt foxes, rats, and other small animals. In this story, Herriot and his wife, Helen, follow up on an advertisement for Border terrier puppies.

James Herriot
In several popular books published in the 1970s and 1980s, James Herriot wrote warm, humorous stories about the animals he cared for.

◀ **Border terriers**

She [Helen, his wife] turned to me and spoke agitatedly, "I've got Mrs. Mason on the line now. There's only one pup left out of the litter and there are people coming from as far as eighty miles away to see it. We'll have to hurry. What a long time you've been out there!"

We bolted our lunch and Helen, Rosie, granddaughter Emma and I drove out to Bedale. Mrs. Mason led us into the kitchen and pointed to a tiny brindle creature twisting and writhing under the table.

"That's him," she said.

I reached down and lifted the puppy as he curled his little body round, apparently trying to touch his tail with his nose. But that tail wagged furiously and the pink tongue was busy at my hand. I knew he was ours before my quick examination for hernia and overshot jaw.

The deal was quickly struck and we went outside to inspect the puppy's relations. His mother and grandmother were out there. They lived in little barrels which served as kennels and both of them darted out and stood up at our legs, tails lashing, mouths panting in delight. I felt vastly reassured. With happy, healthy ancestors like those I knew we had every chance of a first rate dog.

As we drove home with the puppy in Emma's arms, the warm thought came to me. The wheel had indeed turned. After nearly fifty years I had my Border terrier.

Language Arts Activity

James Herriot describes this scene using dialog and first-person narrative. The narrative describes Herriot's feelings about a memorable event—finally finding the dog he had wanted for so long. Write a first-person narrative describing a memorable event in your life. You might choose a childhood memory or a personal achievement at school. What emotions did you feel? How did you make your decision? If possible, use dialog in your writing.

Background

Facts and Figures James Alfred Wight (1916–1995) wrote under the pseudonym James Herriot. Born in England, but raised in Scotland, Wight graduated from Glasgow Veterinary College in 1939. He established his veterinary practice in England, where he lived for the remainder of his life. Wight wrote books about his experiences as a vet in the English countryside. Works such as *All Creatures Great and Small* and *All Things Bright and Beautiful* relay tales of his animal care in a small, quiet English town. His books were made into a television series in England in the late 1970s. Wight also published several children's books. In 2001, his son, Jim Wight, published a biography about his father entitled *The Real James Herriot: A Memoir to My Father.*

Popular Breeds

The popularity of different breeds of dogs changes over time. For example, the line graph shows how the number of poodles registered with the American Kennel Club changed between 1970 and 2000.

Standard poodle and puppy ▶

Math Activity

Use the table below to create your own line graph for Labrador retrievers and cocker spaniels. Which breed was more popular in 1980, Labrador retrievers or cocker spaniels?

How has the number of Labrador retrievers changed from 1970 to 2000? How has the number of cocker spaniels changed over the same time?

Dog Populations

Breed	1970	1980	1990	2000
Poodle	265,879	92,250	71,757	43,868
Labrador Retriever	25,667	52,398	99,776	172,841
Cocker Spaniel	21,811	76,113	105,642	29,393

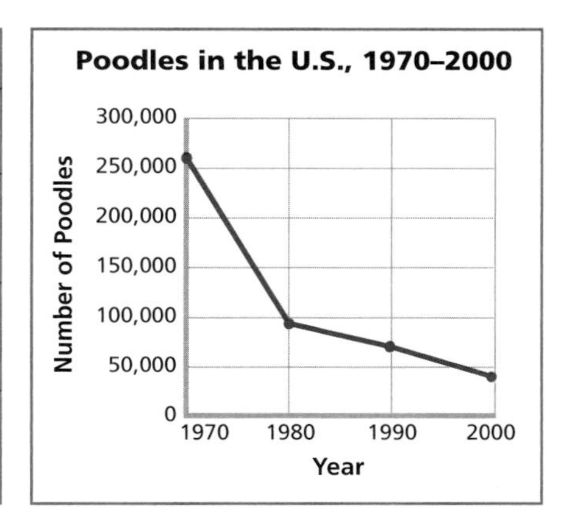

Tie It Together

Best-of-Breed Show

In many places, proud dog owners of all ages bring their animals to compete in dog shows.

Organize your own dog show.

With a partner, choose one specific breed of dog. Pick a breed shown on the map on pages 170–171, or use library resources to research another breed.

- Find out what the breed looks like, the time and place where it originated, and what traits it was first bred for.
- List your breed's characteristics, height, weight, and coloring.
- Research the breed's personality and behavior.
- Find out your breed's strengths. Learn what weaknesses may develop as a result of inbreeding.
- Make a poster for your breed. Include a drawing or photo and the information that you researched.
- With your class, organize the dog displays into categories of breeds, such as hunting dogs, herding dogs, and toy dogs.

Mathematics

Explore Mathematics Concepts

Discuss Encourage students to describe how a graph can successfully picture information from a data table. They can use the information about poodles in the table and graph to illustrate their point.

Math Activity

Focus Remind students to plot the year on the horizontal axis and the number of dogs on the vertical axis. Students can use the graph on this page as a model.

Teach Students can put both sets of data on one graph by using a different color pencil for each. Remind them to make a key for the graph if they choose to do this.

Expected Outcome Check students' graphs for appropriate titles and accurate labeling of axes. Answers: In 1980, cocker spaniels were more popular; the number of Labrador retrievers increased from 1970 to 2000; the number of cocker spaniels increased until 1990, and then significantly decreased by 2000.

Tie It Together

Best-of-Breed Show

Time 3 class periods (1 for research, 1 for designing and making the posters, 1 to organize the display of posters)

Tips Have students work in groups of two. Provide students with examples of dogs from each of the seven categories of dogs: terrier, working, sporting, hound, herding, toy, and nonsporting. Once students have chosen which dog they would like to research, review with students the information they need to complete the assignment.
- Check with each group to make sure no breed of dog is repeated. Make sure that at least one breed from each of the seven categories is represented.
- Provide students with poster board, colored markers, construction paper, and other materials they might need to make their posters.
- Students may be able to use computer graphics to design parts of their posters.
- If possible, have students make color copies of the photos for their posters.

Think Like a Scientist

The Skills Handbook is designed as a reference for students to use whenever they need to review inquiry, reading, or math skills. You can use the activities in this part of the Skills Handbook to teach or reinforce inquiry skills.

Observing

Focus Remind students that an observation is what they can see, hear, smell, taste, or feel.

Teach Invite students to make observations of the classroom. List these observations on the board. Challenge students to identify the senses they used to make each observation. Then, ask: **Which senses will you use to make observations from the photograph on this page?** *(Sight is the only sense that can be used to make observations from the photograph.)*

Activity

Some observations that students might make include that the boy is skateboarding, wearing a white helmet, and flying in the air. Make sure that students' observations are confined to only things that they can actually see in the photograph.

Inferring

Focus Choose one or two of the classroom observations listed on the board, and challenge students to interpret them. Guide students by asking why something appears as it does.

Teach Encourage students to describe their thought processes in making their inferences. Point out where they used their knowledge and experience to interpret the observations. Then invite students to suggest other possible interpretations for the observations. Ask: **How can you find out whether an inference is correct?** *(By further investigation)*

Activity

One possible inference is that the boy just skated off a ramp at a skate park. Invite students to share their experiences that helped them make the inference.

Predicting

Focus Discuss the weather forecast for the next day. Point out that this prediction is an inference about what will happen in the future based on observations and experience.

Teach Help students differentiate between a prediction and an inference. You might organize the similarities and differences in a Venn diagram on the board. Both are interpretations of observations using experience and knowledge, and both can be incorrect. Inferences describe current or past events. Predictions describe future events.

Activity

Students might predict that the boy will land and skate to the other side. Others might predict that the boy will fall. Students should also describe the evidence or experience on which they based their predictions.

SKILLS Handbook

Think Like a Scientist

Scientists have a particular way of looking at the world, or scientific habits of mind. Whenever you ask a question and explore possible answers, you use many of the same skills that scientists do. Some of these skills are described on this page.

Observing

When you use one or more of your five senses to gather information about the world, you are **observing.** Hearing a dog bark, counting twelve green seeds, and smelling smoke are all observations. To increase the power of their senses, scientists sometimes use microscopes, telescopes, or other instruments that help them make more detailed observations.

An observation must be an accurate report of what your senses detect. It is important to keep careful records of your observations in science class by writing or drawing in a notebook. The information collected through observations is called evidence, or data.

Inferring

When you interpret an observation, you are **inferring,** or making an inference. For example, if you hear your dog barking, you may infer that someone is at your front door. To make this inference, you combine the evidence—the barking dog—and your experience or knowledge—you know that your dog barks when strangers approach—to reach a logical conclusion.

Notice that an inference is not a fact; it is only one of many possible interpretations for an observation. For example, your dog may be barking because it wants to go for a walk. An inference may turn out to be incorrect even if it is based on accurate observations and logical reasoning. The only way to find out if an inference is correct is to investigate further.

Predicting

When you listen to the weather forecast, you hear many predictions about the next day's weather—what the temperature will be, whether it will rain, and how windy it will be. Weather forecasters use observations and knowledge of weather patterns to predict the weather. The skill of **predicting** involves making an inference about a future event based on current evidence or past experience.

Because a prediction is an inference, it may prove to be false. In science class, you can test some of your predictions by doing experiments. For example, suppose you predict that larger paper airplanes can fly farther than smaller airplanes. How could you test your prediction?

Activity

Use the photograph to answer the questions below.

Observing Look closely at the photograph. List at least three observations.

Inferring Use your observations to make an inference about what has happened. What experience or knowledge did you use to make the inference?

Predicting Predict what will happen next. On what evidence or experience do you base your prediction?

Classifying

Could you imagine searching for a book in the library if the books were shelved in no particular order? Your trip to the library would be an all-day event! Luckily, librarians group together books on similar topics or by the same author. Grouping together items that are alike in some way is called **classifying.** You can classify items in many ways: by size, by shape, by use, and by other important characteristics.

Like librarians, scientists use the skill of classifying to organize information and objects. When things are sorted into groups, the relationships among them become easier to understand.

Activity

Classify the objects in the photograph into two groups based on any characteristic you choose. Then use another characteristic to classify the objects into three groups.

Activity

This student is using a model to demonstrate what causes day and night on Earth. What do the flashlight and the tennis ball in the model represent?

Making Models

Have you ever drawn a picture to help someone understand what you were saying? Such a drawing is one type of model. A model is a picture, diagram, computer image, or other representation of a complex object or process. **Making models** helps people understand things that they cannot observe directly.

Scientists often use models to represent things that are either very large or very small, such as the planets in the solar system, or the parts of a cell. Such models are physical models—drawings or three-dimensional structures that look like the real thing. Other models are mental models—mathematical equations or words that describe how something works.

Communicating

Whenever you talk on the phone, write a report, or listen to your teacher at school, you are communicating. **Communicating** is the process of sharing ideas and information with other people. Communicating effectively requires many skills, including writing, reading, speaking, listening, and making models.

Scientists communicate to share results, information, and opinions. Scientists often communicate about their work in journals, over the telephone, in letters, and on the Internet. They also attend scientific meetings where they share their ideas with one another in person.

Activity

On a sheet of paper, write out clear, detailed directions for tying your shoe. Then exchange directions with a partner. Follow your partner's directions exactly. How successful were you at tying your shoe? How could your partner have communicated more clearly?

Inquiry Skills

Classifying

Focus Encourage students to think of common things that are classified.

Teach Ask: **What things at home are classified?** *(Clothing might be classified in order to place it in the appropriate dresser drawer; glasses, plates, and silverware are grouped in different parts of the kitchen; screws, nuts, bolts, washers, and nails might be separated into small containers.)* **What are some things that scientists classify?** *(Scientists classify many things they study, including organisms, geological features and processes, and kinds of machines.)*

Activity

Some characteristics students might use include color, pattern of color, use of balls, and size. Students' criteria for classification should clearly divide the balls into two, and then three, distinct groups.

Making Models

Focus Ask: **What are some models you have used to study science?** *(Students might have used human anatomical models, solar system models, maps, or stream tables.)* **How have these models helped you?** *(Models can help you learn about things that are difficult to study because they are very large, very small, or highly complex.)*

Teach Be sure students understand that a model does not have to be three-dimensional. For example, a map is a model, as is a mathematical equation. Have students look at the photograph of the student modeling the causes of day and night on Earth. Ask: **What quality of each item makes this a good model?** *(The flashlight gives off light, and the ball is round and can be rotated by the student.)*

Activity

The flashlight represents the sun and the ball represents Earth.

Communicating

Focus Have students identify the methods of communication they have used today.

Teach Ask: **How is the way you communicate with a friend similar to and different from the way scientists communicate about their work to other scientists?** *(Both may communicate using various methods, but scientists must be very detailed and precise, whereas communication between friends may be less detailed and precise.)* Encourage students to communicate like a scientist as they carry out the activity.

Activity

Students' answers will vary but should identify a step-by-step process for tying a shoe. Help students identify communication errors such as leaving out a step, putting steps in the wrong order, or disregarding the person's handedness.

Making Measurements

Students can refer to this part of the Skills Handbook whenever they need to review how to make measurements with SI units. You can use the activities here to teach or reinforce SI units.

Measuring in SI

Focus Review SI units with students. Begin by providing metric rulers, graduated cylinders, balances, and Celsius thermometers. Use these tools to reinforce that the meter is the unit of length, the liter is the unit of volume, the gram is the unit of mass, and the degree Celsius is the unit of temperature.

Teach Ask: **If you want to measure the length and the width of the classroom, which SI unit would you use?** *(Meter)* **Which unit would you use to measure the amount of mass in your textbook?** *(Gram)* **Which would you use to measure how much water a drinking glass holds?** *(Liter)* **When would you use the Celsius scale?** *(To measure the temperature of something)* Then use the measuring equipment to review SI prefixes. For example, ask: **What are the smallest units on the metric ruler?** *(Millimeters)* **How many millimeters are there in one centimeter?** *(10 millimeters)* **How many in 10 centimeters?** *(100 millimeters)* **How many centimeters are there in one meter?** *(100 centimeters)* **What does 1,000 meters equal?** *(One kilometer)*

Activity

Length The length of the shell is 7.8 centimeters, or 78 millimeters. If students need more practice measuring length, have them use meter sticks and metric rulers to measure various objects in the classroom.

Activity

Liquid Volume The volume of water in the graduated cylinder is 62 milliliters. If students need more practice, have them use a graduated cylinder to measure different volumes of water.

Making Measurements

By measuring, scientists can express their observations more precisely and communicate more information about what they observe.

Measuring in SI

The standard system of measurement used by scientists around the world is known as the International System of Units, which is abbreviated as SI (**Système International d'Unités,** in French). SI units are easy to use because they are based on multiples of 10. Each unit is ten times larger than the next smallest unit and one tenth the size of the next largest unit. The table lists the prefixes used to name the most common SI units.

Common SI Prefixes		
Prefix	**Symbol**	**Meaning**
kilo-	k	1,000
hecto-	h	100
deka-	da	10
deci-	d	0.1 (one tenth)
centi-	c	0.01 (one hundredth)
milli-	m	0.001 (one thousandth)

Length To measure length, or the distance between two points, the unit of measure is the **meter (m).** The distance from the floor to a doorknob is approximately one meter. Long distances, such as the distance between two cities, are measured in kilometers (km). Small lengths are measured in centimeters (cm) or millimeters (mm). Scientists use metric rulers and meter sticks to measure length.

Common Conversions		
1 km	=	1,000 m
1 m	=	100 cm
1 m	=	1,000 mm
1 cm	=	10 mm

Activity

The larger lines on the metric ruler in the picture show centimeter divisions, while the smaller, unnumbered lines show millimeter divisions. How many centimeters long is the shell? How many millimeters long is it?

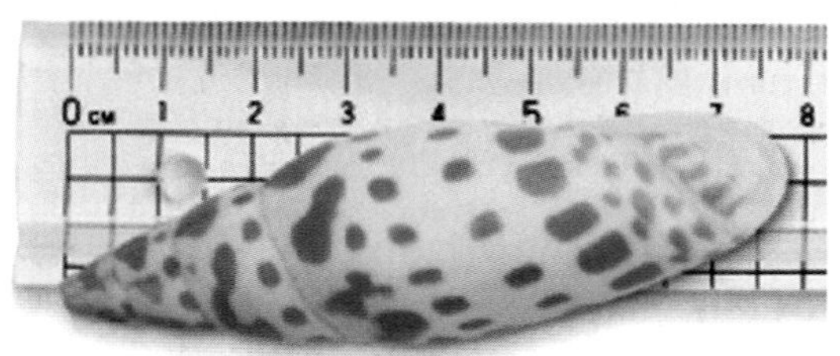

Liquid Volume To measure the volume of a liquid, or the amount of space it takes up, you will use a unit of measure known as the **liter (L).** One liter is the approximate volume of a medium-size carton of milk. Smaller volumes are measured in milliliters (mL). Scientists use graduated cylinders to measure liquid volume.

Activity

The graduated cylinder in the picture is marked in milliliter divisions. Notice that the water in the cylinder has a curved surface. This curved surface is called the *meniscus*. To measure the volume, you must read the level at the lowest point of the meniscus. What is the volume of water in this graduated cylinder?

Common Conversion		
1 L	=	1,000 mL

Mass To measure mass, or the amount of matter in an object, you will use a unit of measure known as the **gram (g).** One gram is approximately the mass of a paper clip. Larger masses are measured in kilograms (kg). Scientists use a balance to find the mass of an object.

Common Conversion
1 kg = 1,000 g

Activity

The mass of the potato in the picture is measured in kilograms. What is the mass of the potato? Suppose a recipe for potato salad called for one kilogram of potatoes. About how many potatoes would you need?

0.25 KG

Temperature To measure the temperature of a substance, you will use the **Celsius scale.** Temperature is measured in degrees Celsius (°C) using a Celsius thermometer. Water freezes at 0°C and boils at 100°C.

Time The unit scientists use to measure time is the **second (s).**

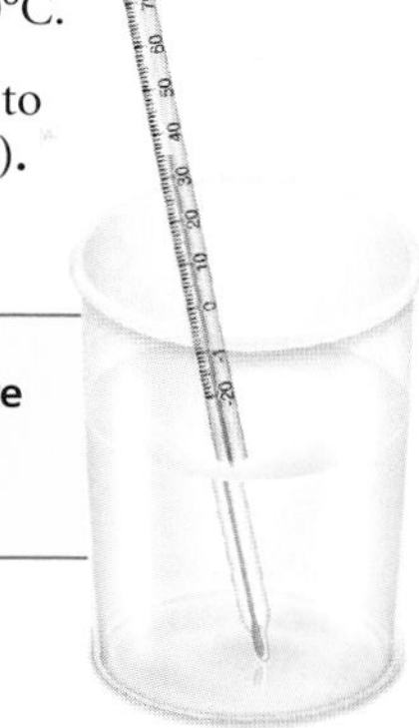

Activity

What is the temperature of the liquid in degrees Celsius?

Converting SI Units

To use the SI system, you must know how to convert between units. Converting from one unit to another involves the skill of **calculating,** or using mathematical operations. Converting between SI units is similar to converting between dollars and dimes because both systems are based on multiples of ten.

Suppose you want to convert a length of 80 centimeters to meters. Follow these steps to convert between units.

1. Begin by writing down the measurement you want to convert—in this example, 80 centimeters.
2. Write a conversion factor that represents the relationship between the two units you are converting. In this example, the relationship is 1 meter = 100 centimeters. Write this conversion factor as a fraction, making sure to place the units you are converting from (centimeters, in this example) in the denominator.
3. Multiply the measurement you want to convert by the fraction. When you do this, the units in the first measurement will cancel out with the units in the denominator. Your answer will be in the units you are converting to (meters, in this example).

Example

80 centimeters = ■ meters

$$80 \text{ centimeters} \times \frac{1 \text{ meter}}{100 \text{ centimeters}} = \frac{80 \text{ meters}}{100}$$

$$= 0.8 \text{ meters}$$

Activity

Convert between the following units.

1. 600 millimeters = ■ meters
2. 0.35 liters = ■ milliliters
3. 1,050 grams = ■ kilograms

Activity

Mass The mass of the potato is 0.25 kilograms. You would need 4 potatoes to make one kilogram. If students need more practice, give them various objects, such as coins, paper clips, and books, to measure mass.

Activity

Temperature The temperature of the liquid is 35°C. Students who need more practice can measure the temperatures of various water samples.

Converting SI Units

Focus Review the steps for converting SI units, and work through the example with students.

Teach Ask: **How many millimeters are in 80 centimeters?** *(With the relationship 10 millimeters = 1 centimeter, students should follow the steps to calculate that 80 centimeters is equal to 800 millimeters.)* Have students do the conversion problems in the activity.

Activity

1. *600 millimeters = 0.6 meters*
2. *0.35 liters = 350 milliliters*
3. *1,050 grams = 1.05 kilograms*

If students need more practice converting SI units, have them make up conversion problems to trade with partners.

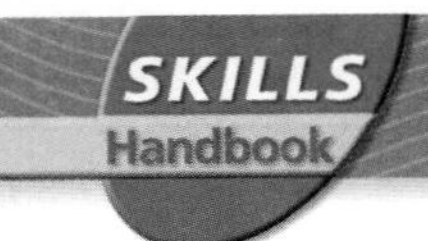

Conducting a Scientific Investigation

Students can refer to this part of the Skills Handbook whenever they need to review the steps of a scientific investigation. You can use the activities here to teach or reinforce these steps.

Posing Questions

Focus Ask: **What do you do when you want to learn about something?** *(Answers might include asking questions about it or looking for information in books or on the Internet.)* Explain that scientists go through the same process to learn about something.

Teach Tell students that the questions scientists ask may have no answers or many different answers. To answer their questions, scientists often conduct experiments. Ask: **Why is a scientific question important to a scientific investigation?** *(It helps the scientist decide if an experiment is necessary; the answer might already be known. It also helps focus the idea so that the scientist can form a hypothesis.)* **What is the scientific question in the activity on the next page?** *(Is a ball's bounce affected by the height from which it is dropped?)*

Developing a Hypothesis

Focus Emphasize that a hypothesis is one possible explanation for a set of observations. It is *not* a guess. It is often based on an inference.

Teach Ask: **On what information do scientists base their hypotheses?** *(Their observations and previous knowledge or experience)* Point out that a hypothesis does not always turn out to be correct. Ask: **When a hypothesis turns out to be incorrect, do you think the scientist wasted his or her time? Explain.** *(No. The scientist learned from the investigation and will develop another hypothesis that could prove to be correct.)*

Designing an Experiment

Focus Have a volunteer read the Experimental Procedure in the box. Invite students to identify the manipulated variable *(amount of salt)*, the variables kept constant *(amount and temperature of water, location of containers)*, the control *(Container 3)*, and the responding variable *(time required for the water to freeze)*.

Conducting a Scientific Investigation

In some ways, scientists are like detectives, piecing together clues to learn about a process or event. One way that scientists gather clues is by carrying out experiments. An experiment tests an idea in a careful, orderly manner. Although experiments do not all follow the same steps in the same order, many follow a pattern similar to the one described here.

Posing Questions

Experiments begin by asking a scientific question. A scientific question is one that can be answered by gathering evidence. For example, the question "Which freezes faster—fresh water or salt water?" is a scientific question because you can carry out an investigation and gather information to answer the question.

Developing a Hypothesis

The next step is to form a hypothesis. A **hypothesis** is a possible explanation for a set of observations or answer to a scientific question. In science, a hypothesis must be something that can be tested. A hypothesis can be worded as an *If . . . then . . .* statement. For example, a hypothesis might be *"If I add salt to fresh water, then the water will take longer to freeze."* A hypothesis worded this way serves as a rough outline of the experiment you should perform.

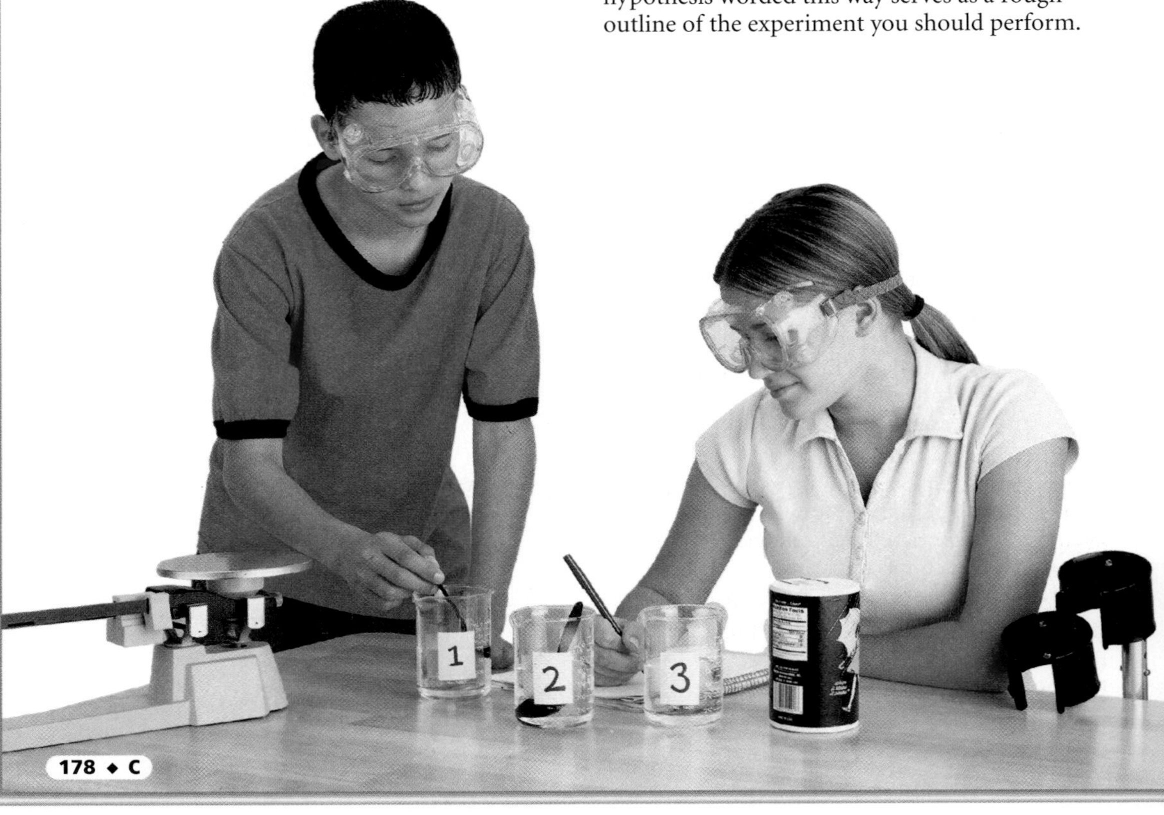

178 ◆ C

Teach Ask: **How might the experiment be affected if Container 1 had only 100 milliliters of water?** *(It wouldn't be an accurate comparison with the containers that have more water.)* Also make sure that students understand the importance of the control. Then, ask: **What operational definition is used in this experiment?** *("Frozen" means the time at which a wooden stick can no longer move in a container.)*

Designing an Experiment

Next you need to plan a way to test your hypothesis. Your plan should be written out as a step-by-step procedure and should describe the observations or measurements you will make.

Two important steps involved in designing an experiment are controlling variables and forming operational definitions.

Controlling Variables In a well-designed experiment, you need to keep all variables the same except for one. A **variable** is any factor that can change in an experiment. The factor that you change is called the **manipulated variable**. In this experiment, the manipulated variable is the amount of salt added to the water. Other factors, such as the amount of water or the starting temperature, are kept constant.

The factor that changes as a result of the manipulated variable is called the **responding variable.** The responding variable is what you measure or observe to obtain your results. In this experiment, the responding variable is how long the water takes to freeze.

An experiment in which all factors except one are kept constant is called a **controlled experiment.** Most controlled experiments include a test called the control. In this experiment, Container 3 is the control. Because no salt is added to Container 3, you can compare the results from the other containers to it. Any difference in results must be due to the addition of salt alone.

Forming Operational Definitions Another important aspect of a well-designed experiment is having clear operational definitions. An **operational definition** is a statement that describes how a particular variable is to be measured or how a term is to be defined. For example, in this experiment, how will you determine if the water has frozen? You might decide to insert a stick in each container at the start of the experiment. Your operational definition of "frozen" would be the time at which the stick can no longer move.

Experimental Procedure

1. Fill 3 containers with 300 milliliters of cold tap water.
2. Add 10 grams of salt to Container 1; stir.
   Add 20 grams of salt to Container 2; stir.
   Add no salt to Container 3.
3. Place the 3 containers in a freezer.
4. Check the containers every 15 minutes.
   Record your observations.

Interpreting Data

The observations and measurements you make in an experiment are called **data.** At the end of an experiment, you need to analyze the data to look for any patterns or trends. Patterns often become clear if you organize your data in a data table or graph. Then think through what the data reveal. Do they support your hypothesis? Do they point out a flaw in your experiment? Do you need to collect more data?

Drawing Conclusions

A **conclusion** is a statement that sums up what you have learned from an experiment. When you draw a conclusion, you need to decide whether the data you collected support your hypothesis or not. You may need to repeat an experiment several times before you can draw any conclusions from it. Conclusions often lead you to pose new questions and plan new experiments to answer them.

Activity

Is a ball's bounce affected by the height from which it is dropped? Using the steps just described, plan a controlled experiment to investigate this problem.

Interpreting Data

Focus Ask: **What kind of data would you collect from the experiment with freezing salt water?** *(Time and state of the water)*

Teach Ask: **What if you forgot to record some data during an investigation?** *(You wouldn't be able to draw valid conclusions because some data are missing.)* Then, ask: **Why are data tables and graphs a good way to organize data?** *(They make it easier to record data accurately, as well as compare and analyze data.)* **What kind of data table and graph might you use for this experiment?** *(A table would have columns for each container with a row for each time interval in which the state of water is recorded. A bar graph would show the time elapsed until water froze for each container.)*

Drawing Conclusions

Focus Help students understand that a conclusion is not necessarily the end of a scientific investigation. A conclusion about one experiment may lead right into another experiment.

Teach Point out that in scientific investigations, a conclusion is a summary and explanation of the results of an experiment. For the Experimental Procedure described on this page, tell students to suppose that they obtained the following results: Container 1 froze in 45 minutes, Container 2 in 80 minutes, and Container 3 in 25 minutes. Ask: **What conclusions can you draw from this experiment?** *(Students might conclude that water takes longer to freeze as more salt is added to it. The hypothesis is supported, and the question of which freezes faster is answered—fresh water.)*

Activity

You might wish to have students work in pairs to plan the controlled experiment. Students should develop a hypothesis, such as, "If I increase the height from which a ball is dropped, then the height of its bounce will increase." They can test the hypothesis by dropping a ball from varying heights (the manipulated variable). All trials should be done with the same kind of ball and on the same surface (constants). For each trial, they should measure the height of the bounce (responding variable). After students have designed the experiment, provide rubber balls, and invite them to carry out the experiment so they can collect and interpret data and draw conclusions.

SKILLS Handbook

Technology Design Skills

Students can refer to this part of the Skills Handbook whenever they need to review the process of designing new technologies. You can use the activities here to teach or reinforce the steps in this process.

Identify a Need

Focus Solicit from students any situations in which they have thought that a tool, machine, or other object would be really helpful to them or others. Explain that this is the first step in the design of new products.

Teach Point out that identifying specific needs is very important to the design process. Ask: **If it was specified that the toy boat be wind-powered, how might that affect the design?** *(The boat would likely be designed with sails.)*

Research the Problem

Focus Explain that research focuses the problem so that the design is more specific.

Teach Ask: **What might happen if you didn't research the problem before designing the solution?** *(Answers include developing a design that has already been found to fail, using materials that aren't the best, or designing a solution that already exists.)* **What would you research before designing your toy boat?** *(Students might research designs and materials.)*

Design a Solution

Focus Emphasize the importance of a design team. Ask: **Why are brainstorming sessions important in product design?** *(A group will propose more new ideas than one person.)*

Teach Divide the class into teams to design the toy boat. Instruct them to brainstorm design ideas. Then, ask: **Why do you think engineers evaluate constraints after brainstorming?** *(Evaluating constraints while brainstorming often stops the flow of new ideas.)* **What design constraints do you have for your toy boat?** *(Materials must be readily available and teacher-approved. The boat must be 15 centimeters or less in length and must travel 2 meters in a straight line carrying a load of 20 pennies.)*

SKILLS Handbook

Technology Design Skills

Engineers are people who use scientific and technological knowledge to solve practical problems. To design new products, engineers usually follow the process described here, even though they may not follow these steps in the exact order. As you read the steps, think about how you might apply them in technology labs.

Identify a Need

Before engineers begin designing a new product, they must first identify the need they are trying to meet. For example, suppose you are a member of a design team in a company that makes toys. Your team has identified a need: a toy boat that is inexpensive and easy to assemble.

Research the Problem

Engineers often begin by gathering information that will help them with their new design. This research may include finding articles in books, magazines, or on the Internet. It may also include talking to other engineers who have solved similar problems. Engineers often perform experiments related to the product they want to design.

For your toy boat, you could look at toys that are similar to the one you want to design. You might do research on the Internet. You could also test some materials to see whether they will work well in a toy boat.

Drawing for a boat design ▼

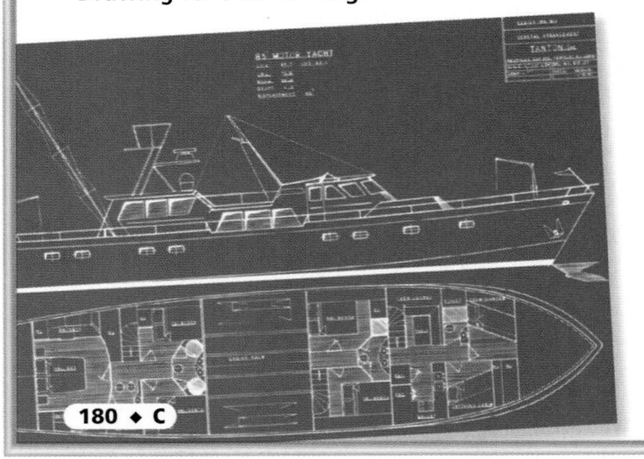

Design a Solution

Research gives engineers information that helps them design a product. When engineers design new products, they usually work in teams.

Generating Ideas Often design teams hold brainstorming meetings in which any team member can contribute ideas. **Brainstorming** is a creative process in which one team member's suggestions often spark ideas in other group members. Brainstorming can lead to new approaches to solving a design problem.

Evaluating Constraints During brainstorming, a design team will often come up with several possible designs. The team must then evaluate each one.

As part of their evaluation, engineers consider constraints. **Constraints** are factors that limit or restrict a product design. Physical characteristics, such as the properties of materials used to make your toy boat, are constraints. Money and time are also constraints. If the materials in a product cost a lot, or if the product takes a long time to make, the design may be impractical.

Making Trade-offs Design teams usually need to make trade-offs. In a **trade-off,** engineers give up one benefit of a proposed design in order to obtain another. In designing your toy boat, you will have to make trade-offs. For example, suppose one material is sturdy but not fully waterproof. Another material is more waterproof, but breakable. You may decide to give up the benefit of sturdiness in order to obtain the benefit of waterproofing.

Build and Evaluate a Prototype

Once the team has chosen a design plan, the engineers build a prototype of the product. A **prototype** is a working model used to test a design. Engineers evaluate the prototype to see whether it works well, is easy to operate, is safe to use, and holds up to repeated use.

Think of your toy boat. What would the prototype be like? Of what materials would it be made? How would you test it?

Troubleshoot and Redesign

Few prototypes work perfectly, which is why they need to be tested. Once a design team has tested a prototype, the members analyze the results and identify any problems. The team then tries to **troubleshoot,** or fix the design problems. For example, if your toy boat leaks or wobbles, the boat should be redesigned to eliminate those problems.

Communicate the Solution

A team needs to communicate the final design to the people who will manufacture and use the product. To do this, teams may use sketches, detailed drawings, computer simulations, and word descriptions.

Activity

You can use the technology design process to design and build a toy boat.

Research and Investigate

1. Visit the library or go online to research toy boats.
2. Investigate how a toy boat can be powered, including wind, rubber bands, or baking soda and vinegar.
3. Brainstorm materials, shapes, and steering for your boat.

Design and Build

4. Based on your research, design a toy boat that
   - is made of readily available materials
   - is no larger than 15 cm long and 10 cm wide
   - includes a power system, a rudder, and an area for cargo
   - travels 2 meters in a straight line carrying a load of 20 pennies
5. Sketch your design and write a step-by-step plan for building your boat. After your teacher approves your plan, build your boat.

Evaluate and Redesign

6. Test your boat, evaluate the results, and troubleshoot any problems.
7. Based on your evaluation, redesign your toy boat so it performs better.

Activity

The design possibilities are endless. Students might use small plastic containers, wood, foil, or plastic drinking cups for the boat. Materials may also include toothpicks, straws, or small wooden dowels. Brainstorm with students the different ways in which a toy boat can be propelled. The boats may be any shape, but must be no longer than 15 centimeters.

As student groups follow the steps in the design process, have them record their sources, brainstorming ideas, and prototype design in a logbook. Also give them time to troubleshoot and redesign their boats. When students turn in their boats, they should include assembly directions with a diagram, as well as instructions for use.

Build and Evaluate a Prototype

Focus Explain that building a prototype enables engineers to test design ideas.

Teach Relate building and testing a prototype to conducting an experiment. Explain that engineers set up controlled experiments to test the prototype. Ask: **Why do you think engineers set up controlled experiments?** *(From the data, they can determine which component of the design is working and which is failing.)* **How would you test your prototype of the toy boat?** *(Answers will vary depending on the toy boat's propulsion system.)*

Troubleshoot and Redesign

Focus Make sure students know what it means to troubleshoot. If necessary, give an example. One example is a stapler that isn't working. In that case, you would check to see if it is out of staples or if the staples are jammed. Then you would fix the problem and try stapling again. If it still didn't work, you might check the position of staples and try again.

Teach Explain that engineers often are not surprised if the prototype doesn't work. Ask: **Why isn't it a failure if the prototype doesn't work?** *(Engineers learn from the problems and make changes to address the problems. This process makes the design better.)* Emphasize that prototypes are completely tested before the product is made in the factory.

Communicate the Solution

Focus Inquire whether students have ever read the instruction manual that comes with a new toy or electronic device.

Teach Emphasize the importance of good communication in the design process. Ask: **What might happen if engineers did not communicate their design ideas clearly?** *(The product might not be manufactured correctly or used properly.)*

Creating Data Tables and Graphs

Students can refer to this part of the Skills Handbook whenever they need to review the skills required to create data tables and graphs. You can use the activities provided here to teach or reinforce these skills.

Data Tables

Focus Emphasize the importance of organizing data. Ask: **What might happen if you didn't use a data table for an experiment?** *(Possible answers include that data might not be collected or they might be forgotten.)*

Teach Have students create a data table to show how much time they spend on different activities during one week. Suggest that students first list the main activities they do every week. Then they should determine the amount of time they spend on each activity each day. Remind students to give the data table a title. A sample data table is shown below.

Bar Graphs

Focus Have students compare and contrast the data table and the bar graph on this page. Ask: **Why would you make a bar graph if the data are already organized in a table?** *(The bar graph organizes the data in a visual way that makes them easier to interpret.)*

Teach Students can use the data from the data table they created to make a bar graph that shows the amount of time they spend on different activities during a week. The vertical axis should be divided into units of time, such as hours. Remind students to label both axes and give their graph a title. A sample bar graph is shown below.

Creating Data Tables and Graphs

How can you make sense of the data in a science experiment? The first step is to organize the data to help you understand them. Data tables and graphs are helpful tools for organizing data.

Data Tables

You have gathered your materials and set up your experiment. But before you start, you need to plan a way to record what happens during the experiment. By creating a data table, you can record your observations and measurements in an orderly way.

Suppose, for example, that a scientist conducted an experiment to find out how many Calories people of different body masses burn while doing various activities. The data table shows the results.

Notice in this data table that the manipulated variable (body mass) is the heading of one column. The responding variable (for Experiment 1, the number of Calories burned while bicycling) is the heading of the next column. Additional columns were added for related experiments.

Calories Burned in 30 Minutes

Body Mass	Experiment 1: Bicycling	Experiment 2: Playing Basketball	Experiment 3: Watching Television
30 kg	60 Calories	120 Calories	21 Calories
40 kg	77 Calories	164 Calories	27 Calories
50 kg	95 Calories	206 Calories	33 Calories
60 kg	114 Calories	248 Calories	38 Calories

Bar Graphs

To compare how many Calories a person burns doing various activities, you could create a bar graph. A bar graph is used to display data in a number of separate, or distinct, categories. In this example, bicycling, playing basketball, and watching television are the three categories.

To create a bar graph, follow these steps.

1. On graph paper, draw a horizontal, or x-, axis and a vertical, or y-, axis.
2. Write the names of the categories to be graphed along the horizontal axis. Include an overall label for the axis as well.
3. Label the vertical axis with the name of the responding variable. Include units of measurement. Then create a scale along the axis by marking off equally spaced numbers that cover the range of the data collected.
4. For each category, draw a solid bar using the scale on the vertical axis to determine the height. Make all the bars the same width.
5. Add a title that describes the graph.

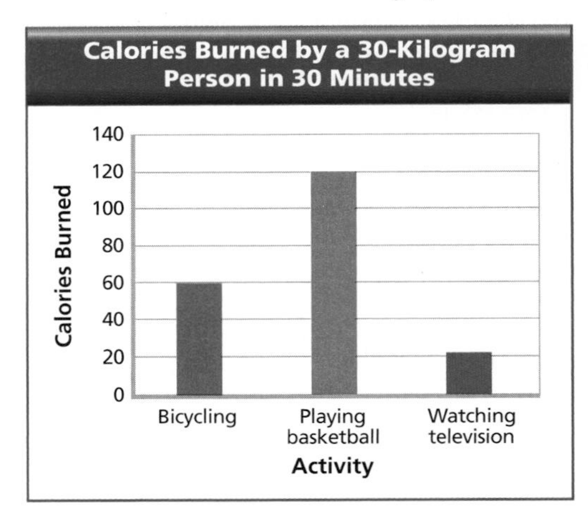

Time Spent on Different Activities in a Week

	Going to Classes	Eating Meals	Playing Soccer	Watching Television
Monday	6	2	2	0.5
Tuesday	6	1.5	1.5	1.5
Wednesday	6	2	1	2
Thursday	6	2	2	1.5
Friday	6	2	2	0.5
Saturday	0	2.5	2.5	1
Sunday	0	3	1	2

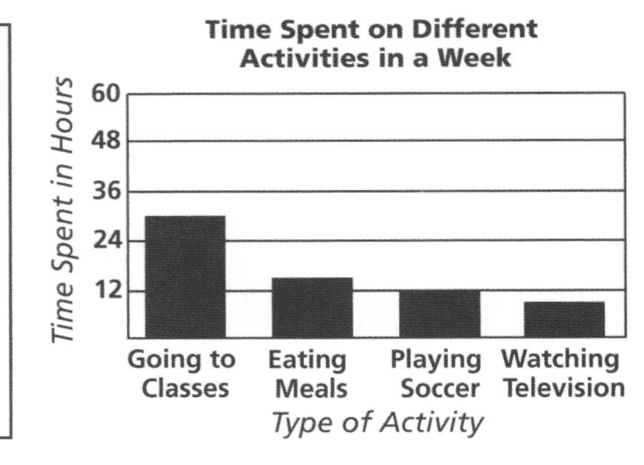

Line Graphs

To see whether a relationship exists between body mass and the number of Calories burned while bicycling, you could create a line graph. A line graph is used to display data that show how one variable (the responding variable) changes in response to another variable (the manipulated variable). You can use a line graph when your manipulated variable is **continuous,** that is, when there are other points between the ones that you tested. In this example, body mass is a continuous variable because there are other body masses between 30 and 40 kilograms (for example, 31 kilograms). Time is another example of a continuous variable.

Line graphs are powerful tools because they allow you to estimate values for conditions that you did not test in the experiment. For example, you can use the line graph to estimate that a 35-kilogram person would burn 68 Calories while bicycling.

To create a line graph, follow these steps.

1. On graph paper, draw a horizontal, or x-, axis and a vertical, or y-, axis.
2. Label the horizontal axis with the name of the manipulated variable. Label the vertical axis with the name of the responding variable. Include units of measurement.
3. Create a scale on each axis by marking off equally spaced numbers that cover the range of the data collected.
4. Plot a point on the graph for each piece of data. In the line graph above, the dotted lines show how to plot the first data point (30 kilograms and 60 Calories). Follow an imaginary vertical line extending up from the horizontal axis at the 30-kilogram mark. Then follow an imaginary horizontal line extending across from the vertical axis at the 60-Calorie mark. Plot the point where the two lines intersect.

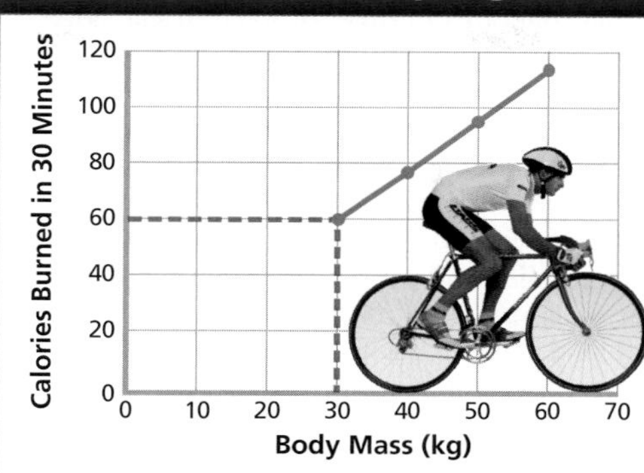

5. Connect the plotted points with a solid line. (In some cases, it may be more appropriate to draw a line that shows the general trend of the plotted points. In those cases, some of the points may fall above or below the line. Also, not all graphs are linear. It may be more appropriate to draw a curve to connect the points.)
6. Add a title that identifies the variables or relationship in the graph.

Activity

Create line graphs to display the data from Experiment 2 and Experiment 3 in the data table.

Activity

You read in the newspaper that a total of 4 centimeters of rain fell in your area in June, 2.5 centimeters fell in July, and 1.5 centimeters fell in August. What type of graph would you use to display these data? Use graph paper to create the graph.

Line Graphs

Focus Ask: **Would a bar graph show the relationship between body mass and the number of Calories burned in 30 minutes?** *(No. Bar graphs can only show data in distinct categories.)* Explain that line graphs are used to show how one variable changes in response to another variable.

Teach Walk students through the steps involved in creating a line graph using the example illustrated on the page. For example, ask: **What is the label on the horizontal axis? On the vertical axis?** *(Body Mass (kg); Calories Burned in 30 Minutes)* **What scale is used on each axis?** *(10 kg on the x-axis and 20 Calories on the y-axis)* **What does the second data point represent?** *(77 Calories burned for a body mass of 40 kg)* **What trend or pattern does the graph show?** *(The number of Calories burned in 30 minutes of cycling increases with body mass.)*

Activity

Students should make a different graph for each experiment. Each graph should have a different x-axis scale that is appropriate for the data. See sample graphs below.

Activity

Students should conclude that a bar graph would be best for displaying the data.

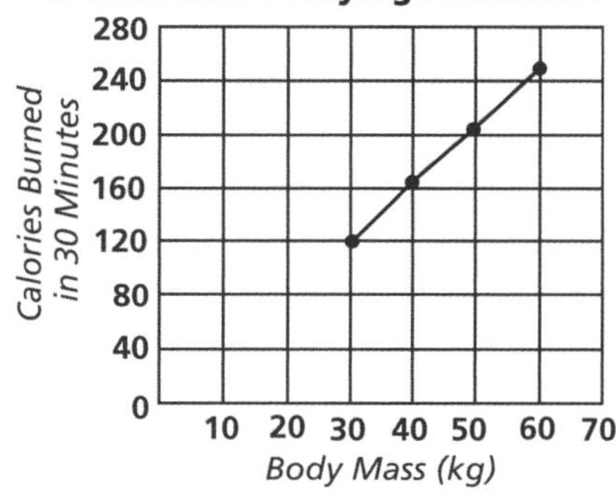

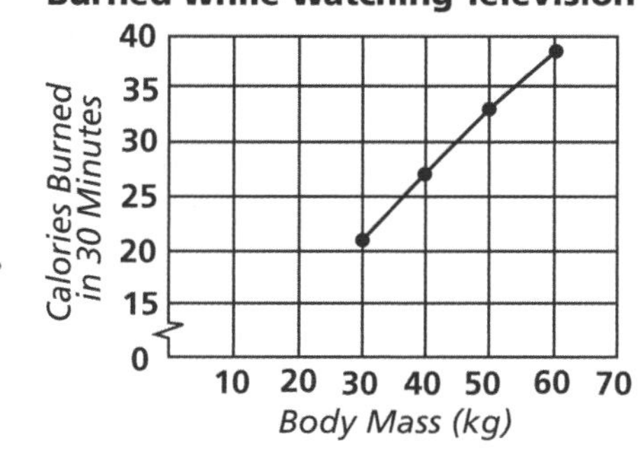

Circle Graphs

Focus Emphasize that a circle graph must include 100 percent of the categories for the topic being graphed. For example, ask: **Could the data in the bar graph titled "Calories Burned by a 30-kilogram Person in Various Activities" (on the previous page) be shown in a circle graph? Why or why not?** *(No. It does not include all the possible ways a 30-kilogram person can burn Calories.)*

Teach Walk students through the steps for making a circle graph. If necessary, help them with the compass and the protractor. Use the protractor to illustrate that a circle has 360 degrees. Make sure students understand the mathematical calculations involved in making a circle graph.

Activity

You might have students work in pairs to complete the activity. Students' circle graphs should look like the graph below.

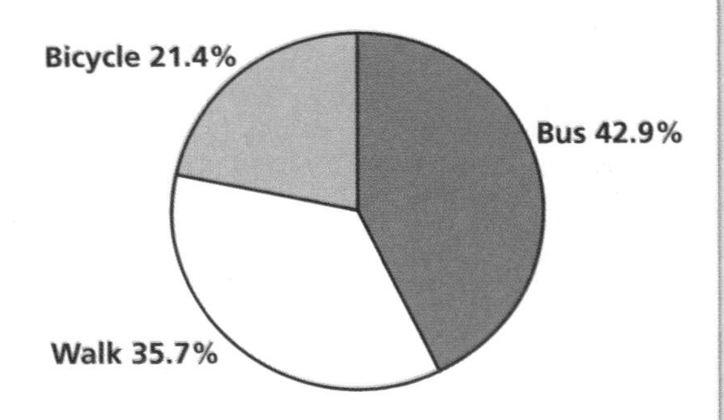

Circle Graphs

Like bar graphs, circle graphs can be used to display data in a number of separate categories. Unlike bar graphs, however, circle graphs can only be used when you have data for *all* the categories that make up a given topic. A circle graph is sometimes called a pie chart. The pie represents the entire topic, while the slices represent the individual categories. The size of a slice indicates what percentage of the whole a particular category makes up.

The data table below shows the results of a survey in which 24 teenagers were asked to identify their favorite sport. The data were then used to create the circle graph at the right.

Favorite Sports

Sport	Students
Soccer	8
Basketball	6
Bicycling	6
Swimming	4

To create a circle graph, follow these steps.

1. Use a compass to draw a circle. Mark the center with a point. Then draw a line from the center point to the top of the circle.
2. Determine the size of each "slice" by setting up a proportion where x equals the number of degrees in a slice. (*Note:* A circle contains 360 degrees.) For example, to find the number of degrees in the "soccer" slice, set up the following proportion:

$$\frac{\text{Students who prefer soccer}}{\text{Total number of students}} = \frac{x}{\text{Total number of degrees in a circle}}$$

$$\frac{8}{24} = \frac{x}{360}$$

Cross-multiply and solve for x.

$$24x = 8 \times 360$$
$$x = 120$$

The "soccer" slice should contain 120 degrees.

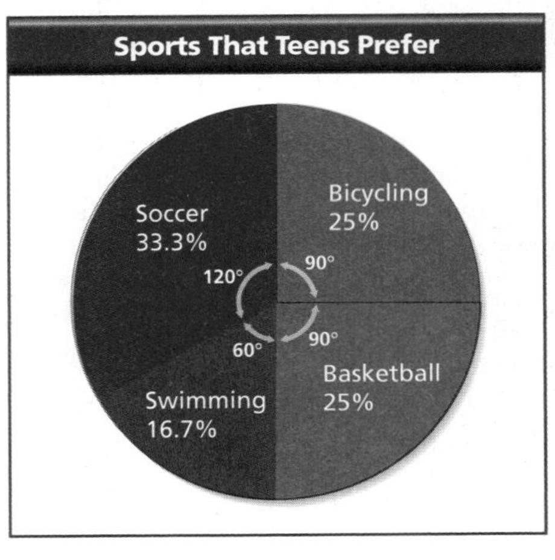

3. Use a protractor to measure the angle of the first slice, using the line you drew to the top of the circle as the 0° line. Draw a line from the center of the circle to the edge for the angle you measured.
4. Continue around the circle by measuring the size of each slice with the protractor. Start measuring from the edge of the previous slice so the wedges do not overlap. When you are done, the entire circle should be filled in.
5. Determine the percentage of the whole circle that each slice represents. To do this, divide the number of degrees in a slice by the total number of degrees in a circle (360), and multiply by 100%. For the "soccer" slice, you can find the percentage as follows:

$$\frac{120}{360} \times 100\% = 33.3\%$$

6. Use a different color for each slice. Label each slice with the category and with the percentage of the whole it represents.
7. Add a title to the circle graph.

Activity

In a class of 28 students, 12 students take the bus to school, 10 students walk, and 6 students ride their bicycles. Create a circle graph to display these data.

Math Review

Scientists use math to organize, analyze, and present data. This appendix will help you review some basic math skills.

Mean, Median, and Mode

The **mean** is the average, or the sum of the data divided by the number of data items. The middle number in a set of ordered data is called the **median.** The **mode** is the number that appears most often in a set of data.

Example

A scientist counted the number of distinct songs sung by seven different male birds and collected the data shown below.

Male Bird Songs

Bird	A	B	C	D	E	F	G
Number of Songs	36	29	40	35	28	36	27

To determine the mean number of songs, add the total number of songs and divide by the number of data items—in this case, the number of male birds.

$$\text{Mean} = \frac{231}{7} = 33 \text{ songs}$$

To find the median number of songs, arrange the data in numerical order and find the number in the middle of the series.

27 28 29 35 36 36 40

The number in the middle is 35, so the median number of songs is 35.

The mode is the value that appears most frequently. In the data, 36 appears twice, while each other item appears only once. Therefore, 36 songs is the mode.

Practice

Find out how many minutes it takes each student in your class to get to school. Then find the mean, median, and mode for the data.

Probability

Probability is the chance that an event will occur. Probability can be expressed as a ratio, a fraction, or a percentage. For example, when you flip a coin, the probability that the coin will land heads up is 1 in 2, or $\frac{1}{2}$, or 50 percent.

The probability that an event will happen can be expressed in the following formula.

$$P(\text{event}) = \frac{\text{Number of times the event can occur}}{\text{Total number of possible events}}$$

Example

A paper bag contains 25 blue marbles, 5 green marbles, 5 orange marbles, and 15 yellow marbles. If you close your eyes and pick a marble from the bag, what is the probability that it will be yellow?

$$P(\text{yellow marbles}) = \frac{15 \text{ yellow marbles}}{50 \text{ marbles total}}$$

$$P = \frac{15}{50}, \text{ or } \frac{3}{10}, \text{ or } 30\%$$

Practice

Each side of a cube has a letter on it. Two sides have *A*, three sides have *B*, and one side has *C*. If you roll the cube, what is the probability that *A* will land on top?

Math Review

Students can refer to this part of the Skills Handbook whenever they need to review some basic math skills. You can use the activities provided here to teach or reinforce these skills.

Mean, Median, and Mode

Focus Remind students that data from an experiment might consist of hundreds or thousands of numbers. Unless analyzed, the numbers likely will not be helpful.

Teach Work through the process of determining mean, median, and mode using the example in the book. Make sure students realize that these three numbers do not always equal each other. Point out that taken together, these three numbers give more information about the data than just one of the numbers alone.

Practice

Answers will vary based on class data. The mean should equal the total number of minutes divided by the number of students. The median should equal the number in the middle after arranging the data in numerical order. The mode should equal the number of minutes that is given most frequently.

Probability

Focus Show students a coin and ask: **What is the chance that I will get tails when I flip the coin?** *(Some students might know that there is a 1 in 2, or 50 percent, chance of getting tails.)*

Teach Set up a bag of marbles like the one in the example. Allow students to practice determining the probabilities of picking marbles of different colors. Then, encourage them to actually pick marbles and compare their actual results with those results predicted by probability.

Practice

$P(A) = 2$ sides with $\frac{A}{6}$ sides total

$P = \frac{2}{6}$, or $\frac{1}{3}$, or 33%

Area

Focus Ask: **Who knows what area is?** *(Area is equal to the number of square units needed to cover a certain shape or object.)* On the board, write the formulas for the area of a rectangle and a circle.

Teach Give students various objects of different shapes. Have them measure each object and determine its area based on the measurements. Point out that the units of the answer are squared because they are multiplied together. If students are interested, you might also explain that π is equal to the ratio of the circumference of a circle to its diameter. For circles of all sizes, π is approximately equal to the number 3.14, or $\frac{22}{7}$.

Practice

The area of the circle is equal to $21\text{ m} \times 21\text{ m} \times \frac{22}{7}$, or $1{,}386\text{ m}^2$.

Circumference

Focus Draw a circle on the board. Then trace the outline with your finger and explain that this is the circumference of the circle, or the distance around it.

Teach Show students that the radius is equal to the distance from the center of the circle to any point on it. Point out that the diameter of a circle is equal to two times the radius. Give students paper circles of various sizes, and have them calculate the circumference of each.

Practice

The circumference is equal to $2 \times 28\text{ m} \times \frac{22}{7}$, or 176 m.

Volume

Focus Fill a beaker with 100 milliliters of water. Ask: **What is the volume of water?** *(100 milliliters)* Explain that volume is the amount of space that something takes up. Then point out that one milliliter is equal to one cubic centimeter (cm^3).

Teach Write on the board the formulas for calculating the volumes of a rectangle and a cylinder. Point out that volume is equal to the area of an object multiplied by its height. Then measure the beaker to show students the relationship between liquid volume (100 milliliters) and the number of cubic units it contains (100 cubic centimeters).

Practice

The volume of the rectangular object is equal to $17\text{ cm} \times 11\text{ cm} \times 6\text{ cm}$, or $1{,}122\text{ cm}^3$.

Area

The **area** of a surface is the number of square units that cover it. The front cover of your textbook has an area of about 600 cm^2.

Area of a Rectangle and a Square To find the area of a rectangle, multiply its length times its width. The formula for the area of a rectangle is

$$A = \ell \times w, \text{ or } A = \ell w$$

Since all four sides of a square have the same length, the area of a square is the length of one side multiplied by itself, or squared.

$$A = s \times s, \text{ or } A = s^2$$

Example

A scientist is studying the plants in a field that measures 75 m × 45 m. What is the area of the field?

$$A = \ell \times w$$
$$A = 75\text{ m} \times 45\text{ m}$$
$$A = 3{,}375\text{ m}^2$$

Area of a Circle The formula for the area of a circle is

$$A = \pi \times r \times r, \text{ or } A = \pi r^2$$

The length of the radius is represented by r, and the value of π is approximately $\frac{22}{7}$.

Example

Find the area of a circle with a radius of 14 cm.

$$A = \pi r^2$$
$$A = 14 \times 14 \times \frac{22}{7}$$
$$A = 616\text{ cm}^2$$

Practice

Find the area of a circle that has a radius of 21 m.

Circumference

The distance around a circle is called the circumference. The formula for finding the circumference of a circle is

$$C = 2 \times \pi \times r, \text{ or } C = 2\pi r$$

Example

The radius of a circle is 35 cm. What is its circumference?

$$C = 2\pi r$$
$$C = 2 \times 35 \times \frac{22}{7}$$
$$C = 220\text{ cm}$$

Practice

What is the circumference of a circle with a radius of 28 m?

Volume

The volume of an object is the number of cubic units it contains. The volume of a wastebasket, for example, might be about $26{,}000\text{ cm}^3$.

Volume of a Rectangular Object To find the volume of a rectangular object, multiply the object's length times its width times its height.

$$V = \ell \times w \times h, \text{ or } V = \ell wh$$

Example

Find the volume of a box with length 24 cm, width 12 cm, and height 9 cm.

$$V = \ell wh$$
$$V = 24\text{ cm} \times 12\text{ cm} \times 9\text{ cm}$$
$$V = 2{,}592\text{ cm}^3$$

Practice

What is the volume of a rectangular object with length 17 cm, width 11 cm, and height 6 cm?

186 ◆ C

Fractions

A **fraction** is a way to express a part of a whole. In the fraction $\frac{4}{7}$, 4 is the numerator and 7 is the denominator.

Adding and Subtracting Fractions To add or subtract two or more fractions that have a common denominator, first add or subtract the numerators. Then write the sum or difference over the common denominator.

To find the sum or difference of fractions with different denominators, first find the least common multiple of the denominators. This is known as the least common denominator. Then convert each fraction to equivalent fractions with the least common denominator. Add or subtract the numerators. Then write the sum or difference over the common denominator.

Example

$$\frac{5}{6} - \frac{3}{4} = \frac{10}{12} - \frac{9}{12} = \frac{10 - 9}{12} = \frac{1}{12}$$

Multiplying Fractions To multiply two fractions, first multiply the two numerators, then multiply the two denominators.

Example

$$\frac{5}{6} \times \frac{2}{3} = \frac{5 \times 2}{6 \times 3} = \frac{10}{18} = \frac{5}{9}$$

Dividing Fractions Dividing by a fraction is the same as multiplying by its reciprocal. Reciprocals are numbers whose numerators and denominators have been switched. To divide one fraction by another, first invert the fraction you are dividing by—in other words, turn it upside down. Then multiply the two fractions.

Example

$$\frac{2}{5} \div \frac{7}{8} = \frac{2}{5} \times \frac{8}{7} = \frac{2 \times 8}{5 \times 7} = \frac{16}{35}$$

Practice

Solve the following: $\frac{3}{7} \div \frac{4}{5}$.

Decimals

Fractions whose denominators are 10, 100, or some other power of 10 are often expressed as decimals. For example, the fraction $\frac{9}{10}$ can be expressed as the decimal 0.9, and the fraction $\frac{7}{100}$ can be written as 0.07.

Adding and Subtracting With Decimals To add or subtract decimals, line up the decimal points before you carry out the operation.

Example

$$\begin{array}{r} 27.4 \\ +\ 6.19 \\ \hline 33.59 \end{array} \qquad \begin{array}{r} 278.635 \\ -\ 191.4 \\ \hline 87.235 \end{array}$$

Multiplying With Decimals When you multiply two numbers with decimals, the number of decimal places in the product is equal to the total number of decimal places in each number being multiplied.

Example

$$\begin{array}{rl} 46.2 & \text{(one decimal place)} \\ \times\ 2.37 & \text{(two decimal places)} \\ \hline 109.494 & \text{(three decimal places)} \end{array}$$

Dividing With Decimals To divide a decimal by a whole number, put the decimal point in the quotient above the decimal point in the dividend.

Example

$$15.5 \div 5$$

$$5\overline{)15.5} = 3.1$$

To divide a decimal by a decimal, you need to rewrite the divisor as a whole number. Do this by multiplying both the divisor and dividend by the same multiple of 10.

Example

$$1.68 \div 4.2 = 16.8 \div 42$$

$$42\overline{)16.8} = 0.4$$

Practice

Multiply 6.21 by 8.5.

Fractions

Focus Draw a circle on the board, and divide it into eight equal sections. Shade in one of the sections, and explain that one out of eight, or one eighth, of the sections is shaded. Also use the circle to show that four eighths is the same as one half.

Teach Write the fraction $\frac{3}{4}$ on the board. Ask: **What is the numerator?** *(Three)* **What is the denominator?** *(Four)* Emphasize that when adding and subtracting fractions, the denominators of the two fractions must be the same. If necessary, review how to find the least common denominator. Remind students that when multiplying and dividing, the denominators do not have to be the same.

Practice

$$\frac{3}{7} \div \frac{4}{5} = \frac{3}{7} \times \frac{5}{4} = \frac{15}{28}$$

Decimals

Focus Write the number *129.835* on the board. Ask: **What number is in the ones position?** *(9)* **The tenths position?** *(8)* **The hundredths position?** *(3)* Make sure students know that 0.8 is equal to $\frac{8}{10}$ and 0.03 is equal to $\frac{3}{100}$.

Teach Use the examples in the book to review addition, subtraction, multiplication, and division with decimals. Make up a worksheet of similar problems to give students additional practice. Also show students how a fraction is converted to a decimal by dividing the numerator by the denominator. For example, $\frac{1}{2}$ is equal to 0.5.

Practice

$6.21 \times 8.5 = 52.785$

Ratio and Proportion

Focus Differentiate a ratio from a fraction. Remind students that a fraction tells how many parts of the whole. In contrast, a ratio compares two different numbers. For example, $\frac{12}{22}$, or $\frac{6}{11}$, of a class are girls. But the ratio of boys to girls in the class is 10 to 12, or $\frac{5}{6}$.

Teach Use the example in the book to explain how to use a proportion to find an unknown quantity. Provide students with additional practice problems, if needed.

Practice

$6 \times 49 = 7x$
$294 = 7x$
$294 \div 7 = x$
$x = 42$

Percentage

Focus On the board, write $50\% = \frac{50}{100}$. Explain that a percentage is a ratio that compares a number to 100.

Teach Point out that when calculating percentages, you are usually using numbers other than 100. In this case, you set up a proportion. Go over the example in the book. Emphasize that the number representing the total goes on the bottom of the ratio, as does the 100%.

Practice

Students should set up the proportion

$$\frac{42 \text{ marbles}}{300 \text{ marbles}} = \frac{x\%}{100\%}$$

$42 \times 100 = 300x$

$4200 = 300x$

$4200 \div 300 = 14\%$

Ratio and Proportion

A **ratio** compares two numbers by division. For example, suppose a scientist counts 800 wolves and 1,200 moose on an island. The ratio of wolves to moose can be written as a fraction, $\frac{800}{1,200}$, which can be reduced to $\frac{2}{3}$. The same ratio can also be expressed as 2 to 3 or 2 : 3.

A **proportion** is a mathematical sentence saying that two ratios are equivalent. For example, a proportion could state that $\frac{800 \text{ wolves}}{1,200 \text{ moose}} = \frac{2 \text{ wolves}}{3 \text{ moose}}$. You can sometimes set up a proportion to determine or estimate an unknown quantity. For example, suppose a scientist counts 25 beetles in an area of 10 square meters. The scientist wants to estimate the number of beetles in 100 square meters.

Example

1. Express the relationship between beetles and area as a ratio: $\frac{25}{10}$, simplified to $\frac{5}{2}$.
2. Set up a proportion, with x representing the number of beetles. The proportion can be stated as $\frac{5}{2} = \frac{x}{100}$.
3. Begin by cross-multiplying. In other words, multiply each fraction's numerator by the other fraction's denominator.

   $5 \times 100 = 2 \times x$, or $500 = 2x$
4. To find the value of x, divide both sides by 2. The result is 250, or 250 beetles in 100 square meters.

Practice

Find the value of x in the following proportion: $\frac{6}{7} = \frac{x}{49}$.

Percentage

A **percentage** is a ratio that compares a number to 100. For example, there are 37 granite rocks in a collection that consists of 100 rocks. The ratio $\frac{37}{100}$ can be written as 37%. Granite rocks make up 37% of the rock collection.

You can calculate percentages of numbers other than 100 by setting up a proportion.

Example

Rain falls on 9 days out of 30 in June. What percentage of the days in June were rainy?

$$\frac{9 \text{ days}}{30 \text{ days}} = \frac{d\%}{100\%}$$

To find the value of d, begin by cross-multiplying, as for any proportion:

$9 \times 100 = 30 \times d$ $\quad d = \frac{900}{30}$ $\quad d = 30$

Practice

There are 300 marbles in a jar, and 42 of those marbles are blue. What percentage of the marbles are blue?

Significant Figures

The **precision** of a measurement depends on the instrument you use to take the measurement. For example, if the smallest unit on the ruler is millimeters, then the most precise measurement you can make will be in millimeters.

The sum or difference of measurements can only be as precise as the least precise measurement being added or subtracted. Round your answer so that it has the same number of digits after the decimal as the least precise measurement. Round up if the last digit is 5 or more, and round down if the last digit is 4 or less.

Example

Subtract a temperature of 5.2°C from the temperature 75.46°C.

$$75.46 - 5.2 = 70.26$$

5.2 has the fewest digits after the decimal, so it is the least precise measurement. Since the last digit of the answer is 6, round up to 3. The most precise difference between the measurements is 70.3°C.

Practice

Add 26.4 m to 8.37 m. Round your answer according to the precision of the measurements.

Significant figures are the number of nonzero digits in a measurement. Zeroes between nonzero digits are also significant. For example, the measurements 12,500 L, 0.125 cm, and 2.05 kg all have three significant figures. When you multiply and divide measurements, the one with the fewest significant figures determines the number of significant figures in your answer.

Example

Multiply 110 g by 5.75 g.

$$110 \times 5.75 = 632.5$$

Because 110 has only two significant figures, round the answer to 630 g.

Scientific Notation

A **factor** is a number that divides into another number with no remainder. In the example, the number 3 is used as a factor four times.

An **exponent** tells how many times a number is used as a factor. For example, $3 \times 3 \times 3 \times 3$ can be written as 3^4. The exponent ^{4} indicates that the number 3 is used as a factor four times. Another way of expressing this is to say that 81 is equal to 3 to the fourth power.

Example

$$3^4 = 3 \times 3 \times 3 \times 3 = 81$$

Scientific notation uses exponents and powers of ten to write very large or very small numbers in shorter form. When you write a number in scientific notation, you write the number as two factors. The first factor is any number between 1 and 10. The second factor is a power of 10, such as 10^3 or 10^6.

Example

The average distance between the planet Mercury and the sun is 58,000,000 km. To write the first factor in scientific notation, insert a decimal point in the original number so that you have a number between 1 and 10. In the case of 58,000,000, the number is 5.8.

To determine the power of 10, count the number of places that the decimal point moved. In this case, it moved 7 places.

$$58{,}000{,}000 \text{ km} = 5.8 \times 10^7 \text{ km}$$

Practice

Express 6,590,000 in scientific notation.

Significant Figures

Focus Measure the length of a paper clip using two different rulers. Use one ruler that is less precise than the other. Compare the two measurements. Ask: **Which measurement is more precise?** *(The ruler with the smallest units will give the more precise measurement.)*

Teach Give students the opportunity to take measurements of an object using tools with different precision. Encourage students to add and subtract their measurements, making sure that they round the answers to reflect the precision of the instruments. Go over the example for significant digits. Check for understanding by asking: **How many significant digits are in the number 324,000?** *(Three)* **In the number 5,901?** *(Four)* **In the number 0.706?** *(Three)* If students need additional practice, create a worksheet with problems in multiplying and dividing numbers with various significant digits.

Practice

26.4 m + 8.37 m = 34.77 m
This answer should be rounded to 34.8 m because the least precise measurement has only one digit after the decimal. This number is rounded up to 8 because the last digit is more than 5.

Scientific Notation

Focus Write a very large number on the board, such as 100 million, using all the zeros. Then, write the number using scientific notation. Ask: **Why do you think scientists prefer to write very large numbers using scientific notation?** *(Possible answers include that it is easier to do calculations, convert units, and make comparisons with other numbers.)*

Teach Go over the examples, and ask: **In the second example, which numbers are the factors?** *(5.8 and 10^7)* **Which number is the exponent?** *(^{7})* Explain that very small numbers have a negative exponent because the decimal point is moved to the right to produce the first factor. For example, 0.00000628 is equal to 6.28×10^{-6}.

Practice

$6{,}590{,}000 = 6.59 \times 10^6$

Reading Comprehension Skills

Students can refer to this part of the Skills Handbook whenever they need to review a reading skill. You can use the activities provided here to teach or reinforce these skills.

All in One Teaching Resources

- Target Reading Skills Handbook

Using Prior Knowledge

Focus Explain to students that using prior knowledge helps connect what they already know to what they are about to read.

Teach Point out that prior knowledge might not be accurate because memories have faded or perspectives have changed. Encourage students to ask questions to resolve discrepancies between their prior knowledge and what they have learned.

Asking Questions

Focus Demonstrate to students how to change a text heading into a question to help them anticipate the concepts, facts, and events they will read about.

Teach Encourage students to use this reading skill for the next section they read. Instruct them to turn the text headings into questions. Also challenge students to write at least four *what, how, why, who, when,* or *where* questions. Then, have students evaluate the skill. Ask: **Did asking questions about the text help you focus on the reading and remember what you read?** *(Answers will vary, but encourage honesty.)* If this reading skill didn't help, challenge them to assess why not.

Previewing Visuals

Focus Explain to students that looking at the visuals before reading will help them activate prior knowledge and predict what they are about to read.

Teach Assign a section for students to preview the visuals. First, instruct them to write a sentence describing what the section will be about. Then, encourage them to write one or two questions for each visual to give purpose to their reading. Also have them list any prior knowledge about the subject.

Reading Comprehension Skills

Each section in your textbook introduces a Target Reading Skill. You will improve your reading comprehension by using the Target Reading Skills described below.

Using Prior Knowledge

Your prior knowledge is what you already know before you begin to read about a topic. Building on what you already know gives you a head start on learning new information. Before you begin a new assignment, think about what you know. You might look at the headings and the visuals to spark your memory. You can list what you know. Then, as you read, consider questions like these.

- How does what you learn relate to what you know?
- How did something you already know help you learn something new?
- Did your original ideas agree with what you have just learned?

Asking Questions

Asking yourself questions is an excellent way to focus on and remember new information in your textbook. For example, you can turn the text headings into questions. Then your questions can guide you to identify the important information as you read. Look at these examples:

Heading: Using Seismographic Data
Question: How are seismographic data used?
Heading: Kinds of Faults
Question: What are the kinds of faults?

You do not have to limit your questions to text headings. Ask questions about anything that you need to clarify or that will help you understand the content. *What* and *how* are probably the most common question words, but you may also ask *why*, *who*, *when*, or *where* questions.

Previewing Visuals

Visuals are photographs, graphs, tables, diagrams, and illustrations. Visuals contain important information. Before you read, look at visuals and their labels and captions. This preview will help you prepare for what you will be reading.

Often you will be asked what you want to learn about a visual. For example, after you look at the normal fault diagram below, you might ask: What is the movement along a normal fault? Questions about visuals give you a purpose for reading—to answer your questions.

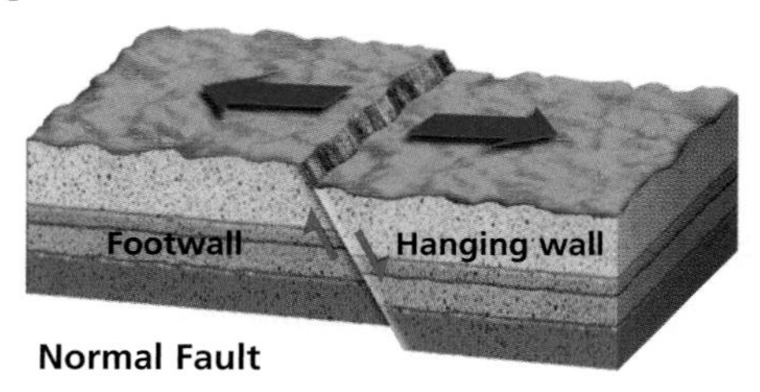

Normal Fault

Outlining

An outline shows the relationship between main ideas and supporting ideas. An outline has a formal structure. You write the main ideas, called topics, next to Roman numerals. The supporting ideas, called subtopics, are written under the main ideas and labeled A, B, C, and so on. An outline looks like this:

Technology and Society

I. Technology through history
II. The impact of technology on society
  A.
  B.

Outlining

Focus Explain that using an outline format helps organize information by main topic, subtopic, and details.

Teach Choose a section in the book, and demonstrate how to make an outline for it. Make sure students understand the structure of the outline by asking: **Is this a topic or a subtopic? Where does this information go in the outline? Would I write this heading next to a Roman numeral or a capital letter?** *(Answers depend on the section being outlined.)* Also show them how to indent and add details to the outline using numerals and lowercase letters.

Identifying Main Ideas

When you are reading science material, it is important to try to understand the ideas and concepts that are in a passage. Each paragraph has a lot of information and detail. Good readers try to identify the most important—or biggest—idea in every paragraph or section. That's the main idea. The other information in the paragraph supports or further explains the main idea.

Sometimes main ideas are stated directly. In this book, some main ideas are identified for you as key concepts. These are printed in boldface type. However, you must identify other main ideas yourself. In order to do this, you must identify all the ideas within a paragraph or section. Then ask yourself which idea is big enough to include all the other ideas.

Comparing and Contrasting

When you compare and contrast, you examine the similarities and differences between things. You can compare and contrast in a Venn diagram or in a table.

Venn Diagram A Venn diagram consists of two overlapping circles. In the space where the circles overlap, you write the characteristics that the two items have in common. In one of the circles outside the area of overlap, you write the differing features or characteristics of one of the items. In the other circle outside the area of overlap, you write the differing characteristics of the other item.

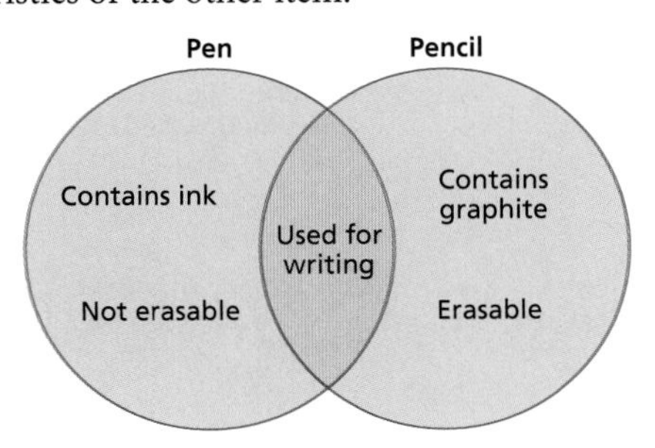

Table In a compare/contrast table, you list the characteristics or features to be compared across the top of the table. Then list the items to be compared in the left column. Complete the table by filling in information about each characteristic or feature.

Blood Vessel	Function	Structure of Wall
Artery	Carries blood away from heart	
Capillary		
Vein		

Identifying Supporting Evidence

A hypothesis is a possible explanation for observations made by scientists or an answer to a scientific question. Scientists must carry out investigations and gather evidence that either supports or disproves the hypothesis.

Identifying the supporting evidence for a hypothesis or theory can help you understand the hypothesis or theory. Evidence consists of facts—information whose accuracy can be confirmed by testing or observation.

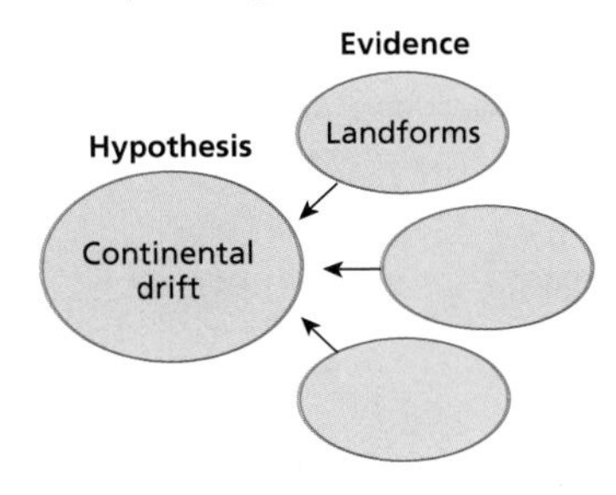

Identifying Main Ideas

Focus Explain that identifying main ideas and details helps sort the facts from the information into groups. Each group can have a main topic, subtopics, and details.

Teach Tell students that paragraphs are often written so that the main idea is in the first or second sentence, or in the last sentence. Assign students a page in the book. Instruct them to write the main idea for each paragraph on that page. If students have difficulty finding the main idea, suggest that they list all of the ideas given in the paragraph, and then choose the idea that is big enough to include all the others.

Comparing and Contrasting

Focus Explain that comparing and contrasting information shows how concepts, facts, and events are similar or different. The results of the comparison can have importance.

Teach Point out that Venn diagrams work best when comparing two things. To compare more than two things, students should use a compare/contrast table. Have students make a Venn diagram or compare/contrast table using two or more different sports or other activities, such as playing musical instruments. Emphasize that students should select characteristics that highlight the similarities and differences in the activities.

Identifying Supporting Evidence

Focus Explain to students that identifying the supporting evidence will help them to understand the relationship between the facts and the hypothesis.

Teach Remind students that a hypothesis is neither right nor wrong, but it is either supported or not supported by the evidence from testing or observation. If evidence is found that does not support a hypothesis, the hypothesis can be changed to accommodate the new evidence, or it can be dropped.

Sequencing

Focus Tell students that organizing information from beginning to end will help them understand a step-by-step process.

Teach Encourage students to create a flowchart to show the things they did this morning to get ready for school. Remind students that a flowchart should show the correct order in which events occur. *(A typical flowchart might include: got up ➤ took a shower ➤ got dressed ➤ ate breakfast ➤ brushed teeth ➤ gathered books and homework ➤ put on jacket.)*

Then explain that a cycle diagram shows a sequence of events that is continuous. Point out the cycle diagram that shows how the weather changes with the seasons of the year. Ask: **Why is a cycle diagram used instead of a flowchart to show the sequence of the seasons?** *(A cycle diagram shows that the sequence is continuous, not just a series of events.)* Challenge students to make a sequence diagram for a section of the text. Have them explain why they chose either a cycle diagram or a flowchart. Remind them to include at least four steps in the sequence.

Relating Cause and Effect

Focus Explain to students that cause is the reason for what happens. The effect is what happens in response to the cause. Relating cause and effect helps students relate the reason for what happens to what happens as a result.

Teach Emphasize that not all events that occur together have a cause-and-effect relationship. For example, tell students that you went to the grocery store and your car stalled. Ask: **Is there a cause-and-effect relationship in this situation? Explain.** *(No. Going to the grocery store could not cause a car to stall. There must be another cause to make the car stall.)*

Sequencing

A sequence is the order in which a series of events occurs. A flowchart or a cycle diagram can help you visualize a sequence.

Flowchart To make a flowchart, write a brief description of each step or event in a box. Place the boxes in order, with the first event at the top of the page. Then draw an arrow to connect each step or event to the next.

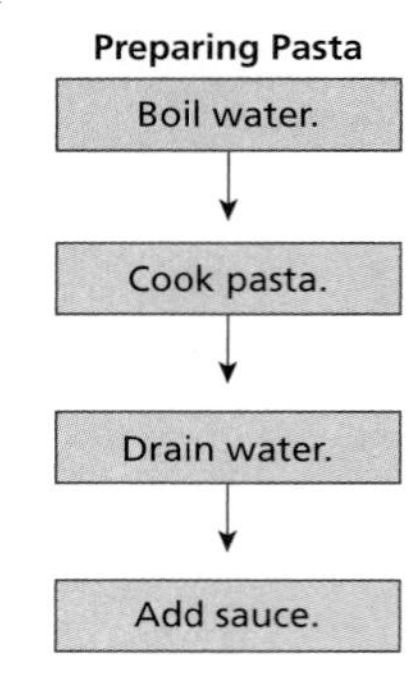

Cycle Diagram A cycle diagram shows a sequence that is continuous, or cyclical. A continuous sequence does not have an end because when the final event is over, the first event begins again. To create a cycle diagram, write the starting event in a box placed at the top of a page in the center. Then, moving in a clockwise direction, write each event in a box in its proper sequence. Draw arrows that connect each event to the one that occurs next.

Seasons of the Year

Winter
Spring
Summer
Fall

Relating Cause and Effect

Science involves many cause-and-effect relationships. A cause makes something happen. An effect is what happens. When you recognize that one event causes another, you are relating cause and effect.

Words like *cause, because, effect, affect,* and *result* often signal a cause or an effect. Sometimes an effect can have more than one cause, or a cause can produce several effects.

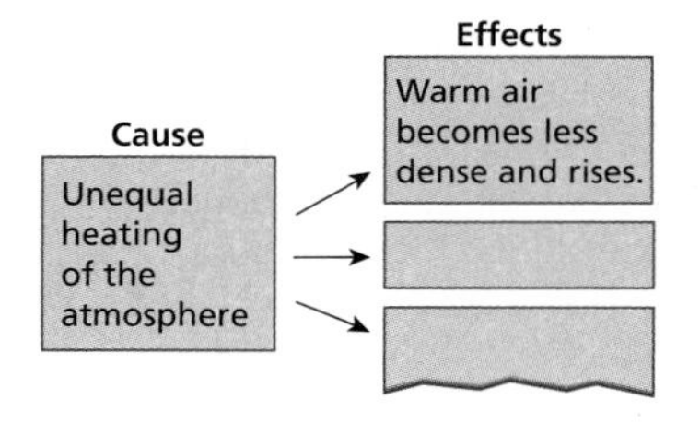

Concept Mapping

Concept maps are useful tools for organizing information on any topic. A concept map begins with a main idea or core concept and shows how the idea can be subdivided into related subconcepts or smaller ideas.

You construct a concept map by placing concepts (usually nouns) in ovals and connecting them with linking words (usually verbs). The biggest concept or idea is placed in an oval at the top of the map. Related concepts are arranged in ovals below the big idea. The linking words connect the ovals.

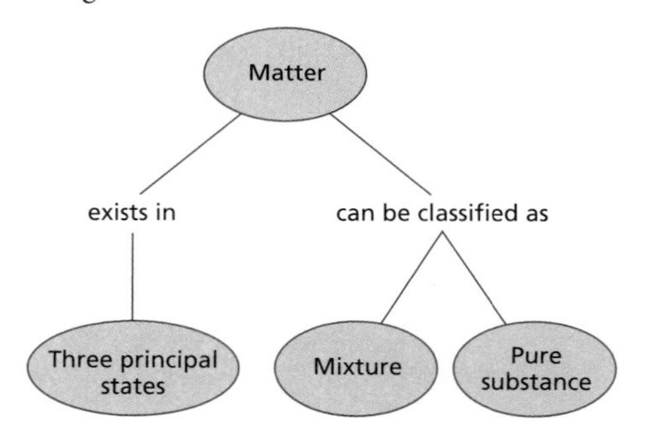

Concept Mapping

Focus Elicit from students how a map shows the relationship of one geographic area to another. Connect this idea to how a concept map shows the relationship between terms and concepts.

Teach Challenge students to make a concept map with at least three levels of concepts to organize information about types of transportation. All students should start with the phrase *Types of transportation* at the top of the concept map. After that point, their concepts may vary. *(For example, some students might place* private transportation *and* public transportation *at the next level, while other students might choose* human-powered *and* gas-powered.*)* Make sure students connect the concepts with linking words.

Building Vocabulary

Knowing the meaning of these prefixes, suffixes, and roots will help you understand the meaning of words you do not recognize.

Word Origins Many science words come to English from other languages, such as Greek and Latin. By learning the meaning of a few common Greek and Latin roots, you can determine the meaning of unfamiliar science words.

Prefixes A prefix is a word part that is added at the beginning of a root or base word to change its meaning.

Suffixes A suffix is a word part that is added at the end of a root word to change the meaning.

Greek and Latin Roots

Greek Roots	Meaning	Example
ast-	star	astronaut
geo-	Earth	geology
metron-	measure	kilometer
opt-	eye	optician
photo-	light	photograph
scop-	see	microscope
therm-	heat	thermostat
Latin Roots	**Meaning**	**Example**
aqua-	water	aquarium
aud-	hear	auditorium
duc-, duct-	lead	conduct
flect-	bend	reflect
fract-, frag-	break	fracture
ject-	throw	reject
luc-	light	lucid
spec-	see	inspect

Prefixes and Suffixes

Prefix	Meaning	Example
com-, con-	with	communicate, concert
de-	from; down	decay
di-	two	divide
ex-, exo-	out	exhaust
in-, im-	in, into; not	inject, impossible
re-	again; back	reflect, recall
trans-	across	transfer
Suffix	**Meaning**	**Example**
-al	relating to	natural
-er, -or	one who	teacher, doctor
-ist	one who practices	scientist
-ity	state of	equality
-ology	study of	biology
-tion, -sion	state or quality of	reaction, tension

Building Vocabulary

Reading in a content area presents challenges different from those encountered when reading fiction. Science texts often have more new vocabulary and more unfamiliar concepts that place greater emphasis on inferential reasoning. Students who can apply vocabulary strategies will be more successful in reading and understanding a science textbook. Challenge students to use Greek and Latin word origins and the meanings of prefixes and suffixes to learn the Key Terms in each section.

Word Origins

Focus Explain that word origins describe the older, foreign words that many modern English words have come from. Many science words come from Greek and Latin.

Teach Tell students that most dictionaries give the word origin just before the definition. Choose a section that has a Key Term with a Greek or Latin word origin. Encourage students to learn the meaning of the root word. Ask: **How does knowing the word origin help you remember the meaning of the Key Term?** *(Answers will vary, but the meaning of the Latin or Greek root should provide a clue to the definition of the Key Term.)* Ask: **What other words do you know that come from the same word origin?** *(Students may mention other words related to the Key Term.)* Challenge students to use word origins to figure out the meanings of unfamiliar words as they read. Students should confirm their definitions as necessary by checking a dictionary.

Prefixes

Focus Tell students that learning the meaning of common prefixes can help them determine the meaning of words they don't recognize. They will also increase their vocabulary.

Teach Remind students that a prefix is a word part that is added at the beginning of a root word to change its meaning. List some of the familiar prefixes and meanings, such as *de-* and *re-*, on the chalkboard. Ask: **What words do you know that use these same prefixes?** *(Students should list at least two words for each prefix.)* Ask: **How does the prefix affect the meaning of the root word?** *(Students should explain how it changes the meaning.)* Challenge students to learn the meaning of common prefixes and to use the skill to increase their vocabulary.

Suffixes

Focus Explain to students that learning the meanings of common suffixes and recognizing them in words are two effective strategies for learning word meanings and building vocabulary.

Teach Remind students that a suffix is added to the end of a word to change its meaning. In addition, students can use suffixes to discover the part of speech of an unfamiliar word. On the chalkboard, draw a four-column chart. Label the columns Noun, Verb, Adjective, and Adverb. Choose a Key Term that has a familiar base word, such as *tension.* Ask: **What are the noun, verb, adjective, and adverb forms of this word?** *(Students should give all possible answers, which may include only two forms of the word.)* Ask: **What endings signal that the word is a noun, adjective, or adverb?** *(Students should list the suffixes.)* Challenge students to learn the meanings of suffixes and to use them to decode new words.

- Complete student edition
- Video and audio
- Simulations and activities
- Section and chapter activities

Laboratory Safety

Laboratory safety is an essential element of a successful science class. Students need to understand exactly what is safe and unsafe behavior and what the rationale is behind each safety rule.

All in One Teaching Resources

- Laboratory Safety Teacher Notes
- Laboratory Safety Rules
- Laboratory Safety Symbols
- Laboratory Safety Contract

General Precautions

- Post safety rules in the classroom, and review them regularly with students before beginning every science activity.
- Familiarize yourself with the safety procedures for each activity before introducing it to your students.
- For open-ended activities like Chapter Projects, have students submit their procedures or design plans in writing and check them for safety considerations.
- Always act as an exemplary role model by displaying safe behavior.
- Know how to use safety equipment, such as fire extinguishers and fire blankets, and always have it accessible.
- Have students practice leaving the classroom quickly and orderly to prepare them for emergencies.
- Explain to students how to use the intercom or other available means of communication to get help during an emergency.
- Never leave students unattended while they are engaged in science activities.
- Provide enough space for students to safely carry out science activities.
- Instruct students to report all accidents and injuries to you immediately.

Safety Symbols

These symbols warn of possible dangers in the laboratory and remind you to work carefully.

Safety Goggles Wear safety goggles to protect your eyes in any activity involving chemicals, flames or heating, or glassware.

Lab Apron Wear a laboratory apron to protect your skin and clothing from damage.

Breakage Handle breakable materials, such as glassware, with care. Do not touch broken glassware.

Heat-Resistant Gloves Use an oven mitt or other hand protection when handling hot materials such as hot plates or hot glassware.

Plastic Gloves Wear disposable plastic gloves when working with harmful chemicals and organisms. Keep your hands away from your face, and dispose of the gloves according to your teacher's instructions.

Heating Use a clamp or tongs to pick up hot glassware. Do not touch hot objects with your bare hands.

Flames Before you work with flames, tie back loose hair and clothing. Follow instructions from your teacher about lighting and extinguishing flames.

No Flames When using flammable materials, make sure there are no flames, sparks, or other exposed heat sources present.

Corrosive Chemical Avoid getting acid or other corrosive chemicals on your skin or clothing or in your eyes. Do not inhale the vapors. Wash your hands after the activity.

Poison Do not let any poisonous chemical come into contact with your skin, and do not inhale its vapors. Wash your hands when you are finished with the activity.

Fumes Work in a ventilated area when harmful vapors may be involved. Avoid inhaling vapors directly. Only test an odor when directed to do so by your teacher, and use a wafting motion to direct the vapor toward your nose.

Sharp Object Scissors, scalpels, knives, needles, pins, and tacks can cut your skin. Always direct a sharp edge or point away from yourself and others.

Animal Safety Treat live or preserved animals or animal parts with care to avoid harming the animals or yourself. Wash your hands when you are finished with the activity.

Plant Safety Handle plants only as directed by your teacher. If you are allergic to certain plants, tell your teacher; do not do an activity involving those plants. Avoid touching harmful plants such as poison ivy. Wash your hands when you are finished with the activity.

Electric Shock To avoid electric shock, never use electrical equipment around water, or when the equipment is wet or your hands are wet. Be sure cords are untangled and cannot trip anyone. Unplug equipment not in use.

Physical Safety When an experiment involves physical activity, avoid injuring yourself or others. Alert your teacher if there is any reason you should not participate.

Disposal Dispose of chemicals and other laboratory materials safely. Follow the instructions from your teacher.

Hand Washing Wash your hands thoroughly when finished with the activity. Use antibacterial soap and warm water. Rinse well.

General Safety Awareness When this symbol appears, follow the instructions provided. When you are asked to develop your own procedure in a lab, have your teacher approve your plan before you go further.

End-of-Experiment Rules

- Always have students use warm water and soap for washing their hands.

Heating and Fire Safety

- No flammable substances should be in use around hot plates, light bulbs, or open flames.
- Test tubes should be heated only in water baths.
- Students should be permitted to strike matches to light candles or burners *only* with strict supervision. When possible, you should light the flames, especially when working with younger students.
- Be sure to have proper ventilation when fumes are produced during a procedure.
- All electrical equipment used in the lab should have GFI (Ground Fault Interrupter) switches.

Science Safety Rules

General Precautions

Follow all instructions. Never perform activities without the approval and supervision of your teacher. Do not engage in horseplay. Never eat or drink in the laboratory. Keep work areas clean and uncluttered.

Dress Code

Wear safety goggles whenever you work with chemicals, glassware, heat sources such as burners, or any substance that might get into your eyes. If you wear contact lenses, notify your teacher.

Wear a lab apron or coat whenever you work with corrosive chemicals or substances that can stain. Wear disposable plastic gloves when working with organisms and harmful chemicals. Tie back long hair. Remove or tie back any article of clothing or jewelry that can hang down and touch chemicals, flames, or equipment. Roll up long sleeves. Never wear open shoes or sandals.

First Aid

Report all accidents, injuries, or fires to your teacher, no matter how minor. Be aware of the location of the first-aid kit, emergency equipment such as the fire extinguisher and fire blanket, and the nearest telephone. Know whom to contact in an emergency.

Heating and Fire Safety

Keep all combustible materials away from flames. When heating a substance in a test tube, make sure that the mouth of the tube is not pointed at you or anyone else. Never heat a liquid in a closed container. Use an oven mitt to pick up a container that has been heated.

Using Chemicals Safely

Never put your face near the mouth of a container that holds chemicals. Never touch, taste, or smell a chemical unless your teacher tells you to.

Use only those chemicals needed in the activity. Keep all containers closed when chemicals are not being used. Pour all chemicals over the sink or a container, not over your work surface. Dispose of excess chemicals as instructed by your teacher.

Be extra careful when working with acids or bases. When mixing an acid and water, always pour the water into the container first and then add the acid to the water. Never pour water into an acid. Wash chemical spills and splashes immediately with plenty of water.

Using Glassware Safely

If glassware is broken or chipped, notify your teacher immediately. Never handle broken or chipped glass with your bare hands.

Never force glass tubing or thermometers into a rubber stopper or rubber tubing. Have your teacher insert the glass tubing or thermometer if required for an activity.

Using Sharp Instruments

Handle sharp instruments with extreme care. Never cut material toward you; cut away from you.

Animal and Plant Safety

Never perform experiments that cause pain, discomfort, or harm to animals. Only handle animals if absolutely necessary. If you know that you are allergic to certain plants, molds, or animals, tell your teacher before doing an activity in which these are used. Wash your hands thoroughly after any activity involving animals, animal parts, plants, plant parts, or soil.

During field work, wear long pants, long sleeves, socks, and closed shoes. Avoid poisonous plants and fungi as well as plants with thorns.

End-of-Experiment Rules

Unplug all electrical equipment. Clean up your work area. Dispose of waste materials as instructed by your teacher. Wash your hands after every experiment.

Handling Organisms Safely

- In an activity where students are directed to taste something, be sure to store the material in clean, *nonscience* containers. Distribute the material to students in *new* plastic or paper dispensables, which should be discarded after the tasting. Tasting or eating should never be done in a lab classroom.
- When growing bacterial cultures, use only disposable petri dishes. After streaking, the dishes should be sealed and not opened again by students. After the lab, students should return the unopened dishes to you.
- Two methods are recommended for the safe disposal of bacterial cultures. *First method:* Autoclave the petri dishes and discard them without opening. *Second method:* If no autoclave is available, carefully open the dishes (never have a student do this), pour full-strength bleach into the dishes, and let them stand for a day. Then pour the bleach from the petri dishes down a drain, and flush the drain with lots of water. Tape the petri dishes back together, and place them in a sealed plastic bag. Wrap the plastic bag with a brown paper bag or newspaper, and tape securely. Throw the sealed package in the trash. Thoroughly disinfect the work area with bleach.
- To grow mold, use a new, sealable plastic bag that is two to three times larger than the material to be placed inside. Seal the bag and tape it shut. After the bag is sealed, students should not open it. To dispose of the bag and mold culture, make a small cut near an edge of the bag, and cook the bag in a microwave oven on a high setting for at least one minute. Discard the bag according to local ordinance, usually in the trash.
- Students should wear disposable nitrile, latex, or food-handling gloves when handling live animals or nonliving specimens.

Using Glassware Safely

- Use plastic containers, graduated cylinders, and beakers whenever possible. If using glass, students should wear safety goggles.
- Use only nonmercury thermometers with anti-roll protectors.

Using Chemicals Safely

- When students use both chemicals and microscopes in one activity, microscopes should be in a separate part of the room from the chemicals so that when students remove their goggles to use the microscopes, their eyes are not at risk.

Using a Microscope

The microscope is an essential tool in the study of life science. It allows you to see things that are too small to be seen with the unaided eye.

You will probably use a compound microscope like the one you see here. The compound microscope has more than one lens that magnifies the object you view.

Typically, a compound microscope has one lens in the eyepiece, the part you look through. The eyepiece lens usually magnifies 10 ×. Any object you view through this lens would appear 10 times larger than it is.

The compound microscope may contain one or two other lenses called objective lenses. If there are two objective lenses, they are called the low-power and high-power objective lenses. The low-power objective lens usually magnifies 10 ×. The high-power objective lens usually magnifies 40 ×.

To calculate the total magnification with which you are viewing an object, multiply the magnification of the eyepiece lens by the magnification of the objective lens you are using. For example, the eyepiece's magnification of 10 × multiplied by the low-power objective's magnification of 10 × equals a total magnification of 100 ×.

Use the photo of the compound microscope to become familiar with the parts of the microscope and their functions.

The Parts of a Compound Microscope

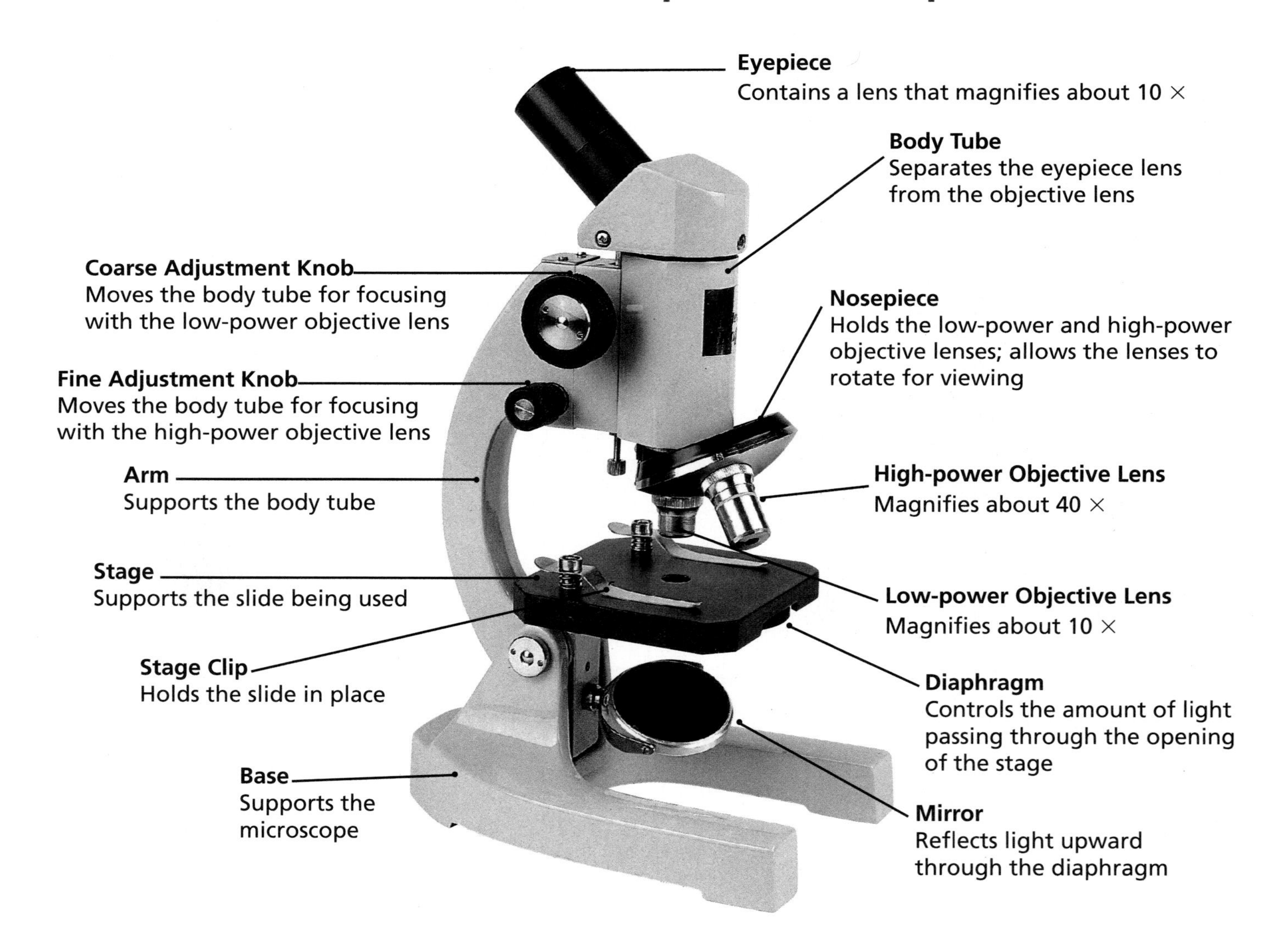

Using the Microscope

Use the following procedures when you are working with a microscope.

1. To carry the microscope, grasp the microscope's arm with one hand. Place your other hand under the base.
2. Place the microscope on a table with the arm toward you.
3. Turn the coarse adjustment knob to raise the body tube.
4. Revolve the nosepiece until the low-power objective lens clicks into place.
5. Adjust the diaphragm. While looking through the eyepiece, also adjust the mirror until you see a bright white circle of light. **CAUTION:** *Never use direct sunlight as a light source.*
6. Place a slide on the stage. Center the specimen over the opening on the stage. Use the stage clips to hold the slide in place. **CAUTION:** *Glass slides are fragile.*
7. Look at the stage from the side. Carefully turn the coarse adjustment knob to lower the body tube until the low-power objective almost touches the slide.
8. Looking through the eyepiece, very slowly turn the coarse adjustment knob until the specimen comes into focus.
9. To switch to the high-power objective lens, look at the microscope from the side. Carefully revolve the nosepiece until the high-power objective lens clicks into place. Make sure the lens does not hit the slide.
10. Looking through the eyepiece, turn the fine adjustment knob until the specimen comes into focus.

Making a Wet-Mount Slide

Use the following procedures to make a wet-mount slide of a specimen.

1. Obtain a clean microscope slide and a coverslip. **CAUTION:** *Glass slides and coverslips are fragile.*
2. Place the specimen on the slide. The specimen must be thin enough for light to pass through it.
3. Using a plastic dropper, place a drop of water on the specimen.
4. Gently place one edge of the coverslip against the slide so that it touches the edge of the water drop at a 45° angle. Slowly lower the coverslip over the specimen. If air bubbles are trapped beneath the coverslip, tap the coverslip gently with the eraser end of a pencil.
5. Remove any excess water at the edge of the coverslip with a paper towel.

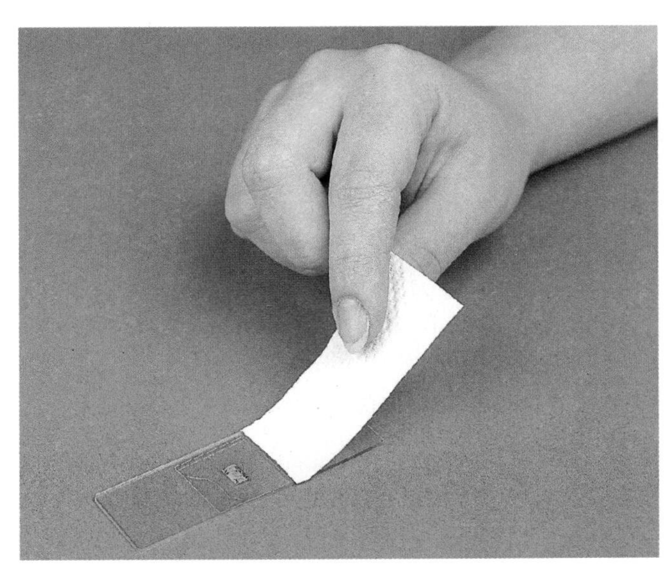

English and Spanish Glossary

active transport The movement of materials through a cell membrane using cellular energy. (p. 36)
transporte activo Movimiento de materiales a través de la membrana celular que usa energía de la célula.

adaptation A trait that helps an organism survive and reproduce. (p. 141)
adaptación Rasgo que ayuda a sobrevivir y a reproducirse a un organismo.

alleles The different forms of a gene. (p. 79)
alelos Diferentes formas de un gen.

amino acid A small molecule that is linked chemically to other amino acids to form proteins. (p. 28)
aminoácido Pequeña molécula que se une químicamente a otros aminoácidos para formar proteínas.

autotroph An organism that makes its own food. (p. 45)
autótrofo Organismo que produce su propio alimento.

branching tree A diagram that shows how scientists think different groups of organisms are related. (p. 152)
árbol ramificado Diagrama que muestra cómo piensan los científicos que se relacionan diferentes grupos de organismos.

cancer A disease in which some body cells grow and divide uncontrollably, damaging the parts of the body around them. (p. 65)
cáncer Enfermedad en la que algunas células del cuerpo crecen y se dividen sin control, dañando las partes del cuerpo que están a su alrededor.

carbohydrate Energy-rich organic compound, such as a sugar or a starch, that is made of the elements carbon, hydrogen, and oxygen. (p. 27)
carbohidrato Compuesto orgánico rico en energía, como azúcar o almidón, que está formado por carbono, hidrógeno y oxígeno.

carrier A person who has one recessive allele for a trait, but does not have the trait. (p. 115)
portador Persona que tiene un alelo recesivo para un determinado rasgo, pero que no tiene el rasgo.

cast A type of fossil that forms when a mold becomes filled in with minerals that then harden. (p. 156)
vaciado Tipo de fósil se forma cuando un molde se llena con minerales que luego se endurecen.

cell The basic unit of structure and function in living things. (p. 7)
célula Unidad básica de estructura y función de los seres vivos.

cell cycle The regular sequence of growth and division that cells undergo. (p. 56)
ciclo celular Secuencia regular de crecimiento y división de las células.

cell membrane A cell structure that controls which substances can enter or leave the cell. (p. 17)
membrana celular Estructura celular que controla qué sustancias pueden entrar y salir de la célula.

cell theory A widely accepted explanation of the relationship between cells and living things. (p. 10)
teoría celular Explicación ampliamente aceptada sobre la relación entre las células y los seres vivos.

cell wall A rigid layer of nonliving material that surrounds the cells of plants and some other organisms. (p. 17)
pared celular Capa rígida de material no vivo que rodea las células vegetales y de algunos organismos.

chemotherapy The use of drugs to treat diseases such as cancer. (p. 66)
quimioterapia Uso de medicamentos para tratar enfermedades como el cáncer.

chlorophyll A green pigment found in the chloroplasts of plants, algae, and some bacteria. (p. 46)
clorofila Pigmento verde que se encuentra en los cloroplastos de las plantas, algas y algunas bacterias.

chloroplast A structure in the cells of plants and some other organisms that captures energy from sunlight and uses it to produce food. (p. 22)
cloroplasto Estructura en las células vegetales y algunos otros organismos que captan la energía de la luz solar y la usan para producir alimento.

chromosome A doubled rod of condensed chromatin; contains DNA that carries genetic information. (p. 57)
cromosoma Doble bastón de cromatina condensada; contiene ADN que transporta información genética.

clone An organism that is genetically identical to the organism from which it was produced. (p. 125)
clon Organismo que es genéticamente idéntico al organismo del que proviene.

codominance A condition in which neither of two alleles of a gene is dominant or recessive. (p. 89)
codominancia Condición en la que ninguno de los dos alelos de un gen es dominante ni recesivo.

compound Two or more elements that are chemically combined. (p. 26)
compuesto Dos o más elementos que se combinan químicamente.

cytokinesis The final stage of the cell cycle, in which the cell's cytoplasm divides, distributing the organelles into each of the two new cells. (p. 60)
citocinesis Fase final del ciclo celular en la cual se divide el citoplasma de la célula y se distribuyen los organelos en cada una de las dos nuevas células.

cytoplasm The region between the cell membrane and the nucleus; in organisms without a nucleus, the region located inside the cell membrane. (p. 19)
citoplasma Región entre la membrana celular y el núcleo; en los organismos sin núcleo, la región ubicada dentro de la membrana celular.

diffusion The process by which molecules move from an area of higher concentration to an area of lower concentration. (p. 33)
difusión Proceso por el cual las moléculas se mueven de un área de mayor concentración a otra de menor concentración.

dominant allele An allele whose trait always shows up in the organism when the allele is present. (p. 79)
alelo dominante Alelo cuyo rasgo siempre se manifiesta en el organismo, cuando el alelo está presente.

DNA Deoxyribonucleic acid; the genetic material that carries information about an organism and is passed from parent to offspring. (p.29)
ADN Ácido desoxirribonucleico; material genético que lleva información sobre un organismo y que se pasa de padres a hijos.

element Any substance that cannot be broken down into simpler substances. (p. 25)
elemento Cualquier sustancia que no puede descomponerse en sustancias más pequeñas.

endoplasmic reticulum A cell structure that forms a maze of passageways in which proteins and other materials are carried from one part of the cell to another. (p. 19)
retículo endoplasmático Estructura celular que forma un laberinto de pasajes por los que se transportan las proteínas y otros materiales de una parte de la célula a otra.

enzyme A type of protein that speeds up a chemical reaction in a living thing. (p. 28)
enzima Tipo de proteína que acelera la reacciones químicas en un ser vivo.

evolution The gradual change in a species over time. (p. 142)
evolución Cambio gradual de una especie a través del tiempo.

extinct Term used to indicate a species that does not have any living members. (p. 159)
extinto Término que se usa para indicar una especie que ya no tiene miembros vivos.

fermentation The process by which cells break down molecules to release energy without using oxygen. (p. 52)
fermentación Proceso por el cual las células descomponen las moléculas para liberar energía sin usar oxígeno.

fertilization the process in which an egg cell and a sperm cell join to form a new organism. (p. 77)
fecundación Proceso por el cual un óvulo y un espermatozoide se unen para formar un organismo nuevo.

fossil The preserved remains or traces of an organism that lived in the past. (p. 139)
fósil Restos o huellas preservados de un organismo que vivió en el pasado.

fossil record The millions of fossils that scientists have collected. (p. 158)
registro fósil Los millones de fósiles que han descubierto los científicos.

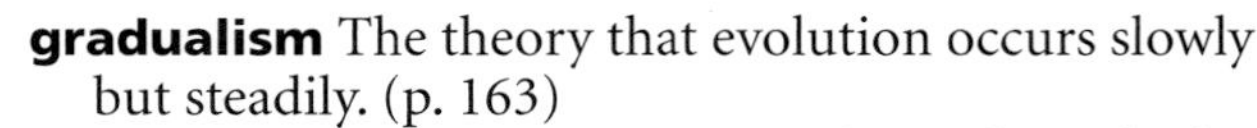

gene The set of information that controls a trait; a segment of DNA on a chromosome that codes for a specific trait. (p. 79)
gen Conjunto de información que controla un rasgo; un segmento de ADN en un cromosoma el cual codifica un rasgo determinado.

gene therapy The insertion of working copies of a gene into the cells of a person with a genetic disorder in an attempt to correct the disorder. (p. 127)
terapia génica Inserción de copias activas de un gen en las células de una persona con un trastorno genético para intentar corregir dicho trastorno.

genetic disorder An abnormal condition that a person inherits through genes or chromosomes. (p. 118)
trastorno genético Condición anormal que hereda una persona a través de genes o cromosomas.

genetic engineering The transfer of a gene from the DNA of one organism into another organism, in order to produce an organism with desired traits. (p. 126)
ingeniería genética Transferencia de un gen desde el ADN de un organismo a otro, para producir un organismo con los rasgos deseados.

genetics The scientific study of heredity. (p. 76)
genética Ciencia que estudia la herencia.

genome All of the DNA in one cell of an organism. (p. 128)
genoma Todo el ADN de una célula de un organismo.

genotype An organism's genetic makeup, or allele combinations. (p. 88)
genotipo Composición genética de un organismo, es decir, las combinaciones de los alelos.

Golgi body A structure in a cell that receives proteins and other newly formed materials from the endoplasmic reticulum, packages them, and distributes them to other parts of the cell. (p. 22)
aparato de Golgi Estructura en la célula que recibe del retículo endoplasmático las proteínas y otros materiales recientemente formados, los empaqueta y los distribuye a otras partes de la célula.

gradualism The theory that evolution occurs slowly but steadily. (p. 163)
gradualismo Teoría que enuncia que la evolución ocurre lenta pero continuamente.

half-life The time it takes for half of the atoms in a radioactive element to break down. (p. 158)
vida media Tiempo que demoran en desintegrarse la mitad de los átomos de un elemento radioactivo.

heredity The passing of traits from parents to offspring. (p. 76)
herencia Transmisión de rasgos de padres a hijos.

heterotroph An organism that cannot make its own food. (p. 45)
heterótrofo Organismo que no puede producir su propio alimento.

heterozygous Having two different alleles for a trait. (p. 88)
heterocigoto Tener dos alelos diferentes para el mismo rasgo.

homologous structures Body parts that are structurally similar in related species; provide evidence that the structures were inherited from a common ancestor. (p. 150)
estructuras homólogas Partes del cuerpo que son estructuralmente similares entre las especies relacionadas; proveen evidencia de que las estructuras se heredaron de un antepasado común.

homozygous Having two identical alleles for a trait. (p. 88)
homocigoto Tener dos alelos idénticos para el mismo rasgo.

hybrid An organism that has two different alleles for a trait; an organism that is heterozygous for a particular trait. (p. 80)
híbrido Organismo que tiene dos alelos diferentes para un rasgo; un organismo que es heterocigoto para un rasgo en particular.

hybridization A selective breeding method in which two genetically different individuals are crossed. (p. 124)
hibridación Método de cruce selectivo en el cual se cruzan dos individuos genéticamente diferentes.

200 • C

inbreeding A selective breeding method in which two individuals with identical or similar sets of alleles are crossed. (p. 124)
endogamia Método de cruce selectivo en el que se cruzan dos individuos con pares de alelos idénticos o semejantes.

interphase The stage of the cell cycle that takes place before cell division occurs. (p. 56)
interfase Fase del ciclo celular que ocurre antes de la división; durante esta fase la célula crece, copia su ADN y se prepara para la división.

karyotype A picture of all the chromosomes in a cell arranged in pairs. (p. 120)
cariotipo Imagen de todos los cromosomas de una célula, organizados en parejas.

lipid Energy-rich organic compound, such as a fat, oil, or wax, that is made of carbon, hydrogen, and oxygen. (p. 27)
lípido Compuesto orgánico rico en energía, como grasa, aceite y cera, formado por carbono, hidrógeno y oxígeno.

lysosome A small, round cell structure containing chemicals that break down large food particles into smaller ones. (p. 22)
lisosoma Pequeña estructura celular redonda que contiene sustancias químicas que descomponen las partículas de alimento grandes en otras más simples.

meiosis The process that occurs in the formation of sex cells (sperm and egg) by which the number of chromosomes is reduced by half. (p. 94)
meiosis Proceso que ocurre en la formación de las células sexuales (espermatozoide y óvulo) por el cual el número de cromosomas se reduce a la mitad.

messenger RNA RNA that copies the coded message from DNA in the nucleus and carries the message into the cytoplasm. (p. 99)
ARN mensajero ARN que copia el mensaje codificado del ADN en el núcleo y lo lleva al citoplasma.

microscope An instrument that makes small objects look larger. (p. 7)
microscopio Instrumento que hace que los objetos pequeños se vean más grandes.

mitochondria Rod-shaped cell structures that convert energy in food molecules to energy the cell can use to carry out its functions. (p. 19)
mitocondria Estructura celular con forma de bastón que transforma la energía de las moléculas de alimentos en energía que la célula puede usar para llevar a cabo sus funciones.

mitosis The stage of the cell cycle during which the cell's nucleus divides into two new nuclei and one copy of the DNA is distributed into each daughter cell. (p. 57)
mitosis Fase del ciclo celular durante la cual el núcleo de la célula se divide en dos nuevos nucleolos y se distribuye una copia del ADN a cada célula hija.

mold A type of fossil formed when a shell or other hard part of an organism dissolves, leaving an empty space in the shape of the part. (p. 156)
molde Tipo de fósil que se forma cuando la caparazón, concha u otra parte dura de un organismo enterrado se disuelve y deja un área hueca con la forma de esa parte.

multiple alleles Three or more forms of a gene that code for a single trait. (p. 112)
alelo múltiple Tres o más formas de un gen que codifican un solo rasgo.

mutation A change in a gene or chromosome. (p. 65)
mutación Cambio en un gen o cromosoma.

natural selection The process by which individuals that are better adapted to their environment are more likely to survive and reproduce than other members of the same species. (p. 143)
selección natural Proceso por el cual los individuos que se adaptan mejor a sus ambientes tienen más posibilidades de sobrevivir y reproducirse que otros miembros de la misma especie.

nucleic acid Very large organic molecule made of carbon, oxygen, hydrogen, nitrogen, and phosphorus, that contains the instructions cells need to carry out all the functions of life. (p. 29)
ácido nucléico Molécula orgánica muy grande compuesta de carbono, oxígeno, hidrógeno, nitrógeno y fósforo, que contiene las instrucciones que las células necesitan para realizar todas las funciones vitales.

nucleus A cell structure that contains nucleic acids, the chemical instructions that direct all the cell's activities. (p. 18)
núcleo Estructura celular que contiene ácidos nucleicos, es decir, las instrucciones químicas que dirigen las actividades de la célula.

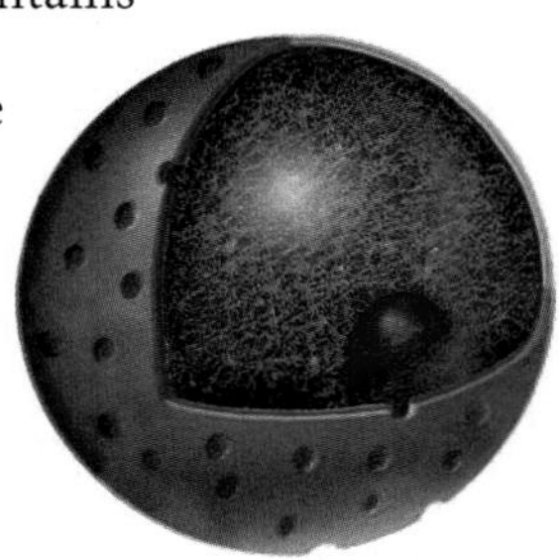

O

organelle A tiny cell structure that carries out a specific function within the cell. (p. 16)
organelo Diminuta estructura celular que realiza una función específica dentro de la célula.

osmosis The diffusion of water molecules through a selectively permeable membrane. (p. 34)
ósmosis Difusión de las moléculas de agua a través de una membrana con permeabilidad selectiva.

P

passive transport The movement of materials through a cell membrane without using energy. (p. 36)
transporte pasivo Movimiento de materiales a través de la membrana celular sin el uso de energía.

pedigree A chart or "family tree" that tracks which members of a family have a particular trait. (p. 119)
genealogía Tabla o "árbol genealógico" que muestra qué miembros de una familia tienen un rasgo en particular.

petrified fossil A fossil formed when minerals replace all or part of an organism. (p. 156)
fósil petrificado Fósil que se forma cuando los minerales reemplazan todo el organismo o parte de él.

phenotype An organism's physical appearance, or visible traits. (p. 88)
fenotipo Apariencia física de un organismo, es decir, los rasgos visibles.

photosynthesis The process by which plants and some other organisms capture the energy in sunlight and use it to make food. (p. 45)
fotosíntesis Proceso por el cual las plantas y otros organismos captan la energía de la luz solar y la usan para producir alimento.

pigment A colored chemical compound that absorbs light. (p. 46)
pigmento Compuesto químico de color que absorbe luz.

probability A number that describes how likely it is that an event will occur. (p. 84)
probabilidad Número que describe la posibilidad de que ocurra un suceso.

protein Large organic molecule made of carbon, hydrogen, oxygen, nitrogen, and sometimes sulfur. (p. 28)
proteína Molécula orgánica grande compuesta de carbono, hidrógeno, oxígeno, nitrógeno y, a veces, azufre.

punctuated equilibria The theory that species evolve during short periods of rapid change. (p. 163)
equilibrio puntuado Teoría que enuncia que las especies evolucionan durante períodos breves de cambios rápidos.

Punnett square A chart that shows all the possible combinations of alleles that can result from a genetic cross. (p. 86)
cuadrado de Punnett Tabla que muestra todas las combinaciones posibles de los alelos que pueden resultar de una cruza genética.

purebred The offspring of many generations that have the same traits. (p. 77)
raza pura Descendiente de muchas generaciones que tienen los mismos rasgos.

R

radioactive dating A technique used to determine the actual age of a fossil on the basis of the amount of a radioactive element it contains. (p. 158)
datación radiactiva Técnica que se usa para determinar la edad real de un fósil basándose en la cantidad de elementos radiactivos que contiene.

radioactive element An unstable element that breaks down into a different element. (p. 158)
elemento radiactivo Elemento inestable que se descompone en un elemento diferente.

recessive allele An allele that is masked when a dominant allele is present. (p. 79)
alelo recesivo Alelo que queda oculto cuando está presente un alelo dominante.

202 • C

relative dating A technique used to determine which of two fossils is older. (p. 157)
datación relativa Técnica que se usa para determinar cuál de dos fósiles es más antiguo.

replication The process by which a cell makes a copy of the DNA in its nucleus. (p. 56)
replicación Proceso por el cual una célula copia el ADN en su núcleo.

respiration The process by which cells break down simple food molecules to release the energy they contain. (p. 50)
respiración Proceso por el cual las células descomponen moléculas simples de alimento para liberar la energía que contienen.

ribosome A small grain-like structure in the cytoplasm of a cell where proteins are made. (p.19)
ribosoma Estructura pequeña parecida a un grano en el citoplasma de una célula donde se fabrican las proteínas.

RNA Ribonucleic acid; a nucleic acid that plays an important role in the production of proteins. (p. 29)
ARN Ácido ribonucleico; ácido nucleico que juega un papel importante en la producción de proteínas.

S

scientific theory A well-tested concept that explains a wide range of observations. (p. 142)
teoría científica Concepto comprobado que explica una amplia gama de observaciones.

selective breeding The process of selecting a few organisms with desired traits to serve as parents of the next generation. (p. 124)
cruce selectivo Proceso de selección de algunos organismos con los rasgos deseados para que sirvan de como progenitores de la siguiente generación.

selectively permeable A property of cell membranes that allows some substances to pass through, while others cannot. (p. 32)
permeabilidad selectiva Propiedad de las membranas celulares que permite que algunas sustancias pasen y otras no.

sex chromosomes A pair of chromosomes carrying genes that determine whether a person is male or female. (p. 113)
cromosomas sexuales Par de cromosomas portadores de genes que determinan si una persona es macho o hembra.

sex-linked gene A gene that is carried on the X or Y chromosome. (p. 114)
gen ligado al sexo Gen portador del cromosoma X o Y.

species A group of similar organisms that can mate with each other and produce fertile offspring. (p. 139)
especie Grupo de organismos similares que pueden aparearse entre ellos y producir descendencia fértil.

stomata Small openings on the underside of a leaf through which oxygen and carbon dioxide can move. (p. 47)
estomas Pequeños orificios en la superficie inferior de la hoja a través de los cuales se intercambia oxígeno y dióxido de carbono.

T

trait A characteristic that an organism can pass on to its offspring through its genes. (p. 76)
rasgo Característica que un organismo puede transmitir a su descendencia a través de sus genes.

transfer RNA RNA in the cytoplasm that carries an amino acid to the ribosome and adds it to the growing protein chain. (p. 99)
ARN de transferencia ARN en el citoplasma que lleva un aminoácido al ribosoma y lo suma a la cadena proteínica que se está formando.

tumor A mass of abnormal cells that develops when cancerous cells divide and grow uncontrollably. (p. 65)
tumor Masa de células anormales que se desarrolla cuando las células cancerosas se dividen y crecen sin control.

V

vacuole A sac inside a cell that acts as a storage area. (p. 22)
vacuola Saco dentro de la célula que actúa como área de almacenamiento.

variation Any difference between individuals of the same species. (p. 143)
variación Cualquier diferencia entre individuos de la misma especie.

Index

Page numbers for key terms are printed in **boldface** type.
Page numbers for illustrations, maps, and charts are printed in *italics*.

Teacher's Edition entries appear in blue type. The page on which a term is defined is indicated in **boldface** type.

Index

Page numbers for key terms are printed in **boldface** type.
Page numbers for illustrations, maps, and charts are printed in *italics*.

Index

Page numbers for key terms are printed in **boldface** type.
Page numbers for illustrations, maps, and charts are printed in *italics.*

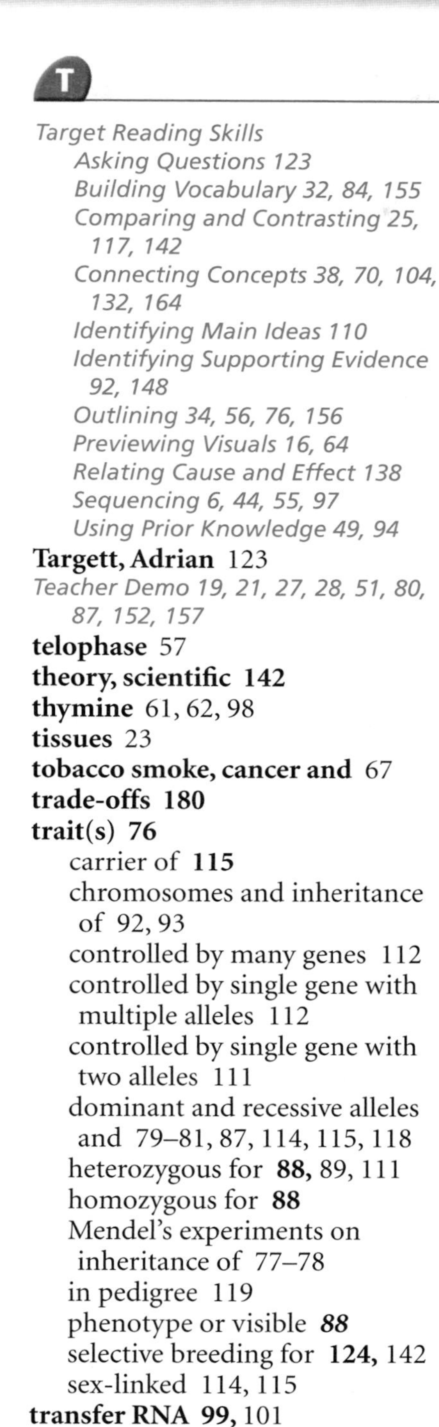

T

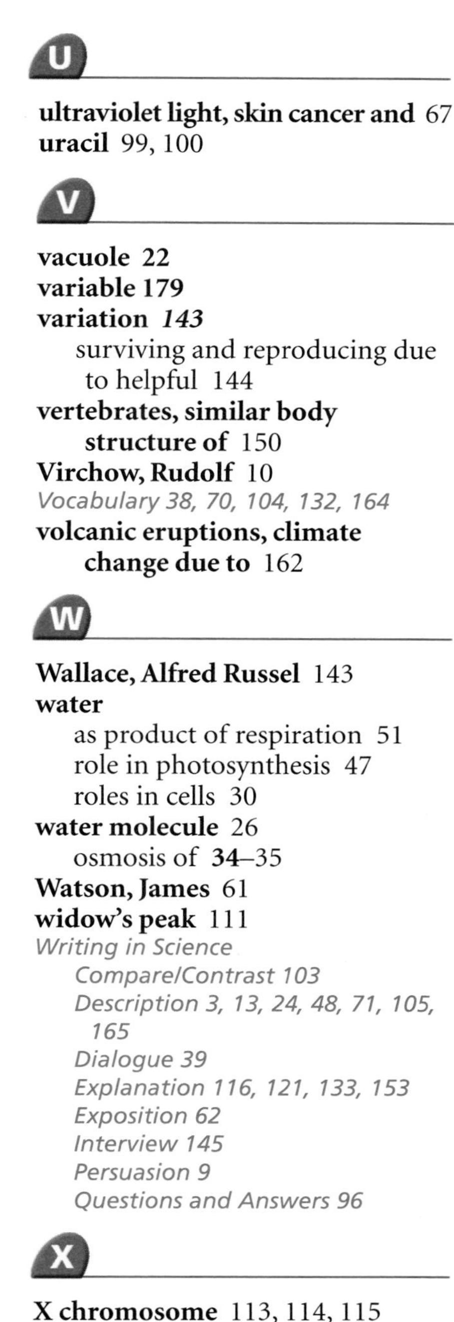

U

V

W

X

Y

Acknowledgments

Acknowledgment for page 172: From *James Herriot's Dog Stories* by James Herriot. Copyright © 1986 by the author and reprinted by permission of St. Martin's Press, LLC for US & reprinted by permission of Harold Ober Associated Incorporated for Canada.

Staff Credits

Diane Alimena, Scott Andrews, Jennifer Angel, Michele Angelucci, Laura Baselice, Carolyn Belanger, Barbara A. Bertell, Suzanne Biron, Peggy Bliss, Stephanie Bradley, James Brady, Anne M. Bray, Sarah M. Carroll, Kerry Cashman, Jonathan Cheney, Joshua D. Clapper, Lisa J. Clark, Bob Craton, Patricia Cully, Patricia M. Dambry, Kathy Dempsey, Leanne Esterly, Emily Ellen, Thomas Ferreira, Jonathan Fisher, Patricia Fromkin, Paul Gagnon, Kathy Gavilanes, Holly Gordon, Robert Graham, Ellen Granter, Diane Grossman, Barbara Hollingdale, Linda Johnson, Anne Jones, John Judge, Kevin Keane, Kelly Kelliher, Toby Klang, Sue Langan, Russ Lappa, Carolyn Lock, Rebecca Loveys, Constance J. McCarty, Carolyn B. McGuire, Ranida Touranont McKneally, Anne McLaughlin, Eve Melnechuk, Natania Mlawer, Janet Morris, Karyl Murray, Francine Neumann, Baljit Nijjar, Marie Opera, Jill Ort, Kim Ortell, Joan Paley, Dorothy Preston, Maureen Raymond, Laura Ross, Rashid Ross, Siri Schwartzman, Melissa Shustyk, Laurel Smith, Emily Soltanoff, Jennifer A. Teece, Elizabeth Torjussen, Amanda M. Watters, Merce Wilczek, Amy Winchester, Char Lyn Yeakley. **Additional Credits** Tara Alamilla, Louise Gachet, Allen Gold, Andrea Golden, Terence Hegarty, Etta Jacobs, Meg Montgomery, Stephanie Rogers, Kim Schmidt, Adam Teller, Joan Tobin.

Illustration

Art developed and produced by **Michelle Barbera:** 143–145; **Kerry Cashman:** 96, 106; **John Ceballos:** 30; **David Corrente:** 86–87; **John Edwards and Associates:** 10, 19t, 19b, 22, 33, 52, 87b, 152, 159; **Kevin Jones Associates:** 156–157; **Keith Kasnot:** 18; **Steve McEntee:** 35, 36, 61, 62, 99, 100–101; **Richard McMahon:** 46–47; **Karen Minot:** 45, 77, 78, 166; **Morgan-Cain & Associates:** 26, 58–59, 94–95; **J/B Woolsey Associates:** 40, 66–67, 72, 89, 126, 150; **XNR Productions:** 138–139. **All charts and graphs by Matt Mayerchak.**

Photography

Photo Research Paula Wehde

Cover Image top, David Madison/Getty Images, Inc.; **bottom,** Ian Walton/Getty Images, Inc.

Page vi, AP/Wide World Photos; **vii,** Richard Haynes; **viii,** E.R. Degginger/Color-Pic, Inc.; **x,** Rensselear Polytechnic Institute; **1l,** Angel E. Garcia (Los Alamos National Laboratory) and Jose N. Onuchic (University of California at San Diego); **1r**, Rensselear Polytechnic Institute; **2,** Bettmann/Corbis; **3,** Rensselear Polytechnic Institute.

Chapter 1
Pages 4–5, Dr. David E. Scott/Phototake; **5r,** Richard Haynes; **6t,** Richard Haynes; **6b,** McDonald Wildlife Photo, Inc./DRK Photo; **7t,** Photo Researchers, Inc.; **7b,** Richard Haynes; **8l,** FSU Research Foundation; **8m,** The Granger Collection; **8r,** Bettmann/Corbis; **9l,** Bettmann/Corbis; **9m,** Pascal Goetgheluck/SPL/Photo Researchers, Inc.; **9r,** Lawrence Migdale/Stock Boston; **10,** John Locke/Dembinsky Photo Associates; **11,** Getty Images, Inc.; **12t,** Photo Researchers, Inc.; **12bl,** Sinclair Stammers/SPL/Photo Researchers, Inc.; **12br,** SPL/Photo Researchers, Inc.; **13,** CRNI/SPL/Photo Researchers, Inc.; **14,** Richard Haynes; **16t,** Runk/Schoenberger/Grant Heilman Photography, Inc.;**16b,** Corbis; **17l,** Runk/Schoenberger/Grant Heilman Photography; **17r,** Mike Abbey/Visuals Unlimited; **18,** Alfred Paskieka/SPL/Photo Researchers, Inc.; **19t,** Bill Longcore/Photo Researchers, Inc.; **19b,** SPL/Photo Researchers, Inc.; **22,** Photo Researchers, Inc.; **23t,** Dr. David Scott/CRNI/Phototake; **23br,** Motta & S. Correr/SPL/Photo Researchers, Inc.; **23bl,** Eric V. Grave/Photo Researchers, Inc.; **24l,** Dr. Gary Gaugler/Photo Researchers, Inc.; **24m,** SNRI/Phototake; **24r,** Phototake; **25t,** Russ Lappa; **25b,** Jeffrey A. Scovil; **26,** Digital Vision/Getty Images, Inc.; **27t,** Japack Company/Corbis; **27m,** Andrew Syred/SPL/Photo Researchers, Inc.; **27bl,** Vittoriano Rastelli/Corbis; **27br,** Getty Images, Inc.; **28,** Scheidermeyer/OSF/Animals Animals/Earth Scenes; **31,** Richard Haynes; **32–33,** Damilo P. Donadomi/Bruce Coleman, Inc.; **35l,** Stanley Flegler/Visuals Unlimited; **35m,** David M. Phillips/Visuals Unlimited; **35r,** David M. Phillips/Visuals Unlimited; **37,** M. Abbey/Visuals Unlimited; **40,** Runk/ Schoenberger/Grant Heilman Photography.

Chapter 2
Pages 42–43, Michael J. Doolittle/The Image Works; **43r,** Russ Lappa; **44t,** Russ Lappa; **44–45b,** Todd Gustafson/Panoramic Images; **45** inset, Stephen J. Krasemann/Photo Researchers, Inc.; **46,** Biophoto Associates/Photo Researchers, Inc.; **47,** Dr. Jeremy Burgess/SPL/Photo Researchers, Inc.; **48,** Superstock, Inc.; **49,** Royalty-Free/Corbis; **50l,** Stephen Dalton/Photo Researchers, Inc.; **50r,** Phil Dotson/Photo Researchers, Inc.; **53,** Richard Hutchins/PhotoEdit; **55t,** David Scharf/Peter Arnold, Inc.; **55b,** AP/Wide World Photos; **56–57t,** Royalty-Free/Corbis; **57b,** Biophoto Associates/Science Source/Photo Researchers, Inc.; **58–59 all,** M. Abbey/Photo Researchers, Inc.; **60,** Visuals Unlimited; **63,** Runk/Schoenberger/Grant Heilman Photography; **64t,** Richard Haynes; **64b,** Corbis; **65,** National Cancer Institute/SPL/Photo Researchers, Inc.; **68t,** Bettmann/Corbis; **68b,** Pallava Bagla/Corbis Sygma; **69t,** Royalty-Free/Corbis; **69b,** Gabe Palmer/Corbis; **70,** Royalty-Free/Corbis.

Chapter 3
Pages 74–75, Ron Kimball Studios; **75r,** Richard Haynes; **76t,** Getty Images, Inc.; **76bl,** Hulton Archive/Getty Images, Inc.; **76br,** Jerry Howard/Positive Images; **77,** Jerry Howard/Positive Images; **79,** Dorling Kindersley; **80 both,** Meinrad Faltner/Corbis; **81t,** David Young-Wolff/PhotoEdit; **81b,** Villanova University; **82tl,** Michael Newman/PhotoEdit; **82tml,** David Young-Wolff/PhotoEdit; **82tmr,** David Young-Wolff/PhotoEdit; **82tr,** David Young Wolff/PhotoEdit; **82bl,** Mary Kate Denny/PhotoEdit; **82bml,** Nicolas Russell/Getty Images, Inc.; **82bmr,** David Young-Wolff/PhotoEdit; **82br,** Corbis; **84t,** U.S. Mint/Omni-Photo Communications, Inc.; **84b,** David Young-Wolff/PhotoEdit; **85,** Jim Cummins/Getty Images, Inc.; **90,** Dorling Kindersley; **91t,** Dorling Kindersley; **91b,** Richard Haynes; **92,** Dennis Kunkel/Phototake; **93l,** Michael Abbey/Photo Researchers, Inc.; **93r,** E.R. Degginger/Color-Pic, Inc.; **97,** Adrian Warren/Last Refuge Ltd.; **103,** Dorling Kindersley; **104,** Adrian Warren/Last Refuge Ltd.

Chapter 4
Pages 108–109, Royalty-Free/Corbis; **109 inset,** Richard Haynes; **110b,** Michael Newman/PhotoEdit; **110t,** Richard Haynes; **111 grid, all,** David Young-Wolff/PhotoEdit; **111l,** Michael Newman/PhotoEdit; **111m,** David Urbina/PhotoEdit; **111r,** Everett Collection; **112,** Camille Tokerud/Getty Images, Inc.; **113l,** Biophoto Associates/Photo Researchers, Inc.; **113r,** Biophoto Associates/Photo Researchers, Inc.; **114l,** Corbis; **114r,** Michael Douma, Institute for Dynamic Educational Advancement; **116,** Amy Etra/PhotoEdit; **117b,** Jonathan Nourok/PhotoEdit; **117t,** CNRI/Photo Researchers, Inc.; **118 both,** Stanley Flegler/Visuals Unlimited; **119,** Craig Farraway; **121 both,** National Hemophilia Foundation; **122,** White Packert/Getty Images, Inc.; **123,** South West News Service; **124bl,** Foodpix; **124bm,** Photo Researchers, Inc.; **124br,** Foodpix; **124m,** Paul McCormick/Getty Images, Inc.; **124t,** Grant Heilman Photography, Inc.; **125,** Image Works; **127l,** 5-D and Segrest Farms/AP/Wide World Photos; **127r,** Animals Animals/Earth Scenes; **128,** Photo Researchers, Inc.; **129,** David Parker/Photo Researchers, Inc.; **130t,** Nathan Benn/Corbis; **130b,** Getty Images, Inc.; **131,** Andrew Brooks/Corbis; **132b,** Craig Farraway; **132t,** The Image Works.

Chapter 5
Pages 136–137, Tui De Roy/Minden Pictures; **137r,** Richard Haynes; **138t,** Portrait by George Richmond/Down House, Downe/Bridgeman Art Library; **138b,** Christopher Ralling; **138 frame,** Dorling Kindersley; **139 all,** Tui De Roy/Minden Pictures; **140t,** Photo Researchers, Inc.; **140b,** Jeremy Woodhouse/Masterfile; **141,** Dr. Jeremy Burgess/SPL/Photo Researchers, Inc.; **142t,** Barbara D. Livingston; **142m,** Barbara D. Livingston **142b,** AP/Wide World; **142 horseshoe,** Dorling Kindersley; **147,** Richard Haynes; **148t,** Richard Haynes; **148b,** Dorling Kindersley; **149 all,** Michael K. Richardson; **150l,** Photo Researchers, Inc.; **150m,** G. Alamany & E. Vicouns/Corbis; **150r,** Robert Pearcy; **151l,** Gary Milburn/Tom Stack & Associates, Inc.; **151r,** Betty K. Bruce/Animals Animals/Earth Scenes; **155t,** James L. Amos/Photo Researchers, Inc.; **155b,** AP/Wide World Photos; **157,** Peter Pavlovsky/Fossils.de; **162 all,** Douglas Henderson; **163,** Breck P. Kent; **164,** Photo Researchers, Inc.

Page 168b, Myrleen Ferguson Cate/PhotoEdit; **168t,** Bridgeman Art Library; **169,** Ron Kimball; **170 all except greyhound,** Corel Corp.; **170 greyhound,** Jack Daniels/Getty Images, Inc.; **171bl,** C. Jeanne White/Photo Researchers, Inc.; **171br,** Corel Corp.; **171m,** Corel Corp.; **171tl,** Corel Corp.; **171tr,** Dorling Kindersley; **172l,** G. K. & Vikki Hart/Getty Images, Inc.; **172r,** AP/Wide World Photos; **173,** Corbis; **174,** Tony Freeman/PhotoEdit; **175t,** Russ Lappa; **175m,** Richard Haynes; **175b,** Russ Lappa; **176,** Richard Haynes; **178,** Richard Haynes; **180,** Morton Beebe/Corbis; **181,** Richard Haynes; **183t,** Dorling Kinderlsey; **183b,** Richard Haynes; **185,** Image Stop/Phototake; **188,** Richard Haynes; **195,** Richard Haynes; **196,** Russ Lappa; **197 both,** Russ Lappa.